Begonia mortality, 299
Blood samples, 390
Cholesterol levels, 400
Dietary delights, 299
Egg weights, 377
Emergency room admissions, 443
Fertility of pheasant eggs, 384
Gas mileages, 404
Hay yields, 452
Highway speeds, 372, 417
Male color blindness, 386
Meal planning, 269
Medical diagnostics, 294
Medical records, 247
Medical research, 348, 349, 353, 360, 447
Mercury contamination, 443
Motion sickness, 292
Nutrition, 36
Nutrition & Weight Training, 46, 83, 119
Pulse rates, 407
Radiation treatments, 348
Radon study, 360
Seedling mortality, 443
Sight & hearing deficiencies, 250
Steroids and strength, 369
Time to failure, 401, 439
Travel times, 372, 411
Trepidation precipitation, 372
Trout lengths, 389
Weather patterns, 564
Wind velocity, 402, 408, 439

Social Sciences

Achievement tests, 380
Chancy games, 328
Choosing personnel, 269
College enrollment patterns, 564
Communication network, 90
Comparison of distributions, 344
Competitive ranking, 231
Divorce statistics, 443
Dominance relations, 91, 94, 98, 117
Effectiveness of studying, 292
Emission control standards, 249
Energy survey, 253, 254
Error detection, 299
Exercise patterns, 524
G.P.A. data, 452
Jury selection, 319, 445

Leisure pursuits, 5
Life-span of island
Majority decisions,
Maze experiments, 566
Military strategies, 501
Music selection, 321
Opinion surveys, 218, 314, 442, 443, 453
Optimal routing, 501
Percentile rankings, 379
Preference relations, 95, 99, 117, 218, 231, 239
Prisoner's dilemma, 300
Rat cognition, 386
Supermarket shopping patterns, 539
Sex discrimination, 445
Task assignments, 272
Taste testing, 99, 390
Traffic study, 347
Transportation networks, 98, 116

General Interest

Air defense missiles, 289
College admissions, 240
Cryptography, 141, 142, 143, 145, 146
Duck hunting, 274
Engine troubleshooting, 226, 228
Gambler's Ruin, 544, 554, 559
Games of chance, 231, 232, 238, 239, 244, 245, 266, 270, 274, 282, 290, 291, 292, 299, 313, 316
G.P.A. computations, 77
Graduate school admissions, 292
Magazine delivery times, 327
Mail promotion, 460
Menu selections, 220
Missile detection, 360
Movie reviews, 238
Mud wrestling, 390
Newspaper readership, 218
Odds-making, 254
Rain probabilities, 291
Relative frequency, 246, 247, 249, 250
Roulette, 241, 244
SAT scores, 439
Scrabble choices, 222
Sports, 39, 239, 240, 250, 252, 261, 275, 325, 359, 371, 372, 399, 407, 409, 439, 443, 450, 524, 538
Subjective probability, 248, 254
Teaching assignments, 269
Times to failure, 360, 381
Writing style analysis, 396

FINITE
MATHEMATICS

FINITE MATHEMATICS

William B. Owen
CENTRAL WASHINGTON UNIVERSITY

Wm. Frederick Cutlip
CENTRAL WASHINGTON UNIVERSITY

Harcourt Brace Jovanovich, Publishers
and its subsidiary, Academic Press
San Diego   New York   Chicago   Austin   Washington, D.C.
London   Sydney   Tokyo   Toronto

To Our Wives

Pam Owen

and

Jean Cutlip

ISBN: 0-15-527546-1

Library of Congress Catalog Number: 90-82259

Printed in the United States of America

Preface

Finite Mathematics is an intuitive, applications-oriented approach to finite mathematics for students of business, the life sciences, and the social sciences. The only mathematics presumed is a year of high school algebra. In Chapter 0 we begin with a brief review of those algebra elements essential to finite mathematics. Many instructors will skip this chapter, leaving it for student reference. As new topics are encountered in Chapters 1–12, we include a discussion of any algebraic details necessary.

FLEXIBILITY   While the usual topics of finite mathematics are included in this book— linear mathematics, probability and statistics, and mathematics of finance—many of them are covered in considerably more depth than in most textbooks, *without a need for any more depth in mathematics*. This additional coverage provides instructors with alternative avenues. We have, for example, included some elementary ideas that are treated only marginally, if at all, in other books at this level. Section 7.6, Reliability of Systems, is a wonderful application of elementary probability which students find extraordinarily interesting and useful. While optional, this section is highly recommended. The discussion of descriptive statistics in Sections 9.1–9.4 is up-to-date and employs such modern concepts of data analysis as stem-and-leaf displays, box plots, Tukey's five-number summary, and detection of outliers. Sections 3.3 (Some Elementary Cryptography), 4.4 (Integer Programming), and 10.2 (Human Mortality and the Insurance "Game") also furnish variety without demanding a huge investment in time.

Along these same lines, Markov chains (Chapter 11) afford a nice vehicle for studying probability conveniently through matrices. This material contains many results which, while elementary, are not usually found in texts at this level. Finally, there is an entire chapter (Chapter 3) devoted to applications of matrices, including a thorough discussion of both the open and closed Leontief input–output models.

The book is divided into three main areas:

    I. Linear Mathematics (Chapters 1–5)

    II. Probability, Statistics, and Decisions (Chapters 6–11)

    III. Financial Mathematics (Chapter 12)

The following diagram shows some possible paths through these areas.

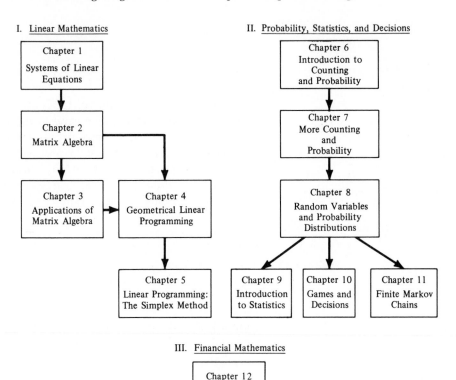

For those who wish to minimize probability, Chapter 6 and the nonoptional sections of Chapters 7 and 8 should provide sufficient coverage.

COMPUTER USE   In various places we use MINITAB to illustrate matrix computations and statistical ideas. The Instructor's Manual also contains several MINITAB simulations that illustrate significant probabilistic and statistical concepts. Although by no means required, we hope that MINITAB's easy-to-use features and widespread availability on campuses, both in micro-computer and mainframe versions, will encourage students and instructors to experiment with its many *nonstatistical* uses.

When discussing linear programming and the simplex method, we include a section on LINDO, an inexpensive software package available both in microcomputer and mainframe versions. The software is *not* required in order to benefit from reading this section.

STYLE

There is more narrative in *Finite Mathematics* than in most competitive textbooks. The intention is to talk *with* rather than *at* the student. The discussions are purposely intuitive and are intended to motivate and develop a common sense understanding of why a particular method or formula works.

Having discovered that students learn better while having fun, we have used a bit of humor in both examples and exercises. Learning is the ultimate objective, so why not make the experience enjoyable? Nonetheless, whenever a humorous example is used, a more serious real-world oriented example follows.

EXAMPLES AND PRACTICE PROBLEMS

Included are almost 250 fully worked, thoroughly discussed examples illustrating the necessary ingredients of finite mathematics. There are also about 150 practice problems at strategic locations to help students obtain immediate understanding of newly introduced ideas. Rather than hiding answers in obscure locations (where enterprising students will find them anyway), they are placed immediately after problems. In several practice problems, we also discuss solutions, giving these practice problems much the same flavor as the examples.

EXERCISE SETS

The book contains more than 2400 exercises, half of which provide drill and are called "Practicing the Moves and Maneuvers." The other half are application problems that require the student to read and think. We call these "Applying the Concepts." *Those exercises that are either more difficult or more time-consuming are marked with an asterisk.*

SUPPLEMENTS FOR INSTRUCTORS

- *Instructor's Manual with Tests*
- *Solutions Manual* provides solutions to all the even-numbered exercises in the textbook.

- *Computerized Testbank* (Micro-Pac Genie) by Microsystems Software, Ltd., is the most complete test-generating and authoring system with graphics on the market. Available for the IBM PC, XT, and compatible system and for the Apple Macintosh.

SUPPLEMENTS FOR STUDENTS

- *Student Solutions Manual* provides solutions to all the odd-numbered exercises in the textbook.

- *Software Tutorial*

ACKNOWLEDGMENTS

Our greatest thanks are due our wives, Pam Owen and Jean Cutlip, for their steadfast patience, understanding, and encouragement during a period when the two of us would have vied mightily for last place in any "Best Husband" contest.

Among the many students who helped, we especially appreciate the work of Barbara Hillegoss, Jim Whitmore, Michael-Ann McAboy, Lorijo Claunch, Michael Williams, Jay Powers, and Lisa Owen. Pam Owen also spent many hours reviewing the manuscript and class-testing certain sections in advanced secondary classes. Colleagues David Anderson, Mike Arcidiacono, Bill Eberly, Ken Gamon, Steve Hinthorne, C.T. Lin, Bernie Martin, Ron Stokes, and Dale Width have class-tested the material and furnished us with many suggestions. David Anderson and C.T. Lin have provided especially helpful and insightful ideas. Giles Maloof and Louis Talman made valuable contributions to solutions. And departmental secretary Nancy Oakes-Width has helped in myriad ways.

The following individuals reviewed the manuscript and contributed many helpful suggestions: Ron Barnes, University of Houston; Carl Bedell, Philadelphia College of Textiles and Science; Joan Dykes, Edison Community College; Joseph Fadyn, Southern College of Technology; Susan Friedman, CUNY-Bernard Baruch College; Art C. Heinricher, Jr., University of Kentucky; Robert Moreland, Texas Technical University; Robert Pruitt, San Jose State University; Cathleen Zucco, LeMoyne College.

Thanks also go to our Harcourt Brace Jovanovich editor Michael Johnson and to associate editor Pamela Whiting for their efforts in support of our endeavor. They demonstrate that good-natured encouragement and enthusiasm are far more effective than threats. We are especially indebted to copy editor Marjii James for her many helpful suggestions, and to Elise Oranges for her support and production skills.

We welcome suggestions and comments.

Contents

Preface   v

Chapter 0   ALGEBRA BASICS   xiii

         Introduction   xiii

     0.1   Real Numbers and Rational Arithmetic   xiii

     0.2   Number Lines and Coordinate Systems   xxiii

     0.3   Linear Equations and Graphs   xxviii

     0.4   Word Problems and Mathematical Models   xliv

     0.5   Algebraic Alteration of Equations   xlvii

Chapter 1   SYSTEMS OF LINEAR EQUATIONS   1

         Introduction   1

     1.1   Solution Methods for Linear Systems   1

     1.2   Matrix Methods for Solving Linear Systems   17

     1.3   Systems with More than One Solution; Systems with No Solution   26

         A Brief Summary of Important Ideas   *36*

         Review Exercises   *37*

Chapter 2   MATRIX ALGEBRA   41

         Introduction   41

     2.1   Matrices: Equality and Addition   42

     2.2   Matrix Multiplication   47

     2.3   Identity Matrices and Transposes   59

     2.4   Matrix Inversion   63

     2.5   Using MINITAB to Perform Matrix Algebra on a Computer (Optional)   72

         A Brief Summary of Important Ideas   *74*

         Review Exercises   *74*

Chapter 3   APPLICATIONS OF MATRIX ALGEBRA   **77**
              Introduction   77
        3.1   Applications of Matrix Multiplication   77
        3.2   Elementary Graph Theory   86
        3.3   Some Elementary Cryptography   99
        3.4   Leontief Economic Models   104
              A Brief Summary of Important Ideas   *115*
              Review Exercises   *115*

Chapter 4   GEOMETRICAL LINEAR PROGRAMMING   **119**
              Introduction   119
        4.1   Graphing Linear Inequalities   121
        4.2   Maximizing or Minimizing Linear Objective Functions   130
        4.3   Linear Programming in Three or More Variables (Optional)   139
        4.4   Integer Programming (Optional)   146
              A Brief Summary of Important Ideas   *148*
              Review Exercises   *149*

Chapter 5   LINEAR PROGRAMMING: THE SIMPLEX METHOD   **153**
              Introduction   153
        5.1   The Simplex Method   154
        5.2   The Simplex Algorithm—The Moves Without the Justification   167
        5.3   Minimization Problems: The Dual   186
        5.4   Solving Linear Programming Problems by Computer   195
              A Brief Summary of Important Ideas   *205*
              Review Exercises   *206*

Chapter 6   INTRODUCTORY COUNTING AND PROBABILITY   **209**
              Introduction   209
        6.1   Sorting a Population   209
        6.2   The Fundamental Counting Principle   219
        6.3   What Is Probability?   223
        6.4   Experiments, Sample Spaces, and Events   224
        6.5   Probability Beginnings, the Additive Law, and the Complement
              Rule   232
        6.6   Equally Likely Probability   240
        6.7   Relative Frequency and Subjective Probability   245
              A Brief Summary of Important Ideas   *251*
              Review Exercises   *252*

Chapter 7   MORE COUNTING AND PROBABILITY   **257**
              Introduction   257
        7.1   Counts of Arrangements and Sets   258
        7.2   Variations on Counting Schemes   270

7.3 Conditional Probability and Independence   276
7.4 The Multiplicative Rule, Tree Diagrams, and More on Independence   283
7.5 Bayes' Theorem (Optional)   292
7.6 Reliability of Systems (Optional But Recommended)   300
A Brief Summary of Important Ideas   311
Review Exercises   312

Chapter 8 RANDOM VARIABLES AND PROBABILITY DISTRIBUTIONS   319
8.1 Random Variables   319
8.2 Describing Random Variables   328
8.3 Measuring Dispersion: The Variance and the Standard Deviation   335
8.4 The Binomial Distribution   348
8.5 An Introduction to Continuous Random Variables   361
8.6 The Normal Distribution: An Introduction   366
8.7 Applying the Normal Distribution   372
8.8 The Normal Approximation to the Binomial Distribution (Optional)   381
A Brief Summary of Important Ideas   387
Review Exercises   388

Chapter 9 INTRODUCTION TO STATISTICS   393
Introduction   393
9.1 Descriptive Statistics I: Graphical Methods   395
9.2 Descriptive Statistics II: Measures of Central Tendency   402
9.3 Descriptive Statistics III: Measures of Dispersion   408
9.4 Measuring Relative Standing: Tukey's Five-Number Summary and Box Plots   414
9.5 Sampling Distributions, Point Estimation, and the Central Limit Theorem   421
9.6 Large Sample Confidence Intervals for the Population Mean μ 434
9.7 Confidence Intervals on p, the Binomial Success Probability (Optional)   440
9.8 A Brief Introduction to Hypothesis Testing (Optional)   444
A Brief Summary of Important Ideas   450
Review Exercises   452

Chapter 10 GAMES AND DECISIONS   455
Introduction   455
10.1 Outcomes and Values; The Value of a Game   455
10.2 Human Mortality and the Insurance "Game"   460
10.3 Choosing a Course of Action   464

10.4   Marginal Analysis   474
10.5   Strictly Determined Games Between Intelligent Players   481
10.6   Mixed Strategy 2 × 2 Games   487
10.7   Solving "Large" Games (Optional)   502
       A Brief Summary of Important Ideas   *508*
       Review Exercises   *509*

Chapter 11   FINITE MARKOV CHAINS   515
11.1   Conditional Probabilities and Transition Matrices   515
11.2   The *m*-Step Probability Vector and Regular Transition Matrices   526
11.3   Absorbing Markov Chains   540
       A Brief Summary of Important Ideas   *561*
       Review Exercises   *563*

Chapter 12   MONEY MATTERS   569
       Introduction   569
12.1   Simple and Compound Interest   570
12.2   Comparing Interest Rates: The Effective Rate of Interest   583
12.3   Present Value of an Investment   587
12.4   Time Diagrams and Equations of Value   592
12.5   Annuities: Future Values and Sinking Funds   599
12.6   More on Annuities: Amortizations   606
       A Brief Summary of Important Ideas   *616*
       Review Exercises   *617*

Appendix TABLES   675
   Table I   Binomial Probability Distributions   621
   Table II   Compound Accumulation Factors   623
   Table III Future Value of an Annuity   627

Answers to Odd-Numbered Exercises   631

Index   675

Standard Normal Distribution Table   Inside Back Cover

0 *Algebra Basics*

Students typically bring a tremendous variety of backgrounds to their study of finite mathematics. Recognizing this, and having seen that many of our students' difficulties trace to certain not-quite-remembered concepts, we offer here a brief review of some of the skills and ideas essential in later chapters. These include:

Section 0.1: Real Numbers and Rational Arithmetic
Section 0.2: Number Lines and Coordinate Systems
Section 0.3: Linear Equations and Graphs
Section 0.4: Word Problems and Mathematical Models
Section 0.5: Algebraic Alteration of Equations

Some topics traditionally included in introductory or review chapters are not represented here. They are either introduced (with suitable emphasis) at appropriate points of application in later chapters or are intentionally omitted. In making these judgments, your authors resisted that tendency to tell you again everything you should know, whether important in the present context or not. Enough is enough!

0.1 REAL NUMBERS AND RATIONAL ARITHMETIC

There is a well-established development leading from the simplest of our number systems, the *natural numbers* or counting numbers, to the richest system we shall consider, the *real numbers*. We remind ourselves of the following systems:

- N, the **set** or complete collection of **natural numbers:** $N = \{1, 2, 3, 4, \ldots\}$.
  We describe N using conventional notation: **braces**—{ }—enclosing the members, or elements, of the set N. The elements are

listed (a list is begun); the ellipsis ". . ." means "and so on, in the given pattern."

- W, the set of **whole numbers:** $W = \{0, 1, 2, 3, 4, . . .\}$.
- Z, the set of **integers:** $Z = \{. . . -2, -1, 0, 1, 2, . . .\}$.
- Q, the set of **fractions** or **rational numbers** (or quotients of integers, hence the "Q").
  Q includes such numbers as 1/2, 9/5, 12/3, (−7)/32—which could be written −(7/32), −25/5, and the like. The number "9/5" suggests that Q contains all improper fractions or mixed numbers. The numbers "−25/5" and "12/3" convey that all positive and negative integers are in **Q**; "0/3," or "0," is also in Q. Thus, Q contains all of the preceding number systems N, W, and Z, and a lot more, filling in many numbers between the evenly separated integers. In "set language,"

N is completely contained in, or is a **subset** of, W: $N \subset W$

In fact, we note that $N \subset W \subset Z \subset Q$.

Graphic Representation of Numbers

Every number in Q (including every number in Z, W, and N) can be assigned to a specific location or point on a number line (see Figure 0.1). Each number represents the distance (positive or negative) of its assigned point from the **origin,** or 0-point. The number assigned to a point is the **coordinate** of that point.

Figure 0.1
Number line with some rational numbers

However, some points in Figure 0.1 are not assigned rational numbers. The usual first example of a point without a rational number is the point P, $\sqrt{2}$ units to the right of the origin. (There is no a/b, a quotient of two integers, such that $(a/b)^2 = 2$. Thus, $\sqrt{2}$ is not rational.) Our labeling of number-line points using only rational numbers is sadly incomplete. The task requires real numbers, and nothing less.

REAL NUMBERS: A WORKING DEFINITION

The set of all numbers required to label every point on a number line with its distance from the origin is called the set of **real numbers,** denoted by R. The real numbers include all previously defined number systems:

$N \subset W \subset I \subset Q \subset R$

Rational Number Arithmetic

Students once proficient at rational number (fraction) arithmetic often find that their skills are rusty. We review here the most frequently forgotten skills for adding, subtracting, multiplying, and dividing rational numbers (fractions), and for converting rational numbers to equivalent rational numbers having the same values but new forms. (For example, 2/5 and 6/15 are equivalent.)

Why Emphasize Fractions?

The real number system R contains Q, the system of rational numbers. To many readers, real numbers are numbers which one enters into or reads from a calculator. However, all entered or displayed numbers are decimal expressions of relatively few digits. A calculator displaying eight digits may use ten digits internally; but neither eight nor ten digits exactly represents the real number $\sqrt{2}$ or even the rational number 1/3.

Some rational numbers have exact decimal equivalents: $1/2 = 0.5$, $13/8 = 1.625$, etc.; but 0.3333 (or a decimal point followed by any number of copies of the digit 3) always inaccurately represents 1/3. One benefit of fractional arithmetic is exactness. As a further benefit, skills with ordinary fractions apply equally well to algebraic fractions (quotients of algebraic expressions) having no decimal approximation.

Numerators and Denominators

Every rational number has the form p/q, pronounced "p over q," where p and q are integers and q is not zero. In such a form, p is the **numerator** and q is the **denominator** of the fraction. Whenever we write such a form, the requirement that the denominator be nonzero is implied, whether stated or not.

Multiplying and Dividing Using Fractions

The product of a/b and c/d, written $a/b \times c/d$ or $a/b \cdot c/d$, is the fraction ac/bd. "The product of two fractions is the product of their numerators over the product of their denominators."

The quotient of a/b and c/d, written $a/b \div c/d$, is obtained as follows: $a/b \div c/d = a/b \cdot d/c = ad/bc$. Forming this quotient requires that c be nonzero, in addition to the usual nonzero requirements on b and d.

Standard Form of a Fraction

A fraction p/q is in standard form if and only if the integer q is positive. If p/q is not in standard form, the denominator q is negative. Multiplying the fraction by $(-1)/(-1)$, another form of 1, produces $(-p)/(-q)$, which is in standard form.

The only possible difference between a fraction and its standard form is in the signs of its numerator and denominator. Changing the signs of both numerator and denominator of a fraction yields an equivalent fraction. As examples, $(-3)/7$ and $42/13$ are in standard form. The standard form of $(-5)/(-11)$ is $5/11$. The standard form of $16/(-29)$ is $(-16)/29$.

■ EXAMPLE 1

Perform the indicated operations. Write results in standard form. All variables r, s, t, and b represent positive integers.

(a) $\dfrac{5}{3} \times \dfrac{-2}{7}$ (b) $\dfrac{4}{r} \cdot \dfrac{s}{-2}$ (c) $\dfrac{b}{3} \cdot \dfrac{2}{5}$ (d) $4 \div \dfrac{5}{-8}$

(e) $\dfrac{r}{4} \div -3$ (f) $\dfrac{t+1}{7} \div \dfrac{2}{9}$

SOLUTION

(a) $\dfrac{5}{3} \times \dfrac{-2}{7} = \dfrac{5(-2)}{3 \cdot 7} = \dfrac{-10}{21}$

(b) $\dfrac{4}{r} \cdot \dfrac{s}{-2} = \dfrac{4 \cdot s}{r(-2)} = \dfrac{4s}{-2r} = \dfrac{-4s}{2r}$

(c) $\dfrac{b}{3} \cdot \dfrac{2}{5} = \dfrac{b \cdot 2}{3 \cdot 5} = \dfrac{2b}{15}$

(d) $4 \div \dfrac{5}{-8} = \dfrac{4}{1} \cdot \dfrac{-8}{5} = \dfrac{-32}{5}$

(e) $\dfrac{r}{4} \div -3 = \dfrac{r}{4} \div \dfrac{-3}{1} = \dfrac{r}{4} \cdot \dfrac{1}{-3} = \dfrac{r}{-12} = \dfrac{-r}{12}$

(f) $\dfrac{t+1}{7} \div \dfrac{2}{9} = \dfrac{t+1}{7} \cdot \dfrac{9}{2} = \dfrac{(t+1) \cdot 9}{7 \cdot 2} = \dfrac{9t+9}{14}$ ■

PRACTICE PROBLEM 1

Perform the indicated operations. Write results in standard form. All variables m, p, r, s, and a represent positive integers.

(a) $\dfrac{11}{9} \times \dfrac{5}{-d}$ (b) $\dfrac{m}{5} \times \dfrac{p}{-4}$ (c) $\dfrac{4}{r} \cdot \dfrac{s+5}{2}$ (d) $\dfrac{13}{32} \div \dfrac{3}{4}$

(e) $\dfrac{2a+6}{5} \div 3$ (f) $9 \div \dfrac{-5}{2}$

ANSWER(S)

(a) $\dfrac{-55}{9d}$ (b) $\dfrac{-mp}{20}$ (c) $\dfrac{4s+20}{2r}$ (d) $\dfrac{52}{96}$

(e) $\dfrac{2a+6}{15}$ (f) $\dfrac{-18}{5}$ □

Adding or Subtracting Like Fractions

Fractions having identical denominators are called **like fractions**. The sum of fractions 2/7 and 3/7 is 2/7 + 3/7 = (2 + 3)/7 = 5/7. The sum of like fractions is the sum of their numerators, over their common denominator. The pattern is: $a/d + c/d = (a + c)/d$.

The difference of fractions a/d and c/d is $a/d - c/d = (a - c)/d$. The difference of like fractions is the difference of their numerators, written over the common denominator.

■ EXAMPLE 2 _____   Perform the indicated operations.

$$\text{(a) } \frac{2}{9} + \frac{5}{9} \quad \text{(b) } \frac{4}{m} - \frac{8}{m} \quad \text{(c) } \frac{5}{3} + \frac{b}{3} \quad \text{(d) } \frac{2}{r} - \frac{a}{r}$$

SOLUTION

$$\text{(a) } \frac{2}{9} + \frac{5}{9} = \frac{2+5}{9} = \frac{7}{9} \qquad \text{(b) } \frac{4}{m} - \frac{8}{m} = \frac{4-8}{m} = \frac{-4}{m}$$

$$\text{(c) } \frac{5}{3} + \frac{b}{3} = \frac{5+b}{3} \qquad \text{(d) } \frac{2}{r} - \frac{a}{r} = \frac{2-a}{r}$$ ■

PRACTICE PROBLEM 2   Perform the indicated operations.

$$\text{(a) } \frac{13}{4} + \frac{6}{4} \quad \text{(b) } \frac{9}{t} - \frac{7}{t}$$

$$\text{(c) } \frac{3}{1-p} + \frac{t}{1-p} \quad \text{(d) } \frac{s+5}{4} - \frac{3}{4}$$

ANSWER(S)

$$\text{(a) } \frac{19}{4} \quad \text{(b) } \frac{2}{t} \quad \text{(c) } \frac{3+t}{1-p} \quad \text{(d) } \frac{s+2}{4}$$ □

We can now multiply or divide any two fractions (avoiding zeros in denominator), but can add or subtract only like fractions. Adding or subtracting **unlike fractions** (having different denominators) requires that we change the form of one or both fractions so that the resulting denominators are identical. Two principles open the way for us:

FRACTION TRANSFORMATION PRINCIPLES

1. If r is any real number, then $r \times 1 = r$. Thus, for any fraction a/b, $a/b \times 1 = a/b$.

2. For any nonzero integer d, d/d is 1.

3. Consequently, for any fraction a/b and any nonzero integer d,

$$\frac{a}{b} \times \frac{d}{d} = \frac{a}{b}$$

Applying the Fraction Transformation Principle

We may change the form of any fraction a/b by multiplying that fraction by 1 in an appropriate form. The original and new fractions are **equivalent** (have the same value). For instance, 2/5 and 6/15 are equivalent, because $2/5 \times 3/3 = 6/15$.

■ EXAMPLE 3

Transform each fraction into an equivalent fraction with denominator 24.

(a) $\dfrac{5}{8}$ (b) $\dfrac{13}{2}$ (c) $\dfrac{m}{6}$ (d) $\dfrac{a+2}{12}$

SOLUTION

(a) We must multiply the denominator 8 by 3 to produce the denominator 24. The appropriate form of 1 by which to multiply 5/8 is thus 3/3:

$$\frac{5}{8}\cdot\frac{3}{3}=\frac{15}{24}$$

(b) $\dfrac{13}{2}\times\dfrac{12}{12}=\dfrac{13\cdot12}{2\cdot12}=\dfrac{156}{24}$ (c) $\dfrac{m}{6}\cdot\dfrac{4}{4}=\dfrac{4m}{24}$

(d) $\dfrac{a+2}{12}\cdot\dfrac{2}{2}=\dfrac{2a+4}{24}$ ■

PRACTICE PROBLEM 3

Write each fraction in an equivalent form having denominator 20.

(a) $\dfrac{1}{-4}$ (b) $\dfrac{17}{5}$ (c) $\dfrac{r}{2}$ (d) $\dfrac{s+3}{10}$

ANSWER(S)

(a) $\dfrac{-5}{20}$ (b) $\dfrac{68}{20}$ (c) $\dfrac{10r}{20}$ (d) $\dfrac{2s+6}{20}$ □

Adding or Subtracting Unlike Fractions

For any fraction, we may obtain an equivalent fraction by multiplying the original fraction by (a suitable form of) 1. The problem of adding or subtracting unlike fractions is solved by replacing the given fractions with equivalent fractions having identical denominators (**a common denominator**). The common denominator must be a multiple of both of the given denominators. In other words, it must be a common multiple of the original denominators. Any common multiple is satisfactory.

■ EXAMPLE 4

Add the fractions 2/3 and 5/4 by first replacing them with equivalent fractions having a common denominator.

SOLUTION

One common multiple of 3 and 4 is 24. (24 = 3 · 8 and 24 = 4 · 6) We multiply 2/3 by 8/8 to produce the common denominator 24 without changing the value of the fraction 2/3. We multiply 5/4 by 6/6 for the same reason.

$$\frac{2}{3}+\frac{5}{4}=\frac{2}{3}\cdot\frac{8}{8}+\frac{5}{4}\cdot\frac{6}{6}=\frac{16}{24}+\frac{30}{24}=\frac{46}{24}$$ ■

We used the common denominator 24 in solving Example 4. A smaller common denominator (common multiple of 3 and 4) is 12. Let us add 2/3 and 5/4 using 12 as the common denominator.

$$\frac{2}{3} + \frac{5}{4} = \frac{2}{3} \cdot \frac{4}{4} + \frac{5}{4} \cdot \frac{3}{3} = \frac{8}{12} + \frac{15}{12} = \frac{23}{12}$$

How do answers 46/24 and 23/12 compare? $46/24 = 23/12 \times 2/2$. That is, 46/24 is 23/12 multiplied by one. The two answers, obtained using different common denominators, are equivalent.

It is more convenient to use the smallest possible common denominator when adding unlike fractions. This smallest denominator is the **lowest** (or **least**) **common denominator (LCD).**

Prime and Composite Numbers

A **prime number** is a natural number or positive integer greater than 1 which is not the product of two smaller positive integers. Thus 3, 5, 23, and 59 are prime. In contrast, 4 and 18 are **composite numbers**—each is a positive integer greater than one which is a product of smaller positive integers: $4 = 2 \cdot 2$; $18 = 2 \cdot 9$.

Every integer can be written as the product of 1 or -1 and prime factors. Disregarding possible reorderings of these factors, there is exactly one such prime factorization of each integer. For instance, the only prime factorization of 30 is $30 = 2 \cdot 3 \cdot 5$, which may be written $3 \cdot 2 \cdot 5$, $5 \cdot 3 \cdot 2$, and so on.

Finding the Lowest Common Denominator (LCD)

Any multiple of an integer has as factors all prime factors (including repeats) of the original integer. Because $72 = 6 \cdot 12$, 72 is a multiple of 12. Also, $72 = 2 \cdot 2 \cdot 2 \cdot 3 \cdot 3$ and $12 = 2 \cdot 2 \cdot 3$. All prime factors of 12 (including sufficient copies of the repeated factor 2) are included in the list of prime factors of 72.

A common multiple of two or more integers must contain all prime factors (including repeats) of each original integer. The lowest common denominator of two or more fractions is easy to construct, as we show in Example 5.

■ EXAMPLE 5

Find the lowest common denominator (LCD) of the given fractions 5/12 and 7/18. Then replace each given fraction by an equivalent fraction having the LCD and obtain $5/12 + 7/18$.

SOLUTION

The prime factorizations of 12 and 18 are:

$$12 = 2 \cdot 2 \cdot 3$$

$$18 = 2 \cdot 3 \cdot 3$$

The prime factors of the LCD are: all prime factors of 12, and any new factors needed to also include the prime factors of 18.

$$LCD = (2 \cdot 2 \cdot 3) \cdot 3 = 36$$

We add 5/12 and 7/18, using the common denominator 36.

$$\frac{5}{12} + \frac{7}{18}$$

$$= \frac{5}{12} \cdot \frac{3}{3} + \frac{7}{18} \cdot \frac{2}{2}$$

$$= \frac{15}{36} + \frac{14}{36}$$

$$= \frac{29}{36}$$

■

PRACTICE PROBLEM 4   Perform the indicated operations:

    (a) $\dfrac{5}{8} + \dfrac{5}{6}$ (b) $\dfrac{2}{5} - \dfrac{3}{20}$ (c) $\dfrac{r}{9} + \dfrac{s}{15}$ (d) $\dfrac{1}{6} - \dfrac{1}{2p}$

     ANSWER(S)   (a) $\dfrac{35}{24}$ (b) $\dfrac{5}{20}$ (c) $\dfrac{5r + 3s}{45}$ (d) $\dfrac{p - 3}{6p}$

□

Reduction to Lowest Terms   A fraction is in **lowest terms** if its numerator and denominator have no common factors. A fraction is **reduced to lowest terms** by removing all common factors from its numerator and denominator. This technique is a reverse use of the principle that two fractions are equivalent if one of them is the other, multiplied by 1. Insertion of a common factor into numerator and denominator multiplies a fraction by 1; deletion of a common factor from numerator and denominator divides a fraction by 1.

■ EXAMPLE 6   Reduce to lowest terms.

    (a) $\dfrac{12}{44}$ (b) $\dfrac{15}{80}$ (c) $\dfrac{56}{21}$

SOLUTION   (a) $\dfrac{12}{44} = \dfrac{2 \cdot 2 \cdot 3}{2 \cdot 2 \cdot 11} = \dfrac{\cancel{2} \cdot \cancel{2} \cdot 3}{\cancel{2} \cdot \cancel{2} \cdot 11} = \dfrac{3}{11}$

    (b) $\dfrac{15}{80} = \dfrac{5 \cdot 3}{2 \cdot 2 \cdot 2 \cdot 2 \cdot 5} = \dfrac{5 \cdot 3}{2 \cdot 2 \cdot 2 \cdot 2 \cdot 5} = \dfrac{3}{16}$

    (c) $\dfrac{56}{21} = \dfrac{2 \cdot 2 \cdot 2 \cdot 7}{3 \cdot 7} = \dfrac{2 \cdot 2 \cdot 2 \cdot \cancel{7}}{3 \cdot \cancel{7}} = \dfrac{8}{3}$

■

PRACTICE PROBLEM 5   Reduce to lowest terms.

    (a) $\dfrac{39}{57}$ (b) $\dfrac{105}{90}$ (c) $\dfrac{255}{300}$

ANSWER(S)   (a) $\dfrac{13}{19}$ (b) $\dfrac{7}{6}$ (c) $\dfrac{17}{20}$

☐

The Distributive Property of Multiplication over Addition

Several patterns describing real number arithmetic are so striking and useful as to deserve names. One such pattern is the **distributive property** relating multiplication and addition. To illustrate, we may calculate the result of $3(2 + 7)$ in two ways:

$$3(2 + 7) = 3 \cdot 9 = 27$$

or

$$3(2 + 7) = 3 \cdot 2 + 3 \cdot 7 = 6 + 21 = 27$$

In the first instance, we added first, then multiplied; in the second, we first distributed the indicated multiplier 3 to the two addends 2 and 7, multiplied, then added. The results are identical.

THE DISTRIBUTIVE PROPERTY

For any real numbers a, b, and c,

$$a(b + c) = a \cdot b + a \cdot c$$

and

$$a(b - c) = a \cdot b - a \cdot c$$

One of the useful ways of changing the forms of equations in Section 0.3 hinges on the distributive property, which applies equally well to multiplying sums or differences. We illustrate the basic use in Example 7.

■ EXAMPLE 7

In each of the following, distribute the multiplier over the indicated sum or difference and form the products.

(a) $6\left(\dfrac{2}{3} + \dfrac{1}{2}\right)$ (b) $15\left(\dfrac{x}{3} - \dfrac{y}{5}\right)$

SOLUTION

(a) $6\left(\dfrac{2}{3} + \dfrac{1}{2}\right) = \dfrac{6}{1} \cdot \dfrac{2}{3} + \dfrac{6}{1} \cdot \dfrac{1}{2}$ (b) $15\left(\dfrac{x}{3} - \dfrac{y}{5}\right) = \dfrac{15}{1} \cdot \dfrac{x}{3} - \dfrac{15}{1} \cdot \dfrac{y}{5}$

$= \dfrac{12}{3} + \dfrac{6}{2}$ $= \dfrac{15x}{3} - \dfrac{15y}{5}$

$= 4 + 3$ $= 5x - 3y$

In each instance, the multiplier was a common multiple of the two denominators, hence a common denominator. In each instance, the fractions vanished.   ■

PRACTICE PROBLEM 6   In each of the following, fill in the blank with the smallest positive integer multiplier which will cause the fractions to vanish, and carry the operations forward as in Example 7. All letters represent positive integers.

(a) ___ $\left(\dfrac{5}{8} - \dfrac{1}{6}\right)$ (b) ___ $\left(\dfrac{2x}{15} + \dfrac{b}{10}\right)$ (c) ___ $\left(\dfrac{3}{4p} + \dfrac{1}{6q}\right)$

ANSWER(S)

(a) Using multiplier 24, the result is $15 - 4$.

(b) Using multiplier 30, the result is $4x + 3b$.

(c) Using multiplier $12pq$, the result is $9q + 2p$.   □

EXERCISES 0.1

PRACTICING THE MOVES AND MANEUVERS

Exercises 1–18: Perform indicated operations. Write all answers in lowest terms, with positive denominators. All letters in the exercises represent positive integers.

1. $\dfrac{2}{5} + \dfrac{17}{-5}$

2. $\dfrac{5}{12} + \dfrac{-3}{12}$

3. $\dfrac{22}{-7} + \dfrac{-15}{3}$

4. $\dfrac{9}{-14} + \dfrac{-7}{4}$

5. $\dfrac{1}{6t} + \dfrac{3}{4t}$

6. $\dfrac{5}{-8} \cdot \dfrac{2}{-3}$

7. $\dfrac{14}{9} \cdot \dfrac{6}{-7}$

8. $\dfrac{24}{5w} \cdot \dfrac{3w}{10}$

9. $\dfrac{16t}{-35} \cdot \dfrac{21}{6t}$

10. $\dfrac{4}{3} \div \dfrac{6}{-5}$

11. $\dfrac{12s}{-28} \div \dfrac{8s}{21}$

12. $\dfrac{48}{5} \div \dfrac{3}{10}$

13. $32n \div \dfrac{10n}{-3}$

14. $45p \div \dfrac{-10p}{7}$

15. $\dfrac{18w}{75} \div 24w$

16. $\dfrac{16}{5} \div (-20)$

17. $\dfrac{8}{9} - \dfrac{5}{6}$

18. $\dfrac{17}{15} - \dfrac{3}{-10}$

Exercises 19–24: Multiply each indicated sum or difference of fractions by the appropriate LCD. Express the result as a sum or difference of integers. (All letters have positive integer values.)

19. $\dfrac{2}{27} - \dfrac{5}{6}$

20. $\dfrac{4}{15m} + \dfrac{7}{6n}$

21. $\dfrac{x}{12} - \dfrac{5y}{8}$

22. $\dfrac{z}{8} + \dfrac{3w}{10}$

23. $6 - \dfrac{5}{2}$

24. $\dfrac{3a}{7} + 10$

0.2 NUMBER LINES AND COORDINATE SYSTEMS

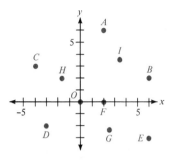

Figure 0.2
Typical two-dimensional
coordinate system
Points plotted:
A (2,6)
B (6,2)
C (−4,3)
D (−3,−2)
E (6,−3)
F (2,0)
G (5/2,−7/3)
H (−√3,2)
I (17/5,2√2)
O (0,0)

A **real number line** is simply a line marked with a scale so that each real number corresponds to a point on that line. The ingredients are: the *origin* (0 point); a *positive direction* (usually to the right on a horizontal line, upward on a vertical line); and a convenient *unit length* (from 0 to 1 on the line). These three specifications determine the exact real number coordinate of each point on the line. A real number line is a *coordinate line* or a **one-dimensional coordinate system.**

A **two-dimensional coordinate system** allows us to show patterns of relationship between pairs of real numbers. Such a system resembles the rectangular grid of streets found in many cities located in relatively flat terrain. To establish a two-dimensional coordinate system, start with a pair of intersecting lines, one horizontal and the other vertical. Coordinatize both lines, taking their intersection as their common origin ("0" point), and convenient unit lengths (usually the same for both lines) to establish positive distances to the right on the horizontal line and upward on the vertical line. The result is a system as in Figure 0.2, in which each pair of real numbers matches a point in the plane of the two lines (the **coordinate plane**). The horizontal coordinate line, or **horizontal axis,** is usually labeled x, and the **vertical axis** is usually labeled y. Just enough detail is shown to establish the scales on the two axes. We follow the convention of using capital letters to name points, sometimes giving the coordinates of a point in parentheses following its name.

The numbers paired at each point are the **coordinates** of that point. Every pair of real numbers (coordinates) locates exactly one point, and every point in the coordinate plane determines exactly one pair of real numbers.

A two-dimensional coordinate system makes relationships between pairs of numbers visible, often with surprising or revealing results. It is sometimes helpful to use different scales on the two axes for convenience in graphing, as in Example 8.

■ EXAMPLE 8

Numbering the months "1" (January) through "12" and tabulating electricity consumption (kilowatt hours) and water consumption (hundreds of gallons) during each two-month billing period, a homeowner organized the following data from his six utility bills:

Month	1	3	5	7	9	11
Electricity (kwh)	7170	6530	3770	1900	1940	2690
Water (100 gal. units)	80	90	270	690	510	200

Plot the bimonthly electrical and water consumption on separate coordinate systems. Try to explain any patterns.

SOLUTION Refer to the homeowner's table while examining the plots.

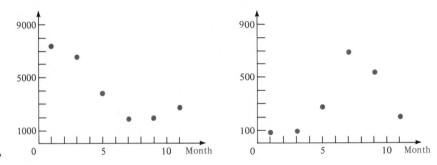

Figure 0.A

Electrical consumption declined during summer months and rose going into autumn. Water consumption, low during winter months, rose sharply during summer, then fell going into autumn. Both patterns are consistent with the dry, continental climate of central Washington state, where electrical home heating and heavy watering of lawns are common practices. ■

   In Example 8 we illustrated the fundamentals of graphing data linking two varying quantities (electrical use and elapsed time, for example). Several principles should be followed:

GRAPHING GUIDELINES

Given data relating two varying quantities (variables), draw a pair of perpendicular axes. Then,

1. Choose and label with an appropriate name or letter one axis for each variable.

2. Survey the values of one variable, and choose a unit size which will display all values of that variable within a suitable span of that variable's axis. Be sure to use steps of equal size in labeling scale marks on the axis. Do likewise for the second variable.

3. Carefully plot points corresponding to pairs of variable values.

PRACTICE PROBLEM 7 Annual income for the Heng household since arriving in the United States in 1983 is as follows (taking 1983 as year #1):

Year	1	2	3	4	5	6	7	8
Income	3200	3800	4000	5600	7000	7800	8300	8000

Plot the data on a suitably designed coordinate system.

ANSWER(S)

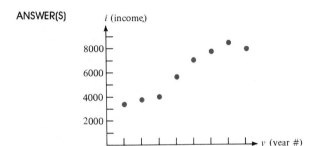

EXERCISES 0.2

PRACTICING THE MOVES AND MANEUVERS

Exercises 25–28: Using suitable choices of scale (not necessarily the same on both axes), plot the given points.

25. $(1,3)$, $(-2,5)$, $(-4,-2.5)$, $(4,-2)$
26. $(4,30)$, $(6,45)$, $(-2,25)$, $(0,-10)$
27. $(0.02,8)$, $(0.06,5)$, $(0.12,3)$, $(0.1,1)$
28. $(0,200)$, $(50,170)$, $(100,140)$, $(150,110)$

Exercises 29–31: List the points in each graph, showing letter and coordinates.

29.
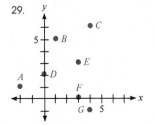

30.
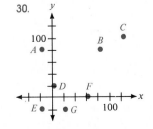

31.
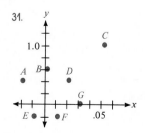

32. On the coordinate system below, plot and label the points A: $(3,6)$, B: $(5,-6)$, C: $(-4,6)$, and D: $(-6,-5)$. Also, plot at least 3 points on the graph of $2w + 3y = 8$, and draw the graph.

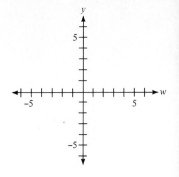

33. On the coordinate system below, plot and label the points R: $(-4,6)$, S: $(5,2)$, TT: $(-3,-6)$, U: $(6,-5)$. Also plot at least three points on the graph of $4j - 3k = -12$, and draw the graph.

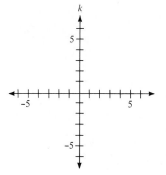

34. On the coordinate system below, sketch and label with capital letters the graphs of the equations

    A: $4x - 7y = -19$ B: $x + 2y = -1$ and C: $-6x + y = -19$

    Then label the intersection of each pair of lines (A and B, A and C, B and C) with coordinates obtained by reading your graph as accurately as possible. Check each pair of coordinates to see if it satisfies the equations of the intersecting graphs.

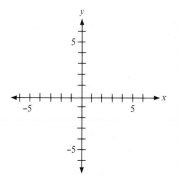

35. On the coordinate system below, sketch and label with capital letters the graphs of the equations

    L: $6x - 4y = -32$ M: $3x + 2y = 4$ and N: $x + 6y = -12$

    Then label the intersection of each pair of lines with its coordinates, determined as accurately as possible by reading your graph, and check each coordinate pair to see if it satisfies the corresponding two equations.

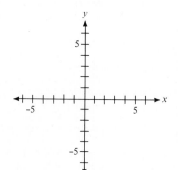

36. In a home with three television sets and four children aged 11 to 18, a seven-day audit of total hours of television from Sunday (day #1) through Saturday (day #7) produced the following record. Plot the data on a suitable graph.

Day	1	2	3	4	5	6	7
Hours	10	6	5	2	4.5	7	12

37. Rick Railston, just resuming daily jogging after three months' convalescence from a back injury, measures his progress by occasionally jogging a timed mile on a Saturday morning. His record of weeks since resumption and corresponding times (expressed in decimal parts of a minute) is as follows. Plot the data on a suitable graph.

Week #	5	12	19	35	40	48
Mile Time	10.4	8.8	8.2	7.9	8.4	7.7

38. The percentages of aluminum beverage cans recycled in the years 1980 to 1989 were as follows. Plot the data on a suitable graph.

Year	'80	'81	'82	'83	'84	'85	'86	'87	'88	'89
% Recycled	17	26	32	34	31	37	40	43	45	50

39. An urban planner sought information correlating number of nationally franchised fast-food outlets to community size (measured to the nearest 5,000), and came up with the following measurements. Plot the data.

City size	10,000	20,000	35,000	45,000	70,000
Fast-food outlets	3	5	11	13	19

0.3 LINEAR EQUATIONS AND GRAPHS

In Example 8, we saw that plotting number pairs derived from real-world data can be illuminating. We can also plot number pairs determined by mathematical statements of relationship. The pairs of numbers satisfying an equation in x and y often form interesting patterns. For instance, let us tabulate and plot some of the pairs satisfying the equation $-x + y = 2$ (or, equivalently, $y = x + 2$):

Figure 0.3
Table and plot for some points satisfying $y = x + 2$

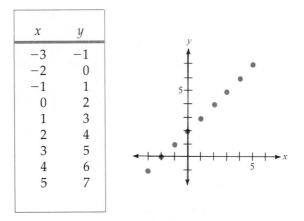

x	y
-3	-1
-2	0
-1	1
0	2
1	3
2	4
3	5
4	6
5	7

The plotted points in Figure 0.3 display a definite pattern. In fact, all points whose coordinates satisfy $y = x + 2$ fall into this pattern—they lie on the line determined by the present points. Furthermore, all coordinate pairs of points on this line satisfy the given equation. For this reason, "$-x + y = 2$" is called a *linear equation*. It is easy to recognize linear equations and to classify their graphs.

LINEAR EQUATIONS IN STANDARD FORM

> If A, B, and C are real numbers, with A and B not both zero, then
>
> $$Ax + By = C$$
>
> is a **linear equation in standard form,** and its graph is a **line in the coordinate plane.** The numbers A and B are the x and y **coefficients,** respectively; the number C is called the **constant term** of the equation.

In our equation $-x + y = 2$, $A = -1$, $B = 1$, and $C = 2$. The "standard form" definition suggests A or B may equal zero, so long as at least one coefficient (A or B) is nonzero. In the equation $-x + y = 2$, both A and B were nonzero; the graph was an **oblique** (slanting) line. What if one coefficient is zero?

■ EXAMPLE 9

Plot graphs of

(a) $2x = 8$ (or "$2x + 0y = 8$")

(b) $3y = 6$ (or "$0x + 3y = 6$")

SOLUTION

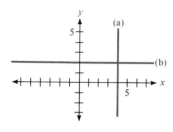

Equation (a) is satisfied only if $x = 4$, no matter what value is given to y. Typical points of its graph are $(4,0)$, $(4,0.5)$, $(4,-1)$, $(4,3)$, etc. As expected, these points are on a line, marked "(a)" in the graph. (Also, solving for x in $2x = 8$ yields $x = 4$.)

Likewise, (b) is satisfied only if $y = 2$. Typical points are $(-3,2)$, $(0,2)$, $(2,2)$, $(3.5,2)$, etc. All such points are on line (b) in the graph.

■

In Example 9, the graph of $2x = 8$ turned out to be a vertical line at $x = 4$; the graph of $3y = 6$ was a horizontal line at $y = 2$. Every horizontal or vertical line has an easily recognized equation.

HORIZONTAL AND VERTICAL LINES

> If $A \neq 0$, the graph of $Ax = C$ is a vertical line.
> If $B \neq 0$, the graph of $By = C$ is a horizontal line.

PRACTICE PROBLEM 8

Graph the equations (a) $x = -3$, (b) $x = 6$, (c) $y = 4$, and (d) $y = -2$.

ANSWER(S)

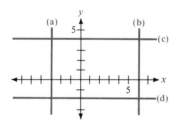

Graphing linear equations is easy. If either A or B is zero, the graph is a horizontal or vertical line. If both A and B are nonzero, the graph is an oblique line; one can substitute convenient values for x or y, find the corresponding values of the other variable, and plot a few points to determine the graph.

ELEMENTARY GRAPHING TECHNIQUE FOR LINEAR EQUATIONS

> Given any linear equation in two variables x and y, substitute any convenient value x_1 for x and solve for y_1, the corresponding value of y. Plot the point $P_1(x_1, y_1)$. Repeat, using a new value of x (or of y) to obtain a second point $P_2(x_2, y_2)$. The graph is the line through P_1 and P_2. Plot a third point as a check.

■ EXAMPLE 10

Graph the equation $4x - 5y = 10$.

SOLUTION

Substitute 0 for x and solve for y

$$4x - 5y = 10$$
$$4(0) - 5y = 10$$
$$-5y = 10$$
$$y = \frac{10}{(-5)}$$
$$y = -2$$

Substitute 0 for y and solve for x

$$4x - 5y = 10$$
$$4x - 5(0) = 10$$
$$4x = 10$$
$$x = \frac{10}{4}$$
$$x = 2.5$$

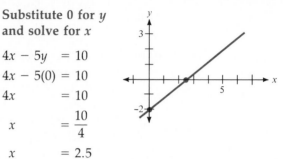

Two points on the graph are thus $(0, -2)$ and $(2.5, 0)$. Plot these and draw the graph. As a check, plot $(5,2)$, obtained by substituting 5 for x and solving to obtain $y = 2$. Note that $(5,2)$ is also on the line. ■

PRACTICE PROBLEM 9

Graph **(a)** $2y - 5 = x$ and **(b)** $3x = 8y$.

ANSWER(S)

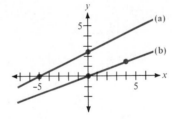

Example 10 displayed an especially convenient way of graphing a linear equation by plotting two points. Substituting 0 for x in the equation produced $y = -2$, where the desired graph crossed the y-axis. This point is the **y-intercept** of the graph. Substituting 0 for y yielded $x = 2.5$, the **x-intercept** of the graph. Finding such intercepts of the graph and drawing the line through them provides a quick and accurate graph, provided the intercepts are not too close to each other (and to $(0,0)$, the origin). If both intercepts are near the origin, a more distant value of x or y will yield a point more suitable for accurate graphing.

Special Case: Zero y-intercept

If substituting $x = 0$ into the given equation produces $y = 0$, then both the x- and y-intercepts are zero. The graph passes through the origin, and a second point must be found using a nonzero value of x or y.

In the pages to follow, we shall emphasize graphing from equations. Such skills directly support our work in later chapters. We shall also learn to write equations of lines, given certain information about their graphs. This knowledge will enhance our ability to make accurate graphs using information from the form of the equation itself. Basic principles of operations on real numbers and their representatives, algebraic expressions, allow us to creatively alter equations into useful forms.

CHANGING THE FORMS OF EQUATIONS

If a, b, and c are real numbers or algebraic expressions, and if $a = b$, then:

1. $a + c = b + c$ The same quantity may be added to (or
   $a - c = b - c$ subtracted from) both members of an
                                equation.

2. If $c \neq 0$ The same nonzero quantity may multiply (or
   $a \cdot c = b \cdot c$ divide) both members of an equation.

   $\dfrac{a}{c} = \dfrac{b}{c}$

In transforming an equation through a succession of forms toward a simpler or more useful form, write "=" ("equals") only between the left and right sides of each individual equation, never between successive equations. Each equation is a complete mathematical sentence. The next equation is a new sentence. No connector between the equations is needed. A few examples should revive most essential skills.

■ EXAMPLE 11

Write each of the following equations in standard form, with integer coefficients. Classify each line as horizontal, vertical, or oblique.

(a) $x - 3y - 10 = -x - 8y$ **(b)** $6y - 1 = -\dfrac{1}{4}y + \dfrac{3}{2}$

(c) $x + \dfrac{2}{3} = \dfrac{2}{3}x + 1$ **(d)** $-2y + 2x = -2x + 2y$

SOLUTION

(a) $x - 3y - 10 = -x - 8y$ Add x to both sides.
      $+x \qquad\qquad +x$

   $2x - 3y - 10 = \qquad - 8y$ Add 10 to both sides.

   $2x - 3y \qquad = 10 - 8y$ Add $8y$ to both sides.

   $2x + 5y \qquad = 10$ $A = 2$; $B = 5$; $C = 10$;   oblique

(b) $6y - 1 = -\dfrac{1}{4}y + \dfrac{3}{2}$ Multiply both sides by 4.

   $24y - 4 = -1y + 6$ Add 4 to both sides.

   $24y \qquad = -y + 10$ Add y to both sides.

   $25y \qquad = \qquad 10$ $A = 0$; $B = 25$; $C = 10$;   horizontal

(c) $x + \dfrac{2}{3} = \dfrac{2}{3}x + 1$ Multiply by 3.

$3x + 2 = \;\; 2x + 3$ Subtract $2x$.

$x + 2 = \qquad\;\; 3$ Subtract 2.

$x \quad\;\; = \quad\;\; 1$ $A = 1;\; B = 0;\; C = 1;$ vertical

(d) $-2y + 2x = -2x + 2y$ Add $2x$ to both sides.

$-2y + 4x = \qquad\;\; 2y$ Subtract $2y$ from both sides.

$4x - 4y = 0$ $A = 4;\; B = -4;\; C = 0;$ oblique.   ■

PRACTICE PROBLEM 10   Graph each equation in Example 11.

ANSWER(S)   **(a)** $2x + 5y = 10$. If $y = 0$, $x = 5$. If $x = 0$, $y = 2$. Plot $(5,0)$, $(0,2)$.

(b) $25y = 10$. Solve for y. $y = 10 \div 25 = \dfrac{2}{5}$. Horizontal line.

(c) $x = 1$. Vertical line.

(d) $4x - 4y = 0$. If $x = 0$, $y = 0$. If $y = 0$, $x = 0$. If $x = 5$, $y = 5$.

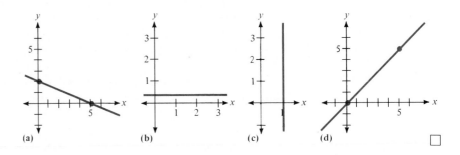

In Practice Problem 10, part **(a)**, setting $y = 0$ gave us the x-intercept 5, where the graph crosses the x-axis. Similarly, $x = 0$ gave us the y-intercept 2. The graph immediately followed.

  In part **(d)**, the x-intercept and y-intercept were both 0 (both at the origin). In this case we chose a convenient nonzero value of one variable and determined the corresponding value of the other. Choosing $x = 5$ gave us $y = 5$.

Slope of a Line   Through any single point in the coordinate plane, it is possible to draw infinitely many lines. These lines differ from one another only in their steepness. Figure 0.4 shows several lines through the origin. Speaking intuitively, line **(a)** is steeper (rises more rapidly to the right) than line **(b)**, and line **(c)** is steeper than either line **(a)** or **(b)**, but falls, rather than rising, to the right.

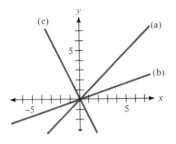

Figure 0.4
Lines through the origin, with
differing "steepness"

For each line in Figure 0.4 (and for any other nonvertical line in the coordinate plane) there is a corresponding real number which measures its steepness. This number is called the **slope** of the line. To see how slope is measured, refer carefully to Figure 0.5, showing only line **(b)** from Figure 0.4, while reading the following discussion.

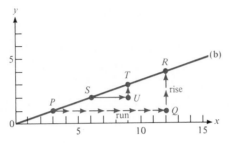

Figure 0.5
Line **(b)**, with two triangles for
measuring slope

Having selected points $P(3,1)$ and $R(12,4)$ on line **(b)**, imagine traveling from P to R by way of Q. You could describe the trip by saying "from P, go 9 units to the right (the "run" in Figure 0.5), then 3 units up (the "rise" in Figure 0.5)." The slope of line **(b)** is the ratio of these two numbers:

$$\text{slope of line } \textbf{(b)} = \frac{\text{rise during travel from } P \text{ to } R}{\text{run during travel from } P \text{ to } R} = \frac{3}{9} = \frac{1}{3}$$

The rise (during travel) from $P(3,1)$ to $R(12,4)$ is exactly $4 - 1$, the y-coordinate of the ending point R minus the y-coordinate of the starting point P. The run from P to R is $12 - 3$, the x-coordinate of R minus the x-coordinate of P.

The slope measurement of line **(b)** (Figure 0.5) does not depend upon which two points of line **(b)** we choose as starting point and ending point. We recalculate the slope using points S and T on line **(b)**, again traveling first horizontally, then vertically from S to reach T.

$$\text{slope of line } \textbf{(b)} = \frac{\text{rise from } S \text{ to } T}{\text{run from } S \text{ to } T} = \frac{3 - 2}{9 - 6} = \frac{1}{3}$$

We obtain the same measurement of slope of line **(b)**, whether we travel from P to R or from S to T. In fact, even the direction of travel does not matter. This time, travel from R to S, first moving horizontally, then vertically (dashed lines in Figure 0.5). The "rise" in this case is negative.

$$\text{slope of line } \textbf{(b)} = \frac{\text{rise from } R \text{ to } S}{\text{run from } R \text{ to } S} = \frac{2 - 4}{6 - 12} = \frac{-2}{-6} = \frac{1}{3}$$

The reason for this agreement of slope values, no matter which two points of line **(b)** are used, is clear to those having experience with similar triangles. In Figure 0.5, triangle PQR and triangle SUT are similar (have the same shape). Both are right triangles. In triangle PQR the two sides forming the right angle at Q are PQ and QQR. These are called the legs of the right angle. When two right triangles are similar, the quotient "short leg divided by long leg" is the same in both triangles. This quotient is "rise over run" in the present illustration. We can generalize:

SLOPE OF A NONVERTICAL LINE IN A COORDINATE SYSTEM

> Given nonvertical line L in a coordinate system, pick any two points $P_1(x_1, y_1)$ and $P_2(x_2, y_2)$ on L. Then the slope of L is
>
> $$m = \frac{y_2 - y_1}{x_2 - x_1}$$

■ **EXAMPLE 12**

Using the origin $O(0,0)$ and one other point on the line, find the slopes of lines **(a)** and **(c)** in Figure 0.4.

SOLUTION

For line **(a),** using points $O(0,0)$ and $A(5,5)$, the slope is

$$m_a = \frac{5 - 0}{5 - 0} = \frac{5}{5} = 1$$

For line **(c),** using points $O(0,0)$ and $C(-3,6)$, the slope is

$$m_c = \frac{6 - 0}{-3 - 0} = \frac{6}{-3} = -2$$ ■

Relationship of Slope to Steepness

Studying lines **(a)**, **(b)**, and **(c)**, with slopes $m_a = 1$, $m_b = 1/3$, and $m_c = -2$, respectively, we can draw general conclusions about slope and "steepness." Lines with large slopes (positive or negative) are steeper (more nearly vertical) than lines with small slopes (positive or negative). Lines with positive slopes rise toward the right; lines with negative slopes fall toward the right.

Two special cases remain:

1. The slope of a horizontal line is $m = 0$. To see this, calculate the slope of the horizontal line through $(0,3)$ and $(4,3)$.

2. The slope of a vertical line is undefined. To see this, attempt to calculate the slope of the vertical line through $(2,0)$ and $(2,6)$.

Drawing a Line with a Desired Slope Through a Given Point

Each nonvertical line through the origin has a specific slope, obtained using any two points on the line. Now, reversing the process, if we want a line through the origin to have a given slope, we may start at the origin and use the idea that slope = rise/run to move to a second point on the line, then draw the line through the origin and second point.

In fact, given any point and a desired slope, we may progress from that given point by a "run, then rise" route to a second point on the line, and draw the line through the given and second points.

EXAMPLE 13

Graph the following lines:

(a) through the origin, with slope $-2/5$;

(b) through the origin, with slope 3;

(c) through $P(3,1)$ with slope $3/2$.

SOLUTION

To graph line (a), start at the origin $O(0,0)$ and move horizontal ("run") distance 5 followed by vertical ("rise") distance -2, to the point $Q(5,-2)$. Line (a) passes through $O(0,0)$ and $Q(5,-2)$.

To graph line (b), first express the slope, 3, as the fraction $3/1$. Start at $O(0,0)$; move horizontal distance 1, then vertical distance 3, to the point $R(1,3)$. Line (b) passes through O and R.

To graph (c), start at $P(3,1)$. Move run distance 2, then rise distance 3 to point $S(5,4)$. Line (c) passes through P and S.

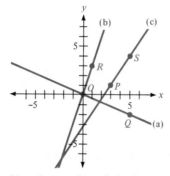

PRACTICE PROBLEM 11

Sketch graphs of the line

(a) through $P(-3,-2)$ with slope $m = -1$;

(b) through $Q(3,-4)$ with slope $m = 1/2$;

(c) through $R(1,2)$ with slope 3.

SOLUTION

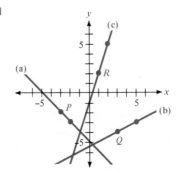

Equation Forms to Ease Graphing

Now let us look at two special forms of linear equations for oblique lines. These forms help us to quickly graph linear equations, and also to quickly write equations of given graphs—something we have not yet attempted. The forms are:

1. Point-slope form

2. Slope-intercept form

Both forms follow from a single observation: through a given point in the plane, there is one and only one line with a given slope.

Point-Slope Equation of a Line

In Figure 0.6(a) we show the line obtained as follows: given the point $P_1(1,3)$ and desired slope $m = 1/4$, from $P_1(1,3)$ we moved horizontal (run) distance 4, then vertical (rise) distance 1 to locate point $P_2(5,4)$. We then drew line **(a)** through P_1 and P_2.

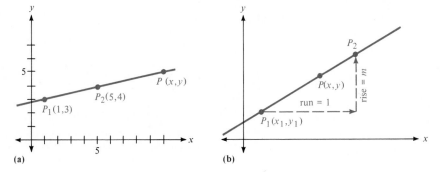

Figure 0.6
(a) A line through $P_1(1,3)$ with slope $m = 1/4$. **(b)** A line through $P_1(x_1, y_1)$ with slope $m = m/1$

Still referring to Figure 0.6(a), consider any "general" point $P(x, y)$ on line **(a)**, with P different from P_1. Line **(a)** has exactly one slope. This slope is $m = 1/4$. The calculated slope using $P(x, y)$ and $P_1(1,3)$ must also be 1/4. Expressing this sameness of slope in equation form,

$$\text{slope using } P \text{ and } P_1 = \frac{1}{4}$$

$$\frac{y - 3}{x - 1} = \frac{1}{4}$$

Multiplying by $x - 1$,

$$y - 3 = \frac{1}{4}(x - 1) \tag{0-1}$$

Equation **(0-1)** is an equation for line **(a)**. (Notice where the coordinates of the given point $P(1,3)$ and the given slope $m = 1/4$ show up in the equation.) Every point on line **(a)** has coordinates which satisfy equation **(0-1)**. Even the coordinates of $P_1(1,3)$ check in the equation:

$$y - 3 = \frac{1}{4}(x - 1)$$

$$3 - 3 = (?)\frac{1}{4}(1 - 1)$$

$$0 = 0$$

In Figure 0.6(b), line **(b)** passes through point $P_1(x_1, y_1)$ and has slope m. Using P_1 and any point $P(x, y)$ different from P_1 but also on line **(b)**, the calculated slope must be exactly m. In equation form,

slope using P and $P_1 = m$

$$\frac{y - y_1}{x - x_1} = m$$

Multiplying by $x - x_1$,

$$y - y_1 = m(x - x_1) \tag{0-2}$$

In equation **(0-2)**, the given slope m and the coordinates of the given point $P_1(x_1, y_1)$ are plainly visible.

POINT-SLOPE EQUATION OF A LINE

Given any point $P_1(x_1, y_1)$ in the coordinate plane and any slope m, an equation for the line through P_1 with slope m is

$$y - y_1 = m(x - x_1) \tag{0-2}$$

■ EXAMPLE 14

Write an equation of the line

(a) through (5,11) with slope $m = 2$;

(b) through (9,−6) with slope −2.

SOLUTION (a) Using equation **(0-2)**,

$$y - y_1 = m(x - x_1)$$
$$y - 11 = 2(x - 5)$$
$$y - 11 = 2x - 10$$
$$y = 2x + 1$$

(b)
$$y - y_1 = m(x - x_1)$$
$$y - (-6) = -2(x - 9)$$
$$y + 6 = -2x + 18$$
$$y = -2x + 12$$

■

PRACTICE PROBLEM 12 Write an equation, solved for y (that is, with y isolated on the left side of the equation), of the line

(a) through (12,−5) with slope 4/3;

(b) through (−6,−2) with slope 5.

ANSWER(S) (a) $y = \frac{4}{3}x - 21$ (b) $y = 5x + 28$ □

Slope-Intercept Equation of a Line

If a line with slope m has y-intercept b, this is equivalent to saying the line passes through the point $P_1(0,b)$. Let us use this special point $P_1(0,b)$ and the slope value m in equation **(0-2)**:

$$y - y_1 = m(x - x_1) \tag{0-2}$$
$$y - b = m(x - 0)$$
$$y - b = mx$$
$$y \quad\;\; = mx + b \tag{0-3}$$

Study equation **(0-3)** carefully. In particular, notice where the given y-intercept b and given slope m appear in the equation. This is the slope-intercept form for the equation of a line.

SLOPE-INTERCEPT EQUATION OF A LINE

> An equation for the line with slope m and y-intercept b is
> $$y = mx + b \tag{0-3}$$

Τhe point-slope form (equation **(0-2)**) is useful for writing an equation for a line, given a description in the form of a single point and desired slope. In contrast, the slope-intercept form (equation **(0-3)**) is useful both for writing an equation and for graphing an equation.

GRAPHING THE SLOPE-INTERCEPT FORM

> To graph the equation $y = mx + b$:
>
> **1.** Plot the point $P(0,b)$ on the y-axis.
>
> **2.** Use the slope m to start from $(0,b)$ and locate a second point Q on the desired line. (If m is a fraction c/d, then the form c/d suggests "run" d and "rise" c. If m is not a fraction, think of m as $m/1$, for example.)
>
> **3.** Draw the line through P and Q.

■ EXAMPLE 15

If the given equation is not in slope-intercept form, solve for y. (Isolate y on the left side of the equation, using the familiar tools for changing the form of an equation.) Then identify slope and y-intercept of the graph of the equation.

(a) $y = -3x + 7$

(b) $2x + 5y = 4x + 3y - 12$

(c) $x + 2y = 10$

SOLUTION   **(a)** The equation is in slope-intercept form. $m = -3; b = 7$

(b) Not in slope-intercept form. Solve for y.

$$2x + 5y = 4x + 3y - 12$$
$$5y = 4x + 3y - 12 - 2x$$
$$5y = 2x + 3y - 12$$
$$5y - 3y = 2x - 12$$
$$2y = 2x - 12$$
$$y = x - 6 \qquad m = 1; b = -6$$

(c) Not in slope-intercept form. Solve for y.

$$x + 2y = 10$$
$$2y = 10 - x$$
$$2y = -x + 10$$
$$y = -\frac{1}{2}x + 5 \qquad m = -\frac{1}{2}; b = 5$$

PRACTICE PROBLEM 13   Find slopes and y-intercepts, and draw the graphs, of

(a) $2y - 12 = 3(x - 2)$

(b) $3x + 8y = 72$

ANSWER(S)   See figure.

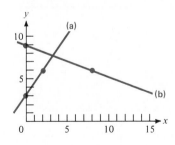

(a) $m = 3/2; b = 3$

(b) $m = -3/8; b = 9$. Can write and use m in form $m = (-3)/8$ or $m = 3/(-8)$. ☐

Equation of a Line through Two Given Points   Through any two points in the plane, there is exactly one line. If both points have the same x-coordinate, the line is vertical, and its equation is of the form $x = c$ (c a real number). If the points have different *x*-coordinates, we can calculate the slope of the line through the points, and then use either point and the calculated slope to write the point-slope equation of the line. No special form is needed for the two-point case.

■ EXAMPLE 16

Write an equation of the line through

    (a) $(5,11)$ and $(5,-2)$

    (b) $(-2,4)$ and $(6,4)$

    (c) $(10,6)$ and $(3,1)$

SOLUTION

(a) Both points have the same *x*-coordinate. The graph is a vertical line. An equation is $x = 5$.

(b) The *x*-coordinates of the two points are different, so one could calculate slope using the two points. However, noting that the *y*-coordinates are both 4, we recognize that the line is horizontal. An equation is $y = 4$.

(c) Neither *x*- nor *y*-coordinates match. The line through the two points is oblique. Its slope is

$$m = \frac{6 - 1}{10 - 3} = \frac{5}{7}$$

Using the calculated slope $m = 5/7$ with the point $(10,6)$ in the point-slope form,

$$y - y_1 = m(x - x_1)$$

$$y - 6 = \frac{5}{7}(x - 10)$$

$$y - 6 = \frac{5}{7}x - \frac{50}{7}$$

$$y = \frac{5}{7}x - \frac{50}{7} + 6$$

$$y = \frac{5}{7}x - \frac{8}{7}$$

The final equation is in the convenient slope-intercept form.   ■

PRACTICE PROBLEM 14

Write an equation, in slope-intercept form, of the line through the given points.

    (a) $(5,-3)$ and $(-13,3)$ **(b)** $(4,0)$ and $(-6,2)$

ANSWER(S)

(a) $y = -\dfrac{1}{3}x - \dfrac{4}{3}$ **(b)** $y = -\dfrac{1}{5}x + \dfrac{4}{5}$

☐

Equations of Parallel Lines   Two distinct (noncoinciding) lines with the same slope (hence same steepness) must be parallel. Two lines that do not have the same slope are not parallel, and must intersect (cross) at exactly one point.

How can one tell from their equations if two lines are parallel? First, we state the obvious: vertical lines (with equations of the form $x = c$, c a real number) are parallel. Horizontal lines (with equations of form $y = c$) are parallel.

If both equations are in slope-intercept form, simply compare the slopes: parallel lines have identical slopes. If both equations are in standard form, multiply either equation by a constant that makes the x-coefficients of the two equations match. If the y-coefficients also match, the lines are parallel. For any pair of equations, write both equations in either slope-intercept or standard form, then compare.

■ EXAMPLE 17

Find all five pairs of equations of parallel lines:

    (a) $y = 2x + 7$ **(f)** $9x + 12y = 2$

    (b) $3x + 5y = -1$ **(g)** $y - 5 = 0$

    (c) $x = 4.3$ **(h)** $x = 17$

    (d) $y = -2$ **(i)** $4y + 3x = 11$

    (e) $2x - y - 5 = 0$ **(j)** $0.6x + 2 + y = 0$

SOLUTION   **(c)** and **(h)** are equations of parallel vertical lines; **(d)** and **(g)** are equations of parallel horizontal lines.

The graph of **(a)** has slope 2. To compare **(a)** (in slope-intercept form) with remaining equations, rewrite them in slope-intercept form:

    (b) $3x + 5y = -1$ Subtract $3x$ from both sides.

           $5y = -3x + 1$ Divide both sides by 5.

           $y = -\dfrac{3}{5}x + \dfrac{1}{5}$

The graph of **(b)** has slope 3/5; of **(a)**, 2. Not equal.

    (e) $2x - y - 5 = 0$ Subtract $2x$.

          $-y - 5 = -2x$ Multiply by -1.

          $y + 5 = 2x$ Subtract 5.

          $y \quad\ = 2x - 5$

The graph of **(e)** has slope 2, as does that of **(a)**. Both **(a)** and **(e)** are equations of parallel lines with slope 2.

Still unpaired: **(b)**, **(f)**, **(i)**, **(j)**. Compare **(b)** and **(f)**.

(b) $3x + 5y = -1$ **(f)** $9x + 12y = 2$

Both equations are in standard form. Multiply **(b)** by 3 to change coefficient of x to 9 (producing matching x-coefficients), then compare:

$3 \cdot$ **(b):** $9x + 15y = -3$ **(f)** $9x + 12y = 2$

Because y-coefficients do not match, graphs are not parallel.

Compare **(b)** and **(i)**. Though x-coefficients match, y-coefficients do not. Not parallel.

Compare **(b)** and **(j)**.

(b) $3x + 5y = -1$ **(j)** $0.6x + 2 - y = 0$

Put **(j)** into standard form, then match x-coefficients:

(j) $0.6x + 2 + y = 0$	Subtract 2.
$0.6x + y = -2$	Multiply by 5.
$3x + 5y = -10$	Compare to **(b)**; x and y coefficients match.

Both **(b)** and **(j)** are equations of parallel lines.

Only **(f)** and **(i)** remain.

(f) $9x + 12y = 2$ **(i)** $4y + 3x = 11$

Rearrange **(i)**, then multiply **(i)** by 3.

(i)	$4y + 3x = 11$
	$3x + 4y = 11$
$3 \cdot$ **(i)**	$9x + 12y = 33$

Coefficients of x and y in $3 \cdot$ **(i)** exactly match those of x and y in **(f)**; **(f)** and **(i)** are equations of parallel lines.   ■

PRACTICE PROBLEM 15   Find all pairs of equations of parallel lines:

(a) $2x + 3y - 12 = 0$ **(b)** $x = 13$

(c) $y = 22$ **(d)** $y - 7 = 2x + 1$

(e) $10x + 6y = 16$ **(f)** $x - \dfrac{1}{2}y = -1$

(g) $5x + 3y = 12$ **(h)** $6 - x = 0$

(i) $y + 4 = -1$ **(j)** $y = -\dfrac{2}{3}x + 5$

ANSWER(S)   Parallel pairs: **(a)** and **(j)**; **(b)** and **(h)**; **(c)** and **(i)**; **(d)** and **(f)**; **(e)** and **(g)**

□

Careful Graphing Pays Off   In graphing, as in other endeavors, care and pride in one's craft are attributes worth cultivating. Graphing is a useful problem-solving tool. Sometimes, as in the study of linear programming in Chapters 4 and 5, a complex process is made understandable by drawing and studying accurate graphs.

When you draw graphs in rectangular coordinate systems, use a straightedge to draw axes and lines. Work with a sharp pencil, lightly until certain of correctness, then darken the graphed points and lines. Label axes, scales, and graphs clearly.

EXERCISES 0.3

PRACTICING THE MOVES AND MANEUVERS

Exercises 40–49: Graph each equation without first changing the form of the equation. Take advantage of slope-intercept form, vertical line form, and horizontal line form when you find them. Otherwise, plot at least three points and draw the graph.

40. $x = 2.5$

41. $y = 2x + 1$

42. $y = \dfrac{2}{3}x - 2$

43. $\dfrac{x}{4} + \dfrac{y}{6} = 1$

44. $y = 4$

45. $x = -3$

46. $2x - 7y = 14$

47. $5x + 2y = 15$

48. $\dfrac{x}{3} + \dfrac{y}{-5} = 1$

49. $y = -2$

Exercises 50–61: Write an equation of the line with the given description.

50. Slope $= 3/4$, y-intercept $= 3$
51. x-intercept -5, y-intercept 3
52. passing through $(-2,5)$ and $(3,-4)$
53. vertical, with x-intercept 13
54. horizontal, through $(6,12)$
55. through $(-3,6)$ and $(10,6)$
56. passing through $(10,2)$ and $(-5,5)$
57. y-intercept -12, x-intercept 8
58. slope -2, y-intercept -4
59. through $(5,5)$ and $(5,8)$
60. through $(14,-6)$, slope $5/2$
61. through $(5,2)$, slope -4

62. On one coordinate system, graph the equations $y = 3x$, $y = 3x + 2$, $y = 3x - 1$, and $y = 3x + 5$.

63. On one coordinate system, graph the equations $2x + 6y = 36$, $2x + 6y = 12$, $2x + 6y = 15$, and $2x + 6y = -12$.

64. Write an equation of the line through $(-3,3)$ parallel to the graph of $y = -6x + 10$.

65. Write an equation of the line through $(6,8)$ parallel to the graph of $5x - 2y = -1$.

66. Does the line with slope 5 and y-intercept $3/8$ intersect the line through points $(19,55)$ and $(23,74)$? Explain without graphing.

67. Does the line through points $(113,86)$ and $(93,66)$ intersect the graph of $x/5 - y/5 = 1$? Explain without graphing.

68. Are $(10,42)$, $(18,58)$, and $(24,75)$ on the same line? Explain without graphing.

0.4 WORD PROBLEMS AND MATHEMATICAL MODELS

Equations are powerful and compact statements of quantitative relationships. For example: a company's internal auditor sees an unitemized charge of $116 for 20 reams of paper and two boxes of felt-tip pens. She remembers that the pens cost $9.60 per box, and wishes to know the unit cost of the paper. Letting c denote the *cost per ream,* she reasons: "The cost for each of the 20 reams of paper is c. The two boxes of pens cost 2($9.60). Paper and pens together cost $116. Then $20c + 2(9.60) = 116$."

Key steps in starting to solve a word problem by algebra are:

1. Represent the unknown quantity or quantities (in this case, the number of reams of paper) by appropriate letters.

   Let c = the cost per ream of paper.

2. Describe the unknown quantity or quantities using one or more equations.

   $$20c + 2(9.60) = 116$$

These are the first two steps in every algebraic solution, no matter how complicated the problem may be. Execute these steps carefully; your entire solution depends upon their accuracy. If relationships about the unknown quantity or quantities are correctly expressed as equations, a correct solution is (almost) assured. Continuing the solution:

3. Solve the equation. In this example, change its form until the unknown quantity c is isolated.

   $$20c + 2(9.60) = 116 \qquad \text{Arithmetic}$$
   $$20c + 19.20 = 116 \qquad \text{Subtract 19.20.}$$
   $$20c = 116 - 19.20$$
   $$20c = 96.80 \qquad \text{Divide by 20.}$$
   $$c = 4.84$$

4. Interpret the solution, answering any questions posed in the original problem. The paper cost $4.84 per ream.

■ EXAMPLE 18

In each of the following, represent the unknown quantity or quantities by appropriate letters (that is, letters suggestive of the quantities they represent), and describe the unknown quantity or quantities using an equation:

(a) How many one-dozen egg cartons can be filled from a crate containing 576 eggs?

(b) If chicken sandwiches cost $2 and grilled cheese sandwiches cost $1, what mixes of the two kinds will cost exactly $10?

(c) The total staff of a school (teachers, administrators, and nonacademic employees, such as cooks and custodians) is to be 17 people. How many of each employment classification are possible?

SOLUTION

(a) Let d represent the unknown number of dozens. Then, $12d = 576$.

(b) Let c be the number of chicken sandwiches, and g the number of grilled cheese sandwiches. Then, $2c + 1g = 10$.

(c) Let t = the number of teachers (avoid nonsensical phrases like "t = teachers"; after all, t stands for a number or quantity), a = the number of administrators, and e = the number of nonacademic employees. Then, $t + a + e = 17$. ∎

Linear Equations in Standard Form

The Example 18 equations have some common characteristics. To see these characteristics, we list the original equations:

(a) $12d = 576$ **(b)** $2c + 1g = 10$ **(c)** $t + a + e = 17$

Common characteristics:

1. Each variable appears in only one term, and only to the first power. (For example, in equation **(b)**, no term involves c^2 or $\sqrt{g}$.)

2. All terms containing variables are on the left side of the equation; **constant terms** (not containing variables) are on the right side of the equation. (This is standard form, described in Section 0.3.)

We have already described as "linear" any equation in two variables having these two characteristics, because the graph of such an equation is a line. In fact, any equation which can be manipulated into a form having these characteristics is called a linear equation. Example 18 does provide one surprise: that linear equations emerge from such a variety of problem settings. Linear equations and their applications will occupy us in Chapters 1, 4, and 5, and will crop up in other chapters.

Mathematical Models

Most applications of mathematics arise in response to questions phrased in words: What is the cost per ream? How many sandwiches of each kind could be purchased? What velocity must the rocket reach to go into earth orbit? What mix of two diet supplements will provide essential nutrients at minimum cost? As in Example 18, the starting point for answering such a question is to use variables (letters) to represent unknown quantities, then write equations to interrelate those variables.

The equation(s) describing relationships among variables are called a **mathematical model** of the problem. Such a model is helpful if it is

1. Accurate: The equations in the model tell only the truth about the quantities they contain.

2. Complete: The equations represent all essential facts in the problem.

An accurate, complete model allows us to answer all questions which can be phrased in the original problem setting.

Example 18 showed the first stages of model building. Practice this essential skill in Practice Problem 16.

PRACTICE PROBLEM 16   Define variables, and write one or more equations, to model each of the following situations:

(a) The total staff of a school (teachers, administrators, and other employees) is 17, and the number of teachers is triple the number of administrators. Use two equations to express the relationships among numbers of the three employee categories.

(b) A salesperson at Robinson's Department Store is paid a base salary of $140 per week, plus a 2% commission on all of her sales. Express her week's pay in terms of her week's sales.

(c) Discount City wants aggressive salespeople, and pays each a base weekly salary of $50, plus a 3% commission on all sales after the first $800. How should Sam Emory (some people find him abrasive) calculate his week's pay if his sales exceed $800?

ANSWER(S)   (a) Let t = number of teachers, a = number of administrators, and e = number of other employees. Then a two-equation model is: $t + a + e = 17$, $t = 3a$.

(b) Let p = total pay for the week, and s = total sales for the week. Then $p = 140 + 0.02s$.

(c) Let p = Sam's total pay for the week, and s = his total sales for the week. $p = 50 + 0.03 (s - 800)$.   □

EXERCISES 0.4

APPLYING THE CONCEPTS

Exercises 69–76:   Define a suitable variable or variables and write an equation or equations describing the given relationship(s):

69. The company cafeteria offers only sandwiches and beverages. All sandwiches cost $2.50; all beverages cost $1. Write an equation which describes the total bill at any table in the cafeteria.

70. Wheat weighs 58 pounds per bushel. Write an equation describing the number of bushels in a truckload of wheat if the weight of the load is known.

71. The company bowling team plans to lunch together in the cafeteria of Exercise 69. The captain plans to spend exactly $28 for the team's lunch. Relate this fact to the prices for sandwiches and beverages.

72. The spring on a garage door is designed so that the spring stretches one foot for each 35 pounds of force applied to it. Write an equation describing the amount of force applied, if the amount of stretch is known.

73. Express total monthly dues income for a racquet club in terms of the membership, if each family membership pays $35 per month, each individual active membership pays $25 per month, and each social membership pays $10 per month.

74. Repulsive Pizza Co. sells one size pizza (small; the pizza is so terrible no one would order a larger size). The basic pizza costs $4; there is an additional charge of $.50 for each optional topping. Express the total price of a single pizza in terms of the number of toppings.

75. Repulsive Pizza's major competitor, Disgusting Deli, offers a basic sandwich for $2, and charges $.75 per extra ingredient. Express a family's total sandwich bill in terms of the number of sandwiches and the number of "extras."

76. The racquet club of Exercise 73 took in $1800 in dues last month. How is this related to the dues structure (family, individual, and social memberships)?

0.5 ALGEBRAIC ALTERATION OF EQUATIONS

In Section 0.3 we listed two principles for changing the forms of equations:

1. The same number or algebraic expression may be added to (subtracted from) both sides of an equation.

2. The same nonzero number or expression may be used to multiply (divide) both sides of an equation.

We used these principles to transform linear equations in x and y into slope-intercept form.

In the present section we attack the following problem: Given an algebraic equation involving numbers and letters (variables or unknowns), solve that equation for any one of its variables using only the operations of addition, subtraction, multiplication, and division. To solve an equation for a given variable v, we must change the form of the equation so that only one copy of the variable appears in the entire equation, isolated on one side of the equation.

Though we shall not become expert enough to solve every equation built up in this manner, we shall refresh or acquire the skills we will need in the chapters to come.

■ EXAMPLE 19

Solve for x:

$$\frac{2x}{3} + \frac{x}{4} = \frac{4x - 3}{6}$$

SOLUTION   Survey the denominators in the equation:

- Denominators: 3, 4, 6.

- Denominators, in factored form: 3, $2 \cdot 2$, $2 \cdot 3$.

- LCD (product of shortest list of factors containing each denominator separately): $3 \cdot 2 \cdot 2$, or 12.

Conclusion: multiply both sides of the equation by 12.

$$12 \cdot \left[\frac{2x}{3} + \frac{x}{4}\right] = \left[\frac{4x-3}{6}\right] \cdot 12 \qquad \text{Distribute 12 on left side, and simplify.}$$

$$8x + 3x = (4x - 3) \cdot 2 \qquad \text{Distribute 2 on right.}$$

$$11x = 8x - 6 \qquad \text{Subtract } 8x.$$

$$3x = -6 \qquad \text{Divide by 3.}$$

$$x = -2$$

Even when the denominators in an equation are algebraic expressions, multiplying by the LCD has helpful results:

■ EXAMPLE 20

Solve for z:

$$\frac{4}{z} - \frac{3}{2z+4} = \frac{11}{2z}$$

SOLUTION   The denominators: z, $2z + 4$, $2z$.

The denominators, in factored form: z, $2(z + 2)$, $2 \cdot z$.

The LCD: $z \cdot 2 \cdot (z + 2)$. Use to multiply both sides:

$$z \cdot 2 \cdot (z+2) \cdot \left[\frac{4}{z} - \frac{3}{2(z+2)}\right] = \frac{11}{2 \cdot z} \cdot z \cdot 2 \cdot (z+2) \qquad \text{Simplify.}$$

$$2 \cdot (z+2) \cdot 4 \quad - \quad 3z \quad = 11 \cdot (z+2)$$

$$8z \quad + 16 \quad - \quad 3z \quad = 11z + 22$$

$$5z + 16 = 11z + 22$$

$$-6z = 6$$

$$z = -1$$

PRACTICE PROBLEM 17   Solve each equation for its only variable.

(a) $\dfrac{r}{3} + \dfrac{r-1}{2} = r - 3$ (b) $\dfrac{2}{z} - \dfrac{5}{z+2} = \dfrac{1}{z}$ (c) $\dfrac{x}{3} + \dfrac{x+1}{4} = \dfrac{x+2}{6}$

ANSWER(S)   **(a)** $r = 15$;   **(b)** $z = 1/2$;   **(c)** $x = 1/5$ ☐

PRACTICE PROBLEM 18   Solve for the indicated variable.

(a) Solve for p: $2(1 - p) - 3p = 0$

(b) Solve for t: $35 = 200(0.05)t$

(c) Solve for y: $\dfrac{3y - 7}{2y + 4} = 1$ *Hint:* First, clear of fractions. Multiply equation by LCD.

(d) Solve for P: $A = P(1 + r)$

(e) Solve for r: $A = P(1 + r)$

ANSWER(S)   **(a)** $p = 2/5$ **(b)** $t = 3.5$ **(c)** $y = 11$ **(d)** $P = A/(1 + r)$
(e) $r = A/P - 1$ ☐

EXERCISES 0.5

PRACTICING THE MOVES AND MANEUVERS

Exercises 77–84: Solve for x.

77. $3x - 12 = 2x + 23$

78. $\dfrac{x}{3} + \dfrac{2x}{5} = 26 - x$

79. $\dfrac{4x - 3}{x - 4} = 5$

80. $\dfrac{10}{x} = \dfrac{2}{3x} + \dfrac{70}{3}$

81. $3(1 - 5x) = 2(3x - 2)$

82. $\dfrac{3x + 7}{5} + \dfrac{x + 2}{2} = x + 2$

83. $13 - 10x = 10x + 5$

84. $\dfrac{7 + 4x}{2x - 1} = -8$

Exercises 85–92: Solve for x. (These exercises illustrate specific patterns found in later chapters.)

85. $3(0.3) + (x - 5)(0.7) = 0$

86. $(8 - x)(0.4) + (2 - x)(0.6) = 0$

87. $(x - 7)(0.29) + (-2)(0.71) = 0$

88. $14x + (-8)(1 - x) = 0$

89. $5(0.65) + (x - 2)(0.35) = 0$

90. $(20 - x)(0.38) + (12 - x)(0.62) = 0$

91. $(x - 13)(0.43) + (-9.5)(0.57) = 0$

92. $5x + (-3.3)(1 - x) = 0$

Systems of Linear Equations

INTRODUCTION

This mathematical territory is new to most students. That is not to say it is difficult. Varied, interesting, and even challenging applications require only modest algebraic abilities. We covered most background essentials in Chapter 0, and we continue to provide examples and reminders at appropriate points in the text. We develop other skills at appropriate sites in this and later chapters.

For example, in Chapter 1, we use competent fraction arithmetic to develop methods for solving *systems* of two or more linear equations with two or more variables. These methods pay off in Chapters 4 and 5, where we pursue such goals as maximizing profits, minimizing costs, or serving the greatest number of clients. In Chapter 4 we discuss linear *inequalities* and their graphs and immediately use our understanding to display graphically all of the product mixes available to a manufacturer in search of an optimal blend of products.

It is important that you practice and master all algebra skills as they are introduced. You will then be equipped to give your full attention to the new applications of these skills, confident that your moves will be automatic and reliable when you need them.

1.1 SOLUTION METHODS FOR LINEAR SYSTEMS

A single linear equation (see Chapter 0) sometimes provides an accurate, compact, easily interpreted *model* of the relationship between two variables. The graph of a linear equation is easy to comprehend. The rise or fall of the dependent variable, as the independent variable increases, is clearly visible. Pairs of *values* of the two interrelated variables can be read directly from the graph or can be calculated by specifying one variable's value and solving for the other.

Plotting graphs and estimating coordinates sometimes gives inaccurate results. No matter how sharp the pencil or how careful the plotter, there is a limit to the accuracy one can achieve from a sketch. Algebraic methods yield the accuracy we require.

In this section we study **linear systems**—sets of two or more linear equations using two or more variables. We develop two methods for solving linear systems (finding values of the variables which satisfy all equations in the system): the *substitution method* and the *elimination (of variables) method*.

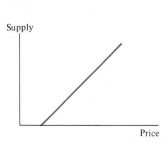
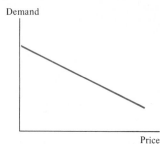

Typical graphic representations of mathematical relationships

■ EXAMPLE 1

Don Schenk, staff writer for a small monthly magazine, needs to produce two more short articles than long articles. Each short article requires two hours of writing time; each long article takes three hours. He has only nine hours of writing time. To use all available time, how many of each type of article should he plan?

SOLUTION

We follow our established pattern for word problems. Let x represent the number of short articles, and let y represent the number of long articles. Look for ways to express relationships between x and y.

Don hopes to write two more short articles than long articles:

$$x = y + 2$$

or, in standard form,

    (a) $x - y = 2$

(For reference, we label equations with letters: **(a)**, **(b)**, etc.)

Each short article takes two hours. Each long article takes three hours. The time available is nine hours. To use all of his time,

    (b) $2x + 3y = 9$

The word problem involving Don Schenk's writing schedule has become *solve the system of two equations in two variables*

    (a) $x - y = 2$
    (b) $2x + 3y = 9$

The Substitution Method

Consider the system of the two equations **(a)** and **(b)** in two variables x and y, and their graphs (Figure 1.1).

(a) $x - y = 2$

(b) $2x + 3y = 9$

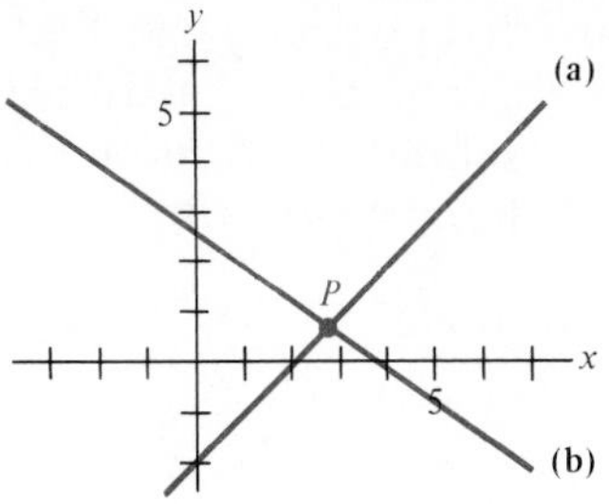

Figure 1.1
Graphs of equations **(a)**
and **(b)**

The intersection point P of the two graphs is on both graphs. The (x, y) coordinates of P therefore must satisfy both equations. "Solve the system of equations **(a)** and **(b)**" means two things:

1. Find values of x and y which satisfy both equations.

2. Find the coordinates of the intersection point P.

Figure 1.1 shapes our thinking; but the substitution method is purely algebraic. First, solve one equation for one of its variables. Equation **(a)** is the easier one to solve:

(a) $x - y = 2$	add y to both sides
$x = y + 2$	

Now substitute the expression $y + 2$—obtained for x from equation **(a)**—in place of x in equation **(b)**. (It is this substitution of an expression obtained from one equation into another equation which gives the method its name.) The substitution step:

(b) $2x + 3y = 9$
$2(y + 2) + 3y = 9$

This last equation is simpler than equations **(a)** and **(b)** because it contains only one variable, y. Solving for y:

$2(y + 2) + 3y = 9$	distribute the 2
$2y + 4 + 3y = 9$	combine the y terms
$5y + 4 = 9$	add -4 to both sides
$5y = 5$	multiply by 1/5
$y = 1$	

If our work is correct, $y = 1$ is the y coordinate of the intersection point P of the two graphs in Figure 1.1. Now substitute the value $y = 1$ into either of the "original equations" **(a)** and **(b)**. Using **(a)**,

(a) $x - y = 2$	substitute 1 for y
$x - 1 = 2$	add 1 to both sides
$x = 3$	

Checking a Solution   To be a solution to a system of equations **(a)** and **(b),** the values $x = 3$ and $y = 1$ must satisfy both equations. A check is essential; an incorrect solution is *always* detectable and correctable. Substituting (3,1) first into **(a),** then into **(b):**

$$\begin{aligned}
\textbf{(a)} \qquad x - y &= \quad 2 \\
3 - 1 &=(?)\ 2 \\
2 &= \quad 2 \qquad \text{(3,1) checks in \textbf{(a)}}
\end{aligned}$$

$$\begin{aligned}
\textbf{(b)}\ \ 2x + 3y &= \quad 9 \\
2(3) + 3(1) &=(?)\ 9 \\
6 + 3 &=(?)\ 9 \\
9 &= \quad 9 \qquad \text{(3,1) checks in \textbf{(b)}}
\end{aligned}$$

Now we may say $x = 3$, $y = 1$ is a solution to the system of equations **(a)** and **(b).** We must now interpret our solution: Don should plan to do three short articles and one long article.   ■

Solution by Graphing   We could have guessed the point (3,1) from Figure 1.1, and checked its correctness in both equations. Such solution by graphing is useful only in two-variable systems, and even then is of limited value: solutions are seldom so easily "read" from the graph. The reasonableness of a supposed solution can be quickly checked using the graph.

In Example 1, it was easy to select one equation (**(a)** $x - y = 2$) to solve for one of its variables. When such a convenient choice does not offer itself, choose arbitrarily and proceed with care.

■ EXAMPLE 2   Solve the following system by substitution.

$$\textbf{(a)}\ \ 4x - 3y = 12$$

$$\textbf{(b)}\ \ 3x + 5y = 15$$

SOLUTION   Neither equation is especially easy to solve for one variable. We choose to solve **(a)** for y:

$$\begin{aligned}
\textbf{(a)}\ \ 4x - 3y &= 12 \qquad\qquad \text{add } -4x \text{ to both sides} \\
-3y &= -4x + 12 \qquad \text{multiply both sides by } -1/3 \\
y &= \frac{4}{3}x - 4
\end{aligned}$$

Substituting $\frac{4}{3}x - 4$—obtained from **(a)**—for y in equation **(b)** and solving for x:

$$\begin{aligned}
\textbf{(b)}\ \ 3x + 5y &= 15 \qquad\qquad \text{replace } y \text{ with } \frac{4}{3}x - 4 \\
3x + 5\left(\frac{4}{3}x - 4\right) &= 15 \qquad\qquad \text{distribute the 5}
\end{aligned}$$

$$3x + \frac{20}{3}x - 20 = 15 \qquad \text{multiply both sides by 3}$$

$$9x + 20x - 60 = 45 \qquad x \text{ terms left, constants right}$$

$$29x = 105$$

$$x = \frac{105}{29}$$

Resist the temptation to whip out a calculator at this point to produce $x \approx 3.621$. Though close to the exact solution value of x, this decimal approximation is slightly off; $x = 105/29$ is exact.

Now substitute this exact x value into **(a)** or **(b)**. Let's use **(b)**:

$$\textbf{(b)} \quad 3x \qquad + \qquad 5y = 15$$

$$3\left(\frac{105}{29}\right) + \qquad 5y = 15$$

$$\frac{315}{29} \qquad + \qquad 5y = 15$$

$$315 \qquad + 29(5y) = 29(15)$$

$$315 \qquad + 145y = 435$$

$$145y = 120$$

$$y = \frac{120}{145} = \frac{24}{29}$$

Checking to see if we have a solution: Substituting exact (fractional) values of x and y into equation **(b)**:

$$\textbf{(b)} \quad 3x \qquad + 5y \qquad = \qquad 15$$

$$3\left(\frac{105}{29}\right) + 5\left(\frac{24}{29}\right) = (?) \; 15 \qquad \text{substituting for } x \text{ and } y$$

$$\frac{315}{29} \qquad + \frac{120}{29} \qquad = (?) \; 15 \qquad \text{arithmetic}$$

$$\frac{435}{29} = (?) \; 15$$

$$15 = \qquad 15 \qquad \text{as we had hoped}$$

The solution checks in **(b)**. Now finish by checking in **(a)**.   ∎

PRACTICE PROBLEM 1   Solve each system by substitution, and check your solution:

$$\textbf{(a)} \; 2m - 5n = -5 \qquad \textbf{(b)} \; 6r - 5t = 5$$
$$m - 4n = 17 \qquad\qquad 3r + 15t = -1$$

ANSWER(S)   **(a)** $m = 5,\ n = 3$ **(b)** $r = \dfrac{2}{3},\ t = -\dfrac{1}{5}$ □

The Elimination Method

The elimination method is also algebraic and also yields an exact solution. The basic idea is to transform the original system of equations into a succession of simpler equivalent systems (systems having the same solution as the original), eliminating variables from certain equations, until the solution becomes apparent. Three moves are sufficient. Each move *always* produces an equivalent new system.

TRANSFORMING A SYSTEM OF LINEAR EQUATIONS INTO AN EQUIVALENT SYSTEM

To transform a given system of linear equations into an equivalent system, one may:

1. Reorder the equations in the system.

2. Multiply any equation by a nonzero constant.

3. Add a nonzero multiple of any equation to any other equation.

Note concerning equation labels (a), (b), etc.: In successive steps of a solution process, the same equation may receive a new label. This is simpler than using a mix of old and new labels. It enables us to point exactly at one appearance of an equation. This use of labels is necessary only in the present section and will soon disappear.

■ EXAMPLE 3

Apply the elimination method to the system of equations from Example 1:

(a) $x - y = 2$ or $1x - 1y = 2$

(b) $2x + 3y = 9$

SOLUTION

We maintain a complete system of two equations at all times, replacing equations with simpler equations until a solution is reached. Successive equivalent systems are shown at left, with explanations in the scratch paper area at right:

Systems of Equations	Scratch Paper Comments
(a) $1x - 1y = 2$	Add $(-2) \cdot$ (a) to (b); this eliminates the x term from (b), producing a new system (c), (d):
(b) $2x + 3y = 9$	

$$\begin{array}{rl} \textbf{(b)} & 2x + 3y = 9 \\ (-2) \cdot \textbf{(a)} & \underline{-2x + 2y = -4} \\ \textbf{(d)} & 0x + 5y = 5 \end{array}$$

(c) $1x - 1y = 2$

(d) $0x + 5y = 5$

(d) has only one unknown. Solve for y, and back-substitute the result into **(c)** to solve for x.

Equation **(d)** has only a single variable. From **(d)**, $y = 1$. Substituting into **(c)**,

(c) $x - y = 2$

$x - 1 = 2$

$x \quad\quad = 3$

The solution ($x = 3$, $y = 1$) was already checked in Example 1.   ■

We again emphasize that all complete systems of equations produced during the elimination method are equivalent systems (have the same solution). To firmly establish this idea, we picture each system in Example 4.

■ EXAMPLE 4

Use the elimination method to solve the system of equations

(a) $5r - 7s = -2$

(b) $3r + 5s = 31$

Interpret each transitional system graphically.

SOLUTION

We show a complete system after each transition, along with the graph of the system. *Transitions do not alter intersection points.*

Original System

(a) $5r - 7s = -2$

(b) $3r + 5s = 31$

The common point of the graphs (circled) *does not change* as the system of equations is taken through transitions.

Original System Graph

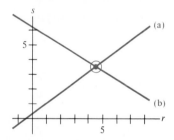

Transitional System 1

(c) $\quad 15r - 21s = -6$

(d) $-15r - 25s = -155$

Equation **(c)** is equation **(a)** multiplied by 3, and **(d)** is equation **(b)** multiplied by -5. *Multiplying an equation by a nonzero constant does not change its graph.*

Transitional System 1 Graph

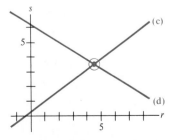

Transitional System 2   **Transitional System 2 Graph**

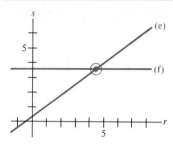

(e) $15r - 21s = -6$

(f) $0r - 46s = -161$

Equation **(f)** is the result of adding **(c)** to **(d)**. *Adding* one equation to another yields a new equation whose graph still passes through the common point of the original graphs.

Equation **(f)** has only one variable. Solving, $s = 161/46 = 3.5$.

As usual, back-substitute 3.5 for s in equation **(e)** and solve for r:

(e) $15r - 21s\quad\ = -6$

   $15r - 21(3.5) = -6$

   $15r - 73.5\quad = -6$

   $15r\qquad\quad = 67.5$

$$r = \frac{67.5}{15} = 4.5$$

The pair of equations

   $r = 4.5$

   $s = 3.5$

may be viewed as a final system revealing values of s and r.

Final System   **Final System Graph**

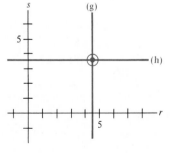

(g) $r = 4.5$

(h) $s = 3.5$

The graphs of equations **(g)** and **(h)** are a vertical and horizontal line, respectively. *These graphs cross at the common point of the original system.*

Study each system and its graph. Each new system is **equivalent to** (has the same solution, or common point, as) the Original System. The common point's coordinates are revealed in the Final System. The Final System values of r and s satisfy both equations in the Original System.

(Checking is an essential step in a complete solution. There is no reason to settle for an incorrect solution. If your solution values do not check in all original equations, you have made a mistake and must retrace your work or carry out a new solution.)   ■

Making Pencil-and-Paper Work Easier

In Example 4, we changed both original system equations to produce Transitional System 1:

Original System	Transitional System 1
(a) $5r - 7s = -2$	**(c)** $15r - 21s = -6$
(b) $3r + 5s = 31$	**(d)** $-15r - 25s = -155$

We made the r coefficients opposite integers to avoid fraction arithmetic. In the methods that follow, you can avoid fractions until the last steps if you wish. Avoiding fractions is convenient in longhand work. However, computers do not find fractions or decimals at all inconvenient. In our next example, we show typical steps in a more formal solution, the way a computer would do it.

■ EXAMPLE 5

Use the elimination method to solve the system

(a) $3x - 4y = 12$

(b) $5x + 8y = 31$

SOLUTION

We again show two columns: transitional systems at left, comments at right. Remember the graphic interpretations of Example 4: The graphs of equations in transitional systems continue to pass through the solution of the original system. We also drop the extra labels found helpful as references in earlier examples, showing a conventionally clean solution.

Systems of Equations

$3x - 4y = 12$
$5x + 8y = 31$

$1x - \dfrac{4}{3}y = 4$

$5x + 8y = 31$

$1x - \dfrac{4}{3}y = 4$

$0x + \dfrac{44}{3}y = 11$

Scratch Paper Comments

Multiply top equation by 1/3, to place "1" in the (first equation, first coefficient) location.

Use top equation as *tool* to change second equation (*target*) by eliminating $5x$: add (-5) times *tool* equation to *target*, producing a new second equation:

$$\begin{array}{r} 5x + 8y = 31 \\ -5x + (20/3)y = -20 \\ \hline 0x + (44/3)y = 11 \end{array}$$

Solving the second equation gives

$$y = 11 \div \left(\frac{44}{3}\right)$$

$$y = 11 \ \left(\frac{3}{44}\right)$$

$$y = \frac{3}{4}$$

Back-substituting into the first equation gives

$$1x - \left(\frac{4}{3}\right)\left(\frac{3}{4}\right) = 4$$

$$1x - 1 \qquad = 4$$

$$x = 5$$

Checking ($x = 5$, $y = 3/4$) in the original equations:

(a) $3x \ - 4y \ = \ 12$ **(b)** $5x \ + 8y \ = \ 31$

$3(5) - 4\left(\frac{3}{4}\right) =(?) \ 12$ $5(5) + 8\left(\frac{3}{4}\right) =(?) \ 31$

$15 \ - 3 \quad =(?) \ 12$ $25 \ + 6 \quad =(?) \ 31$

$12 = \quad 12$ $31 = \quad 31$

Our tedious but orderly process was correct!   ■

PRACTICE PROBLEM 2   Solve by elimination:

(a) $3p + 5q = 9$ **(b)** $4j - k = -1$
$2p + 3q = 2$ $8j + 3k = 13$

ANSWER(S)   **(a)** $p = -17$, $q = 12$ **(b)** $j = \frac{5}{2}$, $k = 11$ □

The elimination or substitution method may also be applied to three linear equations in three unknowns. We will illustrate both processes. In the elimination method for three equations, we will not graph the successive transition systems. Even with no picture, the common point stands revealed in the final system.

■ EXAMPLE 6   Solve by elimination:

$$2x - y + 3z = 1$$
$$3x + y - 4z = 21$$
$$x - 5y + z = -3$$

SOLUTION Recall the three fundamental moves of the elimination method:

1. *Reorder* the list of equations in the system.

2. *Multiply* a given equation by a nonzero constant.

3. *Add* a nonzero multiple of any equation to any other equation in the system. (Think of one equation as the *tool* used to alter the second, and of the second equation as the *target*.)

Systems of Equations	Scratch Paper Comments

Original System

(a) $2x - y + 3z = 1$	In (c), the x coefficient is 1, a perfect tool to eliminate x from the other two equations. Place equation (c) at the top, and relabel.
(b) $3x + y - 4z = 21$	
(c) $x - 5y + z = -3$	

Transitional System 1

(d) $x - 5y + z = -3$	Add -2 times (d) to (e). In the same *frame* (step to System 2), add -3 times equation (d) to equation (f).
(e) $2x - y + 3z = 1$	
(f) $3x + y - 4z = 21$	

Transitional System 2

(g) $x - 5y + z = -3$	Equations (h) and (i) are now a system of 2 equations in two variables. Multiply (h) by 1/9.
(h) $0x + 9y + z = 7$	
(i) $0x + 16y - 7z = 30$	

Transitional System 3

(j) $x - 5y + z = -3$	Add -16 times (k) to (l).
(k) $0x + y + \frac{1}{9}z = \frac{7}{9}$	
(l) $0x + 16y - 7z = 30$	

Transitional System 4

(m) $x - 5y + z = -3$	Equation (o) has only one variable. Solving for z yields $z = 158/9 \div (-79/9)$, hence $z = -2$.
(n) $0x + y + \frac{1}{9}z = \frac{7}{9}$	
(o) $0x + 0y - \frac{79}{9}z = \frac{158}{9}$	

Back-substituting $z = -2$ into equation **(n)**:

$$\textbf{(n)}\ 0x + y + \frac{1}{9}z\ = \frac{7}{9}$$

$$y + \frac{1}{9}(-2) = \frac{7}{9}$$

$$y - \frac{2}{9}\ = \frac{7}{9}$$

$$y = \frac{7}{9} + \frac{2}{9}$$

$$y = 1$$

Back-substituting $y = 1$ and $z = -2$ into **(m)**:

$$\textbf{(m)}\ x - 5y + z\ = -3$$
$$x - 5(1) - 2 = -3$$
$$x - 7\qquad = -3$$
$$x =\quad 4$$

If our work is correct, the solution to the original system of equations **(a)**, **(b)**, and **(c)** is $x = 4$, $y = 1$, $z = -2$. We show a check in equation **(a)**, leaving **(b)** and **(c)** to the reader:

$$\textbf{(a)}\ 2x\ - y + 3z\qquad =\quad 1$$
$$2(4) - 1 + 3(-2) =(?)\ 1$$
$$8\quad - 1 - 6\qquad =(?)\ 1$$
$$1 =\quad 1$$

■

The solution to Example 6 seemed long and tedious. We maintained complete systems through the transitions, to encourage careful, orderly work habits and to prepare for a future solution method. To show that the Example 6 solution was not really all that long, here are the transitions without the explanations. Account for each change from one system to the next by naming the step used. (The steps: *rearrange* equations; *multiply* an equation by a nonzero constant; *add* a nonzero multiple of one equation to another.)

Original System	Transitional System 1
$2x - y + 3z = 1$	$x - 5y + z = -3$
$3x + y - 4z = 21$	$2x - y + 3z = 1$
$x - 5y + z = -3$	$3x + y - 4z = 21$

Transitional System 2

$$x - 5y + z = -3$$
$$0x + 9y + z = 7$$
$$0x + 16y - 7z = 30$$

Transitional System 3

$$x - 5y + z = -3$$
$$0x + y + \frac{1}{9}z = \frac{7}{9}$$
$$0x + 16y - 7z = 30$$

Transitional System 4

$$x - 5y + z = -3$$
$$0x + y + \frac{1}{9}z = \frac{7}{9}$$
$$0x + 0y - \frac{79}{9}z = \frac{158}{9}$$

At this point, the bottom equation has only one variable, z. Solve and back-substitute, etc.

When solving linear systems by elimination, pattern your work after the above. You will find that your work is easy to retrace if checking your solutions reveals the presence of an error.

■ EXAMPLE 7

Solve by the substitution method.

(a) $2x - 3y + z = -5$

(b) $3x + y - 2z = 7$

(c) $-5x + 11y + 3z = 14$

SOLUTION   Scan to see if any variable in any equation would be easy to isolate. We choose to solve (a) for z, yielding

$$z = -2x + 3y - 5$$

Substituting the expression $-2x + 3y - 5$ for z in equations (b) and (c) yields

(d) $3x + y - 2(-2x + 3y - 5) = 7$

(e) $-5x + 11y + 3(-2x + 3y - 5) = 14$

Simplifying yields a system of two equations in x and y:

(f) $7x - 5y = -3$

(g) $-11x + 20y = 29$

Applying the substitution method to (f) and (g), we solve (f) for x:

$$x = \frac{5}{7}y - \frac{3}{7}$$

Substituting $(5/7)y - 3/7$ for x in **(g)** and solving for y yields

$$-11 \left(\frac{5}{7} y - \frac{3}{7} \right) + 20y = 29 \qquad \text{distribute } -11$$

$$-\frac{55}{7} y + \frac{33}{7} + 20y = 29 \qquad \text{multiply by 7}$$

$$-55y + 33 + 140y = 203 \qquad y \text{ terms to left}$$

$$85y = 170 \qquad \text{divide by 85}$$

$$y = 2$$

Back-substituting $y = 2$ into equation **(f)** and solving for x:

$$7x - 5y = -3$$
$$7x - 5(2) = -3$$
$$7x - 10 = -3$$
$$7x = 7$$
$$x = 1$$

Substitute $x = 1$ and $y = 2$ into any original equation; we choose **(b)**:

$$\textbf{(b)}\ 3x + y - 2z = 7$$
$$3(1) + 2 - 2z = 7$$
$$3 + 2 - 2z = 7$$
$$-2z = 2$$
$$z = -1$$

Our solution (subject to checking in all three original equations) is: $x = 1$, $y = 2$, $z = -1$. ■

Our examples have started with integer, rather than fractional, coefficients and constant terms. This is no limitation. If an equation has fractional coefficients, multiply the whole equation by the least common multiple of all the denominators. This gives integer coefficients, without altering solutions. Noninteger decimal coefficients are even easier to clean up: multiply the equation by a power of 10 sufficient to convert all coefficients to integers.

The elimination method creates "1" coefficients at strategic places in the system and uses these 1's to eliminate corresponding coefficients in other equations. Fraction arithmetic sometimes results, with increased chance of errors. If your future involves solving linear systems, you will probably use a computer which requires only that you input the coefficients and stand back! Meanwhile, careful habits now will enhance understanding later.

■ EXAMPLE 8

Universal Computers has just shipped a load of its computers to Midwest Insurance. A competitor, wanting to know what was in the shipment, has learned the following: Computer types R, S, and T were included, and 780 units were shipped. There were 190 more T units than R units. R, S, and T units weigh 30 pounds, 40 pounds, and 60 pounds each, respectively. The shipment weighed 37,100 pounds. How many of each unit were shipped?

SOLUTION We follow the standard steps for a word problem:

1. Read the problem carefully.

2. Identify unknown quantities; represent them by variables.

3. Write equations expressing relationships among variables.

4. Solve the equations for values of the variables.

5. Interpret the values of the variables, and answer the question(s) posed in the original problem.

Represent the numbers of computers of types R, S, and T by variables r, s, and t, respectively. Then,

(a) $r + s + t = 780$
(b) $r + 190 = t$

or, in standard form

(b) $r - t = -190$

(c) $30r + 40s + 60t = 37,100$

We solve this linear system of three equations in three unknowns by elimination: From the original system, proceed by means of the three permissible transition steps through a sequence of equivalent systems to a system ready to solve by back-substitution.

Original System

$$r + s + t = 780$$
$$r - t = -190$$
$$30r + 40s + 60t = 37100$$

Transitional System 1

$$r + s + t = 780$$
$$- s - 2t = -970$$
$$30r + 40s + 60t = 37100$$

Transitional System 2

$$r + s + t = 780$$
$$- s - 2t = -970$$
$$10s + 30t = 13700$$

Transitional System 3

$$r + s + t = 780$$
$$s + 2t = 970$$
$$10s + 30t = 13700$$

Transitional System 4

$$r + s + t = 780$$
$$s + 2t = 970$$
$$10t = 4000$$

Transitional System 5

$$r + s + t = 780$$
$$s + 2t = 970$$
$$t = 400$$

In Transitional System 5 we read $t = 400$. Back-substituting into the second equation in System 5,

$$s + 2(400) = 970$$
$$s + 800\ \ \ \ = 970$$
$$s\ \ \ \ \ \ \ \ \ \ \ = 170$$

Back-substituting $s = 170$ and $t = 400$ into the first System 5 equation,

$$r + 170 + 400 = 780$$
$$r + 570\ \ \ \ \ \ \ \ = 780$$
$$r\ \ \ \ \ \ \ \ \ \ \ \ \ \ = 310$$

The Universal Computers shipment thus consisted of 310 Type R computers, 170 Type S computers, and 400 Type T computers. ∎

EXERCISES 1.1

PRACTICING THE MOVES AND MANEUVERS

Exercises 1–4: Use the substitution method to solve the given system. Check your solution in the original equations.

1. $x - 4y = 7$
    $2x + 5y = 1$

2. $6c + 3d = \ \ 3$
    $2c - \ d = -9$

3. $r + \ s + \ t = 3$
    $2r - 5s - 3t = 7$
    $4r + \ s - \ t = 1$

4. $u - 2v + \ w = -4$
    $2u + 5v + 8w = \ \ 7$
    $4u + \ v + 7w = -4$

5. Solve Exercise 1 by the elimination method.
6. Solve Exercise 2 by the elimination method.
7. Solve Exercise 3 by the elimination method.
8. Solve Exercise 4 by the elimination method.

Exercises 9–12: Solve by the elimination method. Check each solution.

9. $3h + \ j - \ 2k = -2$
    $2h + 3j + \ 8k = \ 15$
    $-4h + 2j + 14k = \ 24$

10. $\dfrac{2}{3}f - \dfrac{1}{4}g + \ 3h = \dfrac{41}{2}$

    $\dfrac{1}{2}f + \dfrac{1}{4}g + \dfrac{1}{3}h = \dfrac{13}{2}$

    $\dfrac{1}{6}f - \dfrac{1}{2}g + \ h = 4$

*11. $r + s + \ t - 2u = -2$
     $2r + s - 3t + \ u = -3$
     $3r - s + 2t + 5u = \ 28$
     $r - s + \ t - \ u = \ \ 3$

*12. $0.3a + 2.6b - 0.4c + d = \ \ 4.5$
     $0.4a - 1.2b + 0.6c - d = -4.6$
     $a - \ \ b - \ \ c + d = \ -8$
     $a + \ \ b + \ \ c + d = \ \ \ 2$

Exercises 13–14: Graph and label all three given equations **(a)**, **(b)**, and **(c)** on one coordinate system. Use elimination or substitution to find the intersection point of each pair of lines. Label each intersection with its coordinates. Check calculated coordinates for agreement with plotted points.

13. (a) $5x + 7y = 89$
     (b) $x + 7y = 29$
     (c) $3x - 7y = -25$

14. (a) $x - y = 2$
     (b) $7x + 4y + 2 = 0$
     (c) $-x - 4y = -9$

APPLYING THE CONCEPTS

Exercises 15–21: Solve in neat, orderly, well-organized fashion, using Steps 1–5 for solving word problems:

15. A meeting of 40 Republicans and Democrats contributed money for a gift for the outgoing mayor. Each Republican gave $5, each Democrat gave $2, and the total contributed was $164. How many were Republicans?

16. Spools of insulated wire are shipped in cartons of two sizes: small (6 spools) and large (8 spools). Drake lost the exact counts he obtained in the storeroom, but recalls that the number of small cartons is four less than double the number of large cartons, and the number of spools in small cartons is four more than the number of spools in large cartons. How many of each carton size are in the storeroom?

17. Carla's entire fortune ($1.25) consists of 29 coins (pennies, nickels, and dimes). The number of pennies is one more than the total number of nickels and dimes. How many of each type of coin does Carla have?

18. A shipment of 60 stereo components (receivers, tuners, and amplifiers) contains half as many amplifiers as receivers. Each amplifier weighs 20 pounds; each tuner, 15 pounds; and each receiver, 25 pounds. The shipment weighs 1,225 pounds. How many of each item were shipped?

19. A 40-pound frammis is worth $15; a 64-pound widget is worth $11. How many of each could Tony purchase for exactly $399 if the total weight must be 1896 pounds?

20. Wheelsport, Inc., makes kneepads, helmets, and wheels for sale to serious skateboarders.

Cost per item of putting these items into stores includes fabrication, packaging, and marketing, according to the following table:

	Knee-pads	Hel-mets	Wheels
Fabrication	$2	$3	$4
Packaging	$1	$2	$2.50
Marketing	$0.50	$1	$1.50

The budget for a production run of these three items includes $3,294 for fabrication, $1,960 for packaging, and $1,034 for marketing. How many items of each type should be produced in order to use the entire budgeted amounts?

*21. Cars, trucks, and buses queue up separately to board a ferry boat. The three vehicle types have average weights of 2,000 pounds, 5,000 pounds, and 20,000 pounds, respectively. They occupy 15 feet, 20 feet, and 30 feet of parking lane, respectively. Their average passenger loads are 2, 1.5, and 40 people, respectively. The ferry's capacities are 264,000 pounds of payload, 1,170 feet of lane space, and 322 passengers. How many vehicles of each type would exhaust the ferry's capacities, assuming use of all lane space?

1.2 MATRIX METHODS FOR SOLVING LINEAR SYSTEMS   In Example 6 we laboriously worked our way from the Original System of three linear equations to Transitional System 4, then solved the final equation and back-substituted our way upward through the middle and top equations. We alluded several times to the importance of orderly work in building toward a more compact method to come later. We shall now honor our promise!

We shall actually develop two closely related methods based upon our work in Section 1.1. They are: **Gaussian elimination,** due to Karl Friedrich Gauss (1775–1855), a German mathematician of prodigious achievements, and Gauss-Jordan elimination, a variation on the basic Gaussian plan. First, we need some new notation. Working through the transition systems of Example 6 involved a lot of extra writing. Every x, y, z, and = sign represented a bit of extra baggage. Our work would be greatly simplified if we could abstract from each system only the essential information: the coefficients on the left sides of all equations and the constant terms on the right. Highlighting all coefficients and constant terms in the Original System (supplying "1" coefficients where necessary), we lift out this information and record it in an orderly number array, enclosed by brackets, called a **matrix.**

Original System	Matrix Representing Original System
$\begin{aligned} 2x - 3y + 1z &= -5 \\ 3x + 1y - 2z &= 7 \\ -5x + 11y + 3z &= 14 \end{aligned}$	$\left[\begin{array}{rrr\|r} 2 & -3 & 1 & -5 \\ 3 & 1 & -2 & 7 \\ -5 & 11 & 3 & 14 \end{array}\right]$

This matrix has three horizontal **rows** and four vertical **columns.** The brackets at left and right indicate that the matrix is a package of information to be kept intact; the vertical line between columns three and four reminds us where = signs belong. This vertical bar will often be omitted.

The matrix

$$\left[\begin{array}{rrr} 2 & -3 & 1 \\ 3 & 1 & -2 \\ -5 & 11 & 3 \end{array}\right]$$

consisting of the coefficients of the x, y, and z terms of the original system is called the **coefficient matrix** of the system. Appending the **constant terms** of the equations in a *constant column* on the right of the coefficient matrix produces the **augmented matrix** of the system.

$$\left[\begin{array}{rrr|r} 2 & -3 & 1 & -5 \\ 3 & 1 & -2 & 7 \\ -5 & 11 & 3 & 14 \end{array}\right]$$

The augmented matrix abbreviates the original system, with each horizontal line (row) of numbers representing an equation. To solve the original system, we execute moves of three permitted types, called **elementary row operations,** to change the original augmented matrix into a standard, ready-to-solve form.

ELEMENTARY ROW OPERATIONS

The three elementary row operations by which we may alter the contents of a matrix are:

1. *Reorder* the rows in the matrix.

2. *Multiply* any row by a nonzero constant.

3. *Add* any matrix row to any other matrix row.

Gaussian Elimination

The three **elementary row operations** on a matrix are exactly the three moves used to transform a system of equations through simpler equivalent systems to one which is then easy to solve. Done on a matrix, these operations produce a final matrix in standard form, called *row echelon form*.

ROW ECHELON FORM OF A MATRIX

A matrix in **row echelon form** has these properties:

1. The leading (leftmost nonzero) entry in any row is "1."

2. Each matrix entry below a row's "leading 1" is zero.

3. The leading 1 in any row is in a column to the right of the leading 1 in any row above the given row.

4. All rows (if any) containing only zeros are below every row containing a 1. (Rows of zeros are grouped at the bottom of the matrix.)

It is property 3 in the Row Echelon definition that gives the matrix its characteristic stairsteps-downward-to-the-right appearance.

■ EXAMPLE 9

For each matrix, specify "yes" if the matrix is in row echelon form and "no" if it is not. For matrices not already in row echelon form, perform one or more elementary row operations on the given matrix to transform (reduce) it to row echelon form.

(a) $\begin{bmatrix} 1 & 2 & 1 & -1 \\ 0 & 1 & \frac{2}{3} & 5 \\ 0 & 0 & 1 & -3 \end{bmatrix}$

(b) $\begin{bmatrix} 2 & 1 & -3 & 0 \\ 0 & 1 & 6 & 2 \\ 0 & 0 & 0 & 0 \end{bmatrix}$

(c) $\begin{bmatrix} 0 & 1 & 5 & 0 \\ 1 & 2 & -2 & 6 \\ 0 & 0 & 1 & .4 \end{bmatrix}$

(d) $\begin{bmatrix} 0 & 1 & 0 & 4 & -2 & 1 \\ 0 & 0 & 0 & 1 & 6 & -1 \\ 0 & 0 & 0 & 0 & 1 & .6 \end{bmatrix}$

(e) $\begin{bmatrix} 1 & 0 & 7 & 2 & -3 \\ 1 & 1 & -2 & .6 & .9 \\ 0 & 0 & 2 & 4 & -8 \\ 0 & 0 & 0 & 0 & 1 \end{bmatrix}$ **(f)** $\begin{bmatrix} 1 & 2 & 1 \\ 0 & 1 & 4 \\ 0 & 0 & 1 \\ 0 & 0 & 0 \end{bmatrix}$

SOLUTION **(a)** yes   **(d)** yes   **(f)** yes

(b) no; leading entry in row 1 is 2. Multiply row 1 by 1/2. Result:

$\begin{bmatrix} 1 & \frac{1}{2} & -\frac{3}{2} & 0 \\ 0 & 1 & 6 & 2 \\ 0 & 0 & 0 & 0 \end{bmatrix}$

(c) no; switch rows 1 and 2. Result:

$\begin{bmatrix} 1 & 2 & -2 & 6 \\ 0 & 1 & 5 & 0 \\ 0 & 0 & 1 & .4 \end{bmatrix}$

(e) no; add (-1) times row 1 to row 2. Result:

$\begin{bmatrix} 1 & 0 & 7 & 2 & -3 \\ 0 & 1 & -9 & -1.4 & 3.9 \\ 0 & 0 & 1 & 2 & -4 \\ 0 & 0 & 0 & 0 & 1 \end{bmatrix}$ ∎

Now to connect "reducing a matrix to row echelon form" with "solving a system of linear equations":

SOLVING A LINEAR SYSTEM BY GAUSSIAN ELIMINATION

> 1. Represent the system as an augmented matrix.
>
> 2. Carry out elementary row operations on the matrix to place it in row echelon ("stairsteps") form.
>
> 3. Interpret the final matrix as a system of equations and, if possible, solve by back-substitution.

■ EXAMPLE 10

Solve by Gaussian elimination the system of equations

$$5r - 2s = 11$$
$$2r + 8s = 11$$

SOLUTION We transform the augmented matrix of the given system into row echelon form, keeping in mind the goal "1's on the left, 0's below them," using only the three elementary row operations.

In any matrix, we refer to Row One as "R1," Row Two as "R2," and so on. For "add Row One to Row Two and write the result in Row Two," we say "Row 1 plus Row 2 replaces Row 2" and write "R1 + R2" at the left of Row Two in the resulting matrix, to show how its new Row Two was produced.

For "exchange Row One and Row Three," we write "R1" at the left of Row Three and "R3" at the left of Row One of the resulting matrix. The term "kR2" at the left of Row Two indicates that Row 2 of the previous matrix was multiplied by the nonzero real number k to produce the new Row Two.

Finally, to show that two matrices represent equivalent systems, we shall use a *tilde* ($\sim$) and not "$=$" between the matrices. We begin with the given system's augmented matrix.

$$\begin{bmatrix} 5 & -2 & 11 \\ 2 & 8 & 11 \end{bmatrix} \sim \frac{1}{5} \cdot \text{R1} \begin{bmatrix} 1 & -\frac{2}{5} & \frac{11}{5} \\ 2 & 8 & 11 \end{bmatrix} \underset{-2 \cdot \text{R1} + \text{R2}}{\sim} \begin{bmatrix} 1 & -\frac{2}{5} & \frac{11}{5} \\ 0 & \frac{44}{5} & \frac{33}{5} \end{bmatrix}$$

$$\underset{\frac{5}{44} \cdot \text{R2}}{\sim} \begin{bmatrix} 1 & -\frac{2}{5} & \frac{11}{5} \\ 0 & 1 & \frac{3}{4} \end{bmatrix}$$

The final matrix is in row echelon form. Viewing R2 as an equation, we see $s = 3/4$.

Substituting 3/4 for s in the equation represented by R1 of the final matrix:

$$1r - \frac{2}{5}s = \frac{11}{5}$$

$$1r - \left(\frac{2}{5}\right)\left(\frac{3}{4}\right) = \frac{11}{5}$$

$$r - \frac{3}{10} = \frac{11}{5}$$

$$r = \frac{11}{5} + \frac{3}{10}$$

$$r = \frac{5}{2}$$

The values $r = 3/4$ and $s = 5/2$ do check in the original pair of equations, and are thus the solution to that system. ∎

In performing elementary row operations on a matrix, it is sometimes possible to combine several operations in one transition to a new matrix. Do so only if you are confident of not becoming confused. It is much more important to be correct than efficient at this stage of your development. To illustrate:

■ EXAMPLE 11

Solve by Gaussian elimination:

$$6x - 2y + 2z = 1$$
$$4x + y - 2z = 2$$
$$-8x + 5y + z = 7$$

Step 1

Get 1 at top of leftmost nonzero column.

$$\begin{bmatrix} 6 & -2 & 2 & | & 1 \\ 4 & 1 & -2 & | & 2 \\ -8 & 5 & 1 & | & 7 \end{bmatrix} \underset{\sim}{(\frac{1}{6})\text{R1}} \begin{bmatrix} 1 & -\frac{1}{3} & \frac{1}{3} & | & \frac{1}{6} \\ 4 & 1 & -2 & | & 2 \\ -8 & 5 & 1 & | & 7 \end{bmatrix}$$

Step 2

Use the 1 at left end of R1, and elementary row operations, to "zero" rest of first column. Park and forget R1.

$$(-4)R1 + R2 \qquad 8R1 \ + R3 \qquad \sim \begin{bmatrix} 1 & -\frac{1}{3} & \frac{1}{3} & \bigm| & \frac{1}{6} \\ 0 & \frac{7}{3} & -\frac{10}{3} & \bigm| & \frac{4}{3} \\ 0 & \frac{7}{3} & \frac{11}{3} & \bigm| & \frac{25}{3} \end{bmatrix}$$

Step 3

Attend to R2 and R3. Opportunity! Use 7/3 in R2 to get "0" in R3.

$$(-1)R2 + R3 \qquad \sim \begin{bmatrix} 1 & -\frac{1}{3} & \frac{1}{3} & \bigm| & \frac{1}{6} \\ 0 & \frac{7}{3} & -\frac{10}{3} & \bigm| & \frac{4}{3} \\ 0 & 0 & 7 & \bigm| & 7 \end{bmatrix}$$

Step 4

Convert leading entries in R2 and R3 to 1's.

$$\left(\tfrac{3}{7}\right) \cdot R2 \qquad \left(\tfrac{1}{7}\right) \cdot R3 \qquad \sim \begin{bmatrix} 1 & -\frac{1}{3} & \frac{1}{3} & \bigm| & \frac{1}{6} \\ 0 & 1 & -\frac{10}{7} & \bigm| & \frac{4}{7} \\ 0 & 0 & 1 & \bigm| & 1 \end{bmatrix}$$

The final matrix is in row echelon form. To finish the solution:

1. Write R3 as an equation; solve for z.

2. Substitute the z value into "equation" R2; solve for y.

3. Substitute the values of z and y into "equation" R1; solve for x.

From R3, $z = 1$. Substituting 1 for z in the equation corresponding to R2, and solving:

$$y - \frac{10}{7}z = \frac{4}{7}$$

$$y - \frac{10}{7} \cdot 1 = \frac{4}{7}$$

$$y = \frac{4}{7} + \frac{10}{7}$$

$$y = 2$$

Substituting 1 for z and 2 for y in the equation from R1:

$$x - \frac{1}{3}y + \frac{1}{3}z = \frac{1}{6}$$

$$x - \frac{1}{3} \cdot 2 + \frac{1}{3} \cdot 1 = \frac{1}{6}$$

$$x - \frac{2}{3} + \frac{1}{3} = \frac{1}{6}$$

$$x = \frac{1}{6} + \frac{2}{3} - \frac{1}{3} = \frac{1}{2}$$

Thus (subject to checking), our solution to the original system of equations is $x = 1/2$, $y = 2$, $z = 1$. These values do check out. ■

Gauss-Jordan Elimination   Taken together, the statements of values for x, y, and z in Example 11 are a new system of equations:

Solution as System of Equations	Solution Equations in Matrix Form
$x = \dfrac{1}{2}$ $y = 2$ $z = 1$	$\begin{bmatrix} 1 & 0 & 0 & \mid & \frac{1}{2} \\ 0 & 1 & 0 & \mid & 2 \\ 0 & 0 & 1 & \mid & 1 \end{bmatrix}$

Compare the row echelon form at the end of Example 11 with the "Solution Equations in Matrix Form" above. The transition from "Row Echelon Form" to "Solution Equations in Matrix Form" is just a matter of elementary row operations:

Step 1   **Row Echelon Form**

Use the lead "1" in R3 to clear the column above it.

$$\begin{bmatrix} 1 & -\frac{1}{3} & \frac{1}{3} & \mid & \frac{1}{6} \\ 0 & 1 & -\frac{10}{7} & \mid & \frac{4}{7} \\ 0 & 0 & 1 & \mid & 1 \end{bmatrix} \begin{matrix} (-\frac{1}{3})R3 + R1 \\ (\frac{10}{7})R3 + R2 \\ \sim \end{matrix} \begin{bmatrix} 1 & -\frac{1}{3} & 0 & \mid & -\frac{1}{6} \\ 0 & 1 & 0 & \mid & 2 \\ 0 & 0 & 1 & \mid & 1 \end{bmatrix}$$

Step 2

Use the lead "1" in R2 to clear the column above it.

$$\begin{matrix} (\frac{1}{3})R2 + R1 \\ \\ \sim \end{matrix} \begin{bmatrix} 1 & 0 & 0 & \mid & \frac{1}{2} \\ 0 & 1 & 0 & \mid & 2 \\ 0 & 0 & 1 & \mid & 1 \end{bmatrix}$$

This final matrix gives Solution Equations in Matrix Form. One can read the matrix rows as

$$x = \frac{1}{2}$$
$$y = 2$$
$$z = 1$$

The Solution Equations in Matrix Form is in row echelon form, with one additional characteristic: each **leading entry** (first nonzero entry in a row) is also the only nonzero entry in its *column*. Such a matrix is in reduced row echelon form, obtained from row echelon form by elementary row operations. **Gaussian elimination** is transforming a matrix into row echelon form; **Gauss-Jordan elimination** is completing the transformation to reduced row echelon form. Reduced form conveniently displays the solutions of the original system, without resorting to back-substitution of values into earlier equations.

PRACTICE PROBLEM 3   Transform each of the following augmented matrices into reduced row echelon form, describing the row operations in each step:

(a) $\begin{bmatrix} 2 & 5 & | & -1 \\ 3 & -1 & | & 24 \end{bmatrix}$ (b) $\begin{bmatrix} 2 & 5 & -1 & | & -3 \\ 1 & -1 & 4 & | & 20 \\ 3 & 2 & -1 & | & 3 \end{bmatrix}$

SOLUTION   (a) $\begin{bmatrix} 2 & 5 & | & -1 \\ 3 & -1 & | & 24 \end{bmatrix}$ $\overset{(\frac{1}{2})R1}{\sim}$ $\begin{bmatrix} 1 & \frac{5}{2} & | & -\frac{1}{2} \\ 3 & -1 & | & 24 \end{bmatrix}$ $\overset{}{\underset{-3R1 + R2}{\sim}}$ $\begin{bmatrix} 1 & \frac{5}{2} & | & -\frac{1}{2} \\ 0 & -\frac{17}{2} & | & \frac{51}{2} \end{bmatrix}$

$\overset{}{\underset{(-\frac{2}{17})R2}{\sim}}$ $\begin{bmatrix} 1 & \frac{5}{2} & | & -\frac{1}{2} \\ 0 & 1 & | & -3 \end{bmatrix}$ $\overset{(-\frac{5}{2})R2 + R1}{\sim}$ $\begin{bmatrix} 1 & 0 & | & 7 \\ 0 & 1 & | & -3 \end{bmatrix}$

Transition explanations for part **(b)** are left to you. Justify each row change by "row replacement" comments as in part **(a)**.

(b) $\begin{bmatrix} 2 & 5 & -1 & | & -3 \\ 1 & -1 & 4 & | & 20 \\ 3 & 2 & -1 & | & 3 \end{bmatrix}$ $\sim$ $\begin{bmatrix} 1 & -1 & 4 & | & 20 \\ 2 & 5 & -1 & | & -3 \\ 3 & 2 & -1 & | & 3 \end{bmatrix}$ $\sim$ $\begin{bmatrix} 1 & -1 & 4 & | & 20 \\ 0 & 7 & -9 & | & -43 \\ 3 & 2 & -1 & | & 3 \end{bmatrix}$

$\sim$ $\begin{bmatrix} 1 & -1 & 4 & | & 20 \\ 0 & 7 & -9 & | & -43 \\ 0 & 5 & -13 & | & -57 \end{bmatrix}$

$\sim$ $\begin{bmatrix} 1 & -1 & 4 & | & 20 \\ 0 & 1 & -\frac{9}{7} & | & -\frac{43}{7} \\ 0 & 5 & -13 & | & -57 \end{bmatrix}$ $\sim$ $\begin{bmatrix} 1 & -1 & 4 & | & 20 \\ 0 & 1 & -\frac{9}{7} & | & -\frac{43}{7} \\ 0 & 0 & -\frac{46}{7} & | & -\frac{184}{7} \end{bmatrix}$

$\sim$ $\begin{bmatrix} 1 & -1 & 4 & | & 20 \\ 0 & 1 & -\frac{9}{7} & | & -\frac{43}{7} \\ 0 & 0 & 1 & | & 4 \end{bmatrix}$ This is row echelon form.

$\sim$ $\begin{bmatrix} 1 & -1 & 4 & | & 20 \\ 0 & 1 & 0 & | & -1 \\ 0 & 0 & 1 & | & 4 \end{bmatrix}$ $\sim$ $\begin{bmatrix} 1 & -1 & 0 & | & 4 \\ 0 & 1 & 0 & | & -1 \\ 0 & 0 & 1 & | & 4 \end{bmatrix}$

$\sim$ $\begin{bmatrix} 1 & 0 & 0 & | & 3 \\ 0 & 1 & 0 & | & -1 \\ 0 & 0 & 1 & | & 4 \end{bmatrix}$ This is *reduced* row echelon form.

If the variables were named r, s, and t, the final matrix would clearly represent the solution "$r = 3$, $s = -1$, $t = 4$." $\square$

Basic Variables   In the reduced row echelon matrix of a system of linear equations, any variable (letter) corresponding to a leading entry (leftmost "1") in a row is called a **basic variable**. Consider the final (reduced row echelon) matrix of Practice Problem 3. If the variables are r, s, and t, the basic variable for row one of the reduced matrix is r. For row 2, the basic variable is s. For row 3, the basic variable is t.

EXERCISES 1.2

PRACTICING THE MOVES AND MANEUVERS

Exercises 22–25: Transform the augmented matrix to row echelon form. Interpret the result as a system of linear equations, and finish solving by back-substitution. Check the solution in a system of equations represented by the given matrix.

22. $\left[\begin{array}{ccc|c} 2 & 5 & -1 & 3 \\ -3 & 4 & 5 & 30 \\ 1 & 1 & 1 & -3 \end{array}\right]$

23. $\left[\begin{array}{ccc|c} 2 & -10 & 1 & 0 \\ 6 & -5 & -5 & 2 \\ 0 & \frac{4}{5} & -\frac{1}{5} & \frac{2}{5} \end{array}\right]$

*24. $\left[\begin{array}{cccc|c} 2 & 0 & 1 & 0 & 5 \\ 0 & 1 & 0 & -2 & 3 \\ 1 & 1 & 0 & 0 & 11 \\ 0 & 0 & 2 & 3 & 0 \end{array}\right]$

25. $\left[\begin{array}{cc|c} \frac{2}{3} & -\frac{1}{3} & \frac{11}{120} \\ \frac{1}{4} & \frac{2}{5} & \frac{1}{10} \end{array}\right]$

Exercises 26–29: Transform the augmented matrix to reduced row echelon form. Interpret the result as the solution to a system of linear equations, and check this solution in a system of equations represented by the original matrix.

*26. $\left[\begin{array}{cccc|c} 3 & -2 & -4 & 2 & 3 \\ 4 & 3 & 2 & 1 & -5 \\ -5 & 0 & 3 & 3 & -1 \\ 1 & 2 & 3 & 4 & -5 \end{array}\right]$

27. $\left[\begin{array}{ccc|c} \frac{1}{2} & \frac{1}{4} & 2 & 0 \\ -\frac{2}{3} & \frac{1}{3} & -1 & \frac{5}{3} \\ 2 & -1 & 1 & 1 \end{array}\right]$

28. $\left[\begin{array}{ccc|c} 6 & -7 & -1 & 0 \\ 1 & 0 & -3 & 2 \\ -2 & 2 & 2 & -10 \end{array}\right]$

29. $\left[\begin{array}{ccc|c} 1 & -4 & 2 & -8 \\ 3 & -1 & 1 & 13 \\ 2 & -2 & -5 & 23 \end{array}\right]$

Exercises 30–33: Solve by Gauss-Jordan elimination. Check your solution.

30.
$$2a + b - c = -5$$
$$7a + 8b + 4c = -1$$
$$4a - 8b - 10c = 14$$

*31.
$$r + 2s - 8t + 4u = -8$$
$$2r - s - 3t + u = 6$$
$$r + t = 5$$
$$5r - 2s + u = -4$$

*32.
$$2w - x + y - z = 2$$
$$3w + 2x + y + 2z = -5$$
$$6w + 4y + z = 5$$
$$w - x + y - z = 3$$

33.
$$2k + 3p - 14q = 17$$
$$k - p + q = 0$$
$$-8k + 6p + 3q = 7$$

APPLYING THE CONCEPTS

34. The cold room of Darwin's Fruit Market contains 200 crates (apples, peaches, and cherries). Darwin paid $4 per crate for peaches, $3 per crate for apples, and $6 per crate for cherries; the total bill was $762. There are 26 more crates of apples than of peaches. How many crates of each did Darwin buy?

35. Wilderness Tours has just organized a trip into the mountains for a number of people using horses and mules. The total number of creatures (horses, mules, and people) is 91. The number of horses is 2.5 times the number of people, and the number of mules is equal to the number of horses plus half the number of

people. How many of each creature are on the trip?

36. Roy Allison has city council permission to develop Mayfair, a new residential area. The council insists that the neighborhood appeal to a variety of households (not singles only, retired only, or families with children only), and it also limits the number of houses and the total number of bedrooms in the development. The restrictions: There must be a mix of one-, two-, and three-bedroom homes. The number of three-bedroom homes must be double the number of one-bedroom homes. At most 65 homes, and at most 145 bedrooms, may be built. How many homes of each type may Allison build if he fully exhausts the limits on number of homes and number of bedrooms?

1.3 SYSTEMS WITH MORE THAN ONE SOLUTION; SYSTEMS WITH NO SOLUTION

Every system of linear equations we have solved up to this point has been very well behaved, presenting us with a single clear, exact solution which checks in all equations of the original system. However, it is also possible for a system to have either more than one or no solution. Let us look at the geometry and the algebra of these new possibilities.

Solution Possibilities for Two Linear Equations in Two Unknowns

The graphs of two linear equations in two unknowns are lines. A solution of the two equations corresponds to a common point on the two graphs. Clearly, not every pair of linear equations in two unknowns need produce a tidy, one-point (one pair of values for the unknowns) solution. The graphs may be related in three possible ways, illustrated at left:

(a) They may be *separate* and *parallel* (no solution).

(b) They may intersect in *one point* (a unique solution).

(c) They may *exactly coincide* (an *infinite family* of solutions).

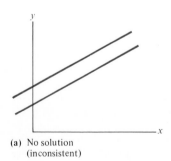

(a) No solution
(inconsistent)

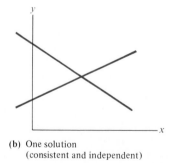

(b) One solution
(consistent and independent)

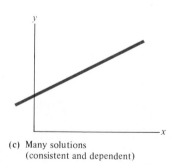

(c) Many solutions
(consistent and dependent)

In graphic terms, condition **(a)** would require any solution point to be on both of two parallel lines. These requirements are inconsistent with each other. Thus, a set of equations with no solution is said to be **inconsis-**

tent. For other reasons beyond the scope of this text, a set of equations with exactly one solution is called consistent and **independent,** and a set of equations with many solutions is called consistent and **dependent.**

EXAMPLE 12

Systems of two linear equations with no, one, or many solutions; solve each of the following systems by substitution.

System 1	System 2	System 3
(a) $2x - 5y = 1$	(c) $x + 2y = 3$	(e) $x + 2y = 3$
(b) $3x + 2y = -1$	(d) $2x + 4y = 6$	(f) $2x + 4y = 4$

SOLUTION

System 1, by substitution. Solving **(a)** for x yields

$$x = \frac{5}{2} y + \frac{1}{2}$$

Substitution into **(b)** and solving for y:

$$3\left(\frac{5}{2} y + \frac{1}{2}\right) + 2y = -1$$

$$\frac{15}{2} y + \frac{3}{2} + 2y = -1$$

$$15y + 3 + 4y = -2$$

$$19y = -5$$

$$y = -\frac{5}{19}$$

Substituting $-5/19$ for y in equation **(a)** or **(b)** will produce a single value for x; so, *System 1 has exactly one solution.*

System 1
(schematic; not to scale)

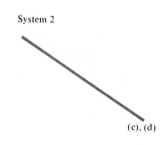

(a)
(b)

System 2, by substitution. From **(c)**, $x = 3 - 2y$. Substituting into **(d)** and solving for y produces

$$2(3 - 2y) + 4y = 6$$
$$6 - 4y + 4y = 6$$
$$0 = 0$$

This last equation ($0 = 0$) is true for *all* values of y; y can be any real number, and, for any selected value $y = t$, it follows from equation **(c)** that $x = 3 - 2t$. The t used to express the many possible pairs of values of y and x is called a **parameter.** (More on this in Examples 13 and 14.)

System 2

(c), (d)

System 3, by substitution. From **(e)**, $x = 3 - 2y$. Substituting into **(f)** and solving for y produces

$$2(3 - 2y) + 4y = 4$$
$$6 - 4y + 4y = 4$$
$$0 = -2$$

System 3

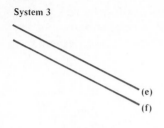

(e)

(f)

This last equation $(0 = -2)$ is *never* true. No y-values satisfy it, hence there is no y-value to substitute into **(e)** or **(f)** to get a corresponding x-value.

Though there is more to learn, we now see that simply carrying out the solution-by-substitution process will reveal the nature of the solutions to a given system.   ◼

PRACTICE PROBLEM 4   Attempt to solve Systems 1, 2, and 3 from Example 12 by elimination, carrying each solution to a point where the nature of the system's solutions is clear.

SOLUTION   In each system, we eliminate x from the second equation. The results (showing just the lower equation from each system) are:

System 1
"One y"

System 2
"Any y"

System 3
"No y"

System 1 **Bottom Equation**	**System 2** **Bottom Equation**	**System 3** **Bottom Equation**
$0x - (11/2)y = 5$	$0x + 0y = 0$	$0x + 0y = -2$

Conclusions. System 1: *one* solution. System 2: *many* solutions. System 3: *no* solution. This agrees with Example 12 conclusions. Solving by elimination also reveals the nature of the solutions.   □

Representing Multiple Solutions With Parameters

◼ EXAMPLE 13

Consider the system of equations

(a) $3x - 6y = -6$

(b) $x - 2y = -2$

Since equation **(a)** is just a constant multiple of equation **(b),** all pairs of values of x and y which satisfy **(b)** also satisfy **(a).** The graphs of the two equations are lines that exactly coincide.

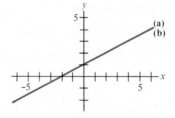

Figure 1.2
Graphs of equations (a)
and (b)

The pairs of (x,y) values which satisfy both equations are exactly the coordinates of points which the two graphs have in common. The graphs reveal that the system consisting of equations **(a)** and **(b)** has infinitely many solutions. Every point on the common graph of **(a)** and **(b)** has coordinates which satisfy both equations.

Solving the system by Gauss-Jordan elimination,

$$\begin{bmatrix} 3 & -6 & | & -6 \\ 1 & -2 & | & -2 \end{bmatrix} \sim \begin{bmatrix} 1 & -2 & | & -2 \\ 3 & -6 & | & -6 \end{bmatrix} \sim \begin{bmatrix} 1 & -2 & | & -2 \\ 0 & 0 & | & 0 \end{bmatrix}$$

Remembering that each augmented matrix represents a system of equations, the bottom row in the final matrix says $0x + 0y = 0$. This is true but not very informative! The final matrix is in reduced row echelon form, and tells us everything about the solutions to the original system, if we can only understand it. What is the message? Reinterpret the top row as an equation:

$$x - 2y = -2$$

Solve this equation for its leading term (the term corresponding to the leftmost "one" in row one of the final matrix above):

$$x = 2y - 2$$

To understand and express the entire solution family, interpret this equation as saying we may give y any value we please; then the corresponding value of x will be 2 times the y-value, minus 2. A conventional way of expressing the solution family is with a pair of equations:

$$y = c \qquad \text{("c" being } any \text{ number)}$$
$$x = 2c - 2$$

The variable c, used to generate pairs of values of x and y, is called a **parameter.** Using c, we express the entire family of solutions. To generate members of the solution family, assign values to c and harvest the corresponding values of y and x. Some c values and solutions are shown in the table in Figure 1.3.

Figure 1.3
Solutions (x,y) to a linear system, expressed in terms of parameter c

c	-2	-1	0	1	1.5	2	3
$y = c$	-2	-1	0	1	1.5	2	3
$x = 2c - 2$	-6	-4	-2	0	1	2	4

The (x,y) pairs in the table are $(-6,-2)$, $(-4,-1)$, $(-2,0)$, $(0,1)$, $(1,1.5)$, $(2,2)$, $(4,3)$. The corresponding points do lie on the line common to the graphs of equations **(a)** and **(b)**. Check several points by plotting them in Figure 1.2. ∎

In Example 13 we saw one row of the matrix "disappear" (become entirely zeros) during Gauss-Jordan Elimination. We still put the matrix into reduced row echelon form, and interpreted the result as a family of solutions to the original system. To strengthen our grasp of the essential ideas, let us look at another example.

■ EXAMPLE 14

Solve the system of linear equations whose augmented matrix is

$$\begin{bmatrix} 2 & -1 & 3 & 4 \\ -3 & 2 & 1 & -1 \\ -5 & 4 & 9 & 5 \end{bmatrix}$$

SOLUTION

$$\begin{bmatrix} 2 & -1 & 3 & 4 \\ -3 & 2 & 1 & -1 \\ -5 & 4 & 9 & 5 \end{bmatrix} \sim \begin{bmatrix} 1 & -\frac{1}{2} & \frac{3}{2} & 2 \\ -3 & 2 & 1 & -1 \\ -5 & 4 & 9 & 5 \end{bmatrix}$$

$$\sim \begin{bmatrix} 1 & -\frac{1}{2} & \frac{3}{2} & 2 \\ 0 & \frac{1}{2} & \frac{11}{2} & 5 \\ -5 & 4 & 9 & 5 \end{bmatrix} \sim \begin{bmatrix} 1 & -\frac{1}{2} & \frac{3}{2} & 2 \\ 0 & \frac{1}{2} & \frac{11}{2} & 5 \\ 0 & \frac{3}{2} & \frac{33}{2} & 15 \end{bmatrix}$$

$$\sim \begin{bmatrix} 1 & -\frac{1}{2} & \frac{3}{2} & 2 \\ 0 & 1 & 11 & 10 \\ 0 & \frac{3}{2} & \frac{33}{2} & 15 \end{bmatrix} \sim \begin{bmatrix} 1 & -\frac{1}{2} & \frac{3}{2} & 2 \\ 0 & 1 & 11 & 10 \\ 0 & 0 & 0 & 0 \end{bmatrix} \sim \begin{bmatrix} 1 & 0 & 7 & 7 \\ 0 & 1 & 11 & 10 \\ 0 & 0 & 0 & 0 \end{bmatrix}.$$

The final matrix is in reduced row echelon form. Giving the names x, y, and z to the system variables, and reinterpreting the rows of the final matrix as equations, the final system is

(a) $x + 0y + 7z = 7$

(b) $0x + y + 11z = 10$

(c) $0x + 0y + 0z = 0$

The graph of a linear equation in three unknowns is a **plane,** even if one or more unknowns is missing, as in equations **(a)** and **(b).** Drop equation **(c),** since it supplies no information. Equations **(a)** and **(b)** are equations of two planes. The points common to the two planes are on a **line** (such as the line where the plane of the wall of a room meets the plane of the floor), and the coordinates of the (infinitely many) points on this line are solutions to the original system of equations.

We represent this infinite solution family as in Example 13. Think of each nonzero row of the reduced matrix as an equation, and solve for its leading (leftmost, with nonzero coefficient) variable:

(d) $x = -7z + 7$

(e) $y = -11z + 10$

Here, x and y are called basic unknowns or basic variables. Since z does not appear on the left side of any equation, we may give z any value we like; then $x = -7z + 7$ and $y = -11z + 10$. Variables which are not basic are assigned arbitrary values called **parameters,** which then express all solutions to the system:

$$z = \quad c \qquad\qquad \text{where } c \text{ is any number we wish}$$
$$x = \quad -7c + 7$$
$$y = \quad -11c + 10$$

Then, by assigning values to c, we may generate as many solutions as we like to the final (and to the original) system:

Figure 1.4
Solutions (x, y, z) expressed using parameter c.

c	-3	-2	-1	0	0.5	1	2	10
$x = \quad -7c + 7$	28	21	14	7	3.5	0	-7	-63
$y = -11c + 10$	43	32	21	10	4.5	-1	-12	-100
$z = \quad\quad c$	-3	-2	-1	0	0.5	1	2	10

Try the solution $x = -7$, $y = -12$, $z = 2$ in the original system represented by the augmented matrix

$$\begin{bmatrix} 2 & -1 & 3 & | & 4 \\ -3 & 2 & 1 & | & -1 \\ -5 & 4 & 9 & | & 5 \end{bmatrix}$$

Substituting these x, y, and z values into the left side of the equation represented by row 1 of the matrix yields

$$2(-7) - 1(-12) + 3(2) = (?)\ 4$$
$$-14 + 12 \quad\quad + 6 \quad = (?)\ 4$$
$$4 = \quad 4$$

Similarly, the solution $(x, y, z) = (-7, -12, 2)$ checks in the other two equations. (Verify the remaining two checks for yourself.) ∎

If Gauss-Jordan elimination produces a reduced system with more than one nonbasic variable, each then becomes a separate parameter for the solution family. One example will illustrate.

■ EXAMPLE 15

Interpret the following matrix as the solution to a system of linear equations in the unknowns r, s, t, and u:

$$\begin{bmatrix} 1 & 3 & 0 & .7 & | & 2 \\ 0 & 0 & 1 & -.6 & | & .5 \\ 0 & 0 & 0 & 0 & | & 0 \\ 0 & 0 & 0 & 0 & | & 0 \end{bmatrix}$$

SOLUTION   Solutions of the final system (above matrix) are solutions of the original system (not shown). Since the last two equations are automatically satisfied ($0 = 0$ is *never* false), we need not write the corresponding equations.

Solving for their leading variables the equations given by the first two rows yields:

(a) $r = -3s - 0.7u + 2$

(b) $t = 0.6u + 0.5$

Since s and u appear on the right sides of equations **(a)** and **(b)**, we reason as follows: s and u are free to be any real numbers (not necessarily the same) that we please. Then values of r and t are determined by the values of s and u. We write:

$s = c$ c is any real number
$u = d$ d is any real number; d need not match c
$r = -3c - 0.7d + 2$
$t = 0.6d + 0.5$

As usual, we obtain as many specific solutions as we like by assigning values to c and d, then reading the resulting values of r, s, t, and u. With no particular pattern of c and d values, but with some representative choices, we obtain:

Figure 1.6
Solutions (r, s, t, u) in terms of parameters c and d

c	-2	-1	0	.4	1	2	1
d	.5	-5	7	0	2	1	1
$r = -3c - .7d + 2$	7.65	8.5	-2.9	.8	-2.4	-4.7	-1.7
$s = \quad c$	-2	-1	0	.4	1	2	1
$t = \quad .6d + .5$	.8	-2.5	4.7	.5	1.7	1.1	1.1
$u = \quad d$	.5	-5	7	0	2	1	1

■

PRACTICE PROBLEM 5   Interpret each reduced matrix as a system of equations in x, y, and z, and give the complete solution family.

(a) $\begin{bmatrix} 1 & 0 & 0 & 2 \\ 0 & 1 & \frac{1}{2} & 3 \\ 0 & 0 & 0 & 0 \end{bmatrix}$ **(b)** $\begin{bmatrix} 1 & 2 & 0 & 5 \\ 0 & 0 & 1 & -8 \\ 0 & 0 & 0 & 0 \end{bmatrix}$ **(c)** $\begin{bmatrix} 1 & 0 & 0 & -.7 \\ 0 & 1 & 0 & 2.2 \\ 0 & 0 & 1 & 3.6 \end{bmatrix}$

(d) $\begin{bmatrix} 1 & 0 & \frac{1}{4} & \frac{3}{5} \\ 0 & 1 & \frac{1}{3} & \frac{3}{4} \\ 0 & 0 & 0 & \frac{2}{5} \end{bmatrix}$

SOLUTION

(a) $z = c$ (arbitrary); $y = 3 - (1/2)c$; $x = 2$
(b) $z = -8$; $y = c$; $x = -2c + 5$.
(c) $z = 3.6$; $y = 2.2$; $x = -0.7$
(d) row 3: $0 = (2/5)$. NO SOLUTION.   □

We have begun to understand what may occur when solving a linear system. The augmented matrix of the system may reduce to a matrix showing exactly one solution to the original system. In such a case, deleting rows consisting entirely of zeros will leave a matrix such as

$$\begin{bmatrix} 1 & 0 & 0 & 0 & | & .6 \\ 0 & 1 & 0 & 0 & | & -2 \\ 0 & 0 & 1 & 0 & | & 0 \\ 0 & 0 & 0 & 1 & | & 4 \end{bmatrix}$$

which we interpret as $w = 0.6$, $x = -2$, $y = 0$, $z = 4$.

In another solution, deleting rows of zeros could leave a reduced matrix such as

$$\begin{bmatrix} 1 & 0 & 2 & -3 & | & 4 \\ 0 & 1 & -.5 & 6 & | & .6 \end{bmatrix}$$

which would lead to a solution family of the form

$$y = c$$
$$z = d$$
$$w = -2c + 3d + 4$$
$$x = 0.5c - 6d + 0.6 \qquad c \text{ and } d \text{ being any real numbers}$$

Only one other thing can happen in the reduction of a matrix: a row may "almost" disappear. Track the next example carefully.

■ EXAMPLE 16

Solve the system of equations

$$2a - 7b + 3c = -1$$
$$a + 3b - 2c = 2$$
$$4a - b - c = 5$$

SOLUTION

We start with the system's augmented matrix and proceed by elementary row operations. The solutions of the original system are solutions of every system represented by a matrix in the following sequence, including the final, completely reduced matrix.

$$\begin{bmatrix} 2 & -7 & 3 & | & -1 \\ 1 & 3 & -2 & | & 2 \\ 4 & -1 & -1 & | & 5 \end{bmatrix} \sim \begin{bmatrix} 1 & 3 & -2 & | & 2 \\ 2 & -7 & 3 & | & -1 \\ 4 & -1 & -1 & | & 5 \end{bmatrix} \sim \begin{bmatrix} 1 & 3 & -2 & | & 2 \\ 0 & -13 & 7 & | & -5 \\ 0 & -13 & 7 & | & -3 \end{bmatrix}$$

$$\sim \begin{bmatrix} 1 & 3 & -2 & 2 \\ 0 & 13 & -7 & 5 \\ 0 & -13 & 7 & -3 \end{bmatrix} \sim \begin{bmatrix} 1 & 3 & -2 & 2 \\ 0 & -13 & 7 & -5 \\ 0 & 0 & 0 & 2 \end{bmatrix}$$

and we stop. Why?

Row 3 of the last matrix says $0x + 0y + 0z = 2$. This last matrix represents a system with exactly the same solutions as the original system. In particular, each solution of the original system must satisfy $0x + 0y + 0z = 2$. What values of x, y, and z satisfy this equation? None at all! The last system (and therefore the original system) has *no solutions*. ∎

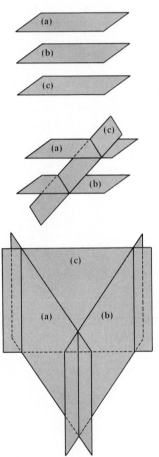

SOLVING SYSTEMS OF LINEAR EQUATIONS

1. A system of linear equations may have no solution, exactly one solution, or infinitely many solutions.

2. Gauss-Jordan elimination solves any linear system, transforming the augmented matrix to matrices of systems with the same solutions as the original.

3. If during the Gauss-Jordan process a row of form "0 0 0 . . . 0 0 n" appears, where n is not zero, halt and write "No solution." (Such a row says "zero equals a nonzero number," and is *never* true.)

4. If no row "0 0 0 . . . 0 n," where n is nonzero, appears, the system has at least one solution.

    a. If every variable is a basic variable in the reduced system, the original system has exactly one solution, given by the equations of the reduced system. Check it in the original system.

    b. If not every variable is basic in the reduced system, the original system has infinitely many solutions. Solve each equation of the reduced system for its basic variable and assign arbitrary letters (parameters) to the non-basic variables. Values of all system variables are then expressed in terms of the parameters. This is called a **general solution.** To generate a **particular solution,** assign number values to the parameters. Check at least one particular solution in the original system.

Two linear equations in *two* unknowns have no solution if their graphs are parallel lines. How can three linear equations in three unknowns fail to have a solution? The graph of each equation is a plane. Can three planes be so arranged that they have no point in common? See the sketches at left.

In general, how is one to know the "nature of the solutions" ("none," "one," or "many") of a linear system? In every case, the reduced matrix tells the entire story:

EXERCISES 1.3

PRACTICING THE MOVES AND MANEUVERS

Exercises 37–44: Use as many variable names v, w, x, y, z as necessary, in alphabetic order, to interpret the reduced row echelon augmented matrix as the solution to a system of linear equations. The vertical line (reminder of the location of $=$ signs) is sometimes omitted.

37. $\begin{bmatrix} 1 & 0 & 0 & | & 5 \\ 0 & 1 & 0 & | & -2 \\ 0 & 0 & 1 & | & .6 \end{bmatrix}$

38. $\begin{bmatrix} 1 & 0 & 0 & 5 \\ 0 & 1 & 0 & -3 \\ 0 & 0 & 0 & 2 \end{bmatrix}$

39. $\begin{bmatrix} 1 & 0 & 0 & | & 2 \\ 0 & 1 & 0 & | & 3 \\ 0 & 0 & 1 & | & -1 \\ 0 & 0 & 0 & | & 0 \end{bmatrix}$

40. $\begin{bmatrix} 1 & 0 & 2 & -1 & 7 \\ 0 & 1 & 0 & 3 & 9 \\ 0 & 0 & 0 & 0 & 0 \\ 0 & 0 & 0 & 0 & 0 \end{bmatrix}$

41. $\begin{bmatrix} 1 & 0 & 6 & 0 & 2 & 5 \\ 0 & 1 & -3 & 0 & 4 & -1 \\ 0 & 0 & 0 & 1 & 6 & 2 \end{bmatrix}$

42. $\begin{bmatrix} 1 & 0 & 0 & | & 4 \\ 0 & 1 & 0 & | & 8 \\ 0 & 0 & 1 & | & -2 \end{bmatrix}$

43. $\begin{bmatrix} 1 & 0 & 0 & 0 & 9 \\ 0 & 1 & 0 & 3 & 0 \\ 0 & 0 & 1 & 5 & 5 \\ 0 & 0 & 0 & 0 & 7 \end{bmatrix}$

44. $\begin{bmatrix} 1 & 0 & 1 & 0 & \frac{1}{3} & 6 \\ 0 & 1 & 2 & 0 & -1 & .9 \\ 0 & 0 & 0 & 1 & 0 & 0 \\ 0 & 0 & 0 & 0 & 0 & 0 \\ 0 & 0 & 0 & 0 & 0 & 0 \end{bmatrix}$

Exercises 45–52: Solve the given system by Gauss-Jordan elimination. Be sure to check the solution, or at least one particular solution in case there are many solutions, in the equations of the original system.

45. $\begin{aligned} 2a - 3b + 6c &= 8 \\ 5a + 2b - 8c &= -20 \\ -6a + 5b + 10c &= 2 \end{aligned}$

*46. $\begin{aligned} 3g + 2h - j + k &= -14 \\ -2g + 7h + 3j - 3k &= 20 \\ -g + 2h - 3j + 4k &= 3 \\ g + h + j + k &= -5 \\ 5g + 3h - 2j - 8k &= -14 \end{aligned}$

47. $\begin{aligned} x + y + z &= 4 \\ 2x - 11y + 3z &= 2 \\ -x + 38y - 4z &= 14 \end{aligned}$

48. $\begin{aligned} 2a + 5b + 2c &= 5 \\ 3a - b - 3c &= 6 \\ 12a + 13b &= 26 \end{aligned}$

*49.
$$\begin{aligned}
2m - 5n - 6p + 2q &= 3 \\
3m + 8n - 13p - 7q &= 3 \\
5m \phantom{{}+8n} + 6p - 10q &= 8 \\
-3m + 2n \phantom{{}+6p} + 8q &= 2
\end{aligned}$$

*50.
$$\begin{aligned}
h + 2i + j + k &= 0 \\
2h - i + 3j - k &= 5 \\
3h + 4i - 2j + k &= -15 \\
4h + 7i + j + 2k &= -10
\end{aligned}$$

51.
$$\begin{aligned}
a + 4b + 20c &= 4 \\
2a - b - 14c &= 19 \\
a + b + 2c &= 8
\end{aligned}$$

52.
$$\begin{aligned}
w + x \phantom{{}+ y} &= 10 \\
x + y &= 2 \\
w \phantom{{}+ x} + y &= -2
\end{aligned}$$

APPLYING THE CONCEPTS

53. Nummy Foods will create a new cereal by mixing three of its present products: Like, Marvels, and Nourismo. The three products supply 40, 20, and 25 calories per ounce, respectively. They also supply 20, 60, and 10 units, respectively, of vitamin B_2 per ounce. Each 16-ounce package of the new cereal must contain 435 calories and 610 units of vitamin B_2. How many ounces of each present product must Nummy put into a package of the new cereal?

54. Quantum Corporation and Megabrain Computers are serious competitors in the microcomputer industry. Quantum knows, through careful attention to trade publications and to rumors overheard at meetings of computer industry people, that Megabrain will soon introduce three new models, code-named Alpha, Bravo, and Charlie. The total number of these computers in the first production batch will be 12,900. Each Alpha uses two TX7 chips; each Bravo uses five TX7's; each Charlie uses three TX7's. Megabrain purchased 41,300 TX7's for use in the first batch. A Megabrain executive remarked that the total number of Alpha and Charlie units is double the number of Bravo units. How many computers of each type does Megabrain plan to build?

A Brief Summary of Important Ideas

The focus of this chapter was upon **linear systems**: sets of linear equations, all to be satisfied by the same values of the variables. **Solution by graphing** received only a nod. Though a sketch of two equations in two unknowns may help detect a solution which is clearly incorrect, graphing seldom yields the accuracy needed for exact solutions. The **substitution** and **elimination** of **variables** methods proved to be much more versatile and reliable. **Matrix methods** (**Gaussian** and **Gauss-Jordan elimination**) grew naturally out of the elimination method.

Matrix methods begin with the **augmented matrix** of the given linear system. **Elementary row operations** produce a sequence of matrices of **equivalent linear systems** leading to **row echelon** (using Gaussian elimination) or **reduced row echelon** (using Gauss-Jordan elimination) **form**. Either form leads to a complete solution to the original linear system; but the reduced row echelon form expresses those solutions most clearly, identifying **basic variables** of the solution family.

If any row of the reduced matrix says "$0 = n$," and n is not zero, the system has **no solution**. If no such row exists, and the variables of the original system are all basic, the system has exactly **one solution**; if the variables are not all basic, the system has an **infinite family of solutions**, all expressed in terms of arbitrary variables called parameters. A system with no solutions is **inconsistent**. A system with one or more solutions is **consistent**. If the system has exactly one solution it is called an **independent** system. A system with more than one solution is **dependent**. Always check at least one solution in all equations of the original system.

REVIEW EXERCISES

PRACTICING THE MOVES AND MANEUVERS

55. Each matrix on the right (A–H) is the coefficient matrix for one or more systems (**a–g**) on the left. Match each system with its possible coefficient matrices.

(a) $3x + 2y - z = 0$
$\quad 2x - y + 2z = 4$

(b) $2x - y = 1$
$\quad x + 4y = -1$
$\quad 0x - 0y = 0$
$\quad 3x - 3y = 2$

(c) $m + 4n = 0$
$\quad 2m - n = 1/3$

(d) $2r - s + 2t = 0.7$
$\quad 3r + 2s - t = 3$

(e) $2x - y = 11$
$\quad 3x - 3y = 0$
$\quad x + 4y = -9$

(f) $x + 2y + 3z + w = 4$

(g) $2a + 2b + 2c + d = 0$
$\quad a - c + d - 2e = 2$
$\quad 2a + 3d + e = 3$
$\quad 4a + b + 2c + 6e = 5$
$\quad 2a - 2c + 2d + 4c = 8$

$$A = \begin{bmatrix} 2 & -1 \\ 1 & 4 \\ 3 & -3 \end{bmatrix} \quad B = \begin{bmatrix} 4 & 1 & 2 & 0 & 6 \\ 1 & 0 & -1 & 1 & -2 \\ 2 & 0 & 0 & 3 & 1 \\ 2 & 2 & 2 & 1 & 0 \\ 2 & 0 & -2 & 2 & 4 \end{bmatrix}$$

$$C = \begin{bmatrix} 1 & 2 & 3 & 1 \end{bmatrix} \quad D = \begin{bmatrix} 2 & -1 \\ 3 & -3 \\ 1 & 4 \end{bmatrix}$$

$$E = \begin{bmatrix} 2 & -1 \\ 1 & 4 \\ 0 & 0 \\ 3 & -3 \end{bmatrix} \quad G = \begin{bmatrix} 2 & -1 \\ 1 & 4 \end{bmatrix}$$

$$F = \begin{bmatrix} 3 & -3 \\ 2 & -1 \\ 1 & 4 \end{bmatrix} \quad H = \begin{bmatrix} 3 & 2 & -1 \\ 2 & -1 & 2 \end{bmatrix}$$

56. Write the augmented matrix of each system of equations in Exercise 55.

Exercises 57–62: Write the system of equations in standard form, solve, and check.

57. $3x + y = 12$

$\quad 2y = 6 - \dfrac{3}{2}x$

58. $2r = 8s + 2$
$\quad 3r = 22 - 7s$

59. $\dfrac{3}{2}a - 5b = -22$

$\quad a + \dfrac{3}{4}b = 18$

60. $\dfrac{d}{6} + e - 3f = -18$

$\dfrac{3}{4}d + e + f = -9$

$d - e + 2f = 0$

61. $\dfrac{3}{7}m - \dfrac{n}{2} = 4$

$\dfrac{m}{4} = -\dfrac{3}{8}n + 3$

62. $0.02x - 0.03y = -.06$

$0.75x + 0.5y = -1.0$

Exercises 63–64: Solve by any method, and check your solutions.

63. $x + 2y + z = 3$
$2x + y + z = 16$
$x + y + 2z = 9$

64. $i + 2j - 5k = 5$
$-3i + 2j + k = -5$
$2i + 2j - 5k = 9$

Exercises 65–66: Solve by substitution, and check.

65. $2x + 3y = 10$
$4x - 9y = 8$

66. $x + y = 0$
$-6x - y + z = 2$
$6x - 9y + 3z = 16$

Exercises 67–70: Solve by the Gauss-Jordan method. Check your solutions.

67. $x - y + z = 2$
$2x + y + 3z = 1$
$4x - 2y + z = 3$

68. $2x + 3y - 4z = 2$
$-x + y - 3z = -6$
$2x + 4y - 6z = 0$

*69. $4r - 2s + 2t + 3u = -5$
$-3r + s + t - 2u = 4$
$2r + 6t = 1$
$-2r + 4t - u = 3$

70. $2a + 3b + 3c = -7$
$-5a + 2b - c = -23$
$-a + 8b + 5c = -13$

Exercises 71–74: Graph the pair of equations, solve the system of equations, and label the intersection of the pair of graphs with its coordinates.

71. $3p - 5q = 9$
$p + q = 3$

72. $-2x - 6y = 18$
$x - 3y = 6$

73. $2s + 3t = -6$
$2s + t = 2$

74. $a + 2b = -3$
$4a - 3b = 1$

Exercises 75–76: Graph the three equations on one coordinate system, plotting at least three points per line. Then, solve each pair of equations, and label each intersection of two graphs with its coordinates. Lastly, shade the interior of the triangle bounded by the three graphs.

75. **(a)** $9y = 4x + 7$ **(b)** $-6y - 6 = 5x + 20$ **(c)** $3x - y = 12$
76. **(a)** $-x + 4y - 21 = 0$ **(b)** $13x - 10y = 21$ **(c)** $10x + 2y = 21$

APPLYING THE CONCEPTS

77. A garden needs 24 kg of phosphates and 16 kg of nitrates, to be supplied by a mixture of Fertilizers A and B with characteristics shown in the table.

(a) Represent the given facts in two equations with appropriate variables.

(b) What will be the cost to fertilize the garden?

	Phosphate per Package	Nitrate per Package	Package Price
Fertilizer A	4 kg	2 kg	$4
Fertilizer B	6 kg	5 kg	$9

78. A service station sells 9,600 gallons of gasoline every day. The station sells twice as much unleaded gas as regular gas. How much of each type of gasoline does the station sell each day?

79. Creek Farm has 10 more cows than Hill Farm and 20 fewer cows than Dale Farm. If Creek Farm triples its herd, it will have 70 less than twice the total of cows on Hill and Dale farms. How many cows has Creek Farm?

*80. A three-digit number is 297 more than the number with the digits reversed. The hundreds digit is 2 more than the tens digit, and the sum of the digits is 13. Find the original number.

*81. The first cyclist in a two-stage relay race rode at a speed of 40 km/hr. The second cyclist rode at 30 km/hr. If they completed the 170 km course in 4 hours 50 minutes, how far did each cyclist ride?

82. $10,000 is put into three investments at rates of 8%, 9%, and 12% per year, respectively. The income from the first two investments is $75 less than the income from the third investment. The total annual income from the three investments is $1,005. Find the amount of each investment.

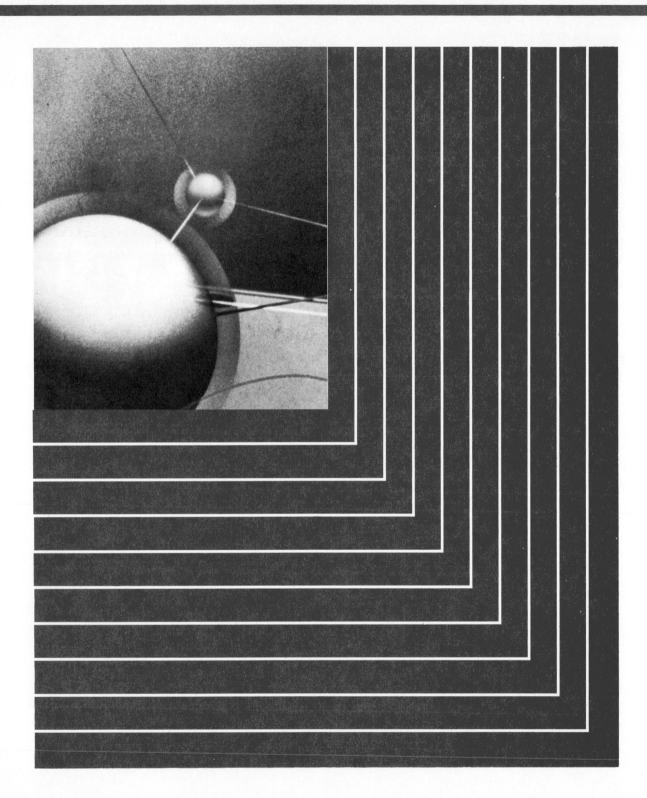

2 *Matrix Algebra*

INTRODUCTION In Chapter 1, you were introduced to the concept of a matrix, and you learned to solve a system of linear equations by manipulating the system's augmented matrix. In this chapter we illustrate some properties of matrices and matrix algebra. In Chapter 3 we then apply the results of this chapter to a variety of situations. The formal definition of a matrix is given below, along with some useful notation.

MATRIX

> A **matrix** is a rectangular array of numbers. A matrix having r rows and c columns is said to be an $r \times c$ (read "r by c") matrix, or to have dimensions $r \times c$. Matrices will be represented by capital letters and their **elements** (number entries) will be represented by the corresponding small letters.

We indicate the dimensions of a matrix with subscripts, the row dimension being shown first. For example, writing $A_{3\times2}$ says A has 3 rows and 2 columns. An example of a 3×2 matrix is

$$A = \begin{bmatrix} 4 & -2 \\ 2 & 1 \\ 1 & 0 \end{bmatrix}$$

The element in the (3,1) position (3rd row, 1st column) is denoted by a_{31}; here, $a_{31} = 1$. Similarly, $a_{12} = -2$.

Row Vectors; Column Vectors Matrices having one row or one column are often called **vectors.** Matrix A shown below is a 1×4 row matrix or a 1×4 **row vector;** the 3×1 column matrix B is also called a **column vector.**

41

$$A = [2 \quad 1 \quad 0 \quad 3]$$

$$B = \begin{bmatrix} 3 \\ 0 \\ -2 \end{bmatrix}$$

An $n \times n$ matrix is said to be **square** because it has the same number of rows and columns.

Matrices will be useful for many reasons. One obvious advantage is "bookkeeping." It is easier to refer to one 6×5 matrix A, than to the 30 numbers that constitute the matrix. We shall discover compelling reasons for using matrices in Chapter 3, but first we shall investigate some properties of matrices.

PRACTICE PROBLEM 1   In matrices A and B, find **(a)** a_{23}, a_{12}, and b_{23}; **(b)** list the elements in the second column of A; **(c)** list the elements in the first row of B.

$$A = \begin{bmatrix} 2 & 1 & -1 \\ 0 & -2 & 5 \\ 2 & 6 & 2 \end{bmatrix} \qquad B = \begin{bmatrix} 2 & 3 & -1 \\ 0 & 2 & 4 \end{bmatrix}$$

ANSWER(S)   **(a)** $a_{23} = 5$, $a_{12} = 1$, and $b_{23} = 4$ **(b)** $1, -2, 6$ **(c)** $2, 3, -1$ □

PRACTICE PROBLEM 2   In Practice Problem 1, find the dimensions of matrices A and B.

ANSWER(S) A is a 3×3 square matrix, while B is 2×3.   □

2.1 MATRICES: EQUALITY AND ADDITION

Matrices can be manipulated much like numbers. In the next few sections we shall discover much about the arithmetic of matrices, but first we need to know when two matrices are equal.

EQUALITY OF TWO MATRICES

Two matrices are **equal** if they have the same dimensions, and if all corresponding elements are equal.

The phrase *corresponding elements* refers to the row-column location in the matrix. The element in matrix B that corresponds to a_{32}, for example, is b_{32}. Thus, if

$$A = \begin{bmatrix} 4 & 1 & 2 \\ 3 & 0 & 1 \end{bmatrix} \quad \text{and} \quad B = \begin{bmatrix} 4 & 1 & x \\ y & 0 & 1 \end{bmatrix}$$

then $A = B$ only when $x = 2$ and $y = 3$. Also,

$$\begin{bmatrix} 4 \\ 2 \end{bmatrix} \neq \begin{bmatrix} 4 & 2 & 1 \\ 2 & 3 & 5 \end{bmatrix} \qquad \text{(dimensions not equal)}$$

Addition and Subtraction of Matrices

Matrices with identical dimensions can be added or subtracted to produce another matrix of those same dimensions by simply adding or subtracting corresponding elements.

ADDING AND SUBTRACTING MATRICES

> If matrices A and B both have dimensions $m \times n$, then their sum, $A + B$, is found by adding each element of B to its corresponding element in A.
>
> Similarly, the difference, $A - B$, is found by subtracting each element of B from the corresponding element in A.

■ EXAMPLE 1

Consider the matrices given below:

$$A = \begin{bmatrix} 4 & 1 \\ 1 & 2 \\ 0 & 2 \end{bmatrix} \quad B = \begin{bmatrix} 2 & 1 & 0 & -3 \\ 1 & -2 & 1 & 3 \end{bmatrix} \quad C = \begin{bmatrix} 1 & -1 \\ 2 & 4 \\ 1 & 3 \end{bmatrix} \quad D = \begin{bmatrix} 0 & 3 \\ 1 & -2 \\ 3 & 1 \end{bmatrix}$$

Find, if possible, the following quantities:

(a) $A + B$ (b) $A + C$ (c) $A - B$ (d) $A - C$

(e) $C + A$ (f) $A + D$ (g) $(C + A) + D$ (h) $C + (A + D)$

SOLUTION

(a) Since A and B do not have the same dimensions, they cannot be added. We say that their *sum is undefined*.

(b) Since A and C are 3×2 matrices, their sum is found by adding each element of C to its corresponding element in A:

$$A + C = \begin{bmatrix} (4 + 1) & (1 + -1) \\ (1 + 2) & (2 + 4) \\ (0 + 1) & (2 + 3) \end{bmatrix} = \begin{bmatrix} 5 & 0 \\ 3 & 6 \\ 1 & 5 \end{bmatrix}$$

(c) $A - B$ does not exist; dimensions of A and B do not match.

(d) Because A and C are 3×2 matrices, $A - C$ is given by

$$A - C = \begin{bmatrix} (4 - 1) & 1 - (-1) \\ (1 - 2) & (2 - 4) \\ (0 - 1) & (2 - 3) \end{bmatrix} = \begin{bmatrix} 3 & 2 \\ -1 & -2 \\ -1 & -1 \end{bmatrix}$$

(e) Since A and C are of the same dimensions, then $C + A$ exists and is found by adding each element of A to its corresponding element in C:

$$C + A = \begin{bmatrix} (1+4) & (-1+1) \\ (2+1) & (4+2) \\ (1+0) & (3+2) \end{bmatrix} = \begin{bmatrix} 5 & 0 \\ 3 & 6 \\ 1 & 5 \end{bmatrix}$$

(f) Matrices A and D have identical dimensions, so $A + D$ exists and is found by adding corresponding elements:

$$A + D = \begin{bmatrix} (4+0) & (1+3) \\ (1+1) & (2+-2) \\ (0+3) & (2+1) \end{bmatrix} = \begin{bmatrix} 4 & 4 \\ 2 & 0 \\ 3 & 3 \end{bmatrix}$$

(g) In finding $(C + A) + D$, the parentheses tell us to first find $C + A$, and then add D to the result. Since D has the same dimensions as $C + A$ (see part **(e)**), the sum $(C + A) + D$ is permissible. To evaluate this sum, add each element of D to its corresponding element in $C + A$:

$$(C + A) + D = \begin{bmatrix} (5+0) & (0+3) \\ (3+1) & (6+-2) \\ (1+3) & (5+1) \end{bmatrix} = \begin{bmatrix} 5 & 3 \\ 4 & 4 \\ 4 & 6 \end{bmatrix}$$

(h) Finding $C + (A + D)$ requires that we first compute $A + D$, done in part **(f)**. Each element of $A + D$ is then added to its corresponding element in C, giving:

$$C + (A + D) = \begin{bmatrix} (1+4) & (-1+4) \\ (2+2) & (4+0) \\ (1+3) & (3+3) \end{bmatrix} = \begin{bmatrix} 5 & 3 \\ 4 & 4 \\ 4 & 6 \end{bmatrix}$$

Discussion. In **(b)** and **(e)**, observe that $C + A$ produces the same matrix as $A + C$, suggesting that order in which we add does not matter. This is true in general, illustrating the **commutative property** of matrix addition. Comparing answers to parts **(g)** and **(h)**, we see that $(C + A) + D = C + (A + D)$, so that it makes no difference whether we first associate matrix A with D (i.e., find $A + D$ first) or with matrix C (by first finding $C + A$). This exemplifies the **associative property** of matrix addition. These properties of matrix addition are summarized below:

PROPERTIES OF MATRIX ADDITION

> **Commutative Property:** If A and B are matrices of the same dimensions, then
>
> $$A + B = B + A$$
>
> **Associative Property:** If matrices A, B, and C all have the same dimensions, then
>
> $$A + (B + C) = (A + B) + C$$

The Zero Matrix.   When you learned to add real numbers, you found that zero was a special number (called the **additive identity**) because $0 + a = a + 0 = a$ for any real number a. There is no single matrix that acts like the real number zero, but for every matrix A, there is a **zero matrix,** or **null matrix** of the same dimensions, denoted by **0,** such that $A + \mathbf{0} = A$. The 1×3 and 2×1 null matrices are, respectively, given by

$$[0 \quad 0 \quad 0] \quad \text{and} \quad \begin{bmatrix} 0 \\ 0 \end{bmatrix}$$

It should be clear, for example, that if A is any 1×3 matrix, then $A + \mathbf{0} = A$, and $\mathbf{0} + A = A$, where $\mathbf{0}$ here refers to the 1×3 null matrix.   ■

EXERCISES 2.1

PRACTICING THE MOVES AND MANEUVERS

Exercises 1–7: Find the dimensions of the given matrices:

1. $\begin{bmatrix} 2 & 4 & 2 & -5 \\ 1 & 0 & 0 & 6 \\ 2 & -1 & 3 & 4 \end{bmatrix}$

2. $\begin{bmatrix} 2 & 5 \\ 3 & 1 \\ 2 & 9 \end{bmatrix}$

3. $[2 \quad -4]$

4. $\begin{bmatrix} 6 \\ 4 \\ -2 \\ 5 \end{bmatrix}$

5. $[-3 \quad -2 \quad 8]$

6. $\begin{bmatrix} 4 & 0 & 1 \\ -2 & 3 & 6 \\ 0 & 0 & 2 \end{bmatrix}$

7. $\begin{bmatrix} 0 \\ 3 \\ 3 \end{bmatrix}$

Exercises 8–15: Find the indicated matrix sum or difference.

8. $\begin{bmatrix} 3 & x \\ 2 & 1 \end{bmatrix} + \begin{bmatrix} 4 & -x \\ 5 & 2 \end{bmatrix}$

9. $\begin{bmatrix} -2 \\ 3 \end{bmatrix} - \begin{bmatrix} 3 \\ 7 \end{bmatrix}$

10. $\begin{bmatrix} 3 & 1 & 0 \\ -3 & -4 & 2 \end{bmatrix} - \begin{bmatrix} 4 & 6 & 1 \\ -2 & 2 & 7 \end{bmatrix}$

11. $\begin{bmatrix} 5 & -6 \\ 2 & 8 \\ 1 & 7 \end{bmatrix} + \begin{bmatrix} 1 & -3 \\ 2 & 4 \\ 5 & x \end{bmatrix}$

12. $[0 \quad 0 \quad 0] + [-2 \quad 4 \quad 7]$

13. $\begin{bmatrix} 1 & 3 \\ 2 & 0 \\ 1 & 5 \\ 0 & 4 \end{bmatrix} - \begin{bmatrix} 1 & 3 \\ 2 & -4 \\ -1 & 5 \\ 6 & 9 \end{bmatrix}$

14. $\begin{bmatrix} x & y \\ 1 & 3 \end{bmatrix} + \begin{bmatrix} 2 & 2-y \\ 3 & x \end{bmatrix}$

15. $[w \quad 4 \quad m] + [m \quad 3 \quad 1]$

Exercises 16–22: Use the matrices given below. Perform the indicated operation if possible; if not, write "NP."

$$A = \begin{bmatrix} 2 & -4 & 2 \\ 1 & 0 & 1 \\ 2 & 1 & 5 \end{bmatrix} \quad B = \begin{bmatrix} 1 & 3 & 5 \\ 2 & 2 & -1 \\ 1 & 0 & -2 \end{bmatrix} \quad C = \begin{bmatrix} 1 & 0 & 0 \\ 0 & 1 & 0 \\ 0 & 0 & 1 \end{bmatrix} \quad D = \begin{bmatrix} 2 \\ 1 \\ 4 \end{bmatrix}$$

16. $A + B$ 17. $A - B$ 18. $B - A$ 19. $A - D$
20. $A + (B + C)$ 21. $B + A$ 22. $(A + B) + C$
23. Does the associative property of matrix addition allow you to say that $A - (B - C) = (A - B) - C$? Justify your answer with examples.
24. Find the values of x and y so that $A + B = C$.

$$A = \begin{bmatrix} 1 & 2 \\ 2 & 1 \\ 3 & 1 \end{bmatrix} \quad B = \begin{bmatrix} x & 0 \\ 3 & 1 \\ y & 0 \end{bmatrix} \quad C = \begin{bmatrix} -2 & 2 \\ 5 & 2 \\ 3 - x & 1 \end{bmatrix}$$

Exercises 25–28: Determine the value of x and/or y.

25. $[x \quad 5 \quad 7] + [3 - 2x \quad 5 \quad 8] = [4 \quad 10 \quad 15]$

26. $\begin{bmatrix} x & 4 \\ 3 & 8 \end{bmatrix} - \begin{bmatrix} 3 & y \\ 2 & 1 \end{bmatrix} + \begin{bmatrix} 2 & 3y \\ 0 & 5 \end{bmatrix} = \begin{bmatrix} 5 & 18 \\ x - 1 & 12 \end{bmatrix}$

27. $\begin{bmatrix} x \\ y \end{bmatrix} - \begin{bmatrix} 4 \\ 2 \end{bmatrix} + \begin{bmatrix} -3x \\ 4y \end{bmatrix} = \begin{bmatrix} 10 \\ 13 \end{bmatrix}$

28. $\begin{bmatrix} 4 \\ 2 + y \end{bmatrix} = \begin{bmatrix} 6 - x \\ 5 \end{bmatrix}$

APPLYING THE CONCEPTS

29. A retail electronics chain has two stores. Normally, the two stores do about the same weekend business in blank cassettes, record albums, and compact discs. To test the effectiveness of an advertising campaign, one store runs a special weekend sale on these three items. Sales data are:

Special Sale		Blank Tape	Records	CD's
Store 1	$A = \begin{matrix} \text{Saturday} \\ \text{Sunday} \end{matrix}$	140 120	45 35	220 180

Regular Pricing		Blank Tape	Records	CD's
Store 2	$B = \begin{matrix} \text{Saturday} \\ \text{Sunday} \end{matrix}$	90 80	35 30	170 154

Present the matrix whose entries describe the estimated additional business generated by the sale. Using the letters A and B, name this matrix.

30. In Exercise 29, find the matrix whose entries describe total sales by category on each of the weekend days. Using letters A and B, name this matrix.

Exercises 31–33: Refer to the following situation. Four undersized NFL linebackers undergo a rigorous, six-week weight-training and diet program designed to add not only strength but weight. At the beginning of the period the respective weights of the linebackers were 220, 218, 224, and 228 pounds, and their respective bench-press amounts were 280, 295, 310, and 260 pounds. At the end of the program, the linebackers weighed 225, 230, 234, and 232 pounds, respectively, and could bench-press the following amounts: 300, 305, 315, and 295 pounds.

31. Find a 4 × 2 matrix that expresses linebacker weights and bench-press amounts at the start of the program. Label completely the rows and columns.

32. Find a 4 × 2 matrix that describes linebacker weights and bench-press amounts at the end of the six-week program.

33. Find a 4 × 2 matrix that describes the gains or losses made by these linebackers during the six-week period.

Exercises 34–37: Refer to the following situation. Salespeople A and B sell only compact disc ("CD") players, preamplifiers and power amplifiers. During November, salesperson A sold 14, 4, and 6, respectively, of these three, while salesperson B sold 12, 5, and 5, respectively. During Thanksgiving vacation, salesperson A undergoes intensive sales training, and puts this training to work in December. During that time she sells 26, 14, and 16 of these three items, respectively, while salesperson B (who did not undergo sales training) sells 18, 9, 9, respectively, of these items.

34. Using a 3 × 2 matrix, express November sales of each product for the two salespeople.

35. Using a 3 × 2 matrix, express December sales of each product for these two salespeople.

36. Using a 3 × 2 matrix, express total sales of each product for these two salespeople in November and December.

37. Using a 3 × 2 matrix, express the increase in sales from November to December. *Note:* For salesperson B, this difference measures "seasonal" effect, while for A it measures seasonal effect, plus the effect of sales training.

2.2 MATRIX MULTIPLICATION

Dreadful Distortion, a stereo salesperson, is paid no salary, but makes a 6% commission on his sales. Below, in matrix format, are the sales figures (in dollars) of what Dreadful sold in various categories during the last weekend:

	Electronics	Speakers	Accessories
Saturday	300	400	100
Sunday	250	300	50

To find how much money Dreadful made on each day in each product category, we multiply each entry of the matrix by 0.06, giving Dreadful's commission matrix:

	Electronics	Speakers	Accessories
Saturday	18	24	6
Sunday	15	18	3

Multiplying every entry in a matrix by the same real number (*scalar* in "matrix talk") is called **scalar multiplication.**

**SCALAR MULTIPLE OF A
MATRIX**

> If c is any real number (scalar), and A is an $m \times n$ matrix, then the scalar multiple cA is the $m \times n$ matrix obtained by multiplying each element of A by c.

PRACTICE PROBLEM 3   If Dreadful's commission rate had been only 5%, instead of 6%, how well would he have fared on the previous weekend?

ANSWER(S)

	Electronics	**Speakers**	**Accessories**
Saturday	15	20	5
Sunday	12.50	15	2.50

**Multiplying a Row Vector
Times a Column Vector**

The stereo shop where Dreadful works stocks three grades of video tape: Standard, High Grade, and Gold (good, better, and best), whose prices (in $) are shown in the 3×1 column vector below.

$$\begin{matrix} \text{S} \\ \text{HG} \\ \text{G} \end{matrix} \begin{bmatrix} 4 \\ 6 \\ 8 \end{bmatrix} \textbf{ Price Vector}$$

The quantities sold of these various tapes during the preceding weekend are shown in the 1×3 row vector below.

$$\begin{matrix} \text{S} & \text{HG} & \text{G} \end{matrix}$$

$[150 \quad 80 \quad 40]$ **Quantity Vector**

The total revenue taken in by the store in video tape is calculated by the following arithmetic expression:

$$150 \cdot 4 + 80 \cdot 6 + 40 \cdot 8 = 1400$$

This arithmetic consists of multiplying each element in the quantity vector times a matching element in the price vector and then adding the results. To see this, write the vectors and the arithmetic side by side:

$$[150 \quad 80 \quad 40] \begin{bmatrix} 4 \\ 6 \\ 8 \end{bmatrix} \qquad 150 \cdot 4 + 80 \cdot 6 + 40 \cdot 8 = 1400$$

Such arithmetic occurs frequently and leads us to define a row vector times a column vector in the following way.

**PRODUCT OF A ROW VECTOR
TIMES A COLUMN VECTOR**

A $1 \times m$ row vector $R = [r_1, \ldots, r_m]$ can be multiplied times a $q \times 1$ column vector $C = \begin{bmatrix} c_1 \\ c_2 \\ \vdots \\ c_q \end{bmatrix}$ in that order only if $m = q$; that is, both vectors must have the same number of elements. When multiplication is possible, the product is the real number RC obtained as follows:

$$RC = r_1 \cdot c_1 + r_2 \cdot c_2 + \cdots + r_q \cdot c_q$$

Study the diagram that follows in order to observe a connection between the dimensions of the row and column vectors and the resulting dimensions of the product:

Row Vector $\times$ **Column Vector**
(left-hand Factor)   **(Right-hand Factor)**

$1 \times q$ $m \times 1$

Inner dimensions must match

\# Rows in   \# Columns in
Product   Product

In particular, note that

1. The product can be found only if inner dimensions match; that is, the number of columns in the left-hand factor must equal the number of rows of the right-hand factor.

2. If the product can be found, its dimensions are the outer dimensions in the above diagram; that is, one row in the left-hand factor means one row in the product; one column in the right-hand factor, means one column in the product.

■ EXAMPLE 2

The owner of the stereo shop carries prerecorded cassettes, record albums, and compact discs. His wholesale costs, respectively, are $4, $7, and $11 each. Upon taking inventory, the owner finds 320 prerecorded cassettes, 400 albums, and 200 compact discs. What is the wholesale value of his stock?

Note: As with most examples in this chapter, this is simple enough to be worked without matrices. Many real world problems, however, will be complex enough to require a computer; this is where the extraordinary power of matrices begins to show. The mechanics of matrix arithmetic are such that large matrices pose no greater theoretical difficulties than small ones. By using matrices in these simple situations, you will "learn the ropes." Extending the ideas to larger problems will pose no difficulty.

SOLUTION   Set up row and column vectors as follows:

$$S = [320 \quad 400 \quad 200] \qquad C = \begin{bmatrix} 4 \\ 7 \\ 11 \end{bmatrix}$$

Row vector S has dimensions 1×3 and column vector C has dimensions 3×1, so inner dimensions match, and we can multiply S times C, getting a matrix with dimensions 1 (number of rows in S) $\times$ 1 (number of columns in C). The resulting arithmetic is

$$SC = 320 \cdot 4 + 400 \cdot 7 + 200 \cdot 11 = 6280 \qquad \text{that is, \$6,280} \qquad \blacksquare$$

PRACTICE PROBLEM 4   In Example 2, suppose we had defined S as a 3×1 column vector, and C as a 1×3 row vector, each having the same elements as before.

(a) What can you say now about the matrix product SC?

(b) Can the wholesale inventory still be found by matrix multiplication?

ANSWER(S)   (a) Nothing at the moment; we know only how to multiply a row vector times a column vector.

(b) Since C is now a row vector, the answer can be found from CS— $6,280, as before.   ☐

PRACTICE PROBLEM 5   Consider the matrices given below.

$$A = [2 \quad 1 \quad -3 \quad 2 \quad 1] \qquad B = [0 \quad 1 \quad 2 \quad 5 \quad -2] \qquad C = [2 \quad 1 \quad 0]$$

$$D = [7 \quad -2 \quad 1] \qquad E = \begin{bmatrix} 0 \\ 2 \\ 1 \\ 2 \\ -1 \end{bmatrix} \qquad F = \begin{bmatrix} 3 \\ 12 \\ 4 \\ -2 \\ 5 \end{bmatrix} \qquad G = \begin{bmatrix} 3 \\ 2 \\ 4 \end{bmatrix}$$

Attempt to find the following matrix products. If a requested operation is not possible, write "NP."

(a) AC (b) AD (c) AE (d) BC (e) DG (f) BF

ANSWER(S)   (a) NP   (b) NP   (c) $AE = 2$ (d) NP   (e) $DG = 21$
(f) $BF = 0$ ☐

Multiplying Two Matrices   The effort devoted to multiplying a row vector times a column vector generalizes, allowing us to multiply matrices having more than one row times matrices having more than one column. The conditions necessary are:

MULTIPLYING TWO MATRICES

> If matrix A has dimensions $m \times n$ and matrix B has dimensions $p \times q$, then the matrix product AB can be found when $n = p$, and the product AB will have dimensions $m \times q$.

To illustrate, suppose A is a 3×2 matrix while B is 2×2. Can we form the product AB? Let's check:

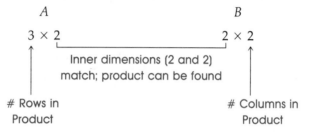

$$\begin{array}{cc} A & B \\ 3 \times 2 & 2 \times 2 \end{array}$$

Inner dimensions (2 and 2)
match; product can be found

\# Rows in
Product

\# Columns in
Product

Since the inner dimensions match, the product AB can be found and its dimensions will be 3×2. Granted, we know that AB can be found, but we still don't know how! We shall demonstrate the procedure for matrix multiplication in the following example.

■ EXAMPLE 3   Using matrices A and B given below, find the product AB.

$$A = \begin{bmatrix} 1 & 1 \\ 2 & 0 \\ 0 & 3 \end{bmatrix} \qquad B = \begin{bmatrix} 2 & 3 \\ -1 & 4 \end{bmatrix}$$

SOLUTION   Our previous check showed that the product AB can indeed be found, and it will be a 3×2 matrix. To find the product, we use repeatedly the only multiplication technique we have at our disposal; namely, multiplying a row vector times a column vector: Multiply each row vector of A times each column vector in B. Each such product is a scalar (real number), and the row-column position of that scalar in the product matrix is determined by the row and column positions of the vectors multiplied.

To find the (1,1) element of the product, we multiply the first row of A times the first column of B:

(1,1) element of product AB:

$$AB = \begin{bmatrix} 1 & 1 \\ 2 & 0 \\ 0 & 3 \end{bmatrix}\begin{bmatrix} 2 & 3 \\ -1 & 4 \end{bmatrix} \qquad 1 \cdot 2 + 1 \cdot (-1) = 1 \qquad AB = \begin{bmatrix} 1 & \\ & \\ & \end{bmatrix}$$

To find the (1,2) element of the product, we multiply the first row of A times the second column of B:

(1,2) element of product AB:

$$AB = \begin{bmatrix} \boxed{1 \quad 1} \\ 2 \quad 0 \\ 0 \quad 3 \end{bmatrix} \begin{bmatrix} 2 & \boxed{3} \\ -1 & \boxed{4} \end{bmatrix} \qquad 1 \cdot 3 + 1 \cdot 4 = 7 \qquad AB = \begin{bmatrix} 1 & \boxed{7} \\ & \\ & \end{bmatrix}$$

To find the (2,1) element of the product, we multiply the second row of A times the first column of B:

(2,1) element of product AB:

$$AB = \begin{bmatrix} 1 \quad 1 \\ \boxed{2 \quad 0} \\ 0 \quad 3 \end{bmatrix} \begin{bmatrix} \boxed{2} & 3 \\ \boxed{-1} & 4 \end{bmatrix} \qquad 2 \cdot 2 + 0 \cdot (-1) = 4 \qquad AB = \begin{bmatrix} 1 & 7 \\ \boxed{4} & \\ & \end{bmatrix}$$

To find the (2,2) element of the product, we multiply the second row of A times the second column of B:

(2,2) element of product AB:

$$AB = \begin{bmatrix} 1 \quad 1 \\ \boxed{2 \quad 0} \\ 0 \quad 3 \end{bmatrix} \begin{bmatrix} 2 & \boxed{3} \\ -1 & \boxed{4} \end{bmatrix} \qquad 2 \cdot 3 + 0 \cdot 4 = 6 \qquad AB = \begin{bmatrix} 1 & 7 \\ 4 & \boxed{6} \\ & \end{bmatrix}$$

To find the (3,1) element of the product, we multiply the third row of A times the first column of B:

(3,1) element of product AB:

$$AB = \begin{bmatrix} 1 \quad 1 \\ 2 \quad 0 \\ \boxed{0 \quad 3} \end{bmatrix} \begin{bmatrix} \boxed{2} & 3 \\ \boxed{-1} & 4 \end{bmatrix} \qquad 0 \cdot 2 + 3 \cdot (-1) = -3 \qquad AB = \begin{bmatrix} 1 & 7 \\ 4 & 6 \\ \boxed{-3} & \end{bmatrix}$$

To find the (3,2) element of the product, we multiply the third row of A times the second column of B:

(3,2) element of product AB:

$$AB = \begin{bmatrix} 1 \quad 1 \\ 2 \quad 0 \\ \boxed{0 \quad 3} \end{bmatrix} \begin{bmatrix} 2 & \boxed{3} \\ -1 & \boxed{4} \end{bmatrix} \qquad 0 \cdot 3 + 3 \cdot 4 = 12 \qquad AB = \begin{bmatrix} 1 & 7 \\ 4 & 6 \\ -3 & \boxed{12} \end{bmatrix}$$

The complete matrix product AB is thus

$$AB = \begin{bmatrix} 1 & 1 \\ 2 & 0 \\ 0 & 3 \end{bmatrix} \begin{bmatrix} 2 & 3 \\ -1 & 4 \end{bmatrix} = \begin{bmatrix} 1 & 7 \\ 4 & 6 \\ -3 & 12 \end{bmatrix}$$

∎

In summary, to determine whether two matrices may be multiplied, write their dimensions side by side, in the same order as the matrix product you hope to find; if the inner dimensions match, then multiplication is possible, and the outer dimensions will be the dimensions of the product. If it is possible to form AB, then multiply each row of A times every column of B and place the result in the position corresponding to the row and column vectors used in your multiplication.

PRACTICE PROBLEM 6 In Example 3, find BA.

ANSWER(S)   Since B is 2×2 and A is 3×2, the product BA is not possible. (The inner dimensions, 2 and 3, do not match.)   ☐

The preceding problem illustrates a major difference between multiplying matrices and multiplying real numbers. When multiplying two real numbers, a and b, $a \cdot b = b \cdot a$. This is the commutative property of multiplication for real numbers. When A and B are matrices, it is not always true that $AB = BA$. In Example 3, BA does not even exist. Even when AB and BA both exist, there is no guarantee that AB will equal BA, as the following problem shows:

PRACTICE PROBLEM 7   Consider the following matrices:

$$A = \begin{bmatrix} 1 & 3 \\ 1 & 0 \end{bmatrix} \qquad B = \begin{bmatrix} 2 & 1 \\ 1 & 1 \end{bmatrix}$$

If possible, find AB and BA.

ANSWER(S)   Since A and B are each 2×2 matrices, the product can be formed in either order. The two products are:

$$AB = \begin{bmatrix} 5 & 4 \\ 2 & 1 \end{bmatrix} \qquad BA = \begin{bmatrix} 3 & 6 \\ 2 & 3 \end{bmatrix}$$

Even though both AB and BA can be found, they are not equal; commutativity does not in general hold for matrix multiplication.   ☐

PRACTICE PROBLEM 8   Perform as many different matrix multiplications as you can by using pairs of the following matrices in any order:

$$A = \begin{bmatrix} 1 & -1 & 3 \\ 2 & 0 & 1 \end{bmatrix} \qquad B = \begin{bmatrix} 4 \\ -2 \\ 1 \end{bmatrix} \qquad C = \begin{bmatrix} 3 & -1 \\ 2 & 0 \\ 1 & -3 \end{bmatrix}$$

ANSWER(S)   Only AB, AC, and CA can be calculated. These products are:

$$AB = \begin{bmatrix} 9 \\ 9 \end{bmatrix} \qquad AC = \begin{bmatrix} 4 & -10 \\ 7 & -5 \end{bmatrix} \qquad CA = \begin{bmatrix} 1 & -3 & 8 \\ 2 & -2 & 6 \\ -5 & -1 & 0 \end{bmatrix}$$ ☐

■ EXAMPLE 4   Using matrices A, B, and C shown below, let us find the following quantities:

(a) AB **(b)** BC **(c)** $A(BC)$ **(d)** $(AB)C$

$$A = \begin{bmatrix} 2 & 1 \\ 1 & 0 \\ 5 & 3 \end{bmatrix} \quad B = \begin{bmatrix} 1 & 2 & 3 & 1 \\ 0 & 1 & 0 & 1 \end{bmatrix} \quad C = \begin{bmatrix} -1 \\ 2 \\ 0 \\ -3 \end{bmatrix}$$

SOLUTION   **(a)** Since A is 3×2 and B is 2×4, the product AB may be found and will be a 3×4 matrix. Successively multiplying each row of A times all columns in B produces the following:

$$AB = \begin{bmatrix} 2 & 1 \\ 1 & 0 \\ 5 & 3 \end{bmatrix} \begin{bmatrix} 1 & 2 & 3 & 1 \\ 0 & 1 & 0 & 1 \end{bmatrix} = \begin{bmatrix} 2 & 5 & 6 & 3 \\ 1 & 2 & 3 & 1 \\ 5 & 13 & 15 & 8 \end{bmatrix}$$

(b) BC is possible as B is 2×4 and C is 4×1. The product is

$$BC = \begin{bmatrix} 1 & 2 & 3 & 1 \\ 0 & 1 & 0 & 1 \end{bmatrix} \begin{bmatrix} -1 \\ 2 \\ 0 \\ -3 \end{bmatrix} = \begin{bmatrix} 0 \\ -1 \end{bmatrix}$$

(c) The parentheses around BC means we should find BC first (done in part **(b)**) and then multiply BC on the left by matrix A. Since A is 3×2 and BC is 2×1, $A(BC)$ is the 3×1 matrix found as follows:

$$A(BC) = \begin{bmatrix} 2 & 1 \\ 1 & 0 \\ 5 & 3 \end{bmatrix} \begin{bmatrix} 0 \\ -1 \end{bmatrix} = \begin{bmatrix} -1 \\ 0 \\ -3 \end{bmatrix}$$

(d) To find $(AB)C$, treat AB as a single matrix (found in **(a)**) and then multiply it on the right by C. Since AB is 3×4 and C is 4×1, the product exists and will be a 3×1 matrix:

$$(AB)C = \begin{bmatrix} 2 & 5 & 6 & 3 \\ 1 & 2 & 3 & 1 \\ 5 & 13 & 15 & 8 \end{bmatrix} \begin{bmatrix} -1 \\ 2 \\ 0 \\ -3 \end{bmatrix} = \begin{bmatrix} -1 \\ 0 \\ -3 \end{bmatrix}. \qquad \blacksquare$$

Associativity   When multiplying real numbers, $4 \cdot 2 \cdot 3$ can be found by first multiplying the 4 and 2, getting 8, and then multiplying $8 \cdot 3$ to get 24. Alternatively, you could first multiply the 2 and 3, getting 6, and then multiply 6 by 4, obtaining 24. This is the associative property of multiplication for real numbers. With Example 4, you have seen a similar result for matrices; namely, $A(BC) = (AB)C$. This result, which illustrates the **associative property of matrix multiplication,** is true in general:

ASSOCIATIVE LAW FOR MATRIX MULTIPLICATION

If matrices A, B, and C are dimensioned so that necessary multiplications can be performed, then

$$A(BC) = (AB)C$$

■ EXAMPLE 5

With matrices A, B, and D as shown, find:

(a) $B + D$ **(b)** AB **(c)** AD **(d)** $A(B + D)$ **(e)** $AB + AD$

$$A = \begin{bmatrix} 2 & 1 \\ 1 & 0 \\ 5 & 3 \end{bmatrix} \quad B = \begin{bmatrix} 1 & 2 & 3 & 1 \\ 0 & 1 & 0 & 1 \end{bmatrix} \quad D = \begin{bmatrix} 1 & 0 & -2 & 1 \\ 0 & 1 & 2 & -3 \end{bmatrix}$$

SOLUTION

(a) B and D are each 2×4, so their sum can be found:

$$B + D = \begin{bmatrix} 1 & 2 & 3 & 1 \\ 0 & 1 & 0 & 1 \end{bmatrix} + \begin{bmatrix} 1 & 0 & -2 & 1 \\ 0 & 1 & 2 & -3 \end{bmatrix} = \begin{bmatrix} 2 & 2 & 1 & 2 \\ 0 & 2 & 2 & -2 \end{bmatrix}$$

(b) A is 3×2 and B is 2×4, so the product AB can be found and will be the following 3×4 matrix:

$$AB = \begin{bmatrix} 2 & 1 \\ 1 & 0 \\ 5 & 3 \end{bmatrix} \begin{bmatrix} 1 & 2 & 3 & 1 \\ 0 & 1 & 0 & 1 \end{bmatrix} = \begin{bmatrix} 2 & 5 & 6 & 3 \\ 1 & 2 & 3 & 1 \\ 5 & 13 & 15 & 8 \end{bmatrix}$$

(c) Since A is 3×2 and D is 2×4, then AD is the 3×4 matrix calculated below:

$$AD = \begin{bmatrix} 2 & 1 \\ 1 & 0 \\ 5 & 3 \end{bmatrix} \begin{bmatrix} 1 & 0 & -2 & 1 \\ 0 & 1 & 2 & -3 \end{bmatrix} = \begin{bmatrix} 2 & 1 & -2 & -1 \\ 1 & 0 & -2 & 1 \\ 5 & 3 & -4 & -4 \end{bmatrix}$$

(d) In finding $A(B + D)$, the parentheses tell us to find $B + D$ first (see part **(a)**), and then multiply the result on the left by A. Since A is 3×2 and $B + D$ is 2×4, the product $A(B + D)$ is a 3×4 matrix:

$$A(B + D) = \begin{bmatrix} 2 & 1 \\ 1 & 0 \\ 5 & 3 \end{bmatrix} \begin{bmatrix} 2 & 2 & 1 & 2 \\ 0 & 2 & 2 & -2 \end{bmatrix} = \begin{bmatrix} 4 & 6 & 4 & 2 \\ 2 & 2 & 1 & 2 \\ 10 & 16 & 11 & 4 \end{bmatrix}$$

(e) AB and AD are each 3×4, so their sum can be found:

$$AB + AD = \begin{bmatrix} 2 & 5 & 6 & 3 \\ 1 & 2 & 3 & 1 \\ 5 & 13 & 15 & 8 \end{bmatrix} + \begin{bmatrix} 2 & 1 & -2 & -1 \\ 1 & 0 & -2 & 1 \\ 5 & 3 & -4 & -4 \end{bmatrix}$$

$$= \begin{bmatrix} 4 & 6 & 4 & 2 \\ 2 & 2 & 1 & 2 \\ 10 & 16 & 11 & 4 \end{bmatrix}$$

Observe that $A(B + D)$ is the same as $AB + AD$. This illustrates the so-called **distributive law for matrix multiplication:**

DISTRIBUTIVE LAW FOR MATRIX MULTIPLICATION

If matrices A, B, and C are such that all necessary multiplications and additions can be performed, then

$$A(B + C) = AB + AC$$

This could be called a **left-hand distributive law.** If dimensions are such that multiplication is possible, there is also a **right-hand distributive law:** $(A + B)C = AC + BC$. ∎

The following example illustrates many matrix arithmetic principles we have encountered thus far.

■ EXAMPLE 6

A highly regarded loudspeaker manufacturer makes three different bookshelf speakers: the Models I, II, and III. Manufacturing these three models requires various amounts of raw materials (speaker cabinets, crossover networks, and speaker drivers). There are also two stages of labor. In stage one, the speaker drivers and crossover networks are installed in the finished cabinets; stage two consists of testing the completed loudspeaker and packing it for shipping to the company's dealers. The raw materials and labor costs (in dollars) of manufacturing one of each model are shown in the expense matrix E:

	Raw Materials	Driver Installation	Testing and Packing	
Model I	10	6	4	
Model II	12	8	5	$= E$
Model III	20	10	7	

Orders for these speakers come from the company's regional representatives, who are paid a sales commission on each speaker: $2, $3, and $5 per speaker, respectively. In addition to manufacturing costs and sales commissions, the company pays the freight to its dealers, and also gives them a co-op advertising allowance in the form of a credit to the dealer's account. Average country-wide freight costs are $2, $3, and $4, respectively, per speaker of each model. The advertising allowance consists of $1, $1.50, and $2, respectively, on each of the three models. The company bills its dealers \$50 for a Model I, \$62 for a Model II, and \$85 for a Model III.

A representative submits a dealer order for 20 Model I's, 16 Model II's, and 12 Model III's. Using matrices, analyze costs, revenue (income the company receives from selling its speakers), and profits (revenue minus costs) for the speaker company in filling this order.

SOLUTION   We introduce 3×1 column vectors C (commission on sales), F (freight), A (advertising allowance), and R (revenue):

$$C = \begin{matrix} \text{I} \\ \text{II} \\ \text{III} \end{matrix}\begin{bmatrix} 2 \\ 3 \\ 5 \end{bmatrix} \quad \begin{matrix} \text{I} \\ \text{II} \\ \text{III} \end{matrix}\begin{bmatrix} 2 \\ 3 \\ 4 \end{bmatrix} = F \quad \begin{matrix} \text{I} \\ \text{II} \\ \text{III} \end{matrix}\begin{bmatrix} 1 \\ 1.50 \\ 2 \end{bmatrix} = A \quad \begin{matrix} \text{I} \\ \text{II} \\ \text{III} \end{matrix}\begin{bmatrix} 50 \\ 62 \\ 85 \end{bmatrix} = R$$

The cost to the company of manufacturing one each of these speakers is given by summing the rows of the expense matrix E. Summing rows of E can be accomplished by multiplying E on the right by a 3×1 column vector of 1's, producing the 3×1 column vector of manufacturing costs, M:

$$M = \begin{bmatrix} 10 & 6 & 4 \\ 12 & 8 & 5 \\ 20 & 10 & 7 \end{bmatrix}\begin{bmatrix} 1 \\ 1 \\ 1 \end{bmatrix} = \begin{matrix} \text{I} \\ \text{II} \\ \text{III} \end{matrix}\begin{bmatrix} \$20 \\ \$25 \\ \$37 \end{bmatrix}$$

The total costs to the company for each speaker delivered are given by the elements of the vector $T = M + C + F + A$:

$$T = M + C + F + A = \begin{bmatrix} 20 \\ 25 \\ 37 \end{bmatrix} + \begin{bmatrix} 2 \\ 3 \\ 5 \end{bmatrix} + \begin{bmatrix} 2 \\ 3 \\ 4 \end{bmatrix} + \begin{bmatrix} 1 \\ 1.50 \\ 2 \end{bmatrix}$$

$$= \begin{matrix} \text{I} \\ \text{II} \\ \text{III} \end{matrix}\begin{bmatrix} 25 \\ 32.50 \\ 48 \end{bmatrix}$$

The profits to the company are computed as revenue minus total costs. Letting vector P stand for profit, we have

$$P = R - T = \begin{bmatrix} 50 \\ 62 \\ 85 \end{bmatrix} - \begin{bmatrix} 25 \\ 32.50 \\ 48 \end{bmatrix} = \begin{matrix} \text{I} \\ \text{II} \\ \text{III} \end{matrix}\begin{bmatrix} 25 \\ 29.50 \\ 37 \end{bmatrix}$$

The total profit from the given order of 20 Model I's, 16 Model II's, and 12 Model III's is given by the matrix product QP, where $Q = [20 \quad 16 \quad 12]$ is an order quantity vector:

$$QP = [20 \quad 16 \quad 12]\begin{bmatrix} 25 \\ 29.50 \\ 37 \end{bmatrix} = 500 + 472 + 444 = \$1416$$

PRACTICE PROBLEM 9   In Example 6, find and interpret the following matrix products: **(a)** Q times C; **(b)** Q times F; **(c)** Q times A; **(d)** Q times R.

ANSWER(S)   **(a)** $QC = \$148$ is the total sales commission paid to the sales representative on the order; **(b)** $QF = \$136$ is the total freight charge (a countrywide average) for an order of this size; **(c)** $QA = \$68$ is the total advertising allowance that the company credits the dealer on an order of this size; **(d)** $QR = \$3{,}012$ is the total revenue due the manufacturer for this order.   □

PRACTICE PROBLEM 10   Using the information from Example 6, suppose a sales representative turns in orders from two dealers at the same time. Dealer 1 wants 30, 20, and 12 of the three models, while Dealer 2 wants 50, 60, and 40 of the three models. Using only matrix multiplication, determine the total sales commission on these two orders.

ANSWER(S)   The total sales commission can be found from the following matrix multiplication:

$$\begin{matrix} \mathbf{I} & \mathbf{II} & \mathbf{III} \end{matrix}$$

$$[1 \quad 1]\begin{bmatrix} 30 & 20 & 12 \\ 50 & 60 & 40 \end{bmatrix}\begin{bmatrix} 2 \\ 3 \\ 5 \end{bmatrix} = [80 \quad 80 \quad 52]\begin{bmatrix} 2 \\ 3 \\ 5 \end{bmatrix} = \$660$$ □

EXERCISES 2.2

PRACTICING THE MOVES AND MANEUVERS

Exercises 38–53: Use the matrices below to find the indicated matrix product; if the product is not defined, write "NP."

$$A = \begin{bmatrix} 3 \\ 1 \\ 5 \end{bmatrix} \quad B = \begin{bmatrix} -1 & 2 & 3 \\ 0 & 1 & 1 \\ 2 & 1 & 0 \end{bmatrix} \quad C = \begin{bmatrix} -2 & 1 & 3 \\ 1 & 4 & 0 \end{bmatrix} \quad D = \begin{bmatrix} 1 & 2 & 1 \\ 0 & 1 & 0 \\ 1 & 1 & 1 \end{bmatrix} \quad E = \begin{bmatrix} 1 & 2 \\ 0 & 1 \\ 0 & 4 \end{bmatrix} \quad F = \begin{bmatrix} -5 & 3 \\ 2 & -3 \end{bmatrix}$$

| 38. AB | 39. BA | 40. DB | 41. BD | 42. AC | 43. CA | 44. BC | 45. CB |
| 46. BE | 47. CE | 48. CD | 49. DE | 50. AD | 51. AF | 52. DA | 53. DF |

Exercises 54–57: Use the matrices A–F defined above.

54. **(a)** Find $B + D$.
   (b) Find $C(B + D)$ by multiplying the answer to **(a)** on the left by matrix C.
   (c) Find $CB + CD$.
   (d) Compare your answers to parts **(b)** and **(c)**; comment.

55. **(a)** Find $(B + D)E$ by multiplying $B + D$ on the right by E.
    (b) Find $BE + DE$.
    (c) Compare your answers to parts **(a)** and **(b)**; comment.
56. **(a)** Find $(BD)E$.   **(b)** Find $B(DE)$.
    (c) Compare your answers to parts **(a)** and **(b)**; comment.
57. **(a)** Find $(CB)D$.   **(b)** Find $C(BD)$.
    (c) Compare your answers to **(a)** and **(b)**; comment.

2.3 IDENTITY MATRICES AND TRANSPOSES

The real number "1" is special in that $1 \cdot a = a \cdot 1 = a$ for every real number a. Keep this in mind during the following example.

■ EXAMPLE 7

Consider matrices A, B, C, and D shown below:

$$A = \begin{bmatrix} 1 & 2 \\ -1 & 0 \\ 3 & -2 \end{bmatrix} \quad B = \begin{bmatrix} 4 & 1 \\ 2 & 1 \end{bmatrix} \quad C = \begin{bmatrix} 1 & 0 \\ 0 & 1 \end{bmatrix} \quad D = \begin{bmatrix} 1 & 0 & 0 \\ 0 & 1 & 0 \\ 0 & 0 & 1 \end{bmatrix}$$

Find, if possible, the following matrix products:

(a) BC **(b)** CB **(c)** AC **(d)** CA **(e)** DA **(f)** AD

SOLUTION

(a) B and C are both 2×2, so the product can be found and will be a 2×2:

$$BC = \begin{bmatrix} 4 & 1 \\ 2 & 1 \end{bmatrix} = B \qquad \text{so that multiplication on the right by } C \text{ has left } B \text{ unchanged}$$

(b) Since B and C are 2×2, CB can also be found:

$$CB = \begin{bmatrix} 4 & 1 \\ 2 & 1 \end{bmatrix} = B \qquad \text{so that multiplication on the left by } C \text{ has left } B \text{ unchanged}$$

The Identity Matrix

Observe that multiplication by the 2×2 square matrix C, in either order, has left matrix B unchanged. In this respect, the matrix C acts precisely like the multiplicative identity "1" of real numbers. For that reason, we shall call matrix C the 2×2 **identity matrix,** and use the notation I_2, the single subscript being all that is necessary since the matrix is square:

$$I_2 = \begin{bmatrix} 1 & 0 \\ 0 & 1 \end{bmatrix}$$

Notice the structure of this matrix: ones on the main diagonal (where row and column positions are identical; positions (1,1) and

(2,2) here). Everywhere else (that is, in the off-diagonal positions) there are zeros in this identity matrix of order 2.

(c) The multiplication AC can be accomplished, producing the following 3×2 matrix:

$$AC = \begin{bmatrix} 1 & 2 \\ -1 & 0 \\ 3 & -2 \end{bmatrix} = A$$

so that multiplication on the right by C has left matrix A unchanged

(d) In attempting CA, we see that the interior dimensions do not match: C has only two columns, while A has three rows.

(e) The product DA is possible because inner dimensions match at 3, giving a 3×2 matrix:

$$DA = \begin{bmatrix} 1 & 2 \\ -1 & 0 \\ 3 & -2 \end{bmatrix} = A$$

so that multiplication on the left by D has left matrix A unchanged

(f) Matrix product AD is not possible: the inner dimensions are incompatible.

In part **(c)** observe that $AC = A$ but CA is not defined. Likewise, in part **(e)**, $DA = A$, but AD is not defined. *For nonsquare matrices like* A, *there is no single matrix that acts like the real number 1.* ∎

The purpose of this example was to introduce the identity matrix and some of its properties. These are summarized in the following box.

IDENTITY MATRIX

The **identity matrix** of order n is the $n \times n$ square matrix whose main diagonal entries are all ones and whose off-diagonal entries are all zeros. The identity matrix of order n is given by

$$I_n = \begin{bmatrix} 1 & 0 & \ldots & \ldots & 0 \\ 0 & 1 & 0 & \ldots & 0 \\ 0 & 0 & 1 & 0 & \ldots 0 \\ & & \ldots & & \\ 0 & 0 & 0 & \ldots & 1 \end{bmatrix}$$

If A is $m \times p$, then $AI_p = A$ and $I_m A = A$. If A is $n \times n$, then $AI_n = I_n A = A$.

Transpose of a Matrix   A vector or matrix may contain the right quantities, but be dimensioned so that multiplication is not possible. Consider our stereo salesperson Dreadful Distortion from Section 2.2. Dreadful is paid a bonus (known as a "spiff") for a car deck he sells from any of three companies. Regardless of company, he is paid $4 for a car deck with no Dolby noise reduction, and $5 for a car deck with Dolby. The pertinent figures are given in matrices S (for spiff) and Q (for quantity):

Dreadful's Sales, by Company

$$S = \begin{matrix} \text{Non-Dolby} \\ \text{Dolby} \end{matrix} \begin{bmatrix} \$4 \\ \$5 \end{bmatrix} \qquad Q = \begin{matrix} \#1 & \#2 & \#3 \\ \begin{bmatrix} 12 & 5 & 7 \\ 8 & 4 & 9 \end{bmatrix} \end{matrix}$$

How much does Dreadful make in commissions? We expect the answer to be provided by matrix multiplication. Checking dimensions, we find that S times Q is not permissible, nor is Q times S. If, however, S had been a 1×2 row vector, we could have multiplied that row vector on the right by Q to get a 1×3 matrix. This can still be done—without changing matrix S—by introducing the *transpose* of a matrix.

TRANSPOSE OF A MATRIX

> If A is an $m \times n$ matrix, then the **transpose** of A, written A^T and pronounced "A transpose," is the $n \times m$ matrix obtained by interchanging rows and columns of A. The element in the i,j-th position of A will become the j,i-th entry of A^T.

Dreadful's spiff and quantity sold matrices and their transposes are:

$$S = \begin{bmatrix} 4 \\ 5 \end{bmatrix} \qquad S^T = [4 \quad 5]$$

$$Q = \begin{bmatrix} 12 & 5 & 7 \\ 8 & 4 & 9 \end{bmatrix} \qquad Q^T = \begin{bmatrix} 12 & 8 \\ 5 & 4 \\ 7 & 9 \end{bmatrix}$$

Dreadful's commission matrix can now be found by multiplying S^T times Q, giving

$$S^TQ = [4 \quad 5] \cdot \begin{bmatrix} 12 & 5 & 7 \\ 8 & 4 & 9 \end{bmatrix} = [88 \quad 40 \quad 73]$$

Dreadful made $88 from Company #1 products, $40 from Company #2, and $73 from the sale of Company #3 products.

PRACTICE PROBLEM 11 In the discussion previous to this problem, determine the total spiff amount Dreadful made on sales of products from Companies A, B, and C by using matrix multiplication.

ANSWER(S) The answer is $88 + 40 + 73 = \$201$, which can be found by the following multiplication:

$$[88 \quad 40 \quad 73] \cdot \begin{bmatrix} 1 \\ 1 \\ 1 \end{bmatrix} = 88 \cdot 1 + 40 \cdot 1 + 73 \cdot 1 = 201$$

Thus, multiplying a row vector on the right by a column vector of ones has the effect of summing the elements in that row. We saw this in Example 5 as well. In general, multiplying any matrix A on the right by an appropriately dimensioned column vector of ones will produce a column vector whose entries are the row sums of matrix A.   □

EXERCISES 2.3

PRACTICING THE MOVES AND MANEUVERS

Exercises 58–63: Find the transpose of the given matrix.

58. $\begin{bmatrix} 5 \\ -3 \\ 5 \end{bmatrix}$

59. $[2 \quad 1 \quad -4]$

60. $\begin{bmatrix} 3 & 2 \\ 2 & 7 \end{bmatrix}$

61. $\begin{bmatrix} 3 & -1 & 2 \\ -2 & 1 & 5 \\ 3 & 0 & 1 \end{bmatrix}$

62. $\begin{bmatrix} 2 & -4 \\ 3 & 0 \\ -1 & 6 \end{bmatrix}$

63. $\begin{bmatrix} 1 & 1 & 1 & 1 \\ 2 & 3 & 4 & 5 \end{bmatrix}$

64. Find the transpose of the matrix A and comment.

65. In Exercise 64, find $(A^T)^T$.

$$A = \begin{bmatrix} 2 & 1 & 5 \\ 1 & 3 & -7 \\ 5 & -7 & 8 \end{bmatrix}$$

Any matrix M such that $M^T = M$ is said to be **symmetric**.

Exercises 66–70: Use the following matrices:

$$A = \begin{bmatrix} 2 & 1 & -2 \\ 0 & 2 & 1 \\ 3 & -1 & 5 \\ 2 & 1 & 4 \end{bmatrix} \quad B = \begin{bmatrix} 4 & -2 \\ -1 & 4 \\ 2 & 0 \end{bmatrix} \quad C = [2 \quad 1 \quad 4]$$

66. **(a)** Find $(AB)^T$.   **(b)** Find B^T, A^T, and $B^T A^T$. Comment.
67. **(a)** Find $(CB)^T$.   **(b)** Find B^T, C^T, and $B^T C^T$. Comment.
68. Find $(A^T)^T$ and comment.
69. Find $(C^T)^T$ and comment.
70. **(a)** Find AC^T.   **(b)** Find CA^T and $(AC^T)^T$. Comment.

71. Consider the matrix X given below:

$$X = \begin{bmatrix} 1 & 2 \\ 1 & 4 \\ 1 & 3 \\ 1 & 2 \\ 1 & 5 \end{bmatrix}$$

   (a) Find $X^{\mathsf{T}}X$.   **(b)** Find $(X^{\mathsf{T}}X)^{\mathsf{T}}$ and comment.

Exercises 72–78: Use the matrices of Exercises 66–70 and find the requested quantities.

72. Find AI_3. 73. Find I_4A. 74. Find CB. 75. Find BI_2.
76. Find I_3B. 77. Find CI_3. 78. Find I_1C.
79. Let

$$C = \begin{bmatrix} 1 & 2 \end{bmatrix} \quad \text{and} \quad D = \begin{bmatrix} \frac{1}{2} & 1 \\ \frac{1}{4} & \frac{1}{2} \end{bmatrix}$$

   (a) Find CI_2.
   (b) Find CD and comment.
   (c) Are there other matrices besides D and I_2 that are special in this way?

80. We have seen that multiplying a matrix on the right by a column vector of ones has the effect of summing the rows. Determine what needs to be done if you want to sum the columns of a matrix. For example, using matrices A and B below, determine what matrix operation needs to be done to matrix A in order that matrix B be the result. *Hint:* See Practice Problem 10.

$$A = \begin{bmatrix} 4 & 1 & 6 \\ 2 & 1 & -1 \\ 3 & 1 & 5 \\ 4 & 1 & 2 \end{bmatrix} \qquad B = \begin{bmatrix} 13 & 4 & 12 \end{bmatrix}$$

81. What is the transpose of an identity matrix I?

2.4 MATRIX INVERSION In this section we consider an alternate way to solve systems of equations. We consider a system that we solved in Example 7 of Chapter 1:

   (a) $2x - 3y + z = -5$

   (b) $3x + y - 2z = 7$

   (c) $-5x + 11y + 3z = 14$

   The **coefficient matrix,** obtained by simply stripping away the x, y, and z, is 3×3 and is given by

$$A = \begin{bmatrix} 2 & -3 & 1 \\ 3 & 1 & -2 \\ -5 & 11 & 3 \end{bmatrix}$$

Write the unknowns as a 3×1 column vector, and the constants on the right-hand side as yet another 3×1 vector, giving

$$\mathbf{X} = \begin{bmatrix} x \\ y \\ z \end{bmatrix} \qquad B = \begin{bmatrix} -5 \\ 7 \\ 14 \end{bmatrix}$$

As a convention, we shall use a boldfaced, capital letter $\mathbf{X}$ to represent a vector of unknowns, and a lowercase x to represent a single unknown. The column vector B is often called the right-hand side or the constant vector. Form the matrix product $A\mathbf{X}$:

$$A\mathbf{X} = \begin{bmatrix} 2 & -3 & 1 \\ 3 & 1 & -2 \\ -5 & 11 & 3 \end{bmatrix} \begin{bmatrix} x \\ y \\ z \end{bmatrix} = \begin{bmatrix} 2 \cdot x + (-3) \cdot y + 1 \cdot z \\ 3 \cdot x + 1 \cdot y + (-2) \cdot z \\ (-5) \cdot x + 11 \cdot y + 3 \cdot z \end{bmatrix}$$

$$= \begin{bmatrix} 2x - 3y + z \\ 3x + y - 2z \\ -5x + 11y + 3z \end{bmatrix}$$

$A\mathbf{X}$ is a 3×1 vector and its $(1,1)$ element is the left-hand side of equation **(a)**. Similarly, the $(2,1)$ and $(3,1)$ elements of $A\mathbf{X}$ represent the left-hand sides of equations **(b)** and **(c)**. Since matrix equality means element-by-element equality, the system of equations can be represented by the single matrix equation $A\mathbf{X} = B$. This equation looks much like the simple equations you solved during your first terrifying exposure to algebra. There you had to solve story problems like the following:

A six-pack of Mother Fletcher's Dandelion Nectar costs $2.10. How much is that per can?

The answer is found easily by solving the equation $6x = 2.10$ for x:

$$6x = 2.10$$
$$(1/6) \cdot 6x = (1/6) \cdot 2.10 \qquad \text{Multiply both sides by 1/6, the inverse or}$$
$$x = 0.35 \qquad \text{reciprocal of 6.}$$

The fraction $1/6$ is called the **inverse** of 6 because $(1/6) \cdot 6 = 6 \cdot (1/6) = 1$, the multiplicative identity for real numbers.

Flushed with success, we might attempt to apply the same thinking to the matrix equation $A\mathbf{X} = B$, which would give us something like $\mathbf{X} = (1/A) \cdot B$. What does $1/A$ mean? Nothing! Remember that A is a matrix. The quantity $1/A$ has no meaning, but for some matrices A there is a matrix which acts much like the reciprocal of a real number. Consider matrices A and B as given below:

$$A = \begin{bmatrix} 4 & 1 \\ 2 & 1 \end{bmatrix} \qquad B = \begin{bmatrix} \frac{1}{2} & -\frac{1}{2} \\ -1 & 2 \end{bmatrix}$$

Since A and B are both 2×2 matrices, we can multiply A times B or B times A. The results of both multiplications are shown:

$$AB = \begin{bmatrix} 4 & 1 \\ 2 & 1 \end{bmatrix}\begin{bmatrix} \frac{1}{2} & -\frac{1}{2} \\ -1 & 2 \end{bmatrix} = \begin{bmatrix} 1 & 0 \\ 0 & 1 \end{bmatrix} \qquad BA = \begin{bmatrix} \frac{1}{2} & -\frac{1}{2} \\ -1 & 2 \end{bmatrix}\begin{bmatrix} 4 & 1 \\ 2 & 1 \end{bmatrix} = \begin{bmatrix} 1 & 0 \\ 0 & 1 \end{bmatrix}$$

Matrix B plays the same role, relative to A, as the number 1/6 plays to 6. In both cases the product of A and B, in either order, produces the appropriate multiplicative identity. For this reason, we say that B is the **inverse** of A and write

$$B = A^{-1} = \begin{bmatrix} \frac{1}{2} & -\frac{1}{2} \\ -1 & 2 \end{bmatrix}$$

MATRIX INVERSE

> If A is a square matrix and there is a square matrix B such that $A \cdot B = B \cdot A = I$, then B is said to be the **inverse** of A, and we write $B = A^{-1}$.

Note that the roles of A and B are interchangeable; thus, we could also say A is the inverse of B and write $A = B^{-1}$. When a matrix has an inverse, that inverse is unique; there is no other matrix that will satisfy the above definition. Two obvious questions arise: **(1)** When does a matrix have an inverse? and **(2)** When a matrix has an inverse, how do we find it?

Before attempting to answer these questions, consider the following example.

■ EXAMPLE 8

Given the system of equations shown below, find the solution by using the inverse of the coefficient matrix.

$$4x + y = 7$$
$$2x + y = 5$$

SOLUTION

This is an easy system to solve by any method used in Chapter 1, but the idea here is to show how a matrix inverse, when it exists, acts like the reciprocal of a real number. In matrix form, the above system can be written $A\mathbf{X} = B$, where

$$A = \begin{bmatrix} 4 & 1 \\ 2 & 1 \end{bmatrix} \qquad \mathbf{X} = \begin{bmatrix} x \\ y \end{bmatrix} \qquad B = \begin{bmatrix} 7 \\ 5 \end{bmatrix}$$

Before solving this particular system, observe what happens in general when the coefficient matrix of system $A\mathbf{X} = B$ has an inverse:

$$AX = B$$
$$A^{-1}(AX) = A^{-1}(B) \qquad \text{multiply both sides on the left by } A^{-1}$$
$$(A^{-1} \cdot A)X = A^{-1}(B) \qquad \text{associate } A \text{ with } A^{-1}$$
$$IX = A^{-1}(B) \qquad A^{-1} \cdot A \text{ is the identity matrix}$$
$$X = A^{-1}(B) \qquad \text{since } I \text{ is the identity matrix, } I \cdot X = X$$

Hence, when the inverse of the coefficient matrix exists, we can find the solution to the system $A \cdot X = B$ by multiplying this inverse times the right-hand side (the constant vector). For our example,

$$X = A^{-1} \cdot B = \begin{bmatrix} \frac{1}{2} & -\frac{1}{2} \\ -1 & 2 \end{bmatrix} \begin{bmatrix} 7 \\ 5 \end{bmatrix} = \begin{bmatrix} 1 \\ 3 \end{bmatrix}$$

so that $x = 1$ and $y = 3$. ■

We are now ready to answer the two questions posed prior to Example 8; namely, when can we expect an inverse, and, when an inverse exists, how do we find it? A matrix can't have an inverse unless it is square. As we saw earlier, each row in the coefficient matrix is associated with an equation, so that there are as many rows as there are equations; similarly, there are as many columns as there are unknowns. Thus, for the coefficient matrix to be square, there must be as many equations as unknowns. This alone does not guarantee that the matrix will have an inverse, but it is necessary. The procedure we will now demonstrate, based on elementary row operations you learned in Chapter 1, will reveal whether or not there is an inverse, and if there is, produce the inverse.

Finding Matrix Inverses   To illustrate the process of finding an inverse, we solve the system from Example 8 (where we used the inverse of the coefficient matrix to find the solution) by using elementary row operations on the augmented matrix. The augmented matrix, $[A \mid B]$, is given by

$$[A \mid B] = \begin{bmatrix} 4 & 1 & | & 7 \\ 2 & 1 & | & 5 \end{bmatrix}$$

You should verify the solution for yourself; below we show one sequence of elementary row operations that leads to the solution,

$$\begin{bmatrix} 4 & 1 & | & 7 \\ 2 & 1 & | & 5 \end{bmatrix} \underset{\frac{1}{4}R_1}{\sim} \begin{bmatrix} 1 & \frac{1}{4} & | & \frac{7}{4} \\ 2 & 1 & | & 5 \end{bmatrix} \underset{R_2 - 2R_1}{\sim} \begin{bmatrix} 1 & \frac{1}{4} & | & \frac{7}{4} \\ 0 & \frac{1}{2} & | & \frac{3}{2} \end{bmatrix}$$

Now we obtain a "1" in the (2,2) position and use it to clear the (1,2) element:

$$\underset{2R_2}{\sim} \begin{bmatrix} 1 & \frac{1}{4} & | & \frac{7}{4} \\ 0 & 1 & | & 3 \end{bmatrix} \underset{R_1 - \frac{1}{4}R_2}{\sim} \begin{bmatrix} 1 & 0 & | & 1 \\ 0 & 1 & | & 3 \end{bmatrix} = [I \mid A^{-1} \cdot B]$$

In this reduced form the solution is seen to be

$$\mathbf{X} = \begin{bmatrix} 1 \\ 3 \end{bmatrix}$$

a result we found earlier.

Notice that we began with the augmented matrix $[A \mid B]$ and row operations reduced this to $[I \mid \mathbf{X}]$. Since $A^{-1} \cdot A = I$, and $\mathbf{X} = A^{-1} \cdot B$, we can say that the row operations we used produced exactly the same result as if we had multiplied the original augmented matrix on the left by A^{-1}:

$$A^{-1} \cdot [A \mid B] = [A^{-1} \cdot A \mid A^{-1} \cdot B] = [I \mid \mathbf{X}]$$

Now suppose we were to form a slightly different augmented matrix, using the same A, but augmenting A not with a constant vector but with an identity matrix of the same dimensions as A. Performing row operations on this new augmented matrix, with the intent of reducing the A-part to I, is equivalent to multiplying on the left by A^{-1}. What do these same operations do to the identity matrix that we appended? By now you are quick to respond: "These operations produce the same result as if we had multiplied on the left by A^{-1}." Since $A^{-1} \cdot I = A^{-1}$, then reducing A, augmented by an identity of the same size, will give us I augmented by A^{-1}. Row operations on $[A \mid I]$ produce

$$A^{-1} \cdot [A \mid I] = [A^{-1} \cdot A \mid A^{-1} \cdot I] = [I \mid A^{-1}]$$

Thus, when a square matrix A has an inverse, you can find A^{-1} by augmenting A with an identity of the same size and reducing this matrix until the A-portion becomes I; the augmented part will be A^{-1}. The following example reinforces this argument.

■ EXAMPLE 9

Find the inverse of matrix A by augmenting A with a 2×2 identity matrix and then performing elementary row operations (transformations) until A has been transformed to the identity

$$A = \begin{bmatrix} 2 & 4 \\ 1 & 1 \end{bmatrix}$$

SOLUTION

One sequence of elementary row operations on the matrix $[A \mid I]$ is shown below:

$$[A \mid I] = \begin{bmatrix} 2 & 4 & | & 1 & 0 \\ 1 & 1 & | & 0 & 1 \end{bmatrix} \underset{R_1}{\overset{R_2}{\sim}} \begin{bmatrix} 1 & 1 & | & 0 & 1 \\ 2 & 4 & | & 1 & 0 \end{bmatrix} \underset{R_2 - 2R_1}{\sim} \begin{bmatrix} 1 & 1 & | & 0 & 1 \\ 0 & 2 & | & 1 & -2 \end{bmatrix}$$

$$\underset{\frac{1}{2}R_2}{\sim} \begin{bmatrix} 1 & 1 & | & 0 & 1 \\ 0 & 1 & | & \frac{1}{2} & -1 \end{bmatrix} \underset{R_1 - R_2}{\sim} \begin{bmatrix} 1 & 0 & | & -\frac{1}{2} & 2 \\ 0 & 1 & | & \frac{1}{2} & -1 \end{bmatrix} = [I \mid A^{-1}]$$

PRACTICE PROBLEM 12 Find the inverses of the following two matrices:

$$A = \begin{bmatrix} 2 & 2 \\ 1 & 2 \end{bmatrix} \qquad B = \begin{bmatrix} 1 & 1 & 2 \\ 1 & 0 & 1 \\ 2 & 0 & 1 \end{bmatrix}$$

ANSWER(S) $\quad A^{-1} = \begin{bmatrix} 1 & -1 \\ -\frac{1}{2} & 1 \end{bmatrix} \qquad B^{-1} = \begin{bmatrix} 0 & -1 & 1 \\ 1 & -3 & 1 \\ 0 & 2 & -1 \end{bmatrix}$ □

In our examples thus far, all matrices have had inverses. What happens if we try to find the inverse when a matrix does not in fact have an inverse?

■ EXAMPLE 10

Find the inverse of matrix A, where

$$A = \begin{bmatrix} 1 & 4 \\ 2 & 8 \end{bmatrix}$$

SOLUTION We form the matrix $[A \mid I]$, and begin row operations, attempting to reduce the A portion to I, knowing that if the matrix has an inverse, these same operations will convert the augmented portion to A^{-1}. Here we go!

$$[A \mid I] = \begin{bmatrix} 1 & 4 \mid 1 & 0 \\ 2 & 8 \mid 0 & 1 \end{bmatrix} \underset{R_2 - 2R_1}{\sim} \begin{bmatrix} 1 & 4 \mid 1 & 0 \\ 0 & 0 \mid -2 & 1 \end{bmatrix}$$

The row of zeros in the A-segment says "stop." The trouble arises because the second row of A is a multiple of the first. For a square matrix to have an inverse, there cannot be such "dependencies" among rows (or columns) of the matrix. It is possible to get nonzero entries in the second row of the A-portion, but we cannot also get the needed 0 and 1 in correct positions. We simply say that A does not have an inverse; the row of zeros in the "A"-portion of $[A \mid I]$ is a "flag" indicating that further efforts are useless. ■

FINDING THE INVERSE OF A SQUARE MATRIX

To find the inverse of an $n \times n$ matrix A:

1. Augment A with an identity matrix of order n.

2. Using elementary row operations, attempt to reduce $[A \mid I]$ to $[I \mid B]$. If you are able to accomplish this, then B will be the inverse of A.

3. If, during this process, you encounter one or more rows consisting entirely of zeros in the left-hand portion, then stop; A does not have an inverse.

Based on the examples just worked, we summarize the procedure to be used in finding the inverse of a square matrix as shown in the box on page 68.

Finding inverses of 2 × 2 matrices will occur frequently in this book. For this reason, we state the conditions under which a 2 × 2 matrix has an inverse and what the inverse is when it exists.

**FINDING THE INVERSE OF A
2 × 2 MATRIX**

Consider the typical 2 × 2 matrix A:

$$A = \begin{bmatrix} a & b \\ c & d \end{bmatrix}$$

Define the quantity D by $D = ad - cb$. (D is known as the **determinant** of the matrix A.) If D is zero, the inverse of A does not exist; if D is not zero, however, then the inverse of matrix A is given by

$$A^{-1} = \frac{1}{D} \begin{bmatrix} d & -b \\ -c & a \end{bmatrix}$$

This result is easily expressed in words:

When the inverse of a 2 × 2 matrix exists, it can be found by interchanging main-diagonal elements, changing the sign of off-diagonal elements, and dividing all elements by determinant D.

Caution: This method works only for 2 × 2 matrices; for 3 × 3 or larger matrices, you should use the row operations procedure on the matrix augmented with an identity matrix of the same order.

■ EXAMPLE 11

Find the inverses of the following matrices:

$$A = \begin{bmatrix} 2 & 1 \\ 3 & 4 \end{bmatrix} \qquad B = \begin{bmatrix} 2 & -4 \\ -1 & 2 \end{bmatrix}$$

SOLUTION

In finding the inverse of matrix A, note that A^{-1} can be found since $D = 2 \cdot 4 - 3 \cdot 1 = 5$, which is not zero. Following our special procedure for 2 × 2 matrix inverses, we interchange the 2 and 4 on the main diagonal while changing the signs of the 1 and the 3 on the off diagonal. We finish our job by dividing each element by $D = 5$ (or the equivalent operation of multiplying each entry by 1/5), obtaining

$$A^{-1} = \frac{1}{5}\begin{bmatrix} 4 & -1 \\ -3 & 2 \end{bmatrix} = \begin{bmatrix} \frac{4}{5} & -\frac{1}{5} \\ -\frac{3}{5} & \frac{2}{5} \end{bmatrix}$$

Either form above is suitable; it is not necessary to perform the scalar multiplication of 1/5 times each element.

In attempting to find B^{-1}, note that $D = 2 \cdot 2 - (-1) \cdot (-4) = 0$, so that B does not have an inverse. This shows why D must not be zero; if it were 0, we would be dividing by 0, a mathematical "no no." ∎

EXERCISES 2.4

PRACTICING THE MOVES AND MANEUVERS

Note: In the rest of this chapter, an asterisk (*) indicates an exercise that, while not difficult, requires more computation.

Exercises 82–89: Find the inverse of the given matrix, if it exists. If not, indicate "No inverse."

82. $\begin{bmatrix} 1 & -2 \\ 2 & 3 \end{bmatrix}$
    83. $\begin{bmatrix} 2 & -3 \\ -2 & 3 \end{bmatrix}$
    84. $\begin{bmatrix} 3 & 4 \\ 2 & 6 \end{bmatrix}$
    85. $\begin{bmatrix} 2 & 0 \\ 1 & 3 \end{bmatrix}$

86. $\begin{bmatrix} 3 & -2 \\ 4 & 1 \end{bmatrix}$
    87. $\begin{bmatrix} 1 & -4 \\ 2 & 3 \end{bmatrix}$
    88. $\begin{bmatrix} 3 & 1 \\ 6 & 2 \end{bmatrix}$
    89. $\begin{bmatrix} 2 & 0 \\ 2 & 3 \end{bmatrix}$

Exercises 90–95: Attempt to find the inverse of the given matrix by augmenting the matrix with I and reducing, if possible, to the form $[I \mid A^{-1}]$. If the inverse does not exist, then indicate "No inverse."

90. $\begin{bmatrix} 2 & 1 & -1 \\ -1 & 0 & 1 \\ 2 & 1 & 0 \end{bmatrix}$
    91. $\begin{bmatrix} 1 & 0 & 2 \\ 2 & 1 & 2 \\ 3 & 1 & 4 \end{bmatrix}$
    *92. $\begin{bmatrix} 2 & 4 & 1 \\ -1 & 1 & 3 \\ 0 & 0 & 1 \end{bmatrix}$

93. $\begin{bmatrix} 1 & 2 & 1 \\ 2 & 0 & 3 \\ 1 & 0 & 1 \end{bmatrix}$
    94. $\begin{bmatrix} 1 & 2 & 0 \\ 2 & 1 & 3 \\ 1 & -1 & 3 \end{bmatrix}$
    95. $\begin{bmatrix} 1 & 0 & 0 \\ 0 & 2 & 0 \\ 0 & 0 & 3 \end{bmatrix}$

Exercises 96–99: Make use of the following matrices:

$$A = \begin{bmatrix} 2 & 1 & 1 \\ 1 & 0 & 0 \\ 1 & 1 & 3 \end{bmatrix} \quad B = \begin{bmatrix} 1 & 3 \\ 2 & 5 \end{bmatrix} \quad C = [6] \quad D = \begin{bmatrix} 1 & 3 \\ 2 & 6 \end{bmatrix}$$

*96. Find (if possible) A^{-1}.

97. Find (if possible) B^{-1}.

98. Find (if possible) C^{-1}.

99. Find (if possible) D^{-1}.

Exercises 100–105: Use the matrices listed below to find the asked-for quantities, if possible. If not possible, so indicate.

$$A = \begin{bmatrix} 1 & 4 \\ 0 & 1 \end{bmatrix} \qquad B = \begin{bmatrix} 1 & 4 \\ 0 & 2 \end{bmatrix} \qquad C = \begin{bmatrix} 1 & 2 \\ 2 & 4 \end{bmatrix}$$

$$D = \begin{bmatrix} 1 & 2 & 3 \\ 3 & 2 & 1 \\ 1 & 1 & 0 \end{bmatrix} \qquad E = \begin{bmatrix} 1 & 1 & 0 \\ 1 & 1 & 2 \\ 0 & 0 & 1 \end{bmatrix} \qquad F = \begin{bmatrix} 1 & 1 & 0 \\ 1 & 1 & 1 \\ 2 & 0 & 0 \end{bmatrix}$$

100. Find A^{-1}.
101. Find B^{-1}.
102. Find C^{-1}.
*103. Find D^{-1}.
104. Find E^{-1}.
105. Find F^{-1}.

Exercises 106–111: Use matrices A and B.

$$A = \begin{bmatrix} 1 & 2 \\ 2 & 3 \end{bmatrix} \qquad B = \begin{bmatrix} 1 & 3 \\ 4 & 2 \end{bmatrix}$$

106. Find A^{-1}, and B^{-1}.
107. Find $(AB)^{-1}$.
108. Find $B^{-1} \cdot A^{-1}$.
109. What did you discover in Exercises 106–108? This result is always true.
110. Find $(B^{-1})^{\mathsf{T}}$ and $(B^{\mathsf{T}})^{-1}$. Comment. This result is true in general.
111. Find **(a)** BA **(b)** $(BA)^{-1}$ **(c)** $A^{-1}B^{-1}$ **(d)** compare answers to **(b)** and **(c)**; comment.
*112. Using matrices D and F from Exercises 100–105, find the following:
    (a) DF **(b)** $(DF)^{-1}$ **(c)** $F^{-1}D^{-1}$ **(d)** compare answers to **(b)** and **(c)**; comment.
*113. Using matrix D from Exercises 100–105, find the following:
    (a) $(D^{-1})^{\mathsf{T}}$ **(b)** $(D^{\mathsf{T}})^{-1}$ **(c)** comment.

APPLYING THE CONCEPTS

114. A and B are square matrices, and $AB = BA = I$; what can be said about A and B?

Note: Exercises 115–117 are interrelated and should be assigned as a group.

115. Solve the following system of equations by first finding the inverse of the coefficient matrix and then multiplying it times the right-hand side:

$$2x + 3y = 8$$
$$5x - 2y = 1$$

116. Solve the system in Exercise 115 by using Gauss-Jordan elimination.
117. In Exercises 115 and 116, you solved the same system in two different ways. There is little advantage to first finding the inverse of the system's coefficient matrix and then multiplying it times the right-hand side. With the same amount of work, you can get the solution with ordinary Gauss-Jordan elimination, thus avoiding the matrix multiplication. There are times, however, when the inverse is helpful. You may encounter several different systems, all with the same coefficient matrix. Under those conditions, it would be better to first find the inverse of the coefficient matrix and then to do matrix multiplications, one for each system of equations. Similarly, in certain problems in statistics, the inverse of the coefficient matrix supplies valuable statistical information, and would ordinarily be found anyway. Considering the work you have already done in Exercises 115 and 116, solve the following systems by the most efficient means possible:

(a) $2x + 3y = 13$ **(b)** $2x + 3y = 14$
    $5x - 2y = 1$ $5x - 2y = 16$

2.5 USING MINITAB TO PERFORM MATRIX ALGEBRA ON A COMPUTER (OPTIONAL)

MINITAB is an easy-to-learn statistical package used widely on college campuses. Though designed for statistics, MINITAB contains all the necessary matrix commands. The symbol "MTB >" is MINITAB's "prompt" for you to enter a command or data. In our discussion, computer responses are shown underlined. Information you enter is shown in boldface. The carriage-return symbol <CR> is an instruction for you to depress the ENTER key. We use the following matrices in our MINITAB illustration. We shall use MINITAB's convention of naming matrices with the symbol M, followed by a number.

$$\text{M1} = \begin{bmatrix} 1 & 3 \\ 4 & -2 \end{bmatrix} \quad \text{M2} = \begin{bmatrix} 2 & -1 & 3 \\ 1 & 0 & 1 \\ 0 & 4 & -3 \end{bmatrix} \quad \text{M3} = \begin{bmatrix} 1 \\ 4 \\ 2 \end{bmatrix} \quad \text{M4} = \begin{bmatrix} 2 & 3 \\ 1 & 5 \end{bmatrix}$$

We shall enter these matrices into the computer and then find the following quantities: **(a)** M1 + M4 **(b)** M1 · M6 **(c)** M2 · M3 **(d)** $(\text{M1})^{-1}$ **(e)** M1 · $(\text{M1})^{-1}$ **(f)** $(\text{M3})^{\text{T}}$ **(g)** 5 · M1

To enter these matrices in MINITAB, proceed as follows:

Comments

MTB > **read 2 2 M1** <CR>	says to store data in 2 × 2 matrix M1
DATA> **1 3** <CR>	entering the first row
DATA> **4 -2** <CR>	entering the second row
2 ROWS READ	

MTB > **read 3 3 M2** <CR>	says to store data in 3 × 3 matrix M2
DATA> **2 -1 3** <CR>	entering the first row
DATA> **1 0 1** <CR>	entering the second row
DATA> **0 4 -3** <CR>	entering the third row
3 ROWS READ	

Matrices M3, M4 are entered in similar fashion. We add matrices M1 and M4, storing their sum in matrix M5:

(a) MTB > **add M1 M4 M5** <CR>   compute M1 + M4; call sum M5

   MTB > **print M5** <CR>   print M5 = M1 + M4

   MATRIX M5

   3   6
   5   3

(b) MTB > **mult M1 M4 M6** <CR>   compute M1 times M4; call product M6

   MTB > **print M6** <CR>   display the product matrix M6

   MATRIX M6

   5   18
   6   2

(c) MTB > mult M2 M3 M7 <CR>   compute M2 times M3; call product M7

MTB > print M7 <CR>   display the product matrix M7

MATRIX M7

13
6
-2

(d) MTB > invert M1 M8 <CR>   find inverse of M1; store in M8

MTB > print M8 <CR>   display the inverse matrix M8

MATRIX M8

0.142857   0.214286
0.285714 -0.071429

(e) MTB > multiply M1 M8 M9 <CR>   compute M1 times $(M1)^{-1}$; store in M9; M9 should be I_2

MTB > print M9 <CR>   checking to see that M9 = I_2

MATRIX M9

1   0
0   1

(f) MTB > transpose M3 M10 <CR>   find $(M3)^T$; call it M10
MTB > print M10 <CR>   print the matrix M3-transpose

MATRIX M10

4   1   2

(g) MTB > Multiply 5 M1 M11 <CR>   multiply all elements in M1 by 5; store scalar multiple 5M1 in matrix M11

MTB > print M11 <CR>   print the scalar multiple 5M1

MATRIX M11

5   15
20   -10

A Brief Summary of Important Ideas

A **matrix** is a rectangular array of numbers. A matrix having only one row is called a **row vector.** A matrix with one column is called a **column vector.** A matrix with as many rows as columns is said to be **square.** Two matrices having the same dimensions may be added or subtracted, element by element. Matrix addition is both commutative and associative.

If matrix A has dimensions $m \times n$ and matrix B has $p \times q$, then the product AB can be found if $n = p$; that is, inner dimensions must match. The product will then be an $m \times q$ matrix. When dimensions are such that multiplication is permissible, matrix multiplication obeys the associative and distributive laws, but matrix multiplication is not commutative.

An $n \times n$ square matrix with 1's on the main diagonal and zeros elsewhere is said to be an **identity matrix,** denoted by I_n. If A is a square matrix and $AB = I_n$, then B is said to be the **inverse** of A, denoted A^{-1}. (When $AB = I_n$ then $BA = I_n$ and A is also the inverse of B.)

When an $n \times n$ square matrix A has an inverse, that inverse is unique and may be found by forming $[A \mid I_n]$ (augmenting A with I_n) and then using elementary row operations to reduce this to $[I_n \mid B]$. The matrix B will then be A^{-1}. If a square matrix does not have an inverse, this procedure will not allow you to obtain the identity matrix in the left-hand part of the augmented matrix; instead you will have one or more rows of zeros.

If a system of equations can be written in matrix form as $AX = B$, then A is said to be the **coefficient matrix** of the system. Solutions to this system, if any, can be found by using elementary row operations. If A is square and has an inverse, then the solution vector $\mathbf{X}$ may also be found by $\mathbf{X} = A^{-1} \cdot B$.

REVIEW EXERCISES

PRACTICING THE MOVES AND MANEUVERS

Exercises 118–134: Use the matrices below to find the requested quantities, if possible. If not possible, so indicate.

$$A = \begin{bmatrix} 2 & 1 & 1 \\ 1 & 0 & 0 \\ 0 & 2 & 3 \end{bmatrix} \quad B = \begin{bmatrix} 1 & 1 & 1 \\ 2 & 1 & 0 \\ -2 & 0 & 3 \end{bmatrix} \quad C = \begin{bmatrix} -4 & 1 & 0 \\ 2 & 1 & -2 \\ 3 & 3 & 5 \end{bmatrix}$$

118. Find AB.   119. Find BA.   120. Find $A + B$.   121. Find $B + A$.
122. What principles are illustrated by Exercises 118–121?
123. Find the following:
    (a) $B + C$ (b) $A(B + C)$ (c) $AB + AC$
    (d) What principle is illustrated by the results of parts (a) through (c)?

124. Find A^{-1}.   125. Find B^{-1}.   *126. Find C^{-1}.
127. Find A^{T}.   128. Find B^{T}.   129. Find C^{T}.
130. **(a)** Find $A(BC)$. **(b)** Find $(AB)C$. **(c)** What principle is shown in **(a)** and **(b)**?
131. **(a)** Find $(A + B)^{\mathrm{T}}$. **(b)** Find $A^{\mathrm{T}} + B^{\mathrm{T}}$.
    (c) What did you discover from parts **(a)** and **(b)**? This result is true in general.
132. Find $(AB)^{\mathrm{T}}$ and show that this is the same matrix as $B^{\mathrm{T}} \cdot A^{\mathrm{T}}$.
*133. Find $(A^{\mathrm{T}})^{-1}$ and show this is the same matrix as $(A^{-1})^{\mathrm{T}}$.
134. **(a)** Find $A^{\mathrm{T}}A$. **(b)** Find $(A^{\mathrm{T}}A)^{\mathrm{T}}$. **(c)** Compare answers in **(a)** and **(b)**. What can you say about the matrix $A^{\mathrm{T}}A$? Do you think this result is true for any matrix A, or only for the A of this problem? *Hint:* See Exercise 64.

APPLYING THE CONCEPTS

Exercises 135–138: A computer retailer has just contracted for 100 computers from a manufacturer. The manufacturer makes three different computer systems, using an 80286, an 80386 or an 80486 microprocessor. Each of these models comes in a Normal (N) or Super (S) version. Matrix A shows the assortment of these versions among the three models. The N and S models differ in the number of RAM chips, and the number of floppy drives and ports, as shown in matrix M below. The vector C details the unit costs for each of the three items.

$$\begin{array}{c}\text{80286}\\\text{80386}\\\text{80486}\end{array}\begin{array}{cc}\text{Normal} & \text{Super}\\\left[\begin{array}{cc}12 & 6\\24 & 36\\6 & 16\end{array}\right]\end{array}=A \quad \begin{array}{c}\text{Normal}\\\text{Super}\end{array}\begin{array}{ccc}\text{RAM Chips} & \text{Floppies} & \text{Ports}\\\left[\begin{array}{ccc}9 & 1 & 2\\36 & 2 & 4\end{array}\right]\end{array}=M \quad \begin{array}{c}\text{RAM chips}\\\text{Floppies}\\\text{Ports}\end{array}\begin{array}{c}\text{Costs}\\\left[\begin{array}{c}\$10\\\$70\\\$18\end{array}\right]\end{array}=C$$

135. Find the matrix product AM and interpret the entries.
136. Find the matrix product $(AM)C$ and interpret the entries.
137. Find the matrix product $T = [1 \ \ 1 \ \ 1] \cdot AM$ and interpret the entries of T.
138. Find the matrix product TC and interpret the entries.

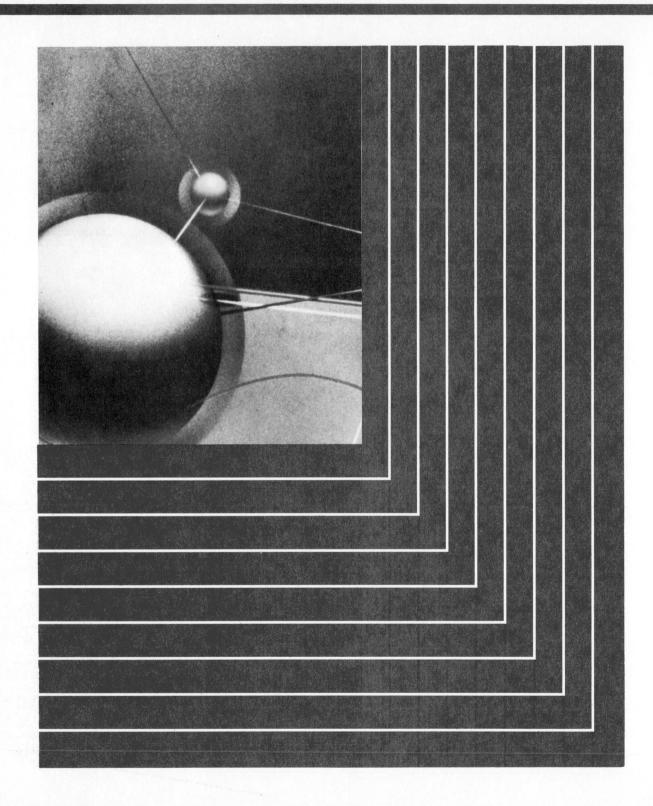

3

Applications of Matrix Algebra

In this chapter you will see diverse applications of the power of matrices in various fields. In Section 3.1 we consider several examples of matrix multiplication. In Section 3.2 we discuss applications of graph theory, a branch of mathematics which enables us to study such diverse areas as trade relations between countries, communication relations between individuals, and even to compare the taste of items or the power of athletic teams. In Section 3.3 we use matrix inverses to help decode messages when we study cryptography. Finally, in Section 3.4, we use most of what we have learned about matrices to study Leontief economic models; specifically we determine how much various segments of an economy should produce to maintain a stable economy.

3.1 APPLICATIONS OF MATRIX MULTIPLICATION

We begin with a simple example that should be of interest to all hard-working students striving for grades.

■ EXAMPLE 1

In Delmo Dweeb's first semester at Anemia Tech, his courses and grades were as follows:

Course	Credit Hours	Grade	Quality Points
Lip Reading for Rodents	5	C = 2	10
The Slide Rule in the 21st Century	3	B = 3	9
Interior Decorating with Walnuts	4	A = 4	16

What was Delmo's Grade Point Average (G.P.A.) the first semester?

77

SOLUTION   Delmo's G.P.A. can be found by totaling his quality points and then dividing by the total number of hours he took. His quality points are found by multiplying the credit hours for a class by its numerical value (4 for A, 3 for B, 2 for C, etc.). Here, Delmo generated 35 quality points in a 12-hour load, so his G.P.A. is 35/12 ≈ 2.92. Let's use matrices to make this computation. Introduce the following row vector L, where

$$\begin{array}{ccc} \text{LR} & \text{SR} & \text{ID} \end{array}$$
$$L = \begin{bmatrix} \dfrac{5}{12} & \dfrac{3}{12} & \dfrac{4}{12} \end{bmatrix}$$

which you can think of as a **load vector.** For example 5/12 of Delmo's load is in the lip-reading class, while only 3/12 is in the slide-rule course. Let us also introduce a **grade vector** G:

$$G = \begin{bmatrix} 2 \\ 3 \\ 4 \end{bmatrix}$$

where, for example, the 2 represents C, the 3 represents B, and the 4 represents the A in the three courses, respectively. Observe that the product LG is the exact arithmetic necessary to compute Delmo's G.P.A.:

$$LG = \begin{bmatrix} \dfrac{5}{12} & \dfrac{3}{12} & \dfrac{4}{12} \end{bmatrix} \begin{bmatrix} 2 \\ 3 \\ 4 \end{bmatrix} = \dfrac{5}{12} \cdot 2 + \dfrac{3}{12} \cdot 3 + \dfrac{4}{12} \cdot 4$$

$$= \dfrac{35}{12} \approx 2.92$$

It is interesting to note that this G.P.A. is a *weighted average* of the numerical score values of the grades. Since Delmo had an A, a B, and a C, there would be good reason for thinking he had a B average, or a 3.0. His G.P.A. being below 3.00 reflects the fact that the C had *more weight* (5 hours) than the A (4 hours). We can build on this idea in Example 2.

■ EXAMPLE 2

Delmo and his three brothers Felmo, Zelmo, and Elmo Dweeb were the only students in "Advanced Lip Reading for Rodents." In this class, there were three hourly exams, worth 20% each, and a final, worth 40%. Scores made by Delmo and his brothers were:

Student	Delmo	Felmo	Zelmo	Elmo
Exam 1	65	75	60	70
Exam 2	80	70	50	75
Exam 3	70	60	90	65
Final Exam	45	50	40	30

Using the professor's weighting, determine the student averages.

SOLUTION   Based on Example 1, we could calculate each student's average separately. To illustrate, Elmo's average is:

$$[.20 \quad .20 \quad .20 \quad .40] \begin{bmatrix} 70 \\ 75 \\ 65 \\ 30 \end{bmatrix} = (0.20) \cdot 70 + (0.20) \cdot 75 \\ + (0.20) \cdot 65 + (0.40) \cdot 30$$

$$= 54$$

This calculation could be repeated for each student, but, using matrix multiplication we can do all such calculations at once:

$$\begin{array}{cccc} \text{Ex 1} & \text{Ex 2} & \text{Ex 3} & \text{Final} \\ [.20 & .20 & .20 & .40] \end{array} \begin{array}{c} \text{Ex1} \\ \text{Ex2} \\ \text{Ex3} \\ \text{Fin} \end{array} \begin{bmatrix} 65 & 75 & 60 & 70 \\ 80 & 70 & 50 & 75 \\ 70 & 60 & 90 & 65 \\ 45 & 50 & 40 & 30 \end{bmatrix}$$

$$= \begin{bmatrix} \text{Delmo} & \text{Felmo} & \text{Zelmo} & \text{Elmo} \\ 61 & 61 & 56 & 54 \end{bmatrix}$$

Delmo and Felmo have 61 averages, while Zelmo is at 56, and Elmo at 54. It looks as if the Dweeb brothers are in dire straits, but what can you expect from quadruplets born three years apart! ■

■ EXAMPLE 3

The local Triplex Theatres has (you guessed it!) four theatres, I, II, III, and IV. Prices of attending these theatres vary and are given, respectively, by the price vector P below:

$$P = \begin{bmatrix} 3.50 \\ 4.00 \\ 4.50 \\ 6.00 \end{bmatrix}$$

On Saturdays only, each of these theatres has a matinee, an evening show, and a late evening show. The theatre has all new features this week, and the manager has estimated attendance for the Saturday showings with the following "Attendance matrix" A:

$$
\begin{array}{c}
\\
\text{Matinee}\\
A = \text{Early Eve.}\\
\text{Late Eve.}
\end{array}
\begin{array}{cccc}
\text{I} & \text{II} & \text{III} & \text{IV}\\
\left[\begin{array}{cccc}
200 & 300 & 350 & 600\\
400 & 500 & 600 & 800\\
500 & 600 & 700 & 1000
\end{array}\right]
\end{array}
$$

Using matrix arithmetic, answer the following questions:

(a) What is estimated total revenue for each showing?

(b) What are estimated ticket sales in each theatre?

(c) What is the estimated grand total revenue for all three showings?

For (a), the matrix product AP yields correct arithmetic:

$$
\begin{array}{c}
\\
\text{Matinee}\\
AP = \text{Early Eve.}\\
\text{Late Eve.}
\end{array}
\begin{array}{ccccc}
\text{I} & \text{II} & \text{III} & \text{IV} & \text{Price}\\
\left[\begin{array}{cccc}
200 & 300 & 350 & 600\\
400 & 500 & 600 & 800\\
500 & 600 & 700 & 1000
\end{array}\right]
&
\left[\begin{array}{c}
3.50\\
4.00\\
4.50\\
6.00
\end{array}\right]
\end{array}
$$

$$
\begin{array}{c}
\\
\text{Matinee}\\
= \text{Early Eve.}\\
\text{Late Eve.}
\end{array}
\begin{array}{c}
\text{Revenue}\\
\left[\begin{array}{c}
7,075\\
10,900\\
13,300
\end{array}\right]
\end{array}
$$

Performing the necessary arithmetic should convince you that each entry in AP is the sum of products having the form "Quantity times price equals revenue."

Part (b) requires that we sum the columns of the A matrix. Defining a row vector S by

$$S = [1 \quad 1 \quad 1]$$

we sum the columns by performing the matrix multiplication SA:

$$
SA = [1 \quad 1 \quad 1]
\begin{array}{cccc}
\text{I} & \text{II} & \text{III} & \text{IV}\\
\left[\begin{array}{cccc}
200 & 300 & 350 & 600\\
400 & 500 & 600 & 800\\
500 & 600 & 700 & 1000
\end{array}\right]
\begin{array}{c}
\text{Matinee}\\
\text{Early Eve.}\\
\text{Late Eve.}
\end{array}
\end{array}
$$

$$
= \begin{array}{cccc}
\text{I} & \text{II} & \text{III} & \text{IV}\\
[1100 & 1400 & 1650 & 2400]
\end{array}
$$

For part **(c),** we need to sum the entries in the 3×1 matrix AP, which was computed in part **(a).** As in part **(b),** this sum can be accomplished by multiplying AP on the left by S:

$$[1 \quad 1 \quad 1] \begin{bmatrix} 7,075 \\ 10,900 \\ 13,300 \end{bmatrix} = 31,275$$

∎

Incidence Matrices

■ EXAMPLE 4

The Dweeb brothers love pizza but have to exercise care as each is allergic to various toppings as shown in matrix A, with "1" in a given row-column position indicating that the person in that row is allergic to the topping in that column; a "0" indicates no allergy. This "allergy" matrix A is given by

$$A = \begin{array}{c} \\ \text{Delmo} \\ \text{Felmo} \\ \text{Zelmo} \\ \text{Elmo} \end{array} \begin{array}{ccccc} \text{Mush-} & & & \text{Kum-} & \text{Ruta-} \\ \text{rooms} & \text{Olives} & \text{Anchovies} & \text{quats} & \text{bagas} \\ \begin{bmatrix} 0 & 0 & 0 & 1 & 0 \\ 1 & 0 & 1 & 0 & 1 \\ 0 & 0 & 1 & 1 & 0 \\ 1 & 1 & 1 & 0 & 1 \end{bmatrix} \end{array}$$

Note that Delmo is allergic only to kumquats, while poor Elmo is allergic to all toppings except kumquats. The Dahmunohs in Dweebsville serves three different pizzas: the Basic, the Deluxe, and the Gastrointestinal Challenge. Matrix B describes toppings, a "1" indicating presence of a topping, and "0" absence.

$$B = \begin{array}{c} \\ \\ \text{Mushrooms (M)} \\ \text{Olives} \quad\text{(O)} \\ \text{Anchovies} \quad\text{(A)} \\ \text{Kumquats} \quad\text{(K)} \\ \text{Rutabagas} \quad\text{(R)} \end{array} \begin{array}{ccc} & & \text{Gastro-} \\ & & \text{intestinal} \\ \text{Basic} & \text{Deluxe} & \text{challenge} \\ \text{(B)} & \text{(D)} & \text{(GIC)} \\ \begin{bmatrix} 1 & 1 & 1 \\ 0 & 1 & 1 \\ 0 & 1 & 1 \\ 0 & 0 & 1 \\ 0 & 1 & 0 \end{bmatrix} \end{array}$$

Matrices A and B, consisting only of 0 and 1 entries, with "1" indicating presence (incidence) of a certain condition and "0" absence, are known as **incidence matrices.** These matrices are important in graph theory, discussed in Section 3.2.

Discuss the matrix products BA and AB as they relate to the culinary delights experienced by the Dweeb brothers.

SOLUTION The matrix product BA does not exist since the number of columns in B does not match the number of rows in A. Matrix AB, however, can be evaluated, and is shown below: (Check this!)

$$AB = \begin{array}{c} \begin{array}{ccccc} \text{M} & \text{O} & \text{A} & \text{K} & \text{R} \end{array} \\ \begin{bmatrix} 0 & 0 & 0 & 1 & 0 \\ 1 & 0 & 1 & 0 & 1 \\ 0 & 0 & 1 & 1 & 0 \\ 1 & 1 & 1 & 0 & 1 \end{bmatrix} \end{array} \begin{array}{c} \begin{array}{ccc} \text{B} & \text{D} & \text{GIC} \end{array} \\ \begin{bmatrix} 1 & 1 & 1 \\ 0 & 1 & 1 \\ 0 & 1 & 1 \\ 0 & 0 & 1 \\ 0 & 1 & 0 \end{bmatrix} \end{array}$$

$$= \begin{array}{c} \\ \text{Delmo} \\ \text{Felmo} \\ \text{Zelmo} \\ \text{Elmo} \end{array} \begin{array}{c} \begin{array}{ccc} \text{B} & \text{D} & \text{GIC} \end{array} \\ \begin{bmatrix} 0 & 0 & 1 \\ 1 & 3 & 2 \\ 0 & 1 & 2 \\ 1 & 4 & 3 \end{bmatrix} \end{array}$$

To understand what the elements in this product matrix indicate, we examine the (2,3) element which, as you know by now, comes from multiplying the *second row of A times the third column of B*:

$$\text{Felmo} \begin{array}{c} \begin{array}{ccccc} \text{M} & \text{O} & \text{A} & \text{K} & \text{R} \end{array} \\ \begin{bmatrix} 1 & 0 & 1 & 0 & 1 \end{bmatrix} \end{array} \begin{array}{c} \begin{array}{c} \text{GIC} \end{array} \\ \begin{bmatrix} 1 \\ 1 \\ 1 \\ 1 \\ 0 \end{bmatrix} \end{array}$$

$$= 1 \cdot 1 + 0 \cdot 1 + 1 \cdot 1 + 0 \cdot 1 + 1 \cdot 0$$
$$= 2$$

Since all entries in both vectors are 0's or 1's, "matching ones" is the only way to get a nonzero answer. "Two" indicates there are two sets of matching 1's. What do "matching ones" mean? A left-hand 1 signifies Felmo is allergic to the topping involved; a right-hand 1 indicates that topping is on the Gastrointestinal Challenge. The "2" thus indicates that there are 2 toppings on the Gastrointestinal Challenge to which Felmo is allergic. ∎

PRACTICE PROBLEM 1 In Example 4, suppose the Dweeb brothers order the Deluxe. Answer the following: **(a)** Who will have the most trouble? **(b)** Who will have the least trouble?

ANSWER(S) **(a)** Elmo, with 4 reactions **(b)** Delmo, with none ☐

PRACTICE PROBLEM 2   If the brothers order Basic on Monday, Deluxe on Tuesday, and the Gastrointestinal Challenge on Wednesday, and each brother eats pizza each night, answer the following: **(a)** What is the total number of allergic reactions each will get? **(b)** How many reactions were caused by each pizza type?

ANSWER(S)   **(a)** Delmo: 1; Felmo: 6; Zelmo: 3; Elmo: 8   **(b)** Basic: 2; Deluxe: 8; "Gastro": 8   □

EXERCISES 3.1

APPLYING THE CONCEPTS

Exercises 1–4: A nutritionist for a yogurt company uses various proportions of two different yogurts, X and Y, to make four different mixes (1 through 4). Amounts of protein, sodium, fat, and carbohydrates (in grams) for one unit of each of the two yogurts is given by matrix A, while units of each yogurt used in making the four mixes are shown in matrix B.

$$A = \begin{matrix} \text{Protein} \\ \text{Sodium} \\ \text{Fat} \\ \text{Carbohydrate} \end{matrix} \begin{bmatrix} \overset{X}{7} & \overset{Y}{10} \\ .1 & .2 \\ 5 & 4 \\ 30 & 46 \end{bmatrix} \qquad \begin{matrix} & \mathbf{Mix} \\ & \mathbf{1}\ \ \mathbf{2}\ \ \mathbf{3}\ \ \mathbf{4} \\ \begin{matrix} X \\ Y \end{matrix} & \begin{bmatrix} 3 & 1 & 1 & 1 \\ 2 & 3 & 1 & 2 \end{bmatrix} \end{matrix} = B$$

1. Find the amount of protein in Mix 2.
2. Find the amount of fat in Mix 3.
3. Find the amount of carbohydrate in mix 3.
4. Both matrix products AB and BA can be calculated. Does either or both of these have any special meaning? Explain.

Exercises 5–7: A fruit packer in Wenatchee, Washington, has a truck loaded with fruit. The load consists of 1,000 boxes of apples, 750 boxes of cherries, and 400 boxes of peaches. Market prices, (\$/box) of the different types of fruit in various Western cities, are given by the entries in the following matrix:

	Apples	**Cherries**	**Peaches**
Portland	3	5	9
San Francisco	4	5	7
Las Vegas	3	6	8
Salt Lake City	3	7	7

5. If the trucker sells his entire load in San Francisco, find the total revenue.
6. If the trucker sells his entire load in Las Vegas, find the total revenue.

7. Suppose it costs the trucker $100 to drive to Portland, $200 to San Francisco, $250 to Salt Lake City, and $300 to Las Vegas. If he wants to maximize his net profit after paying expenses, where should he sell his fruit?

Exercises 8–10: A nursery rents lawn-care equipment. In June, 80 spreaders, 120 sprayers, and 30 post-hole diggers were rented. In July, 90 spreaders, 100 sprayers, and 40 diggers were rented. Based on these figures, projections for August are: $0.8 \times$ July rentals $+ 0.2 \times$ June's rentals.

8. Using matrix multiplication, estimate August rentals for each of the three.
9. Suppose daily rental prices are $15 for spreaders, $12 for sprayers, and $20 for diggers. Using matrix multiplication, calculate rental receipts for June and July.
10. Using prices from Exercise 9, and August projections, estimate August rental receipts.

Exercises 11–14: A company has three factories, each with four production lines: I, II, III, and IV. Matrix A represents the hourly productions of each of the lines in each factory.

$$\text{Factory} \begin{array}{c} \\ 1 \\ 2 \\ 3 \end{array} \overset{\begin{array}{cccc} \text{I} & \text{II} & \text{III} & \text{IV} \end{array}}{\begin{bmatrix} 45 & 50 & 50 & 65 \\ 40 & 50 & 40 & 60 \\ 30 & 60 & 55 & 35 \end{bmatrix}} = A$$

Matrix B represents the number of hours per week each line was run during a recent two-week period.

$$\begin{array}{c} \text{I} \\ \text{II} \\ \text{III} \\ \text{IV} \end{array} \overset{\begin{array}{cc} \text{Week 1} & \text{Week 2} \end{array}}{\begin{bmatrix} 20 & 40 \\ 30 & 25 \\ 40 & 15 \\ 30 & 40 \end{bmatrix}} = B$$

11. What is the total output by Factory 2 during week 2?
12. What is the total output of Factory 1 for the two weeks?
13. What is the total output of all factories for week 2?
14. What is the total output of the three factories for the entire two-week period?

Exercises 15–17: The Eggcetera Breakfast Bar chain specializes in four omelets: the Country Breakfast, the Dieter's Delite, the Liver & Onion Special, and the El Grosso (one each of the other three omelets, mixed in a blender with a pint of goose fat and then fried in castor oil). The costs, respectively, are $4.50, $3.50, $4.00, and $9.50. The Eggcetera has three locations—in North, South, and Central Hepzibah, Idaho, a town consisting of 39 people and 72 severely overworked chickens. Omelet sales in the three locations during the last month were "eggstraordinary," and are given in the matrix below:

	Country Special	Dieter's Delite	Liver & Onion	El Grosso
North	100	150	10	200
South	200	50	100	150
Central	150	200	50	100

Using matrix multiplication, answer the following questions:

15. How many omelets were sold in each store for the month?
16. What were the total receipts for each of the three stores?
17. What were the total receipts by type of omelet?

Exercises 18–20: Mr. L. "Beau" Grease operates three gasoline stations in different parts of town (Hepzibah, Idaho—home of the frazzled and frenzied chickens). During Labor Day weekend, station A sold 500 gallons of super unleaded, 1,200 gallons of unleaded, and 800 gallons of regular; station B sold 700 gallons of super unleaded, 1,500 gallons of unleaded, and 1,000 gallons of regular; station C sold 450 gallons of super unleaded, 900 gallons of unleaded, and 800 gallons of regular (along with 745 bottles of Tums—station C is next to the South outlet of Eggcetera). Price of gasoline during that weekend was $1.29 for super unleaded, $1.10 for unleaded, and $0.95 for regular. Using matrix multiplication

18. Find the Labor Day weekend total revenue taken in by station A.
19. Find the Labor Day weekend total revenue taken in by all stations.
20. Find Labor Day weekend total revenue for station C. Ignore the Tums!

Exercises 21–23: The E-Z Line Company makes two types of notebooks: a deluxe notebook, with index tabs that sells for $1.50, and a regular notebook that sells for $1.00. It costs the company $1.25 to produce each deluxe notebook and $0.80 to produce each regular notebook. The company received orders from four different stores as shown by the following order matrix:

		Deluxe	Regular
	A	1000	1200
Stores	B	600	600
	C	900	750
	D	500	800

Using matrix multiplication, answer the following questions.

21. How much will the bill be for store D?
22. How much will it cost the company to fill all the orders?
23. What will E-Z's profit be for each store?

Exercises 24–27: Consider a manufacturer of tennis rackets. Profit is $9 per racket on their price leader model, the Advantage. On the step-up model, the Match Point, profit is $15, and on the top-of-the-line model, the Ace, they make $20. The manufacturer checks past sales and current economic conditions, and estimates demand for each racket in four geographical regions as shown in the matrix below. Use appropriate matrix manipulations to estimate the profit from:

	Advantage	Match Point	Ace
North	225	75	210
South	110	120	150
East	140	150	100
West	160	100	180

24. the East region.   25. the West region.   26. the South region.   27. the North region.

3.2 ELEMENTARY GRAPH THEORY

Graph theory is a relatively new area of mathematics used to model various phenomena in a variety of disciplines. Graph theory concerns a finite set of objects and relationships among them. Important applications are found in communications, computer science, transportation, sports, and sociology. The only graphs that we shall be concerned with are *directed graphs,* or *digraphs.*

DIRECTED GRAPH (DIGRAPH)

> A **directed graph (digraph)** is a finite set of points $P_1, P_2, \ldots,$ P_n (called **nodes** or **vertices**) along with directed **edges** which connect distinct pairs of points. If there is a sequence of edges that runs from P_i to P_j, we say that P_i is connected to P_j, and write $P_i \longrightarrow P_j$. If connections can be made in either direction, we write $P_i \longleftrightarrow P_j$.

We can visualize these ideas by drawing a diagram where points represent vertices and lines or curves between these dots represent appropriate relationships. The fundamental ideas of digraphs are illustrated in the examples that follow.

■ EXAMPLE 5

Trade relations among four countries (A,B,C,D) are such that

A exports to B, C, D	B exports to C and D
C exports to B and D	D exports to A and B

Illustrate these relationships by drawing an appropriate digraph.

SOLUTION

There are many ways to draw such a digraph. One such digraph is shown in Figure 3.1; there are many other representations. The actual shape is not important, but proper connections are.

Figure 3.1
Digraph for Example 5

In Example 5, note that country A exports to country B: we say there is a **one-step connection** from vertex A to vertex B. (In tracing a path in a digraph, it is important that each edge be traversed *in its indicated direction.*) Examination of a graph enables easy determination of one-step connections. What if there is no one-step connection from one vertex to another? In Example 5, there is no one-step connection from C to A. Can we find an indirect route from C to A that goes through some other vertex? Checking the graph shows that it is possible to get from C to A via D. We say there is a **two-step connection** from C to A, symbolized by C $\longrightarrow$ D $\longrightarrow$ A.

What about higher-step connections? If a digraph has relatively few vertices, then tracing possible routes will resolve the matter. When there are many vertices, however, using matrices is more efficient. We illustrate by analyzing the set of trade relations from Example 5 with matrices. First, introduce a **vertex matrix** M whose i,j-th element is "1" if country i exports to country j and zero otherwise. You may think of the "1" as indicating the presence of trade in a given direction, while zero indicates absence. Clearly, the vertex matrix that follows is an **incidence matrix** (see Example 4) since it indicates presence or absence of a certain condition, in this case trade relations.

$$M = \begin{array}{c} \\ A \\ B \\ C \\ D \end{array} \begin{array}{cccc} A & B & C & D \\ \left[\begin{array}{cccc} 0 & 1 & 1 & 1 \\ 0 & 0 & 1 & 1 \\ 0 & 1 & 0 & 1 \\ 1 & 1 & 0 & 0 \end{array}\right] \end{array}$$

All diagonal entries are 0; a diagonal "1" would say a country exports to itself (which is absurd!). The "1" in the (1,2) position indicates that country A exports to country B; the "0" in the (2,1) position says that B does not reciprocate. ∎

◼ EXAMPLE 6

Lack of two-way trade between all countries in Example 5 leads to interesting questions. Since country B does not export to country A, is it possible for B to send goods to A? If so, how?

SOLUTION

We seek to determine if there is a path from country B to country A. Checking matrix M reveals that although B does not export directly to A, she (countries are traditionally referred to in the female gender) can export to D who can then send the goods to A. We say that country B exports to A by using country D as an intermediary. We call this a **two-step connection** from country B to A. Further checking of the above matrix discloses that this is the only two-step connection. To advance our understanding, we now multiply the B row of M times the A column of M:

$$\begin{array}{c} \text{B row} \end{array} \begin{array}{cccc} A & B & C & D \\ [\,0 & 0 & 1 & 1\,] \end{array} \begin{array}{c} A \text{ column} \\ \left[\begin{array}{c} 0 \\ 0 \\ 0 \\ 1 \end{array}\right] \begin{array}{c} A \\ B \\ C \\ D \end{array} \end{array}$$

$$
= \begin{array}{cccc} \text{B does not} & \text{A does not} & \text{B does not} & \text{B does not} \\ \text{export to A} & \text{export to A} & \text{export to B} & \text{export to A} \\ 0 & \cdot \quad 0 & + \quad 0 & \cdot \quad 0 \end{array}
$$

$$
\begin{array}{cccc} & \text{B exports} & \text{C does not} & \text{B exports} & \text{D exports} \\ & \text{to C} & \text{export to A} & \text{to D} & \text{to A} \\ + & 1 & \cdot \quad 0 & + \quad 1 & \cdot \quad 1 \end{array} = 1
$$

This sum of products produces but a single 1—when both factors are 1. B exporting to C does no good because C refuses to export to A. This particular B-row-times-A-column multiplication gives the number of two-step connections from B to A. Now, form the matrix M^2 (that is, M times M) giving:

$$
M^2 = \begin{array}{c} \\ A \\ B \\ C \\ D \end{array} \begin{array}{cccc} A & B & C & D \\ \begin{bmatrix} 1 & 2 & 1 & 2 \\ 1 & 2 & 0 & 1 \\ 1 & 1 & 1 & 1 \\ 0 & 1 & 2 & 2 \end{bmatrix} \end{array}
$$

What can we say about a typical entry in M^2? In the (2,1) position (representing B to A), we see a "1." Previously we noted one way for B to send goods to A in two steps—namely the path from B to D and then to A. This result generalizes:

The i,j-th element of M^2 expresses the number of two-step connections that go from country i to country j.

For example, "2" in the (1,2) position shows there are two ways to send goods from row 1 (country A) to column 2 (country B) in two steps.

PRACTICE PROBLEM 3 Determine the two ways of getting goods from country A to country B in two steps.

ANSWER(S) **(1)** Country A may send the goods to C who may then send them to B. **(2)** Country A may send the goods to D who may then send them to B on the next step (stage 2). □

PRACTICE PROBLEM 4 Interpret the (4,4) element of the matrix M^2.

ANSWER(S) The (4,4) element of M^2 describes export from country D to herself in two steps. We know that a country cannot export to herself directly, so the two-step communication describes country D exporting goods to country A or B and then that same country simply returning the goods to country D. □

We know what elements in M and M^2 tell us separately. What can be said about a particular element of $M + M^2$?

■ EXAMPLE 7 _____   In Example 5, find $M + M^2$ and interpret its elements.

SOLUTION

$$M = \begin{array}{c} \\ A \\ B \\ C \\ D \end{array} \begin{array}{cccc} A & B & C & D \\ \left[\begin{array}{cccc} 0 & 1 & 1 & 1 \\ 0 & 0 & 1 & 1 \\ 0 & 1 & 0 & 1 \\ 1 & 1 & 0 & 0 \end{array}\right] \end{array} \qquad \begin{array}{c} \\ A \\ B \\ C \\ D \end{array} \begin{array}{cccc} A & B & C & D \\ \left[\begin{array}{cccc} 1 & 2 & 1 & 2 \\ 1 & 2 & 0 & 1 \\ 1 & 1 & 1 & 1 \\ 0 & 1 & 2 & 2 \end{array}\right] \end{array} = M^2$$

$$M + M^2 = \begin{array}{c} \\ A \\ B \\ C \\ D \end{array} \begin{array}{cccc} A & B & C & D \\ \left[\begin{array}{cccc} 1 & 3 & 2 & 3 \\ 1 & 2 & 1 & 2 \\ 1 & 2 & 1 & 2 \\ 1 & 2 & 2 & 2 \end{array}\right] \end{array}$$

Since a given entry in M (0 or 1) indicates direct exporting, while the corresponding element in M^2 indicates two-step exporting, then an element in $M + M^2$ describes the number of export routes from the row country to the column country in two or fewer steps. The "1" entry in the (2,3) position, for example, says that there is but one way of sending goods from country B to country C in two or fewer steps. The 3 in the (1,4) position says there are 3 ways country A is able to export to country D either directly or through 1 intermediary. These three ways are:

1. Directly,

2. Country A can send to B who can send to D (two steps),

or

3. Country A can send to C who can send to D (two steps).   ■

In Examples 5, 6, and 7 we have learned the following:

1. Entries in vertex matrix M describe direct connections.

2. Entries in M^2 describe two-step connections; i.e., connections through one intermediary.

3. Entries in $M + M^2$ describe connections through at most one intermediary.

These results generalize.

CONNECTIONS IN p OR FEWER STEPS

> 1. If M is the incidence matrix of a digraph, then the i,j-th element of M^p gives the number of p-step connections that go from vertex i to vertex j.
>
> 2. The i,j-th element of $M + M^2 + \cdots + M^p$ indicates the number of connections from vertex i to vertex j in p or fewer steps.

Communication Networks

Communication networks provide interesting applications of graph theory.

■ EXAMPLE 8

There are two professors' offices, a secretary's office, and a classroom in a building. Communications between these entities are such that

1. The secretary can talk to everyone.

2. Professors 1 and 2 (we call them P_1 and P_2) communicate with one another, but only P_2 can speak to the secretary.

3. The classroom is able to send messages only to the secretary.

Form the vertex matrix for this digraph and discuss communications. Can Professor P_1 or P_2 send a message to a student in the classroom?

SOLUTION

Using the symbols S, P_1, P_2, and C to represent the four "entities," and remembering that we don't allow entities to talk to themselves, we show a graph and the associated vertex matrix in Figure 3.2.

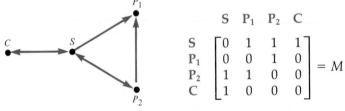

$$
\begin{array}{c@{}c}
 & \begin{array}{cccc} S & P_1 & P_2 & C \end{array} \\
\begin{array}{c} S \\ P_1 \\ P_2 \\ C \end{array} &
\left[\begin{array}{cccc}
0 & 1 & 1 & 1 \\
0 & 0 & 1 & 0 \\
1 & 1 & 0 & 0 \\
1 & 0 & 0 & 0
\end{array}\right] = M
\end{array}
$$

Figure 3.2
Digraph and vertex matrix
for Example 8

As in most offices, the secretary clearly runs the show. Professor P_1 and the classroom appear to have the most trouble in sending messages. Knowing that powers of the vertex matrix M provide us with higher-step communications, we form the matrix products M^2 and M^3, along with $M + M^2$ and $M + M^2 + M^3$:

$$
M^2 = \begin{array}{c@{}c}
 & \begin{array}{cccc} S & P_1 & P_2 & C \end{array} \\
\begin{array}{c} S \\ P_1 \\ P_2 \\ C \end{array} &
\left[\begin{array}{cccc}
2 & 1 & 1 & 0 \\
1 & 1 & 0 & 0 \\
0 & 1 & 2 & 1 \\
0 & 1 & 1 & 1
\end{array}\right]
\end{array}
\qquad
M^3 = \begin{array}{c@{}c}
 & \begin{array}{cccc} S & P_1 & P_2 & C \end{array} \\
\begin{array}{c} S \\ P_1 \\ P_2 \\ C \end{array} &
\left[\begin{array}{cccc}
1 & 3 & 3 & 2 \\
0 & 1 & 2 & 1 \\
3 & 2 & 1 & 0 \\
2 & 1 & 1 & 0
\end{array}\right]
\end{array}
$$

$$M + M^2 = \begin{array}{c} \\ S \\ P_1 \\ P_2 \\ C \end{array}\begin{array}{cccc} S & P_1 & P_2 & C \\ \left[\begin{array}{cccc} 2 & 2 & 2 & 1 \\ 1 & 1 & 1 & 0 \\ 1 & 2 & 2 & 1 \\ 1 & 1 & 1 & 1 \end{array}\right] \end{array} \qquad M + M^2 + M^3 = \begin{array}{c} \\ S \\ P_1 \\ P_2 \\ C \end{array}\begin{array}{cccc} S & P_1 & P_2 & C \\ \left[\begin{array}{cccc} 3 & 5 & 5 & 3 \\ 1 & 2 & 3 & 1 \\ 4 & 4 & 3 & 1 \\ 3 & 2 & 2 & 1 \end{array}\right] \end{array}$$

The entries in matrix $M + M^2$ reveal that a message can get from any entity to any other entity in at most two steps, except that P_1 cannot get a message to a student in the classroom. The P_1 to C entry of M^3 is non-zero, however, so that Professor 1 can get his message to a student in three steps: P_1 to P_2, P_2 to S, and S to C. Since all entries in $M + M^2 + M^3$ are positive, it is possible in three or fewer steps to get a message from any of the four entities to any other. ∎

Dominance Digraphs

Many relationships between pairs are characterized by one element of the pair dominating the other. If A and B represent the items in such a dominance relationship, then either A dominates B or B dominates A, but not both. Let $P_i \to P_j$ now stand for "P_i dominates P_j." Thus, either $P_i \to P_j$ or $P_j \to P_i$ but not both. This is the essence of a *dominance digraph*.

DOMINANCE DIGRAPH

> A digraph such that for any two distinct vertices, P_i and P_j, either P_i dominates P_j ($P_i \to P_j$) or P_j dominates P_i, but not both, is called a **dominance digraph.**

Sports contests, where ties are not allowed, provide a nice example of dominance digraphs. Consider the following example.

■ EXAMPLE 9

A league of six teams—A, B, C, D, E, and F—plays each other once with the following results.

A beats B, D, E, and F   B beats C, D, and F
C beats A and F   D beats C, E, and F
E beats B and C   F beats only E

A vertex matrix for this digraph is shown below.

$$M = \begin{array}{c} \\ A \\ B \\ C \\ D \\ E \\ F \end{array}\begin{array}{cccccc} A & B & C & D & E & F \\ \left[\begin{array}{cccccc} 0 & 1 & 0 & 1 & 1 & 1 \\ 0 & 0 & 1 & 1 & 0 & 1 \\ 1 & 0 & 0 & 0 & 0 & 1 \\ 0 & 0 & 1 & 0 & 1 & 1 \\ 0 & 1 & 1 & 0 & 0 & 0 \\ 0 & 0 & 0 & 0 & 1 & 0 \end{array}\right] \end{array}$$

Interpret the elements in matrices M, M^2, and $M + M^2$.

SOLUTION   Matrix M clearly qualifies as the vertex matrix for a dominance digraph since, with no ties, one of the two teams must win. The i,j-th element of M gives the results of direct competition: a "1" indicates that Team i beat Team j, while a "0" indicates that j won. If there is a "1" in the i,j-th position, then there must be a "0" in the j,i-th position, and vice-versa.

The matrices M^2 and $M + M^2$ are given below:

$$
M^2 =
\begin{array}{c}
 \\
A \\ B \\ C \\ D \\ E \\ F
\end{array}
\begin{array}{cccccc}
A & B & C & D & E & F \\
\left[\begin{array}{cccccc}
0 & 1 & 3 & 1 & 2 & 2 \\
1 & 0 & 1 & 0 & 2 & 2 \\
0 & 1 & 0 & 1 & 2 & 1 \\
1 & 1 & 1 & 0 & 1 & 1 \\
1 & 0 & 1 & 1 & 0 & 2 \\
0 & 1 & 1 & 0 & 0 & 0
\end{array}\right]
\end{array}
\qquad
M + M^2 =
\begin{array}{c}
 \\
A \\ B \\ C \\ D \\ E \\ F
\end{array}
\begin{array}{cccccc}
A & B & C & D & E & F \\
\left[\begin{array}{cccccc}
0 & 2 & 3 & 2 & 3 & 3 \\
1 & 0 & 2 & 1 & 2 & 3 \\
1 & 1 & 0 & 1 & 2 & 2 \\
1 & 1 & 2 & 0 & 2 & 2 \\
1 & 1 & 2 & 1 & 0 & 2 \\
0 & 1 & 1 & 0 & 1 & 0
\end{array}\right]
\end{array}
$$

To help understand what these elements indicate, consider the "3" in the A row, C column position of M^2. This "3" results from multiplying the A row of M times the C column of M:

$$
\begin{array}{c}
 \\
A
\end{array}
\begin{array}{cccccc}
A & B & C & D & E & F \\
[0 & 1 & 0 & 1 & 1 & 1]
\end{array}
\begin{array}{c}
C \\
\left[\begin{array}{c}0\\1\\0\\1\\1\\0\end{array}\right]
\end{array}
\begin{array}{c}
\\A\\B\\C\\D\\E\\F
\end{array}
$$

$$
= 0 \cdot 0 + 1 \cdot 1 + 0 \cdot 0 + 1 \cdot 1 + 1 \cdot 1 + 1 \cdot 0 = 3
$$
$$
\;(1)\quad+\quad(2)\quad+\quad(3)\quad+\quad(4)\quad+\quad(5)\quad+\quad(6)
$$

We examine these six products, one by one, from left to right:

(1) $0 \cdot 0$ says "A did not beat itself" and "A did not beat C."

(2) $1 \cdot 1$ says "A beat B" and "B beat C." A has established a two-stage dominance over team C by beating a team that has beaten C.

(3) $0 \cdot 0$ says "A did not beat C" and "C did not beat itself."

(4) $1 \cdot 1$ says "A beat D" and "D beat C." This is another two-stage dominance shown by A over C.

(5) $1 \cdot 1$ says "A beat E" and "E beat C." This is a third example of a two-stage dominance by A over C.

(6) $1 \cdot 0$ says "A beat F" and "F did not beat C."

The final answer of "3" illustrates the three cases of a two-stage dominance by Team A over Team C. In general we see that:

the *i,j*-th element of M^2 tells us the number of two-stage dominances that Team *i* has over Team j—that is, how many teams that beat Team *j* were defeated by Team *i*.

In Example 9, A beat B and B beat C. This is one indication that A is more powerful than C, but this conclusion is somewhat tainted. Matrix M, which provides the results of direct competition, shows that C beat A. In forming the matrix $M + M^2$, we add corresponding elements from M and M^2. Thus, **the *i,j*-th element of $M + M^2$ tells us the total number of times that Team *i* either beat Team *j* or beat a team that beat Team *j*.** The larger the *i,j*-th entry, the more powerful Team *i* is relative to Team *j*. As we move through all entries in the *i*-th row of $M + M^2$, we can examine the strength of Team *i* versus all other teams. By summing the entries in the *i*-th row of $M + M^2$, we gain an idea of the power of Team *i* relative to its competitors. It seems reasonable that the largest row sum should be associated with the most powerful team. The **power of a vertex** (sports team in our example) in a dominance digraph is defined in just this way:

POWER OF A VERTEX IN A DOMINANCE DIGRAPH

> The **power of vertex *i*** is the total number of one- and two-step dominances from vertex *i* to all other vertices; the power of vertex *i* is the sum of the entries in the *i*th row of $M + M^2$, where M is the vertex matrix.

We now calculate the power of each vertex (sports team) in Example 9. Recalling that row sums for matrix $M + M^2$ can be found by multiplying $M + M^2$ on the right by a column of 1's, we find

$$\begin{array}{c} \\ \begin{array}{c}A\\B\\C\\D\\E\\F\end{array}\end{array}\begin{array}{c}\begin{array}{cccccc}A&B&C&D&E&F\end{array}\\\begin{bmatrix}0&2&3&2&3&3\\1&0&2&1&2&3\\1&1&0&1&2&2\\1&1&2&0&2&2\\1&1&2&1&0&2\\0&1&1&0&1&0\end{bmatrix}\end{array}\begin{bmatrix}1\\1\\1\\1\\1\\1\end{bmatrix}=\begin{bmatrix}13\\9\\7\\8\\7\\3\end{bmatrix}$$

Ranking these teams by power, we obtain:

Team	Power
A	13
B	9
D	8
C	7 ⎤ tie
E	7 ⎦
F	3

Our definition of power produces a ranking that is almost the same as the win-loss record, which is found to be:

Team	Wins	Losses
A	4	1
B	3	2
D	3	2
C	2	3
E	2	3
F	1	4

Strong agreement between our definition of power and the win-loss record is not always the case. Note that our definition of power allows us to differentiate between teams B and D, which have identical win-loss records. Specifically, team B is more powerful than D. Checking the B and D rows of both M and M^2 reveals that B's higher power is due to M^2—B's defeated opponents are stronger than D's. ∎

PRACTICE PROBLEM 5   Each team in a six-team league plays four games, with no team playing any other team more than once. (Since some teams do not play each other, this is not a true dominance diagraph. The definition of power, however, still measures relative strength of the teams.) The results of the games are as follows:

A beats C, E, and F	B beats C, E, and F
C beats only F	D beats A and B
E beats C and D	F beats only D

Rank the teams according to power and compare this ranking with the typical "win-loss" ranking.

ANSWER(S)   The powers and win-loss records are as follows:

Team	Power	Wins	Losses
D	8	2	2
A	7	3	1
B	7	3	1
E	5	2	2
F	3	1	3
C	2	1	3

The "most powerful" team D has only the third best win-loss record! D's power is due to defeating strong opponents A and B.   □

The notion of power is not restricted to sports contests. Power can be used in preference rankings as well. The following example illustrates such a use.

■ EXAMPLE 10

In an experiment actually performed by one of your authors, a student who had never drunk coffee before was led through a pairwise taste-testing experiment designed to determine the coffee that tasted best to him. The following four coffees were brewed, in identical strengths and by the same coffee-maker:

French Roast (FR)   Mexican (M)
Viennese (V)   Colombian (C)

The student was then given a small cup of each of two coffees, and asked to indicate his preference. This procedure was then repeated until he had compared all possible pairs of coffees. The results of the experiment are as follows:

Competing Coffees	FR, V	FR, C	FR, M	V, C	V, M	M, C
Preferences	V	C	M	V	V	C

Using this information, determine the student's preference.

SOLUTION   Using an incidence matrix M, we display these results, using a "1" to indicate the preferred coffee in each pair.

$$M = \begin{array}{c} \\ FR \\ V \\ M \\ C \end{array} \begin{array}{cccc} FR & V & M & C \\ \begin{bmatrix} 0 & 0 & 0 & 0 \\ 1 & 0 & 1 & 1 \\ 1 & 0 & 0 & 0 \\ 1 & 0 & 1 & 0 \end{bmatrix} \end{array}$$

We next compute M^2 and $M + M^2$, getting

$$M^2 = \begin{array}{c} \\ FR \\ V \\ M \\ C \end{array} \begin{array}{cccc} FR & V & M & C \\ \begin{bmatrix} 0 & 0 & 0 & 0 \\ 2 & 0 & 1 & 0 \\ 0 & 0 & 0 & 0 \\ 1 & 0 & 0 & 0 \end{bmatrix} \end{array}$$

$$M + M^2 = \begin{array}{c} \\ FR \\ V \\ M \\ C \end{array} \begin{array}{ccccc} FR & V & M & C & Row\ Sum \\ \begin{bmatrix} 0 & 0 & 0 & 0 \\ 3 & 0 & 2 & 1 \\ 1 & 0 & 0 & 0 \\ 2 & 0 & 1 & 0 \end{bmatrix} & \begin{matrix} 0 \\ 6 \\ 1 \\ 3 \end{matrix} \end{array}$$

Summarizing, we have

Coffee Type	Power	Wins	Losses
Viennese	6	3	0
Colombian	3	2	1
Mexican	1	1	2
French Roast	0	0	3

Here (as opposed to results of Practice Problem 5), there is perfect agreement between powers and the win-loss records. ∎

EXERCISES 3.2

PRACTICING THE MOVES AND MANEUVERS

Exercises 28–30: Find the vertex matrix for the given digraph.

28.

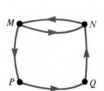

29.

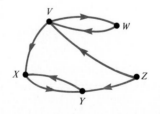

30.

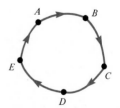

Exercises 31–33: Diagram the digraph represented by the given vertex matrix.

31.
$$\begin{bmatrix} 0 & 1 & 1 \\ 1 & 0 & 0 \\ 1 & 1 & 0 \end{bmatrix}$$

32.
$$\begin{bmatrix} 0 & 0 & 1 \\ 1 & 0 & 1 \\ 0 & 1 & 0 \end{bmatrix}$$

33.
$$\begin{bmatrix} 0 & 1 & 1 & 1 \\ 1 & 0 & 1 & 1 \\ 0 & 0 & 0 & 1 \\ 1 & 1 & 1 & 0 \end{bmatrix}$$

34. Is the vertex matrix of Exercise 31 a dominance digraph? Explain.
35. Is the vertex matrix of Exercise 32 a dominance digraph? Explain.
36. Is the vertex matrix of Exericse 33 a dominance digraph? Explain.

Exercises 37–39: Determine which vertex matrices represent dominance digraphs.

37.
$$\begin{bmatrix} 0 & 1 & 1 & 0 \\ 1 & 0 & 0 & 1 \\ 1 & 1 & 0 & 1 \\ 1 & 0 & 0 & 0 \end{bmatrix}$$

38.
$$\begin{bmatrix} 0 & 1 & 1 & 1 \\ 0 & 0 & 0 & 0 \\ 0 & 1 & 0 & 1 \\ 0 & 1 & 0 & 0 \end{bmatrix}$$

39.
$$\begin{bmatrix} 0 & 1 & 0 \\ 0 & 0 & 1 \\ 1 & 0 & 0 \end{bmatrix}$$

40. Using the vertex matrix in Exercise 37, find the following:
    (a) The number of two-step connections from P_1 to P_3.
    (b) The number of three-step connections from P_1 to P_3.
    (c) The number of connections from P_1 to P_3 that take three or fewer steps.
41. Repeat Exercise 40 for the vertex matrix in Exercise 38.
42. Repeat Exercise 40 for the vertex matrix in Exercise 39.
43. Using the given vertex matrix, answer the following:

$$M = \begin{array}{c} \\ P_1 \\ P_2 \\ P_3 \\ P_4 \end{array} \begin{array}{cccc} P_1 & P_2 & P_3 & P_4 \\ \begin{bmatrix} 0 & 1 & 1 & 1 \\ 0 & 0 & 1 & 0 \\ 0 & 0 & 0 & 0 \\ 0 & 1 & 1 & 0 \end{bmatrix} \end{array}$$

   (a) Does M represent a dominance digraph?
   (b) Find the number of two-step connections from P_1 to P_2.
   (c) Find the number of two-step connections from P_2 to P_4.
   (d) Find the number of three-step connections from P_1 to P_4.

APPLYING THE CONCEPTS

Exercises 44–49: Trade relations among a group of Middle Eastern countries that export are as follows:

   Country A exports to countries B and D.
   Country B exports to countries C and D.
   Country C exports to all other countries.
   Country D exports to only country B.

44. Present the vertex matrix for this digraph.
45. Does the vertex matrix of Exercise 44 represent a dominance digraph? Explain.
46. List those countries that country B can export to in exactly two steps.
47. List those countries that country B can export to in two or fewer steps.
48. Can country A get goods to country D in two or fewer steps? Explain.
49. Can country D get goods to country A in two or fewer steps? Explain.

*50. The five teams in a sports league play each other exactly once, and ties are not possible. The results of *all but one* game are as follows:

Team A beats teams C and D   Team B beats A and C
Team C beats D and E   Team D beats only team E
Team E beats teams A and B

Rank the teams according to power and win-loss records.

Exercises 51–56: A regional airline services four cities—P_1, P_2, P_3, and P_4, as indicated by the digraph below, where an arrow indicates direction of travel.

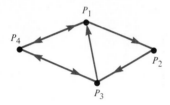

51. Using a "1" to indicate travel from city P_i to city P_j, find the vertex matrix for this digraph.
52. Find the number of two-step connections from P_1 to P_3. List them.
53. Find the number of three-step connections from P_2 to P_3. List them.
54. Find the number of two-step connections from P_2 to P_4. List them.
55. There is no direct flight from P_1 to P_3. How many routes are available that require no more than 2 intermediate stops?
56. Find the number of three-step connections from P_1 to P_4. List them.

Exercises 57–66: Consider the system of streets shown below, where vertices P_1 through P_6 represent intersections in a busy, downtown area.
      *Not difficult, but requiring much matrix arithmetic.

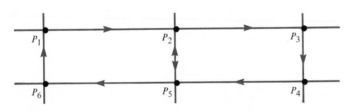

57. Find the vertex matrix M for this digraph.
58. Find M^2 and $M + M^2$. Interpret the entries of each matrix.
59. Is it possible to get from P_1 to P_4 without passing through more than one other intersection? Explain by using matrices.
60. Compute M^3 and $M + M^2 + M^3$. Interpret the entries of each matrix.
61. If now at intersection P_5, how many possible intersections can you reach without driving through more than two other intersections?
62. If you are now at intersection P_2, can you get to P_1 without passing through more than two other intersections? Explain by using matrices.
63. Calculate M^4 and $M + M^2 + M^3 + M^4$. Interpret entries of each matrix.

64. From intersection P_1, are there any other intersections that can't be reached by going through at most three intersections?
65. If now at P_3, what is the minimum number of intersections that need to be traveled to return to P_3?
66. Is it possible to travel from any intersection to any other intersection (including a return to the start) without passing through more than 4 intersections?

Exercises 67–69: An individual is given a pair of each of the following Mexican foods and asked to pick her favorite: Taco (T), Tostada (Tos), Burrito (B), Enchilada (E), and Quesidilla (Q). After tasting each pair, this individual indicates her preference. A summary of the results is given below:

Food Pair	T, Tos	T, B	T, E	T, Q	Tos, B	Tos, E	Tos, Q	B, E	B, Q	E, Q
Preference	Tos	B	T	Q	B	Tos	Q	E	Q	E

67. Find the "win-loss" record for each of these Mexican foods.
68. Find the power of each of the Mexican foods and rank them by power.
69. Compare the win-loss records to the powers and comment.

3.3 SOME ELEMENTARY CRYPTOGRAPHY

Sending secret messages to friends is something you probably did in school at one time. Sending coded messages is not new—there is evidence of secret codes being used in primeval times. The process of sending a message by first encoding it and then having the recipient decode it is called **cryptography.** In this section we examine a simple but interesting use of matrices in the area of cryptography.

A simple code is obtained by "scrambling" alphabet letters. For example, we might use the association given below:

A B C D E F G H I J K L M N O P Q R S T U V W X Y Z   represent this letter
| | | | | | | | | | | | | | | | | | | | | | | | | |
D E G M A H J R P O Z V U F T X I Q W S B Y C N K L   by this letter

To encode the word BUFFOON, you would use an E in place of the B, and B in place of the U, etc., leading to the encoded version EBHHTTF. The recipient of your message would reverse the process, finding the E in the bottom row, replacing it with B, etc., until she arrived at the word BUFFOON. Alternatively, rather than using a code that merely rearranges letters, you might prefer a numerical correspondence like the one below:

A B C D E F G H I J K L M N O P Q R S T U V W X Y Z
4 9 12 8 21 26 25 18 10 19 15 11 23 6 2 3 1 22 5 13 17 20 7 14 24 16

Using this correspondence, the message BUFFOON would get sent as 9 17 26 26 2 2 6. Upon receiving the message, decoding would reverse the process. While it is fun to use such a code, it would not take long to break. Notice that with the first code, the encoded version EBHHTTF contains HH and TT.

Although the HH is a disguise for FF, and TT is code for OO, the occurrence of double letters (or the corresponding double numbers in the numerical code) would be a great help in breaking the code. These considerations, and the fact that certain letters occur with greater frequency, would enable someone knowledgeable in cryptography to discover your code quickly. We shall use matrices to make the code considerably more difficult to break. To allow spacing between words, we introduce a "space" into our alphabet, representing it by "27." (We won't do so, but it would be reasonable to add other forms of punctuation as well.)

■ EXAMPLE 11

To illustrate the use of matrices, we send the following message:

WET BIRDS NEVER FLY AT NIGHT

Begin by dividing the letters into groups of two, remembering that a space, symbolized by "_," is now in our alphabet:

WE   T_   BI   RD   S_   NE   VE   R_   FL   Y_   AT   _N   IG   HT

Using the numerical correspondence above (with a space being "27"), we convert the above groups of two into numerical pairs, representing each pair of numbers by a 2 × 1 column vector:

$$\begin{bmatrix} W \\ E \end{bmatrix} = \begin{bmatrix} 7 \\ 21 \end{bmatrix} \qquad \begin{bmatrix} T \\ \_ \end{bmatrix} = \begin{bmatrix} 13 \\ 27 \end{bmatrix} \qquad \begin{bmatrix} B \\ I \end{bmatrix} = \begin{bmatrix} 9 \\ 10 \end{bmatrix}$$

and so on. Now, as an **encoding matrix**, choose any 2 × 2 matrix A which has an inverse. As we shall see shortly, this inverse will allow the recipient to decode the message. The matrix A that we shall use, and its inverse are given by:

$$A = \begin{bmatrix} 3 & 1 \\ 2 & 1 \end{bmatrix} \qquad A^{-1} = \begin{bmatrix} 1 & -1 \\ -2 & 3 \end{bmatrix}$$

Using the encoding matrix A, we further encode our message by premultiplying (multiplying on the left) each 2 × 1 column vector above by A. Thus, for example, the first two vector pairs, representing "W" and "E," "T" and "space," are now sent to new 2 × 1 vectors given by

$$A \begin{bmatrix} W \\ E \end{bmatrix} = A \begin{bmatrix} 7 \\ 21 \end{bmatrix} = \begin{bmatrix} 3 & 1 \\ 2 & 1 \end{bmatrix} \begin{bmatrix} 7 \\ 21 \end{bmatrix} = \begin{bmatrix} 42 \\ 35 \end{bmatrix}$$

and

$$A \begin{bmatrix} \text{T} \\ \_ \end{bmatrix} = A \begin{bmatrix} 13 \\ 27 \end{bmatrix} = \begin{bmatrix} 3 & 1 \\ 2 & 1 \end{bmatrix} \begin{bmatrix} 13 \\ 27 \end{bmatrix} = \begin{bmatrix} 66 \\ 53 \end{bmatrix}$$

In a similar manner, the next two letter pairs, their number equivalents and the encoded number pairs are as follows:

$$A \begin{bmatrix} \text{B} \\ \text{I} \end{bmatrix} = A \begin{bmatrix} 9 \\ 10 \end{bmatrix} = \begin{bmatrix} 37 \\ 28 \end{bmatrix} \qquad A \begin{bmatrix} \text{R} \\ \text{D} \end{bmatrix} = A \begin{bmatrix} 22 \\ 8 \end{bmatrix} = \begin{bmatrix} 74 \\ 52 \end{bmatrix}$$

Continuing through the remainder of the letter pairs produces the following message:

42 35 66 53 37 28 74 52 42 37 39 33 81 61 93 71 89 63 99
75 25 21 87 60 55 45 67 49

The receiver of the message picks these off in horizontal pairs, converting each pair into a 2 × 1 column vector. To decode the message, she premultiplies each vector by the **decoding matrix,** which we define to be the *inverse of the encoding matrix.* The first pair received, 42 and 35, gets decoded as follows:

$$A^{-1} \begin{bmatrix} 42 \\ 35 \end{bmatrix} = \begin{bmatrix} 1 & -1 \\ -2 & 3 \end{bmatrix} \begin{bmatrix} 42 \\ 35 \end{bmatrix} = \begin{bmatrix} 7 \\ 21 \end{bmatrix} = \begin{bmatrix} \text{W} \\ \text{E} \end{bmatrix}$$

By continuing in this manner, the recipient is able to reconstruct the original message. In this method of coding, observe that a given letter is not always encoded the same. For example, the letter E, which appears three times in our message, gets sent once to 35, once to 33, and once to 61. Not only does the same letter get converted to several different numbers, but a given number can also arise from more than one letter. In the message above, a 37 comes both from a "B," and from a "_." This makes it next to impossible for someone to decode the message based on frequency of occurrence of various numbers. ■

We used a 2 × 2 matrix as an encoding matrix in Example 10. There is no reason we could not have used a 3 × 3 or 4 × 4, or any other square matrix with an inverse. If, for example, we had used a 3 × 3 encoding matrix, we would have divided our message into groups of 3, and then put each "triplet" into a 3 × 1 column vector before premultiplying by the encoding matrix.

Current Uses of Cryptography

A computer uses cryptography to store information, encoding all information as binary numbers. A commonly used character code is the ASCII code. Pronounced "Ask-e," ASCII stands for American Standard Code for Information Interchange. A portion of the ASCII Code is shown in Table 3.1.

Table 3.1

ASCII **Codes**

ASCII Code (Decimal)	Character	ASCII Code (Decimal)	Character	ASCII Code (Decimal)	Character
32	SPACE	64	@	96	
33	!	65	A	97	a
34	''	66	B	98	b
35	#	67	C	99	c
36	$	68	D	100	d
37	%	69	E	101	e
38	&	70	F	102	f
39	'	71	G	103	g
40	(	72	H	104	h
41	)	73	I	105	i
42	*	74	J	106	j
43	+	75	K	107	k
44	'	76	L	108	l
45	−	77	M	109	m
46	.	78	N	110	n
47	/	79	O	111	o
48	0	80	P	112	p
49	1	81	Q	113	q
50	2	82	R	114	r
51	3	83	S	115	s
52	4	84	T	116	t
53	5	85	U	117	u
54	6	86	V	118	v
55	7	87	W	119	w
56	8	88	X	120	x
57	9	89	Y	121	y
58	:	90	Z	122	z
59	;	91	[	123	{
60	<	92	\	124		
61	=	93	]	125	}
62	>	94	^	126	~
63	?	95	_	127	DEL

In Table 3.1, we have shown the decimal code rather than the binary code, which, while longer, is preferred by computers. The ASCII Code for the word CODE (all capital letters) would be

C   67
O   79
D   68
E   69

Computer encoding is routinely done when electronic fund transfers are made between banks. Cryptography is also employed to prevent unauthorized users from gaining access to computers. In order to establish communications with a computer, you must enter a password. If you enter the correct password, the computer is able to decode it, allowing you access. An incorrect code denies you entry, and on some systems the failed attempt is recorded, allowing the proper user of the account to know that an attempt was made to enter his area.

EXERCISES 3.3

APPLYING THE CONCEPTS

Exercises 70–78: Use the following numerical correspondence, along with a "27" representing a space.

A B C D E F G H I J K L M N O P Q R S T U V W X Y Z
4 9 12 8 21 26 25 18 10 19 15 11 23 6 2 3 1 22 5 13 17 20 7 14 24 16

Exercises 70–74: Encode the following messages by using matrix A as the encoding matrix. Ignore all punctuation except spaces between words. Append a final space if necessary to complete a pair.

$$A = \begin{bmatrix} 2 & 3 \\ 3 & 4 \end{bmatrix}$$

70. An early worm gets the bird.
71. Anything worth doing is better done by someone else.

72. A stitch in time is just fine.
73. A pig in a poke.
74. Life goes on.

Exercises 75–78: Decode the given messages, which were sent by using the encoding matrix B given below, and the numerical correspondence above.
    *Not difficult, but requires much matrix arithmetic.

$$B = \begin{bmatrix} 1 & -1 \\ 1 & 0 \end{bmatrix}$$

75. −3 18 20 27   16 18   16 27 −13   4   7 25 −22 5 7 11   −8   5
      4 27   5 10 −16   5 −19   8   −5 13 −6 21   1 3 4 10 −14 13

76. −23   4 −18   3   0   6 −3 24   1   5 −1 20 −19 8 5 10 23
      27 24   27 15 21 −18   6   2 27 −11   2   (Ben Franklin's actual version)

77. −23   4 −8   5 −3 10 −6 12 17   27 −21   6   3 13 2 23 2
      27 −9   4 −3 18 17   22 21 27 −25   2 21 23   0 5

78. −23   4 20 22   0 11   4 10 −2 25   −8 5 −4 2 −6 21 −3 7
      0 11 22 27 −16   1 −1   4 −9 18 −23 4 −6 5   0 21 −7 3
    −19   6 19 27 −14   7   12 21

Exercises 79 and 80:   The messages were sent with the numerical correspondence above and the encoding matrix B shown below. Decode the given messages.

$$B = \begin{bmatrix} 7 & 9 & 2 \\ -3 & -3 & -1 \\ 4 & 5 & 1 \end{bmatrix}$$

*79.

227	−97	126	347	−132	191	163	−72	89	268	−98	149	386
−148	217	301	−123	167	310	−122	175	407	−157	228	278	−105
152	358	−136	201	141	−60	76	114	−51	61	162	−61	89
100	−42	56	427	−161	240	435	−166	242	166	−63	91	

*80.

289	−102	160	284	−104	158	291	−117	164	342	−138	191	426
−162	237	98	−38	54	289	−116	163	256	−104	145	307	−123
171	279	−120	155	309	−115	172	290	−103	160	283	−100	156
369	−144	204	95	−38	53	328	−122	184	275	−102	150	

Exercises 81–84:   Use the ASCII Code given in Table 3.1 to encode the given messages. Be sure to consider capitalization and punctuation.

81. *Beware!*   82. Balderdash.   83. Swing low, sweet chariot.

Exercises 84–86:   Decode the following messages, which were encoded by using the ASCII Codes of Table 3.1.

84.   83 119 105 110 103   32 108 111 119   32 97
      110 100   32 104 105 116   32 102   97 116 33

85.   73 115 110   44 116   32 109   97 116 104   32 102 117 110   63
86.   67 111 109 112 117 116 101 114   32 106 111 107 101 122

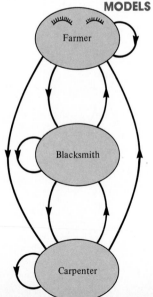

3.4 LEONTIEF ECONOMIC MODELS

In the simple village economy of long ago, interdependence among the people engaged in production was apparent. The blacksmith produced iron goods for his own use and for the farmer and carpenter. The carpenter built not only for himself, but also for the farmer and blacksmith. The farmer produced for the blacksmith and carpenter and for herself. The flow of goods and services among members of the community was easy to trace.

In today's incredibly complex society, the various segments of production are still interdependent. The myriad relationships among producers have not changed: each sector of the economy produces goods and services required by itself and other sectors.

In the mid-1930's Wassily Leontief devised a mathematical way of **modeling** such economic systems with matrices. For a model to be useful, it must both accurately describe the economy at any given time and must allow prediction of the economy at a later time or as a result of demand changes among economic sectors.

A three-sector economy, such as the village of our opening paragraph, requires a matrix with three rows and three columns. Operations on such a small matrix (for example, finding its inverse) are not too demanding. A modern economy, however, may have hundreds of sectors. For example, Leontief required 500 sectors for his model of the U.S. economy, producing a 500-by-500 matrix with 250,000 entries. Though the theory was sound, applications were impractical until large-scale computers were developed in the 1940's. Leontief's important work culminated in his receiving the Nobel Prize in Economics in 1973.

Throughout this section we shall concentrate on understanding and interpreting what we do. We shall encounter major ideas, in the context of small-scale examples. Larger and more realistic models you may encounter later will then pose only computational, not conceptual, difficulties; their computer solutions will hold no mysteries for you. We begin with a simple two-segment economy.

■ EXAMPLE 12

Flow of goods in two-family economy.

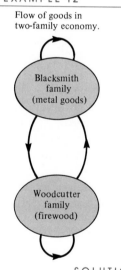

Imagine an isolated pair of families, each growing its own food, producing its own clothing and shelter. (This is to remove all economic concerns except the ones we will now introduce.) Suppose that one family plies the blacksmith trade, producing metal goods for both families, and the other is a family of woodcutters, supplying firewood for both families.

Quantities of metal goods and firewood are expressed in dollars, and all goods produced by the two families are also consumed by the two families. The blacksmith family consumes (requires as inputs) $10 in metal goods and $90 in wood to produce $100 in metal goods. Each dollar unit of metal goods produced requires $0.10 in metal goods and $0.90 in wood as inputs. To complete the model, suppose that the woodcutter family consumes $0.60 in metal goods and $0.40 in wood in producing one dollar's worth of wood. Letting m and w represent total production of metal goods and wood, express the interrelationships of this economy with a matrix equation.

SOLUTION To produce m dollars' worth of metal goods requires, as "inputs" to the blacksmith's family, $0.10m$ in metal and $0.90m$ in wood. To produce w dollars' worth of wood requires, as "inputs" to the woodcutter's family, $0.60w$ in metal goods and $0.40w$ in wood.

The total metal goods production is used up by the two production processes, and is the sum of metal goods used in production by the blacksmith's family and the woodcutter's family:

$$m = 0.10m + 0.60w$$

Similarly, all wood produced is consumed in the two production processes:

$$w = 0.90m + 0.40w$$

In matrix form, this system of two equations in two unknowns is:

$$\begin{bmatrix} m \\ w \end{bmatrix} = \begin{bmatrix} .10 & .60 \\ .90 & .40 \end{bmatrix} \cdot \begin{bmatrix} m \\ w \end{bmatrix}$$

This last matrix equation has the form

$$X = A \cdot X$$

where X is the **total production vector,** A is the **input-output matrix,** or the **technical matrix,** and AX is the **internal demand.** ∎

Closed Leontief Models

In Example 12, matrix A shows required inputs per unit of output for the two-industry economy. Interpreting the equation $X = AX$ as *total production equals internal demand*, we see that everything produced by the two industries is also consumed by the two industries. Further, each dollar of output by the blacksmith requires a dollar in inputs: $0.10 in metal goods and $0.90 in wood. Also, each dollar of woodcutter's output requires a total of $1 in inputs. Since each industry's output value equals its input value, neither economic sector gains or loses money; the economy is stable because neither industry profits at the expense of the other. (In a closed system like this, every profit to one industry is accompanied by a loss to the other.)

The top row of matrix A, (0.10 0.60), multiplied by the production vector X, accounts for the total metal consumed in production. The second row, (0.90 0.40), multiplied by the production vector X, accounts for total wood consumed in production. Thus, each input-output matrix row (multiplied by the production vector X) accounts for internal consumption of one type of product.

In matrix A, the entry 0.10 represents "metal consumed per dollar of metal produced," the entry 0.60 is "metal consumed per dollar of wood produced," the entry 0.90 is "wood consumed per dollar of metal produced," and 0.40 is "wood consumed per dollar of wood produced." Thus the first column of the input-output matrix represents metal and wood costs of producing one dollar worth of metal; the second column represents the metal and wood costs in producing one dollar of wood. Each column total being one indicates that, for each industry, the value of goods produced equals the value of goods consumed. "Both industries break even," reflecting stability of this closed system.

We return to the village economy. We assume that the three interdependent villagers (blacksmith, carpenter, farmer) produce and consume only among themselves (closed model). (Later we examine an open model, allowing production for persons outside the trio.) In a **closed model,** 100% of each sector's production (**output**) is consumed by (serves as **input** to) the sectors. In an **open model,** some production serves as output to consumers (in answer to **consumer demand**).

EXAMPLE 13

The village of Camel Lot (built upon a long-forgotten caravan campsite) consists of the blacksmith, carpenter, and farmer families, each family plying its particular occupation while utilizing goods produced by all three families. Quantities produced and consumed are expressed in dollar values. For long-run stability in the village, it is agreed that each family will "break even," producing goods equal in value to that family's consumption of goods. (Otherwise, in this small closed system, one family's gain becomes another's loss, possibly leading to a family's ruin, departure from the village, and the village's loss of a vital skill.)

Leaders of the three families estimate that each dollar of blacksmith's production will require $0.60 in carpenter's production, and equal amounts from the other two segments. Each dollar of carpenter's production will consume $0.40 in farm products, and equal amounts from the other two industries. Finally, each dollar value produced by the farmer will require $0.30 in blacksmith's goods and $0.50 in carpenter's production.

Find the production dollar amounts for the three economic sectors which will yield a stable economy.

SOLUTION

Let b, c, and f denote dollar values of blacksmith, carpenter, and farmer production, respectively, and set up the input-output matrix to represent a stable closed economy, bearing in mind the observations following Example 12. Recall that the first column of the input-output matrix shows costs, in blacksmith's, carpenter's, and farmer's goods, for one dollar of blacksmith's production. Since the entire cost must also be one dollar, the first column must show $0.60 in carpenter's goods consumed by one dollar of blacksmith's production, with the other two consumptions in column one being $0.20. Similar logic creates columns two and three. The resulting matrix equation, stating that total production equals internal consumption, is

$$I_3 \cdot \begin{bmatrix} b \\ c \\ f \end{bmatrix} = \begin{bmatrix} .20 & .30 & .30 \\ .60 & .30 & .50 \\ .20 & .40 & .20 \end{bmatrix} \cdot \begin{bmatrix} b \\ c \\ f \end{bmatrix}$$

The form of this system is

$$I \cdot X = \qquad A \qquad \cdot X$$

Though not yet in standard form (with all terms containing unknowns gathered on the left sides of the equations), this system has characteristics worth noting:

1. Each entry in the square matrix on the right (input-output matrix) is nonnegative. "No sector consumes a negative amount of any resource in its own production."

2. In the input-output matrix, each column totals 1. "Each dollar of output from any sector requires a total of one dollar in inputs."

Writing the system in standard form $(I - A)X = 0$ yields

$$\begin{bmatrix} .80 & -.30 & -.30 \\ -.60 & .70 & -.50 \\ -.20 & -.40 & .80 \end{bmatrix} \begin{bmatrix} b \\ c \\ f \end{bmatrix} = \begin{bmatrix} 0 \\ 0 \\ 0 \end{bmatrix}$$

Solution by Gauss-Jordan elimination yields the solution family

$$b = \frac{18}{19} t$$

$$c = \frac{29}{19} t$$

$$f = t$$

where the parameter t is an arbitrary constant. There are infinitely many possible production levels for a stable economy, each determined by assigning a value to t. For example, $t = \$38,000$ (chosen because 19 divides $\$38,000$) yields a blacksmith's production of $(18/19) \cdot \$38,000 = \$36,000$, a carpenter's production of $(29/19) \cdot \$38,000 = \$58,000$, and a farmer's production of $\$38,000$. ∎

Study the input-output matrix of Example 13, and its two listed characteristics (nonnegative entries, each column summing to one). Such a matrix guarantees that the system of equations $IX = AX$, where A is the input-output matrix and X is the vector of unknown production levels, will have infinitely many solutions.

PRACTICE PROBLEM 6   Tell whether each of the given matrices could or could not be an input-output matrix for a closed economic system.

(a) $\begin{bmatrix} 1.2 & .3 \\ -.2 & .7 \end{bmatrix}$ (b) $\begin{bmatrix} .65 & .35 \\ .28 & .72 \end{bmatrix}$ (c) $\begin{bmatrix} .25 & .25 & .3 & .2 \\ .35 & .15 & .2 & .3 \\ .15 & .50 & .4 & .1 \\ .25 & .10 & .1 & .4 \end{bmatrix}$

ANSWER(S)   **(a)** no; matrix contains a negative entry; **(b)** no; columns do not total 1; **(c)** yes ☐

The closed model case (producers consume the system's entire production) always leads to a system of linear equations which can be written as a matrix equation of the form $IX = AX$. The standard form of this system is $(I - A)X = 0$. The "**0**" on the right side of this matrix equation is a column vector of zeros.

Such a linear system (with zeros on the right of all equations when the system is in standard form) is called a **homogeneous system.** A homogeneous system of linear equations always has the trivial solution $X = 0$. In Example 13, we obtained an infinite family of solutions (including the trivial solution, obtained by selecting $t = 0$).

In fact, a closed-system input-output matrix (with characteristics "no negative entries; column sums are 1") always leads to a system with infinitely many solutions. That is, the coefficient matrix $(I - A)$ has no inverse, and the matrix equation can be solved by Gauss-Jordan elimination but not by finding $(I - A)^{-1}$.

Not all of the infinitely many solutions of the system $(I - A)X = 0$ are necessarily suitable for the original "real-world" problem. For example, when X is a vector of production levels, as in Example 13, it makes no sense to choose a value of t which yields negative values in X; such values would indicate "negative production." How does one "de-manufacture" something? Indeed, some "minimum level" of productivity might be required to maintain full employment in an economic segment or simply to keep the industrial machinery and personnel functioning at a level which maintains equipment and skills.

■ EXAMPLE 14

What production levels (measured in dollars) would be required in Example 13 if the minimum production for each of the three economic sectors must be $20,000?

SOLUTION   The general solution in Example 13 was

$$b = \frac{18}{19} t$$

$$c = \frac{29}{19} t$$

$$f = t$$

where b, c, and t are the economic outputs of the blacksmith, carpenter, and farmer sectors of the economy. If $t \le 0$, the production levels are also negative or zero. For positive values of t, the smallest of the three production levels a, b, and c is $b = (18/19)t$. The requirement that the smallest production level must be at least $20,000 then becomes

$$b = \frac{18}{19} t \ge 20,000$$

This leads to $t = 20,000 \div (18/19) \approx 21,111$ as the smallest permissible value of t. For example, setting $t = 22,000$ (a convenient value greater than 21,111) leads to the acceptable production levels $b = (18/19)(22,000) \approx \$20,842$, $c = (29/19)(22,000) \approx \$33,579$, and $f = \$22,000$. ■

■ EXAMPLE 15

The input-output matrix

$$A = \begin{bmatrix} .3 & .6 \\ .8 & .4 \end{bmatrix}$$

is not suitable for a stable, closed economic system. Tell why, and investigate setting up a two-industry system with this matrix.

SOLUTION

The first column totals 1.1, not 1.0; this indicates that the first industry requires $1.10 in inputs for each $1 of output—a condition that argues against stability.

   If we insist upon using this matrix in a closed, stable economic system with production levels r and s, the resulting matrix equation $I \cdot X = A \cdot X$ is

$$I \cdot \begin{bmatrix} r \\ s \end{bmatrix} = \begin{bmatrix} .3 & .6 \\ .8 & .4 \end{bmatrix} \cdot \begin{bmatrix} r \\ s \end{bmatrix}$$

In standard form, this becomes

$$\begin{bmatrix} .7 & -.6 \\ -.8 & .6 \end{bmatrix} \cdot \begin{bmatrix} r \\ s \end{bmatrix} = \begin{bmatrix} 0 \\ 0 \end{bmatrix}$$

The only solution of this homogeneous system (check this!) is $r = 0$, $s = 0$; this indicates that the only way for a closed economy with input-output matrix A to be stable is for it to be stagnant! ■

PRACTICE PROBLEM 7

In the input-output matrix in Example 15, replace the entry 0.8 with the value 0.5. Is the resulting matrix suitable as the input-output matrix for a closed system? If not, why not? If this matrix is used to model a closed system, what production levels yield stability?

ANSWER(S)

Not suitable; first column totals 0.8, indicating that one unit of production by the first industry requires only 0.8 units of input. The only stable production levels are "0" for both industries. □

Open Leontief Models

Now consider an open model based upon the three-sector village economy:

■ EXAMPLE 16

In a burst of civic pride, leaders of the three industries in Camel Lot offer to sell some of their production to Onager City, whose name also has ancient origins. The Onagerites eagerly place orders for $12,000 in blacksmith goods, $18,000 of carpenter's products, and $10,000 worth of Camel Lot's farm production. Camel Lot's three economic segments can no longer simply produce $1 of output for each $1 of input. The planners now determine that every dollar of blacksmith production requires $0.20 in blacksmith production, $0.10 in carpenter production, and $0.30 in farm production. The carpenters consume $0.30 in blacksmith production, $0.20 in carpenter production, and $0.20 in farm production for each dollar's worth they produce. Finally, the farm sector requires $0.25 in blacksmith production, $0.20 in carpenter production, and $0.35 in farm production for each dollars worth produced.

What production levels must Camel Lot's sectors attain in order to operate in perfect harmony and also satisfy the external demand imposed by the Onager City orders?

SOLUTION

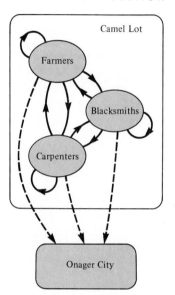

We represent desired production levels by b, c, and f. Blacksmith production must be enough to satisfy Camel Lot's internal needs plus the external demand imposed by the good folk of Onager City. The new ingredient, external demand, can now be shown by a demand vector D. The matrix formulation of "total production equals internal consumption plus external demand" is

$$I \cdot X = A \cdot X + D$$

which, in this example, becomes

$$I \cdot \begin{bmatrix} b \\ c \\ f \end{bmatrix} = \begin{bmatrix} .20 & .30 & .25 \\ .10 & .20 & .20 \\ .30 & .20 & .35 \end{bmatrix} \cdot \begin{bmatrix} b \\ c \\ f \end{bmatrix} + \begin{bmatrix} 12{,}000 \\ 18{,}000 \\ 10{,}000 \end{bmatrix}$$

In this system, matrix A is called the **technological matrix** (accounting for the unit costs of all production), D is called the (external) **demand vector,** and of course X is the **production vector.** In standard form the system becomes $(I - A)X = D$, yielding, in our example, the system

$$\begin{bmatrix} .80 & -.30 & -.25 \\ -.10 & .80 & -.20 \\ -.30 & -.20 & .65 \end{bmatrix} \cdot \begin{bmatrix} b \\ c \\ f \end{bmatrix} = \begin{bmatrix} 12{,}000 \\ 18{,}000 \\ 10{,}000 \end{bmatrix}$$

The system can be solved by Gauss-Jordan elimination or by finding $(I - A)^{-1}$. Solution by finding the inverse of $(I - A)$ offers a significant advantage: if the demand vector D changes, the new system is also readily solved using the same matrix $(I - A)^{-1}$. (See Chapter 2, Exercises 115–117.) Solving $(I - A)X = D$ by using $(I - A)^{-1}$ yields $X = (I - A)^{-1} \cdot D$. In the present example, correct to four decimal places,

$$(I - A)^{-1} = \begin{bmatrix} 1.7052 & .8703 & .9236 \\ .4440 & 1.5808 & .6572 \\ .9236 & .8881 & 2.1670 \end{bmatrix}$$

$$X = (I - A)^{-1} \cdot D \approx \begin{bmatrix} 1.7052 & .8703 & .9236 \\ .4440 & 1.5808 & .6572 \\ .9236 & .8881 & 2.1670 \end{bmatrix}$$

$$\cdot \begin{bmatrix} 12{,}000 \\ 18{,}000 \\ 10{,}000 \end{bmatrix} \approx \begin{bmatrix} 45{,}364 \\ 40{,}354 \\ 48{,}739 \end{bmatrix}$$

Thus, the blacksmith, carpenter, and farm economic segments of the Camel Lot economy must produce approximately $45,364, $40,354, and $48,739 in goods, respectively, to both satisfy internal requirements and meet the external Onager City demand. ∎

PRACTICE PROBLEM 8

(a) What production levels must the three segments of the Camel Lot economy (described in Example 16) achieve if the Onager City demand is for $16,000 in blacksmith goods, $12,000 in carpenters' products, and $20,000 in farm products? *Hint:* Use $(I - A)^{-1}$ from Example 16.

(b) If in addition to the Onager City demands of part **(a)**, Camel Lot receives orders from another city, Bent Lizard—for $4,000 in blacksmith products, $5,000 in carpenters' products, and $15,000 in farm products—what production levels must Camel Lot's economic segments achieve?

ANSWER(S) **(a)** blacksmith: $56,199; carpenter: $39,218; farm: $68,775. **(b)** blacksmith: $81,225; carpenter: $58,756; farm: $109,415. ☐

In a closed system each column of the input-output matrix must sum to 1, indicating that each industry consumes one dollar for each dollar it produces. What happens in an open system (that is, one which tries to satisfy an external demand) if an industry consumes more than it produces? What if one industry simply "breaks even?"

PRACTICE PROBLEM 9 Explain (by interpreting each column) why each of the following seems unsuitable as a two-industry technical matrix for an open system, and then investigate the result of using each matrix to try to satisfy an external demand for 10 units of each of the two products:

(a) $\begin{bmatrix} .4 & .8 \\ .7 & .2 \end{bmatrix}$ (b) $\begin{bmatrix} .4 & .5 \\ .7 & .2 \end{bmatrix}$ (c) $\begin{bmatrix} .4 & .8 \\ .6 & .2 \end{bmatrix}$

ANSWER(S) **(a)** This matrix seems unsuitable since the first industry consumes more in dollar value than it produces ($1.10 consumed for each $1 produced). Trying to satisfy external demand for $10 of each product requires production levels of −$200 and −$162.50 for the two industries—that is, "negative production." Such production is not possible.

(b) Again, the first industry consumes more than it produces. Trying to satisfy given external demand requires production levels of $100 and $100 for the two industries. In this case, such production is possible.

In **(b)**, the second industry is efficient in that it produces more than it consumes; it is able to make up for the inefficiency of the first industry so that the two together can meet external demand. In **(a)** the second industry merely breaks even, with no opportunity to offset the first industry's poor performance.

(c) It seems unlikely that an economic system with this technical matrix could satisfy any external demand, since both industries are break-even industries. This assessment is borne out (the reader should verify our conclusion): there is no solution (not even a "negative production" solution) to the problem of meeting the given external demand. ☐

EXERCISES 3.4

PRACTICING THE MOVES AND MANEUVERS

Exercises 87–90: Determine whether the given A matrix is suitable for a stable, closed economic system. If it is not stable, indicate why.

87. $\begin{bmatrix} .2 & .7 \\ .8 & .3 \end{bmatrix}$
88. $\begin{bmatrix} .23 & .41 \\ .77 & .69 \end{bmatrix}$
89. $\begin{bmatrix} 1.2 & .25 \\ -.2 & .75 \end{bmatrix}$
90. $\begin{bmatrix} .63 & .20 \\ .37 & .80 \end{bmatrix}$

Exercises 91–94: Explain why each of the following matrices seems unsuitable as a two-industry technical matrix for an open system.

91. $\begin{bmatrix} .5 & .9 \\ .5 & .1 \end{bmatrix}$
92. $\begin{bmatrix} .2 & .7 \\ .9 & .4 \end{bmatrix}$
93. $\begin{bmatrix} -.3 & .5 \\ .7 & .4 \end{bmatrix}$
94. $\begin{bmatrix} 0 & .2 \\ 0 & .6 \end{bmatrix}$

APPLYING THE CONCEPTS

Exercises 95–97: Consider the following three-sector (agriculture, lumbering, mining) closed economy which follows the partially completed technical matrix:

$$A = \begin{bmatrix} .2 & * & .3 \\ * & .4 & .3 \\ .6 & .5 & * \end{bmatrix}$$

95. Fill in the entries represented by an asterisk (*) with values which make possible a stable, non-stagnant economy.
96. Interpret (explain fully) row 1 of the matrix.
97. Interpret column 2.

Exercises 98–100: Consider a three-sector (agriculture, fishing, building) economy that has input-output matrix

$$A = \begin{bmatrix} .6 & .2 & .4 \\ .1 & * & .3 \\ .4 & .5 & * \end{bmatrix}$$

98. Fill in the asterisk (∗) entries with values which cause fishing to produce less than it consumes, and building to produce more than it consumes.
99. Interpret row 1.
100. Interpret column 1.

Exercises 101–104: Using the given technical matrix A and external demand vector D, write the matrix equation stating that "gross production is equal to internal consumption plus external demand." Then solve the equation step by step, first obtaining $(I - A)^{-1}$, then substituting the matrix $(I - A)^{-1}$ to finally obtain the required gross production vector.

101. $A = \begin{bmatrix} .2 & 0 \\ .3 & 0 \end{bmatrix} \quad D = \begin{bmatrix} 40 \\ 30 \end{bmatrix}$

102. $A = \begin{bmatrix} .2 & .6 \\ 0 & 0 \end{bmatrix} \quad D = \begin{bmatrix} 100 \\ 80 \end{bmatrix}$

103. $A = \begin{bmatrix} .6 & 0 \\ 0 & .2 \end{bmatrix} \quad D = \begin{bmatrix} 160 \\ 30 \end{bmatrix}$

104. $A = \begin{bmatrix} 0 & .10 \\ 2 & 0 \end{bmatrix} \quad D = \begin{bmatrix} 84 \\ 72 \end{bmatrix}$

105. In Exercise 101, suppose the two products are cattle and corn, in that order. What is the meaning of the zeros in A?
106. If the two products in Exercise 102 are coal and electricity, in that order, what is the meaning of the zeros in A?
*107. If in Exercise 101, the external demands for cattle and corn are doubled, must gross production also be doubled? Support your answer with figures, and explain why the figures are believable (aside from the fact that you calculated them).
108. Interpret the column totals in the technical matrix of Exercise 102.

109. In Exercise 103, if the two products are corn and beans, in that order, what is the meaning of the zeros in matrix A?
110. If the two products in Exercise 104 are lumber and axes, in that order, what is the meaning of the zeros in matrix A?
111. If external demand in Exercise 103 is cut in half, will total production also be cut in half? Explain in a way that would convince one who does not understand your figures.
112. What is the significance of the column totals in the technical matrix of Exercise 104?

Exercises 113–118: Neighboring ranches produce horses and cattle, respectively. The horse ranch annually uses 8 cattle (food for the hands) and 4 horses while producing 100 horses. The cattle ranch uses 8 cattle and 24 horses each year while producing 200 cattle. (Don't ponder the dietary considerations . . . .) Assume that one horse equals one cow in value.

113. Write the technical matrix (horse ranching first) for this small local economy.
114. Is it possible for this economy to be closed and productive? Explain.
115. Murky Puddle, the nearest settlement, wishes to buy 60 horses and 20 cattle per year from the two ranches. What production schedule (production levels) must the two ranches set in order to meet this demand?

116. To the nearest whole horse and cow, what are the production costs (internal resource consumptions) in Exercise 115?
*117. What external demand for the two commodities could be met if annual production is 300 horses and 700 cattle?
*118. Is it possible to fill an external demand for 500 cattle and no horses without producing a surplus of horses? Explain.

A Brief Summary of Important Ideas

In this chapter we have seen how various elements of matrix algebra can be used to solve interesting and diverse problems. Matrices having only 0's and 1's with "1" indicating presence of a certain condition or attribute are called **incidence matrices.** Incidence matrices occurred in many places in this chapter, but especially so in graph theory, where we found that the **vertex matrix** for a **digraph** (directed graph) was an incidence matrix. The p-th power of the vertex matrix describes the number of p-step connections between vertices in the digraph. If, for all pairs of distinct vertices, there is a connection between vertex i and vertex j or between vertex j and vertex i, but not both, then the graph is said to be a **dominance digraph.** The matrix $M + M^2$ (M is the vertex matrix of the dominance digraph) provides an indication of the **power of a vertex.** In this connection, we saw that power could refer to preference ranking, as for example in taste-testing.

Matrices were used to encode messages when we studied cryptography. The **inverse** of the coding matrix provided a way for the recipient to decode the message. The inverse of a matrix proved to be useful not only in decoding messages, but also in determining proper output or production levels necessary to meet certain demands in either an **open** or **closed Leontief model.**

REVIEW EXERCISES

APPLYING THE CONCEPTS

Exercises 119–122: A tailor and a shoemaker stranded on an otherwise undeveloped island devise ways to practice their crafts using locally available, not very durable materials. Before offering their wares (long shirts and moccasins) to the populace, they analyze their small economy, discovering that the shoemaker wears out three coconuts' worth of long shirts and two coconuts' worth of moccasins while making 10 coconuts' worth of moccasins, and the tailor wears out shirts worth three coconuts and moccasins worth four coconuts while making shirts worth 20 coconuts.

119. Write the technical matrix (shirts first).
120. What production levels must the two entrepreneurs attain in order to meet the neighbors' demands for shirts worth 40 coconuts and moccasins worth 60 coconuts?
*121. If production capability is adequate, could the two meet a 1,000-coconut demand for shirts and no demand for moccasins, without causing a surplus of either? Explain.
*122. If their maximum output is 70 coconuts in shirts and 80 coconuts in moccasins, what is the largest external demand they could meet?

Exercises 123–125: The "Homemade Look" Company received an order from Toddlers Anonymous for 600 sweatshirts, 800 t-shirts, and 1200 sweatpants. They also received an order for 500 sweatshirts, 700 t-shirts, and 1000 sweatpants from Kidcare, Inc. Each sweatshirt requires $\frac{3}{4}$ yard of fabric, 10 inches of ribbing, and 28 yards of thread; each t-shirt requires $\frac{3}{8}$ yard of fabric, 6 inches of ribbing, and 16 yards of thread; each pair of sweatpants requires 1 yard of fabric, 5 inches of ribbing, and 24 yards of thread. Fabric costs $7.00 per yard, ribbing costs $0.25 per inch, and thread costs $0.02 per yard. By defining and using matrices, find the following:

123. How much of each material must be purchased for each order?
124. If the "Homemade Look" company sells their products at 1.5 times manufacturing cost, find the total cost of filling each order, and the amount of profit they will make.
125. If the "Homemade Look" company sells their products at twice manufacturing cost, find the total cost of filling each order, and the amount of profit made.

Exercises 126–128: Consider a map that describes two-way roads between three sets of cities $A = \{a_1, a_2, a_3\}$, $B = \{b_1, b_2, b_3\}$, and $C = \{c_1, c_2\}$.

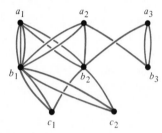

126. Write a matrix D whose i, j-th element is the number of roads connecting a_i to b_j.
127. Write a matrix E whose i, j-th element is the number of roads connecting b_i to c_j.
128. Compute the product DE; interpret the entries in terms of the road map.

Exercises 129–132: Coal and steel industries in a certain small country are heavily interdependent but not efficient. Each million dollars in gross coal production requires $400,000 in coal (power generation for mining equipment, heating the workers' swimming pools, saunas, barbecue pits, etc.) and $400,000 in steel (machinery, recreational equipment, etc.). Each million dollars in steel production consumes $300,000 worth of coal and only $100,000 in steel.

129. Write the technical matrix for this two-sector economy.
130. What gross production levels will allow the two industries to meet external demands for $50 million in coal and $80 million in steel? Round your answer to the nearest million dollars.
*131. What external demand could be met keeping the same gross production obtained in Exercise 130 while cutting in half the amount of steel used in producing a given quantity of coal?
*132. Is it possible to keep the same production as in Exercise 130 and meet a demand for $60 million in coal and $100 million in steel, just by making the coal industry more efficient? Justify your answer with figures.

Exercises 133–136: The admissions committee at the University of Hard Knox anticipates enrollment of 15,000 students in next year's freshman class. It has been determined that incoming freshmen can be classified in the following way concerning TV preferences and whether they wear socks:

	Socks	No socks
Sports	2500	1500
Documentaries	1500	500
Movies	4000	5000

From previous data, the admissions committee has determined that students will enter the College of Leisure, the College of Communications, Couch Potato School, or the School of Flower Repair according to the following matrix proportions:

	Leisure	Communications	Couch potato	Flower repair
Socks	.30	.30	.25	.15
No socks	.40	.05	.25	.30

Using matrix algebra, answer the following questions:

133. How many students who prefer documentaries are expected to enter the College of Communications?
134. How many students who prefer documentaries are expected to enter the College of Flower Repair?
135. How many students are expected in College of Leisure?
136. How many movie buffs are expected to study Couch Potato?

Exercises 137–141: Consider a small school district whose only employees are a superintendent, a principal, a vice-principal, a math teacher, and a janitor. These people influence one another as follows:

The **superintendent** influences everyone but the janitor.
The **principal** influences all but the math teacher and superintendent.
The **vice-principal** influences only the math teacher.
The **math teacher** influences only the principal.
The **janitor** influences everyone but the principal.

137. Find the matrix that expresses these direct influences.
138. Find the matrix that expresses influences through one intermediary.
139. Find the matrix that expresses influences through at most one intermediary.
140. If the vice-principal wants the day off, asking the superintendent will do no good—the superintendent will say "no." Is there a way the vice-principal can get the day off? If so, how? Answer by using matrices.
141. Can the math teacher influence everyone at some stage? Answer with matrices.

Exercises 142–144: A consumer comparing loudspeakers makes all possible pairwise comparisons among four speaker brands, choosing a preferred brand from each pair. The results of his experimentation are shown below:

Brand Pair	A,B	A,C	A,D	B,C	B,D	C,D
Preference	B	A	A	B	D	C

142. Rank the speakers by "win-loss" record.
143. Rank the speakers by power.
144. Discuss and compare the two rankings.

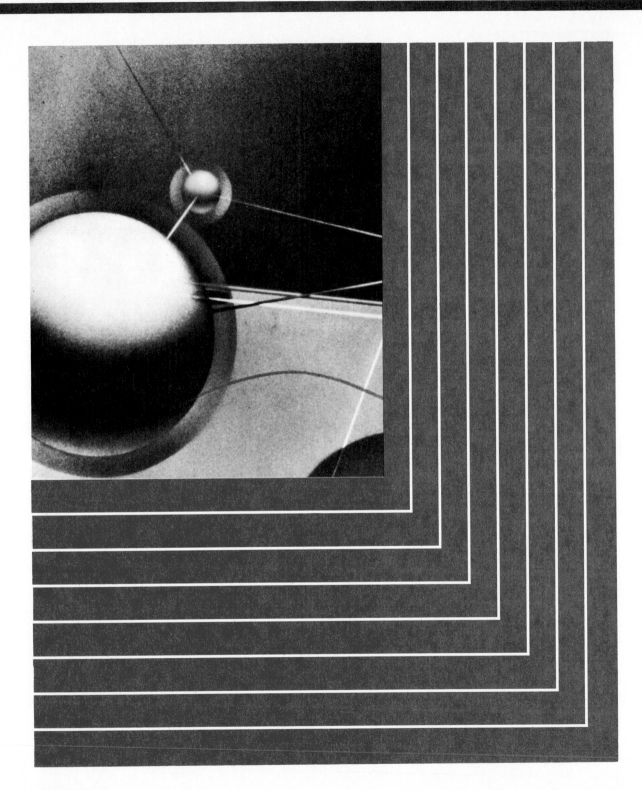

Geometrical Linear Programming

INTRODUCTION   In Chapter 1 we acquired methods for solving systems of linear equations, and encountered assorted applications. Exact answers were the usual outcome: the exact point where two lines crossed or where three planes (linear equations in three unknowns) intersected, or sets of values that exactly satisfied all linear equations in an original system.

Constraints   In government, industry, and commerce, however, an exact requirement like "ship 72 units" may be replaced by a boundary or restriction: "the warehouse holds up to 72 units." Such a restriction is a **constraint**; solving a problem might involve staying within the constraints and yet achieving the **optimal,** or best possible, outcome (for example, maximum profit, minimum production cost, highest level of nutrition). Doing as well as possible within constraints or limitations is called **optimizing** the outcome. The quantity to be optimized is called the **objective function**. Example 1 acquaints us with basic terminology.

■ EXAMPLE 1

Peter Xiang blends two diet supplements (H and K) to provide at least 40 mg of iron and 300 mg of vitamin C daily. Supplement H supplies 2 mg of iron and 30 mg of vitamin C per ounce, and supplement K contains 8 mg of iron and 20 mg of vitamin C per ounce. Peter may have up to 26 ounces of supplement H and 18 ounces of supplement K daily. He also must minimize cholesterol, found in both H (20 mg per ounce) and K (15 mg per ounce). What are the constraints? What is the objective function?

SOLUTION   The constraints are the iron and vitamin C *requirements* and the *limits* on supplement quantities. The objective function (to be minimized within these constraints) is the cholesterol intake. The symbol ≤ means "is less than or equal to" and ≥ means "is greater than or equal to." The constraints are:

total iron from both foods $\geq$ 40 mg

total vitamin C from both foods $\geq$ 300 mg

supplement H consumption $\leq$ 26 ounces

supplement K consumption $\leq$ 18 ounces

The objective function is "total cholesterol from both foods." ■

■ EXAMPLE 2

Using h to denote the number of ounces of supplement H consumed and k to denote the number of ounces of supplement K consumed, write the constraints of Example 1 as linear *inequalities* (algebraic statements using $\geq$ or $\leq$). Write the objective function as an algebraic expression for c (total cholesterol intake) in terms of h and k.

SOLUTION

Constraints

$$2h + 8k \geq 40 \qquad 30h + 20k \geq 300$$

$$h \leq 26 \qquad\qquad k \leq 18$$

Objective Function $c = 20h + 15k$

In addition to the stated constraints, other constraints are **implicit** (implied, but unstated): consumptions of supplements H and K cannot be negative. These implicit constraints (also called nonnegativity constraints) are:

$$h \geq 0 \qquad k \geq 0$$

The Example 1 problem can be stated in a new form: Minimize the objective function $c = 20h + 15k$, subject to the constraints

$$2h + 8k \geq 40 \qquad 30h + 20k \geq 300 \qquad h \geq 0$$

$$h \leq 26 \qquad\qquad k \leq 18 \qquad k \geq 0$$

■

The list of constraint inequalities resembles a list of equations. It is useful to think of the "greater than or equal to" sign as being made up of two parts: "greater than" (>) and "equal to" (=). Graphing an inequality is closely related to graphing the equation obtained by replacing ≥ with =.

4.1 GRAPHING LINEAR INEQUALITIES

Each linear equation in two variables has a clear, precise graph (a line). Each linear inequality also has a graph. The shape of this graph may surprise you. Once you get the basic idea, you will find such graphs very easy to sketch or visualize.

■ EXAMPLE 3

Graph the inequality $x + y \leq 5$.

SOLUTION

We employ two steps:

1. Graph $x + y = 5$ (the solid line in Figure 4.1).

2. Plot other points to identify the graph of $x + y < 5$. That is, find number pairs (x,y) whose sum is less than 5. Some such pairs are $(-5,2)$, $(1,1)$, $(0,4)$, $(-2,3)$, $(0,2)$, and $(-4,3.5)$. (We are not restricted to whole numbers.) Some of these points are plotted in Figure 4.1.

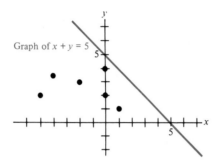

Figure 4.1
Exploring graph of $x + y \leq 5$

The line $x + y = 5$ splits the plane into a half-plane *above* the line and a half-plane *below* the line. All points (x,y) we have found which satisfy $x + y < 5$ lie below the line $x + y = 5$. Also, no point above the line $x + y = 5$ satisfies $x + y < 5$. [Try $(5,2)$.] The graph of $x + y \leq 5$ appears to be the line $x + y = 5$, and the half-plane below that line. A refined version of the graph of $x + y \leq 5$ is shown in Figure 4.2. The solid line graph of the equation $x + y = 5$ indicates that this line is included in the graph of $x + y \leq 5$; the shaded half-plane below the solid line is also included in, and completes, the graph.

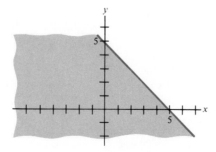

Figure 4.2
Graph of $x + y \leq 5$

■

Strict and Weak Inequalities

An inequality like $x + 2y > 4$ is a **strict inequality**, satisfied only by pairs (x,y) for which $x + 2y$ is strictly larger than 4, with graphs above the line $x + 2y = 4$. The line $x + 2y = 4$ (the *boundary* of the graph of $x + 2y > 4$) is dashed rather than solid in Figure 4.3(a) to show that it is not included in the graph. The graph [Figure 4.3(b)] of the **weak inequality** $x + 2y \geq 4$ includes its boundary, which is therefore solid, not dashed. *In our work, we shall encounter only weak inequalities and their graphs.*

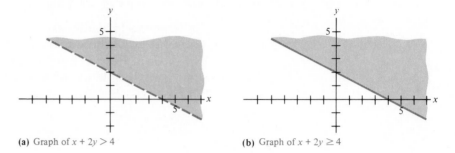

Figure 4.3
Contrasting graphs of weak and strict inequalities

(a) Graph of $x + 2y > 4$ (b) Graph of $x + 2y \geq 4$

The inequalities $x + y \leq 5$ and $x + 2y \geq 4$ are called **linear inequalities**: replacing $\geq$ or $\leq$ with = produces a linear equation, whose graph is the boundary of the graph of the corresponding inequality.

GRAPHING WEAK LINEAR INEQUALITIES

> The graph of a weak linear inequality in two variables is the solid line graph of the corresponding equation, plus the shaded half plane to one side of the line. To detect which half plane, test any point not on the line to see if its coordinates satisfy the inequality.

PRACTICE PROBLEM 1   Sketch the graph of $x + 3y \geq 6$.

ANSWER(S)   We first graph, as a solid line, $x + 3y = 6$. Then, testing any convenient pair (for example, (5,5)), we learn that the half-plane satisfying $x + 3y > 6$ is above the line we have drawn. The complete graph (shaded region and solid-line boundary) is shown in Figure 4.4.

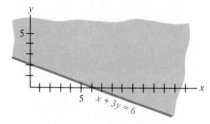

Figure 4.4
Graph of the weak linear inequality $x + 3y \geq 6$

Some prefer an alternative method for determining the half-plane to be included in the graph of a linear inequality in two variables. This method requires that we solve the inequality for its "vertical axis" variable (y in Practice Problem 1). To do so, we must manipulate an inequality much as we manipulate an equation. The fundamental ideas follow:

CHANGING THE FORM OF A LINEAR INEQUALITY

> 1. Adding the same term or number to both sides of an inequality does not change its direction:
>
> If $a \leq b$ then for any term or number c
> $$a + c \leq b + c$$
> If $a \geq b$ then for any term or number c
> $$a + c \geq b + c$$
>
> 2. Multiplying (or dividing) both sides of an inequality by any positive number does not change its direction:
>
> If $a \leq b$, and c is any positive number
> $$ca \leq cb \quad \text{and} \quad \frac{a}{c} \leq \frac{b}{c}$$
> If $a \geq b$, and c is any positive number
> $$ca \geq cb \quad \text{and} \quad \frac{a}{c} \geq \frac{b}{c}$$
>
> 3. Multiplying (or dividing) both sides of an inequality by any negative number reverses its direction:
>
> If $a \leq b$, and c is any negative number
> $$ca \geq cb \qquad \text{The} \leq \text{changed to} \geq.$$
> If $a \geq b$, and c is any negative number
> $$ca \leq cb \qquad \text{The} \geq \text{changed to} \leq.$$
>
> 4. Exchanging the sides of the inequality reverses the inequality symbol:
>
> If $a \leq b$, then $b \geq a$
> If $a \geq b$, then $b \leq a$

The moves for changing the form of a linear inequality are much like our familiar methods for changing the form of a linear equation. The principle source of error is failing to *reverse* the inequality symbol at the appropriate times. When multiplying (or dividing) by a negative number, or when exchanging the two sides of the inequality. Example 4 illustrates the techniques.

■ **EXAMPLE 4**

Solve each inequality for y:

(a) $2x + 5y \geq 7$ (b) $\frac{1}{5}x - \frac{3}{2}y \geq 2$

SOLUTION

(a)
$$2x + 5y \geq 7 \qquad \text{Original inequality}$$
$$5y \geq 7 - 2x \qquad \text{Added } -2x \text{ to both sides}$$
$$y \geq \tfrac{7}{5} - \tfrac{2}{5}x \qquad \text{Multiplied both sides by 1/5}$$

(b) $\frac{1}{5}x - \frac{3}{2}y \geq 2$ Original inequality

$2x - 15y \geq 20$ Multiplied by 10 (Why?)

$-15y \geq 20 - 2x$ Added $-2x$ to both sides

$15y \leq -20 + 2x$ Multiplied by -1. Reversal!

$y \leq -\frac{20}{15} + \frac{2}{15}x$ Multiplied by 1/15   ■

PRACTICE PROBLEM 2   Solve each of the following inequalities for x.

(a) $12(y - 3) - 5(x + 4) \geq x - 2$ (b) $\frac{1}{2}y + \frac{3}{4}x \leq 6 + \frac{1}{2}x$

ANSWER(S)   (a) $x \leq 2y - 9$ (b) $x \leq 24 - 2y$ □

Alternative "Testing for the Solution Half-plane" Procedure

Given a linear inequality in two variables, solve the inequality for its "vertical axis" variable (y in Example 3). If the result is of the form "$y \leq$ some expression," the included half-plane is *below* the boundary of the region. If the result is of the form "$y \geq$ some expression," the included half-plane is *above* the line. Let us explore both techniques in an example:

■ **EXAMPLE 5**

Sketch the graph of $2a + 10 \leq 5b$.

SOLUTION

The graph consists of a solid line (the graph of $2a + 10 = 5b$) and a shaded half-plane. To see which half-plane (above or below the solid boundary) is shaded, test a convenient point in either half-plane. Any point will do; testing $(0,0)$, we obtain $2(0) + 10 \leq 5(0)$, which simplifies to $10 \leq 0$, a false statement. By contrast, testing $(-4,2)$ yields $2 \leq 10$, which is true. We therefore shade the half-plane containing $(-4,2)$. See Figure 4.5.

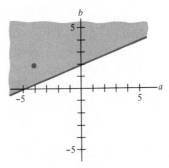

Figure 4.5
Graph of $2a + 10 \leq 5b$

Alternative test procedure: solve $2a + 10 \leq 5b$ for its vertical axis variable b:

$$2a + 10 \le 5b \qquad \text{Original}$$
$$5b \ge 2a + 10 \qquad \text{Exchanged sides—(Reversal!)}$$
$$b \ge \tfrac{2}{5}a + 2 \qquad \text{Divided by 5}$$

The form "$b \ge$ some expression" tells us that the half-plane to be included lies *above* the straight-line graph of $2a + 10 = 5b$. This agrees with our solution. ■

Feasible Regions

Our new graphing skills have immediate application. Requirements (constraints) such as those imposed upon Peter's intakes in Example 1 can now be made visible. The idea is to graph all constraints on one coordinate system. We then carefully identify the **feasible region**: the portion of the coordinate plane that satisfies all the constraints simultaneously. Any point (x,y) in the feasible region is in agreement with all the constraints; it is feasible, practical, or permissible. Any such point is okay because it represents one possible way to satisfy the problem requirements; and only points in the feasible region meet all problem restrictions. Out of the infinitely many possibilities represented by points in the region, we hope to find one (and there may be none, one, or many) to optimize (maximize or minimize, whichever is the goal) the objective function.

We have all the tools; attaining the finished product requires only attention to detail. Before studying Example 6, review the techniques we discovered for graphing linear inequalities in Examples 3–5.

■ EXAMPLE 6

Ace Truck Rentals has 6,000 square feet of storage for vans (200 square feet each) and trucks (300 square feet each). Show in graphic form the numbers of vans and trucks Ace could store.

SOLUTION

Let v and t denote the numbers of vans and trucks, respectively. The stated constraint (available space) is $200v + 300t \le 6000$. (It is not necessary to use all of the storage—only to stay within the 6,000 square feet available.) The implicit constraints, $v \ge 0$ and $t \ge 0$, acknowledge that numbers of vans and trucks cannot be negative. The full list of constraints is:

(a) $200v + 300t \le 6000$

(b) $v \ge 0$

and

(c) $t \ge 0$

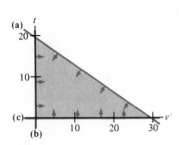

Figure 4.6

Numbers of trucks and vans
Ace could store

Solid line **(a)** in Figure 4.6 corresponds to inequality **(a)**. Testing $(0,0)$ selects the half-plane below line **(a)**, indicated by small arrows pointing downward from line **(a)**. Line **(b)** bounds the region where $v \geq 0$. Testing $(1,1)$ shows that the half-plane to the right of line **(b)** satisfies inequality **(b)**. We so indicate using small arrows pointing rightward from line **(b)**. Similarly, we graph line **(c)** and its attached arrows.

The feasible region is the set of all points in the plane which simultaneously satisfy all three inequalities. These points must be on or below line **(a)** and on or to the right of line **(b)** and on or above line **(c)**. This region consists of the heavy triangle and shaded interior shown in Figure 4.6. For example, since the point $(12,10)$ is in the feasible region, a mix of 12 vans and 10 trucks is feasible (satisfies all constraints). ■

PRACTICE PROBLEM 3   Graph the feasible region of Example 1.

ANSWER(S)   Constraints **(a)** through **(f)** yield the graph (solid boundaries and shaded region) of Figure 4.7. Be sure to track the steps!

Figure 4.7

Graph of feasible region
determined by Peter's dietary
constraints:
(a) $2h + 8k \geq 40$
(b) $30h + 20k \geq 300$
(c) $h \leq 26$
(d) $k \leq 18$
(e) $h \geq 0$
(f) $k \geq 0$

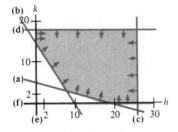

PRACTICE PROBLEM 4   Which of these points are in the Figure 4.7 region? $(15,15)$; $(12,20)$; $(12,18)$; $(12,19)$; $(12,17)$; $(30,10)$; $(2,11)$; $(5,5)$; $(14,3)$. Of what practical use is each feasible point?

ANSWER(S)   Feasible: $(15, 15)$, $(12, 18)$, $(12, 17)$, and $(14, 3)$. Each represents one way for Peter to meet all requirements of nutrition and capacity. □

Bounded and Unbounded Regions   The region in Figure 4.7 is **bounded** (surrounded) by line segments. Each **vertex** (corner) is a point where two boundary segments meet. What if Peter's appetite and capacity were unlimited? Constraints (c) and (d) would disappear; so would lines (c) and (d) in the graph. The result would be the region of Figure 4.8.

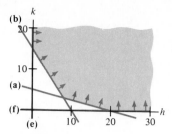

Figure 4.8
Peter's dietary constraints (no
food or appetite limits)

The Figure 4.8 feasible region extends upward and to the right indefinitely. This is an **unbounded region**. One interpretation is that Peter may eat as much as he likes, without limit, so long as his choice corresponds to a point somewhere in the region. Four ounces of supplement H and two ounces of supplement K would not suffice: (4,2) is not in the region. However (60,100) is in the region, so sixty ounces of supplement H and one hundred ounces of supplement K would meet Peter's needs.

The unbounded region of Figure 4.8 represents both unlimited food supplies and an unlimited appetite. In the real world, neither resources nor consumption are unlimited. In this chapter we treat only bounded regions in our examples and exercises, deferring unbounded cases to Chapter 5.

Feasible Vertices   Boundaries of feasible regions are line segments. Two boundaries meet at a **feasible vertex**, with coordinates found from the graph or by solving the appropriate pair of linear equations. Graphing feasible regions and finding coordinates of feasible vertices will be essential in Section 4.2.

PRACTICE PROBLEM 5   For each feasible region sketch, determine the coordinates of feasible vertices, by careful graph reading or by solving appropriate pairs of linear equations. Check all vertex coordinates by substituting into the appropriate equations.

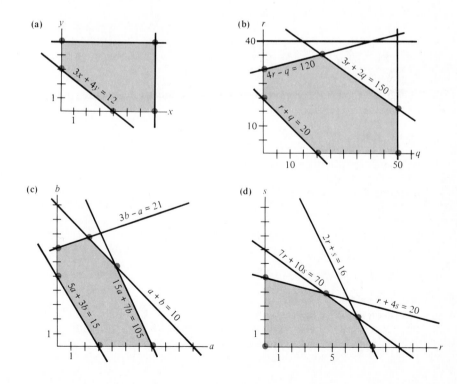

ANSWER(S)   **(a)** $(0,3)$, $(0,5)$, $(7,5)$, $(7,0)$, $(4,0)$

(b) $(0,20)$, $(0,30)$, $\left(\frac{240}{11}, \frac{390}{11}\right)$, $\left(50, \frac{50}{3}\right)$, $(50,0)$, $(20,0)$

(c) $(0,5)$, $(0,7)$, $\left(\frac{29}{4}, \frac{11}{4}\right)$, $\left(\frac{35}{8}, \frac{45}{8}\right)$

(d) $(0,0)$, $(0,5)$, $\left(\frac{80}{18}, \frac{70}{18}\right)$, $\left(\frac{90}{13}, \frac{28}{13}\right)$, $(8,0)$

(In all parts of Practice Problem 5, notice that not every crossing of two linear constraint equations is a feasible vertex.)   □

EXERCISES 4.1

PRACTICING THE MOVES AND MANEUVERS

Exercises 1–16: Graph the given inequality.

1. $x \le 3$
2. $y \ge 2$
3. $x - 2 \le 4$
4. $3 + y \ge -1$
5. $x + y \le 3$
6. $a + b \ge 4$
7. $2r + s \le 6$
8. $j + 5k \le 10$
9. $5m - 8p \ge 20$
10. $36 - 9j \le 6k$
11. $8a \le 4b + 24$
12. $100 \ge 10q + 25r$
13. $3r + 12 \le 4s$
14. $3b - a \ge 3$
15. $5y \ge 4x - 20$
16. $7m - 21 \le 6n$

Exercises 17–24: Sketch the region satisfying the system of inequalities. (*Note:* Grouping of nonnegativity constraints: "$x,y \ge 0$" means "$x \ge 0$ and $y \ge 0$.")

17. **(i)** $x + y \le 5$ **(ii)** $x,y \ge 0$
18. **(i)** $2a + b \le 6$ **(ii)** $a,b \ge 0$
19. **(i)** $2r + 3s \le 12$ **(ii)** $r,s \ge 0$
20. **(i)** $a + b \le 5$ **(ii)** $a,b \ge 0$ **(iii)** $2a + 3b \ge 6$
21. **(i)** $p + q \le 10$ **(ii)** $p,q \ge 0$ **(iii)** $5p + 8q \ge 40$
22. **(i)** $x,y \ge 0$ **(ii)** $x - y \ge 1$ **(iii)** $x - 1 \le \frac{y}{3}$
23. **(i)** $m,n \ge 0$ **(ii)** $m \le 6$ **(iii)** $n \le 4$ **(iv)** $3m + n \ge 7$
24. **(i)** $w,z \ge 0$ **(ii)** $w \le 10$ **(iii)** $z \le 8$ **(iv)** $w + z \le 12$ **(v)** $w - z \le 2$

Exercises 25–27: Tell which points belong to the region of the named exercise. For points which fail, specify a constraint which the point violates.

25. See Exercise 17. Check points $(2,4)$, $(1.5,2.2)$, $(-1,1)$, $(2.5,2.5)$, $(7,-3)$, $(3,3)$.
26. See Exercise 21. Check points $(3,3)$, $(4,4)$, $(5,5)$, $(6,4.1)$, $(12,-2.2)$, $(0,5)$.
27. See Exercise 23. Check points $(2,1)$, $(4,4)$, $(1,3)$, $(5,5)$, $(6,-2.4)$, $(1,4)$.

Exercises 28–35: Give coordinates of all vertices of the named region.

28. Exercise 17.   29. Exercise 18.   30. Exercise 19.   31. Exercise 20.
32. Exercise 21.   33. Exercise 22.   34. Exercise 23.   35. Exercise 24.

Exercises 36–39: Assume $r,s \geq 0$; sketch the feasible region.

36. $r + s \leq 3$ $5r + 2s \geq 10$ 37. $r + s \leq 3$ $5r + 2s \geq 15$ 38. $r + s \leq 3$ $5r + 2s \geq 20$
39. What do Exercises 36, 37, and 38 say about possibilities for feasible regions?

Exercises 40–43: Assuming nonnegativity constraints, sketch the region.

40. $3x + 5y \geq 15$ $6x + 3y \leq 18$ 41. $x \geq 5$ $x + y \leq 10$ $y \leq 3$
42. $3x + 5y \leq 15$ $6x + 3y \geq 18$ $1 \leq y$ 43. $x \leq 5$ $x + y \leq 10$ $y \geq 5$

Exercises 44–47: Give coordinates of all vertices of the named region.

44. Exercise 40.   45. Exercise 41.   46. Exercise 42.   47. Exercise 43.

APPLYING THE CONCEPTS

48. The Cod and Cow restaurant has a 500-pound-capacity freezer. The manager must keep at least 100 pounds of beef and at least 50 pounds of fish on hand at all times. List all constraints, and graph the feasible region.

49. A fruit broker has a controlled-atmosphere warehouse with a capacity of 20,000 boxes of apples. She anticipates a demand for Golden Delicious apples of at least twice the demand for Red Delicious. She plans to buy at least 4,000 boxes of Golden Delicious. List the linear constraints; graph the region.

50. Give the coordinates of all vertices of the feasible region of Exercise 48.

51. Give the coordinates of all vertices of the feasible region of Exercise 49.

52. Bountiful Farms, an agribusiness with large land holdings, has a property with soil seriously lacking plant nutrients. The manager will spend at least $400 per acre on nitrogen and at least $600 per acre on potash. He is willing to spend anywhere from $2,000 per acre to $5,000 per acre. Use n and p for dollars per acre spent on nitrogen and potash; list the constraints; graph the region.

53. Schlock City, purveyor of useless goods of dubious quality, offers two incredible bargains this week: Aardvark, a bath oil guaranteed to make you irresistible to certain four-footed creatures, and Bettergrip contact adhesive for golfer's palms. In a buying frenzy, you take your last $50 and head for Schlock. In a moment of rationality while looking for a parking space you decide to spend no more than $30 on Aardvark and no more than $40 on Bettergrip. Both products are liquids, bottled to order, so that you may purchase any amount you desire. Graph the region of possible purchases.

54. Give the coordinates of all vertices of the feasible region of Exercise 52.

55. Give the coordinates of all vertices of the feasible region of Exercise 53.

56. The parts manager for a trucking company has orders to stock at least 50 filters, including at least 25 air filters and at least 40 oil filters. Graph the region of feasible stock levels and find the coordinates of all vertices.

57. The parts manager of Exercise 56 was fired for overspending. The new manager was told to stock at most 70 filters, including at least 25 air filters and at least 40 oil filters. Graph the region of feasible stock levels and find the coordinates of each vertex of the region.

4.2 MAXIMIZING OR MINIMIZING LINEAR OBJECTIVE FUNCTIONS

In Example 2, Peter's dietary requirements became a system of *constraints* (linear inequalities describing intake requirements and limitations on his two dietary supplements) and an *objective function* describing cholesterol intake in terms of the quantities of the two supplements consumed.

■ EXAMPLE 7

Solve Peter's dietary requirement problem (Examples 1 and 2) by minimizing the objective function $c = 20h + 15k$, subject to the constraints

(a) $2h + 8k \geq 40$

(b) $30h + 20k \geq 300$

(c) $h \leq 26$

(d) $k \leq 18$

(e) $h \geq 0$

and

(f) $k \geq 0$

SOLUTION

All (h,k) pairs which simultaneously satisfy all constraints are feasible. We must find which feasible pairs minimize c.

Let us examine the behavior of the objective function in various parts of the feasible region, enlarged in Figure 4.9. In addition to the boundaries with arrows, we show a sprinkling of values of the objective function $c = 20h + 15k$. We cannot picture the function itself; this would require three dimensions (h, k, and c). At any location in the h,k coordinate system, however, we can show a value of c. For example: at $(h,k) = (10,4)$, $c = 260$. This value of c is written and circled at the point (10,4) in the feasible region. Also circled are $c = 315$ at (12,5), $c = 450$ at (15,10), $c = 460$ at (20,4), and $c = 725$ at (25,15).

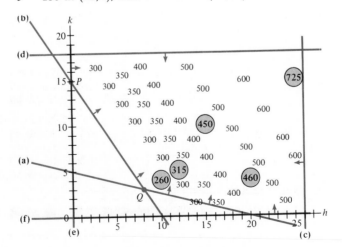

Figure 4.9
Rough plot of values of $c = 20h + 15k$

Other values of c in the feasible region produce strong patterns. Places where $c = 300$ seem to lie on a line angling upward to the left. So do places where $c = 350, 400$, etc. This is no accident. Indeed, in order to find points where c has the value 500, for example, we start with the objective function

$$c = 20h + 15k$$

and specify that c must be 500. The result is the linear equation

$$500 = 20h + 15k$$

whose graph is a line. This line is shown and labeled in Figure 4.10, together with lines on which $c = 300$, $c = 350$, etc.

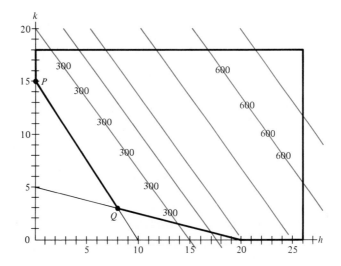

Figure 4.10

Lines of constant value for the objective function $c = 20h + 15k$

The lines on which $c = 300$, $c = 350$, and so on, are called **lines of constant c-value** (or, in general, lines of constant value). Some such lines of constant value are shown in Figure 4.10.

> The lines of constant value in Figure 4.10 have several noteworthy qualities:
>
> **1.** Lines of constant c-value are parallel.
>
> **2.** In the present example, lines of smaller constant c-value occur as one moves toward the origin.
>
> **3.** Every feasible point is on some line of constant value.
>
> **4.** An optimal feasible point is on a line of constant value.

To minimize cholesterol, we want a line of constant c-value *as close as possible* to the origin and intersecting the feasible region. If such a line lies exactly on segment PQ (with endpoints P and Q) (Figure 4.10), then P and Q, and all points on segment PQ, are solutions to the minimization problem. Otherwise, the constant-value line nearest the origin and intersecting the region passes through P or Q, but not both. In either case, an optimal solution occurs at P, or at Q, and perhaps even at both. Figure 4.10 suggests that Q wins the "optimal solution" contest; let us check both P and Q.

The (h,k) coordinates of P are $(0,15)$. The Q coordinates seem to be $(8,3)$; these values of h and k do satisfy equations **(a)** and **(b)**:

(a) $2h + 8k = 40$ $2(8) + 8(3) = (?)\ 40$ $16 + 24 = 40$

(b) $30h + 20k = 300$ $30(8) + 20(3) = (?)300$ $240 + 60 = 300$

[Had Q's coordinates not been obvious, we could have solved the system of equations **(a)** and **(b)**.] Now, checking the values of the objective function c at P and Q:

At $P(0,15)$ $c = 20(0) + 15(15) = 225$

At $Q(8,3)$ $c = 20(8) + 15(3) = 205$

Thus, the minimum value of c in the entire feasible region occurs only at Q. Peter satisfies all dietary constraints, and minimizes cholesterol, with 8 ounces of supplement H and 3 ounces of supplement K daily.   ∎

The Classic Linear Programming Problem

Example 7 has two key elements: a set of linear inequalities (constraints) that determine a feasible region; and a single linear objective function that has a value at each point of the region, and which we wish to maximize or (as in this example) minimize by finding an optimal point in the region. These basic elements occur so frequently that the class of such problems has been named and extensively studied.

THE CLASSIC LINEAR PROGRAMMING PROBLEM

> Given a set of linear inequality constraints, and a linear objective function having a value at each point in the feasible region determined by the constraints, find a point in the region which optimizes (maximizes or minimizes) the value of the objective function.

Look again at Figure 4.10. In this rather typical linear programming situation, we see lines of constant objective function value marching outward from $(0,0)$. Among these is a "first line" and a "last line" intersecting the feasible region at one vertex or, perhaps, at two feasible vertices. The most extreme (minimum or maximum) values of the objective function occur at these extreme "first line" or "last line" positions. A linear objective function always finds its minimum on a closed (completely enclosed) feasible region at a vertex (corner point) of the region. The maximum value of a linear objective function also occurs at a corner of the region.

In Example 8 we both maximize and minimize an objective function.

■ EXAMPLE 8

Given the usual nonnegativity constraints, and the explicit constraints

(a) $2x + 5y \leq 22$

(b) $13x - 9y \leq 60$

and

(c) $11x - 14y \geq -45$

1. maximize $p = -0.4x + 0.1y + 4$ **2.** minimize $p = -0.4x + 0.1y + 4$

SOLUTION

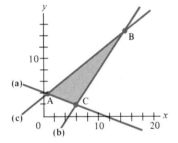

Figure 4.11
Feasible region, with vertex coordinates

Figure 4.11 shows the feasible region, with boundaries lettered to match constraints and with vertices A:(1,4), B:(15,15), and C:(6,2).

We estimated vertex coordinates from the graph, and verified by substituting into appropriate linear equations. (We could have solved pairs of constraint equations to find vertex coordinates.)

Feasible Vertex	Value of p
A: (1,4)	4
B: (15,15)	-0.5
C: (6,2)	1.8

1. The maximum value of p is 4, when $x = 1$ and $y = 4$.

2. The minimum value of p is -0.5, when $x = 15$ and $y = 15$.   ■

Note concerning graphing: In Example 8, we guessed the coordinates of feasible vertices exactly from the graph. Even if such accurate graph reading is not possible, the graph helps us tell which pairs of constraint equations to solve for vertices. In Example 8, part **2**, we minimized $p = -0.4x + 0.1y + 4$ on the feasible region, by evaluating p at the three vertices of the region and selecting the minimum value produced. An alternative approach, important in Chapter 5 where we introduce the Simplex Method for solving linear programming problems in any number of variables, is as follows:

MINIMIZING BY MAXIMIZING

> The minimum of a linear objective function subject to linear constraints occurs where the opposite function takes its maximum.

That is, we do not need a separate method for minimizing; we simply convert the problem into one of maximizing.

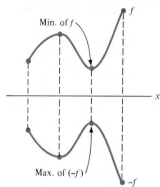

The min. of f is the opposite of the max. is of $-f$.

■ EXAMPLE 9

Minimize the objective function of Example 8 (subject to the Example 8 constraints) by maximizing its opposite.

SOLUTION

Goal: Minimize $p = -0.4x + 0.1y + 4$.

Method: Maximize $q = -p = 0.4x - 0.1y - 4$. The minimum of p occurs exactly where the maximum of q occurs, and is the opposite of the maximum of q.

Result: At A, B, and C of the feasible region of Example 8, q has values -4, 0.5, and -1.8, respectively. The maximum is 0.5, at B, where x and y are 15. Thus, the minimum of p is -0.5, also at B.   ■

PRACTICE PROBLEM 6

The objective function $p = 1.5a + 3.2b - 14$ is to be minimized on a region bounded by linear constraints, with feasible vertices (2,3), (6,1), (4,5), and (5,2).

    (a) Define the function q by making it the opposite of p.

    (b) Find the maximum value of q on the feasible region, and the vertex where the maximum occurs.

    (c) State the minimum value of p on the feasible region, and tell where this minimum occurs.

SOLUTION

(a) $q = -p = -1.5a - 3.2b + 14$.   **(b)** The maximum value of q on the feasible region is 1.8, and occurs at vertex (6,1).   **(c)** The minimum value of p is -1.8, and occurs at vertex (6,1).   □

A General Method of Solving Linear Programming Problems

It may seem that solving a linear programming problem in two variables is highly dependent upon drawing and interpreting an accurate graph of the feasible region. No so! We can gain insight into a general method,

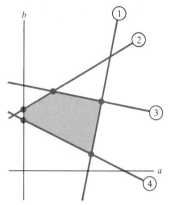

Given a linear objective function in variables a and b, its maximum on the shaded region is at a vertex. (So is its min.)

executable without a picture, by considering and answering two questions:

- **Question 1:** How can we tell if a point (a,b) belongs to the feasible region?
  Answer: Test (a,b) in all of the linear constraints. Point (a,b) belongs to the region if and only if (a,b) satisfies all of the constraint inequalities.

- **Question 2:** How are vertices of the feasible region identified?
  Answer: Each vertex is the crossing point of two edges of the region, or is the solution of a pair of constraint equations. Further, each vertex of the region belongs to the region, hence must satisfy all of the constraint inequalities. Thus, to find all possible vertices of the feasible region, we discover all candidates by solving all possible pairs of constraint equations. Of these candidates, only points whose coordinates satisfy all of the constraint inequalities are vertices of the feasible region.

We can now outline a general plan for solving any linear programming problem in two variables. A thorough understanding of this plan will also form the basis for solving linear programming problems in three or more variables. (Though our present method can in principle handle any number of variables, we shall develop a much more efficient method in Chapter 5.)

SOLVING TWO-VARIABLE LINEAR PROGRAMMING PROBLEMS

1. Find all vertices of the feasible region (by careful graphing and/or by solving appropriate pairs of equations).

2. Calculate the **vertex values** of the objective function p—its values at all corners (vertices) of the feasible region.

3. If the objective function p is to be maximized, a vertex that produces the largest vertex value of p is a solution to the linear programming problem.

4. If the objective function p is to be minimized, a vertex that produces the smallest vertex value of p is a solution. As an alternative, define a new function q by "$q = -p$," and maximize q as in Step 3.

Example 10 shows a typical solution to a two-variable problem.

■ EXAMPLE 10

A new 24,000-square-foot apartment building contains one- and two-bedroom living units that will be sold (not rented) to occupants or inves-

tors. Each one-bedroom unit occupies 1000 square feet; each two-bedroom unit is 1200 square feet. Local zoning restricts the number of units
to 22 or fewer. The builder/developer plans at least 5 two-bedroom
units. How many units of each size should she plan for maximum profit
if her profit is $32,000 per one-bedroom unit and $40,000 per two-bedroom unit?

SOLUTION   Let x and y denote the numbers of one- and two-bedroom units, and P
her profit. We formulate the problem as follows.

Square-footage requirement.   Constructing x one-bedroom units and y
two-bedroom units uses $1000x + 1200y$ square feet. Because the apartment contains 24,000 square feet, we must have

$$1000x + 1200y \le 24{,}000$$

Number of units restriction.   Because local zoning restricts the number
of units to at most 22, we must have

$$x + y \le 22$$

Two-bedroom requirements.   Since there must be at least 5 two-bedroom units, we must have

$$y \ge 5$$

Profit.   By making x one-bedroom units at a profit of $32,000 each and y
two-bedroom units at a profit of $40,000 each, the profit will be $P =
32{,}000x + 40{,}000y$.

The Linear Programming Problem
(Example 10)

Maximize $P = 32{,}000x + 40{,}000y$, subject to
(a) $1000x + 1200y \le 24{,}000$
(b) $x + y \le 22$
(c) $y \ge 5$
(d) $x \ge 0$
(e) $y \ge 0$

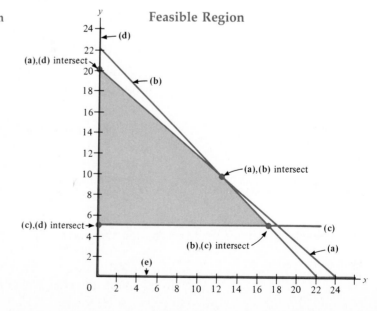

Summarizing, we have the formulation shown in the figure, parts **(a)–(e).**

The careful sketch of the feasible region allows us to select pairs of equations producing feasible vertices (heavy dots in sketch). Solving these pairs of two equations in two unknowns (or estimating solutions from the graph and checking them in the corresponding equations) gives vertices that produce the corresponding P values shown in the following table.

	(a),(d)	(c),(d)	(a),(b)	(b),(c)
Pair of lines:				
Vertex (x,y):	(0,20)	(0,5)	(12,10)	(17,5)
$P = 32{,}000x + 40{,}000y$:	800,000	200,000	424,000	424,000

The vertex producing maximum P is (0,20). The builder should plan 20 two-bedroom units for maximum profit. ■

PRACTICE PROBLEM 7 Zodiac Nectar Company markets two blended fruit juices: "Elysian Fields" (consisting of 50% apple juice, 25% grape juice, and 25% pear juice) and "Jupiter's Joy" (37.5% apple juice, 50% grape juice, and 12.5% pear juice). The company has in its storeroom 72 gallons of apple juice, 64 gallons of grape juice, and 32 gallons of pear juice. Company profit is $10 per gallon of Elysian Fields and $12 per gallon of Jupiter's Joy. How many gallons of each should be produced for maximum profit? (Fractional gallons can be sold.) What is the profit? What ingredients will be unused?

ANSWER(S) The company should produce 76.8 gallons of Elysian Fields and 89.6 gallons of Jupiter's Joy. Only 1.6 gallons of pear juice will be unused. □

EXERCISES 4.2

PRACTICING THE MOVES AND MANEUVERS

Exercises 58–70: Sketch the feasible region determined by the numbered constraints and the usual (implicit) nonnegativity constraints, find the *maximum* of the given objective function on the feasible region, and list all feasible vertices that maximize the objective function.

58. **(i)** $r + s \le 3$ **(ii)** $5r + 2s \le 10$ Objective function $a = 3r + 6s - 2$
59. Constraints of Exercise 58. Objective function $b = 6r - 3s + 2$
60. Constraints of Exercise 58. $c = -2r - 8s + 21$
61. Constraints of Exercise 58. $d = 6r + 5s + 10$
62. **(i)** $r + s \le 3$ **(ii)** $5r + 2s \ge 10$ $f = 12r + 2s - 5$
63. Constraints of Exercise 62. $g = -2r + 10s - 3$
64. **(i)** $-2a + 3b \le 15$ **(ii)** $2a - b \le 8$ **(iii)** $a + b \le 10$ $m = 5a + 12b + 3$
65. Constraints of Exercise 64. $p = 6a + 5b + 2$
66. Constraints of Exercise 64. $r = 6a - 3b + 3$
67. Constraints of Exercise 64. $t = 5a + 5b - 5$
68. **(i)** $w + 4 \ge 2z$ **(ii)** $6 \le 2z + w$ **(iii)** $2z + 3w \le 12$ $m = w + z + 17$
69. **(i)** $w + 4 \ge 2z$ **(ii)** $8 \le 2z + w$ **(iii)** $2z + 3w \le 12$ $m = w + z + 17$
70. **(i)** $w + 4 \ge 2z$ **(ii)** $9 \le 2z + w$ **(iii)** $2z + 3w \le 12$ $m = w + z + 17$

Exercises 71–74: Sketch the feasible region determined by the numbered constraints and the usual (implicit) nonnegativity constraints, find the minimum of the given objective function on the feasible region, and list all feasible vertices which minimize the objective function.

71. **(i)** $45 - 9k \ge 5j$ **(ii)** $7j - 28 - 14k \ge 0$ **(iii)** $6j + 5k \le 60$ $c = 2j - 5k + 1$
72. **(i)** $3m - 2p - 10 \le 0$ **(ii)** $1.5m + p \ge 7$ **(iii)** $2p - m \le 4$ $r = 6 - 10p + 2m$
73. **(i)** $3m - 2p - 10 \le 0$ **(ii)** $1.5m + p \le 7$ **(iii)** $2p - m \le 4$ $r = 6 - 10p + 2m$
*74. **(i)** $2.8r + w \le 14$ **(ii)** $r + 0.6w \ge 3$ **(iii)** $4w \le 10 - r$ $t = 4.3r - 6.2w + 13$

APPLYING THE CONCEPTS

75. Jim Parker has 160 acres to plant in either timothy (highly regarded as racehorse hay) or corn. He will plant at least 40 but no more than 120 acres of corn, and at least 20 but no more than 100 acres of hay, with unused land lying fallow (idle) for the year. He anticipates profits of $1800 per acre of corn and $2400 per acre of hay. How many acres of each should he plant for maximum profit? How much land will lie fallow?
76. Solve Exercise 75 for new market conditions pointing to corn profits of $1200 and timothy profits of $1500 per acre.
77. Solve Exercise 75 for an oversupply of corn in storage from last year that indicates a profit of $1400 per acre of hay but a loss of $500 per acre of corn.
78. Solve Exercise 75 for anticipated profits of $1500 per acre for both crops.
79. Jay Powers has $50,000 to invest for a year. He considers two investments: a mutual fund that he estimates will return a 12% profit and a lakefront condominium that should return 20%. He plans to invest at least $10,000 in the condominium, but, being conservative, will put at least twice as much into the mutual fund as into the condo. How much should he invest in each for maximum profit? How much money does he not invest?
*80. Ben Kreisler, Midget Rent-A-Car manager, stores 28 subcompact cars and 15 luxury cars twelve miles from the airport. He wants the best possible mix of cars at the airport on Friday, knowing that all available cars will be rented. His employees can spend at most 88 hours of labor preparing the cars, and have only 330 gallons of gas to put into them. Subcompact cars take four hours of labor each to make them rental-ready. Luxury cars need only an hour each for clean-up. Subcompacts re-

quire an average of ten gallons of gas; luxury cars, twenty gallons. Each subcompact uses 90 square feet of parking space; each luxury car, 120 square feet. Ben has 2370 square feet of airport parking. Weekend rental rates are $60 per subcompact and $90 per luxury car. What "ready" inventory will maximize revenue? Will any cars be idle?

*81. McGinty Manufacturing, with metal fabricating plants A (in Aurora, Illinois) and B (Buffalo, New York) has a government order for 400 swords, 600 plowshares, and 320 pruning hooks. Production capacities and daily operational costs of the plants are shown in the following table:

Plant	Daily Production			Daily Operation Cost
	Swords	Plows	Hooks	
Aurora	80	150	50	$7000
Buffalo	50	200	40	$5600

Obviously, each plant could fill the order working alone. This imposes limits on the numbers of days required of each plant. How many days should each plant operate to fill this order at minimum operational cost? What surplus items will be produced?

82. The manager of Danlyn Kennels uses a blend of two brands, Rover Ration and Spot-Chow, of dry dog food to supply at least 14,000 units of calcium and 36,000 units of niacin per month to her animals. She wants to meet her dogs' needs at minimum cost. What is the optimal blend of the two foods?

Brand	Contents per Pound		Cost per Pound
	Calcium	Niacin	
Rover	20 units	30 units	$.20
Spot	10 units	40 units	$.30

4.3 LINEAR PROGRAMMING IN THREE OR MORE VARIABLES (OPTIONAL)

Our investment in physical and mental images for two-variable linear programming pays off in the three-or-more variable situations as well. As is often the case in mathematics, a sound understanding grounded in a world we can see and touch (the two-dimensional coordinate plane of

Forming a two-variable feasible region.

the feasible region) extends easily to worlds whose dimensions exceed our drawing ability.

Let us reflect for a moment: In the two-variable case, each linear constraint (inequality) determines a line which splits the two-dimensional coordinate plane into two parts: an open half-plane to be discarded, and a closed half-plane to be retained because it contains the feasible region. Each new constraint has a similar effect: to cut off and discard part of the plane, and retain part of the plane. Imagine making great scissor cuts, successively discarding parts of a large sheet of paper, until only a relatively small region (the feasible region), bounded by scissor cut lines, remains. The vertices of this region are determined by pairs of intersecting scissor cuts.

In the three-variable case, each linear constraint determines a *plane* which splits the three-dimensional coordinate space into two parts: an open half-space to be discarded, and a closed half-space (the plane and all points to one side of it) containing the feasible region. Each new constraint slices through the three-dimensional space like a great knife, discarding part of the remaining space and retaining part. Finally, a relatively small lump of space, bounded by knife-cut planes, remains. The vertices of this solid are determined by trios of knife cuts (constraint planes). (Picture a large potato, whittled away by straight knife cuts so that none of its skin remains. Each "corner" is a place where three cuts meet.)

In the two-dimensional case, we often sketched the constraint equations. Our sketches told us which pairs of constraint equations produced vertices of the feasible region. Any vertex whose coordinates were not obvious could then be obtained by solving the corresponding pair of equations.

In the two-dimensional case, how might we solve without sketching? One approach would be to arbitrarily solve all pairs of constraint equations, sift through the resulting intersections to see which ones satisfy all of the constraint inequalities (these are the feasible vertices), then plug each feasible vertex into the objective function and select one which optimizes the function.

In the three-dimensional case, we could proceed similarly: solve *trios* of constraint equations, obtaining possible corners of the "feasible solid"; retain only corners satisfying all of the constraint inequalities; then find a feasible corner which optimizes the objective function.

■ EXAMPLE 11

Without sketching, maximize $c = 0.3a + 0.4b + 3$, subject to nonnegativity constraints and to $2a + 3b \leq 8$ and $2a - b \geq -2$.

SOLUTION

The four constraint equations (including the nonnegativity constraints) can be paired in exactly six ways:

Pairs of Constraint Equations		Vertex	Feasible?	c-Value
$a = 0$	$b = 0$	(0,0)	yes	3
$a = 0$	$2a + 3b = 8$	(0,8/3)	no*	
$a = 0$	$2a - b = -2$	(0,2)	yes	3.8
$b = 0$	$2a + 3b = 8$	(4,0)	yes	4.2
$b = 0$	$2a - b = -2$	(−1,0)	no**	
$2a + 3b = 8$	$2a - b = -2$	(7/4,3/2)	yes	4.125

* (0,8/3) fails to satisfy $2a - b \geq -2$.
** (−1,0) fails to satisfy $a \geq 0$.   ■

Before proceeding, you should verify the assertions made in the solution of Example 11: obtain the intersections, feasible vertices, and optimal vertex for yourself. Then try the following:

PRACTICE PROBLEM 8 Without sketching, maximize $h = 2.5j + 1.2k + 4$, subject to nonnegativity constraints and to constraints

$$j + 2k \geq 2$$
$$3j + 6k \leq 12$$

and

$$2k \leq j + 3$$

ANSWER(S) The maximum of h occurs at $j = 4$, $k = 0$ and is $h = 14.00$. □

PRACTICE PROBLEM 9 Subject to the Practice Problem 8 constraints, maximize $m = 2.5j + 5.7k + 2$.

ANSWER(S) The maximum of m, 12.175, occurs at (0.5,1.75). □

■ EXAMPLE 12

Minimize the objective function $p = 6x - 2y + 3z + 1$, subject to constraints $3x + 4y + 4z \geq 12$, $10x + 6y + 5z \leq 30$ and to nonnegativity constraints.

SOLUTION In order to solve trios of constraint equations and omit no possibilities, we first list and label the constraints:

(a) $x \geq 0$ (d) $3x + 4y + 4z \geq 12$

(b) $y \geq 0$ (e) $10x + 6y + 5z \leq 30$

(c) $z \geq 0$

We solve sets of three of the constraint equations. For example, solving trio **(a)**, **(d)**, **(e)** by substitution:

Inequality	Equation	Substituting $x = 0$ from (a)
(a) $\quad x \geq 0$	$x = 0$	into (d) and (e) yields
(d) $3x + 4y + 4z \geq 12$	$3x + 4y + 4z = 12$	**(f)** $4y + 4z = 12$
(e) $10x + 6y + 5z \leq 30$	$10x + 6y + 5z = 30$	**(g)** $6y + 5z = 30$

Solving system (f), (g) by substitution

Solving (f) for y $\qquad$ Substituting $3 - z$ for y in (g)

$$\textbf{(g)}\ 6y \qquad\quad + 5z = 30$$
$$4y + 4z = 12 \qquad\qquad 6(3 - z) + 5z = 30$$
$$y + \quad z = 3 \qquad\qquad 18 - 6z + 5z = 30$$
$$y \qquad = 3 - z \qquad\qquad\qquad\ - z = 12$$
$$\qquad\qquad\qquad\qquad\qquad\qquad\qquad z = -12$$

Substituting -12 for z in "$y = 3 - z$" $\quad y = 3 - (-12) \quad y = 15$

Thus, equations **(a)**, **(d)**, and **(e)** determine vertex $(0, 15, -12)$. This and the remaining vertices are shown in Figure 4.12.

Figure 4.12
Table showing solution vertex for each possible trio of constraints

Equation Trio	Vertex	Equation Trio	Vertex
a,b,c	(0,0,0)	a,b,d	(0,0,3)
a,b,e	(0,0,6)	a,c,d	(0,3,0)
a,c,e	(0,5,0)	a,d,e	(0,15,−12)
b,c,d	(4,0,0)	b,c,e	(3,0,0)
b,d,e	(2.4,0,1.2)	c,d,e	(24/11,15/11,0)

Remember: To be a vertex of the feasible region, a vertex must satisfy all five of the constraint inequalities. In table form, with y for "yes" and n for "no," Figure 4.13 shows the results of our checking. (Note that it is not necessary to check a vertex in the three inequalities that produced it, except as an accuracy check.)

Figure 4.13
Testing vertices for feasibility

Vertex	Constraints					Feasible?
	(a)	(b)	(c)	(d)	(e)	
(0,0,0)	y	y	y	N	y	NO
(0,0,3)	y	y	y	y	y	YES
(0,0,6)	y	y	y	y	y	YES
(0,3,0)	y	y	y	y	y	YES
(0,5,0)	y	y	y	y	y	YES
(0,15,−12)	y	y	N	y	y	NO
(4,0,0)	y	y	y	y	N	NO
(3,0,0)	y	y	y	N	y	NO
(2.4,0,1.2)	y	y	y	y	y	YES
(24/11,15/11,0)	y	y	y	y	y	YES

Only six feasible vertices emerge. In the objective function, they yield the values, 10, 19, −5, −9, 19, and $125/11 = 11\frac{4}{11}$. The minimum value is −9, at (0,5,0). ∎

Linear Programming Beyond Three Dimensions

In Example 12, we could have tried to draw a three-dimensional sketch to select trios of constraints which produced feasible vertices. However, three-dimensional sketching is difficult, and it was relatively easy to solve all possible trios of constraint equations, then discard solutions not satisfying all constraint inequalities. Two conclusions are now apparent:

1. Increasing the number of variables beyond three means we no longer can draw pictures.

2. The work required to find all candidate vertices—and, among these, all feasible vertices—grows very rapidly as the numbers of variables and constraints increase.

Our graphic two- and three-variable language carries us into the four-dimensional world we cannot sketch. We may still find the possible "corners" of the feasible region by solving all sets of four constraint equations, testing each candidate vertex in all of the constraint inequalities. The linear objective function still takes its maximum and minimum values at feasible vertices.

How much work is involved? Given four variables and eight constraints, we must solve all possible systems of four equations derived from the eight constraints—a total of 70 systems of equations! Each solution must then be checked in all eight constraints—potentially, 560 checks! In principle we know we could do this job. In Chapter 5 we study a very efficient labor-saving method, the celebrated Simplex Method.

In two-variable problems it was easy to name the variables x and y, p and q, h and k. To prepare for work with larger numbers of variables, we switch to such commonly used names as $x_1, x_2, x_3, x_4, x_5, \ldots$ for as many variables as the problem involves.

We have also used various names for objective functions: c, p, and q, for instance. Our "generic" name for an objective function will be Z.

One final caveat: it is possible for a system of linear equations to have no solution. It is also possible for a system of linear inequalities to have no solution (define an empty feasible region). In such a case, there are no feasible solutions, hence no way to both satisfy the constraints and optimize the objective function.

■ EXAMPLE 13

SOLUTION

Minimize $Z = 2x_1 + 5x_2$, subject to **(a)** $x_1 \geq 0$, **(b)** $x_2 \geq 0$, **(c)** $x_1 + x_2 \geq 10$, **(d)** $2x_1 + 3x_2 \leq 6$, and **(e)** $x_1 - x_2 \geq 1$.

Solving the constraint equations, including nonnegativity constraints **(a)** and **(b)**, in pairs (and you should do so for several pairs) yields the possible feasible vertices $(10,0)$, $(3,0)$, $(1,0)$, $(0,0)$, $(0,2)$, $(0,10)$, $(0,-1)$, $(4.5,5.5)$, $(24,-14)$, and $(1.8,0.8)$. Each of these candidates fails in at least one constraint. [For example, $(0,0)$ fails to satisfy $x_1 + x_2 \geq 10$.] Thus there are no feasible vertices, and there is no solution to the optimization problem.

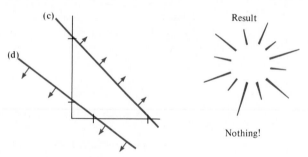

What Does One Do in the "Real World" if the Feasible Region is Empty?

Saying "there is no solution under these constraints" is not usually the end of the matter. Negotiation among interested parties, building more warehouse space, changing the product mix or some similar adjustment may be required to create conditions under which there is a solution.

PRACTICE PROBLEM 10

Find at least one reason for rejecting each candidate vertex in Example 13. Then attempt to sketch the feasible region by graphing the constraint equations and identifying the region satisfying all of the constraints.

ANSWER(S)

$(10,0)$ fails to meet **(d)**; $(3,0)$ fails **(c)**; $(1,0)$ fails **(c)**; $(0,0)$ fails **(c)**; $(0,2)$ fails **(e)**; $(0,10)$ fails **(e)**; $(0,-1)$ fails **(b)**; $(4.5,5.5)$ fails **(d)**; $(24,-14)$ fails **(b)**;

(1.8,0.8) fails **(c)**. In attempting a graph, constraints **(c)** and **(d)** reject the entire plane. (Sketch for yourself.)   □

Nonnegativity Assumption In all work to come, we shall assume, without specific mention, non-negativity of all variables. Remember to include nonnegativity constraints in your analysis of each linear programming problem.

EXERCISES 4.3

PRACTICING THE MOVES AND MANEUVERS

83. Maximize $Z = 5x_1 + 4x_2$ subject to $3x_1 + 3x_2 \leq 12$, $9x_1 - x_2 \leq 46$, and $3x_1 \geq 7x_2 - 8$.
84. Minimize $Z = 3x_1 - 2x_2$ subject to the Exercise 83 constraints.
*85. Minimize $Z = x_1 - 4x_2 + 10$ subject to $14x_1 \leq 73 - 39x_2$, $11x_1 + 8x_2 \geq 80$, and $30x_2 + 17 \geq 38x_1$.
*86. Maximize $Z = 3x_1 + 10x_2$ subject to the Exericse 85 constraints.
87. Maximize $Z = 1.5x_1 + 2.5x_2 + 4x_3$ subject to $4x_1 + 5x_2 + 8x_3 \leq 20$.
88. Minimize $Z = 2.5x_1 - 3x_2 + 1.4x_3$ subject to the Exercise 87 constraints.
89. Minimize $Z = 3x_1 + 1.5x_2 - 4x_3$, subject to $4x_1 + 4x_2 + 5x_3 \leq 20$ and $28x_1 + 7x_2 + 8x_3 \leq 56$.
90. Maximize $Z = 2x_1 + 5x_2 + 3x_3 + x_4$, subject to $36x_1 + 45x_2 + 36x_3 + 40x_4 \leq 360$.
*91. Maximize $Z = 2x_1 + 3x_2 - 5x_3 + 5x_4$, subject to $2x_1 + 5x_2 + x_3 + x_4 \leq 10$ and $x_1 + 4x_2 + 3x_3 + 2x_4 \leq 12$.

APPLYING THE CONCEPTS

*92. Fitness Foods, in a bold bid for market domination, has created four cereals with wholesome names, aimed at the DINK ("double income, no kids") segment of the population. Sold in handy five-pound cans, the cereals are made of oat bran and pine cone bits, in the proportions shown below:

	Cereal			
	Dawn	Homespun	Newday	Sunrise
Ingredients				
Oat bran	2.5 lb	1 lb	3 lb	4 lb
Pine cone	2.5 lb	4 lb	2 lb	1 lb

The company commits 100 pounds of each ingredient to a test-marketing project. The per-package profits are 65 cents (Dawn), 70 cents (Homespun), 55 cents (Newday), and 85 cents (Sunrise).

(a) How many packages of each cereal should be made for maximum profit?
(b) What ingredients, if any, remain unused?

*93. Solve Exercise 92 if profits for the four cereals (in alphabetical order) are 80 cents, 50 cents, 70 cents, and 60 cents.

94. Boondocks Camping Equipment makes three backpacks: the Alpiner, the Biker, and the Cruiser. Each pack requires one hour of cutting time. Each Alpiner and Biker takes one hour of finishing (sewing, plus installing snaps and other hardware) time, but the Cruiser requires five hours of finishing time. Profits are $18 on the Alpiner, $30 on the Biker, and $45 on the Cruiser. The company employs one cutter and two finishers, each of whom works a 40-hour week.

    (a) How many packs per week of each type will maximize profit?
    (b) What employee time, if any, is unutilized?

95. Solve Exercise 94 if profits on the three packs are $35, $30, and $36.

4.4 INTEGER PROGRAMMING (OPTIONAL)

Our linear programming experience has for the most part involved constraints whose graphs intersect neatly at vertices with integer coordinates. (Such points are called **lattice points** because of their pattern when graphed.) This is especially convenient when, for example, "the expression p is maximized at vertex (12,10) of the feasible region" means "12 cars and 10 trucks maximize profit."

    How many cars and trucks should we buy if the solution vertex turns out to be (11.8,10.2)? A quick, easy answer might be "round to nearest whole numbers: 12 cars and 10 trucks." However, (12,10) might be outside our feasible region; 12 cars and 10 trucks might cost more than we can afford. We might then amend our answer to "pick the lattice point nearest to (12,10) and in the feasible region." The reasoning guarantees a feasible solution—but is it optimal? Beware!

■ EXAMPLE 14

Given the constraints $b \geq 1$, $c \geq 0$, and $3.7b + 4.8c \leq 17.76$, maximize the following objective functions, using integer values of b and c:

    (a) $p = 3b + 7c$ **(b)** $q = 3.5b + 4c$

SOLUTION

The feasible region (shaded) and points (b,c) with integer coordinates are plotted in Figure 4.14.

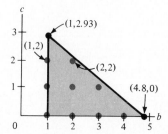

Figure 4.14
Feasible region and lattice points

(a) The maximum of p on the entire region occurs at vertex (1,2.93). The nearest feasible lattice point is (1,2), at which $p = 17$. The feasible point (2,2) yields $p = 20$. No other feasible lattice point does better. Check it out!

(b) Vertex (4.8,0) maximizes q. The feasible lattice point maximizing q is (2,2), which is again not nearest the vertex. ■

The message of Example 14 is clear: If our solutions are restricted to lattice points, we must be very careful. General methods for such integer programming problems, though available, are beyond the scope of our work. However, our now-familiar tools (graphing, and solving systems of equations to find corner points of the feasible region) plus a bit of care will see us through this introductory phase.

EXERCISES 4.4

Exercises 96–99: Make a clear, accurate drawing of the feasible region and its lattice points, preferably on graph paper. Carefully draw a line or two of constant value for the objective function. Use your *drawing* to identify the feasible vertex that solves part **(a)**. Rely heavily on your drawing for parts **(b)** and **(c)**.

96. Subject to the constraints $k \geq 0$, $m \geq 0$, $40m + 35k \geq 140$, $60k + 29m \leq 378$, and $9k + 35m \leq 172$,

   (a) find values of m, k, and r for which $r = 5k + 2m + 3$ is a maximum.
   (b) find integers m and k to maximize r, and the value of r.
   (c) Does the feasible lattice point nearest the vertex in part **(a)** produce the maximum lattice point value of r? If not, by how much does this "nearest" lattice point value of r differ from the maximum lattice point value of r?

*97. Subject to the constraints of Exercise 96,

   (a) find a feasible vertex to minimize $s = 28k + 30m$.
   (b) find a feasible lattice point which minimizes s.
   (c) Does the feasible lattice point nearest the vertex in part **(a)** produce the minimum lattice point value of s? If not, by now much does this "nearest" lattice point value of s differ from the minimum lattice-point value of s?

*98. Subject to $a \geq 0$, $b \geq 0$, $b \leq 4.5$, $6b - 5a \leq 1$, and $5a - 4b \leq 10$,

   (a) find a feasible vertex to minimize $j = 4a - 7b + 10$ (a large-scale drawing is required).
   (b) find a feasible lattice point to minimize j.
   (c) Does the feasible lattice point nearest the vertex in part **(a)** produce the minimum lattice point value of j? If not, by how much does it fail?

99. Subject to the constraints of Exercise 98,

   (a) find a feasible vertex to maximize $p = 4b - 3a$ (a large-scale drawing is required).
   (b) find a feasible lattice point which maximizes p.

(c) Does the feasible lattice point nearest the vertex in part **(a)** produce the maximum lattice point value of *p*? If not, by how much does it fail?

A Brief Summary of Important Ideas

The goal in a linear programming problem is to maximize (or minimize) a linear objective function, within a set of linear constraints (linear inequalities involving the decision variables). Each constraint sets limits on the permissible values of the decision variables. Any set of decision variable values which satisfies *all* the linear constraints is called a **feasible solution** to the linear programming problem. The set of all feasible solutions is called the **feasible region.** A feasible solution which optimizes (maximizes or minimizes, as the goal may be) the objective function is an **optimal solution.**

In Chapters 0 and 1 we developed skills in graphing, and in solving systems of linear equations by efficient methods. Those skills paid off in the present chapter, as we learned to graph feasible regions in two variables. The maximum (or minimum) value of the linear objective function always occurs at a vertex (corner point) of the feasible region. Finding the coordinates of feasible vertices involved solving systems of constraint equations, using the substitution or elimination methods of Chapter 1.

When more than two variables are involved, graphing the feasible region may be difficult (in the three-variable case) or even impossible (more than three variables). Using our two-variable experience, we can still systematically search for feasible vertices by solving all possible sets of appropriate numbers of constraint equations: three equations at a time in three-variable problems, four equations at a time in four-variable problems, and so on. Each vertex so found must first be checked in all linear constraints. Feasible vertices are then substituted, one at a time, into the objective function until a vertex is found which optimizes the objective function. This effective but very cumbersome method will be supplanted by a more efficient method in Chapter 5.

REVIEW EXERCISES

PRACTICING THE MOVES AND MANEUVERS

100. Given nonnegativity constraints on x and y, and the linear constraints $x + 2y \le 24$ and $4x + 3y \ge 24$,

    (a)   carefully sketch the feasible region.
    (b)   find all feasible points which maximize $p = 10 - 3x - 5y$.
    (c)   find all feasible points which minimize $q = 12 - 3x - 6y$.

Exercises 101–103: Maximize the revenue function $r = 15x_1 + 25x_2$, subject to nonnegativity constraints and to the given set of constraints.

101. $3x_1 + 4x_2 \le 15$
102. $x_1 + x_2 \le 25 \quad 2x_1 + 2x_2 \ge 10$
*103. $x_2 \le 70 \quad 5x_1 + 2x_2 \le 300 \quad x_1 + x_2 \le 90 \quad 5x_1 - x_2 \ge -20$

104. Minimize $c = 9x_1 + 12x_2$ subject to the constraints of Exercise 101.
105. Minimize $c = 9x_1 + 12x_2$ subject to the constraints of Exercise 102.
106. Minimize $c = 9x_1 - 12x_2$ subject to the constraints of Exercise 103.
107. Without graphing, find all points satisfying the system of equations $x - 2y + 3z = -5, 5x - 7y - 3z = 11$, and $2x + 2y - 5z = -3$.
108. Without graphing, find all points satisfying the system of equations $x + 2y + 3z = 4, 4x + 3y + 2z = 1$, and $-x - 2y - 3z = 0$.

Exercises 109–115: Execute orderly solutions including defining variables, listing constraints, graphing the feasible set, labeling each feasible vertex with coordinates, and optimizing the objective function.

109. Fantastic Furniture Company makes two types of tables, Type I and Type II. Each Type I table requires one hour of assembling and one hour of finishing. Each Type II table requires one hour of assembling and two hours of finishing. The company has 20 assemblers and 30 finishers, each of whom works 40 hours per week. Each table of Type I brings a profit of $27 and each table of Type II yields a profit of $36. A furniture retailer has agreed to purchase all tables produced. How many tables of each type should be made per week in order to maximize profits? How many hours of each labor type are unused?

110. A Florida citrus company has 480 acres of land for growing oranges and grapefruit. At maturity, each acre of oranges requires 80 hours of labor during the growing season (including harvest); each acre of grapefruit requires 40 hours. Estimated profits are $2200 per acre for oranges and $900 per acre for grapefruit. The company can afford at most 32,000 hours of labor during the growing season. Assuming equal startup costs, equal times to achieve full production, and equal numbers of productive years for the two crops, what is the maximum attainable annual profit? Is any land unused?

111. Major Motors, Inc. must produce at least 5,000 luxury cars, 12,000 intermediate-sized cars, and 21,000 compact cars. The company owns two factories, A and B, at two different locations. Factory A produces 20, 40, and 60 cars, respectively, of the three types each day; factory B, with less modern equipment, produces 10, 30, and 50, respectively, of the three types each day. If operating costs for factory A total $120,000 per day and costs for factory B total $80,000, how many work days should be

scheduled for each factory in order to minimize operating costs and still meet the output demand? What will operating costs be for each factory? Describe any excess production beyond the three required levels.

112. The XYZ Corporation, makers of microcomputers, photocopy machines, and advanced-technology paperweights, has allocated a maximum of $24,000 to a month's advertising, to be split between television and newspaper advertising. One hour of television program sponsorship costs $4,000; one page of newspaper advertising costs $3,000. Surveys indicate that an hour's TV sponsorship reaches 120,000 people and a page of newspaper advertising reaches 80,000 people. The XYZ board of directors includes several members with investments in the local television station and one member who owns the local newspaper. The board agrees to use at least two hours of television time and one page of newspaper advertising. How should the advertising budget be divided so that exposures to the advertisements are maximized?

113. Preparing to build a small neighborhood of budget-priced homes, the developer purchases 100 units of concrete, 160 units of wood, and 400 units of glass. She plans to offer homes of types A and B. Each type A home uses 1 unit of concrete, 2 units of wood, and 2 units of glass; each type B home requires 1 unit of concrete, 1 unit of wood, and 5 units of glass. The devel-

oper anticipates a clear profit of $11,000 per type A home and $10,000 for each type B home. How many of each should she build in order to maximize profits? What materials are left over?

114. A manufacturer of ukulele plinkers and zither picks uses two types of machines—saws and sanders—to shape his products. Each dozen uke plinkers consumes 1 unit of sander time and 2 units of saw time. Each dozen zither picks requires 2 units of sander time and 1 unit of saw time. In each day there are available 12 units of saw time and 15 units of sander time. Each dozen uke plinkers produces $10 profit; each dozen zither picks yields $8 profit. What daily product mix produces maximum profit? Is any available machine time unused?

*115. A trading company is licensed to import at most 300 items of Burmese teak dining room furniture. These may be assorted in any way among chairs, sideboards, and tables, costing the importer $20, $60, and $60 each, respectively. The total cost must not exceed $5,000. Further, all items must fit into one shipping container (900 cubic feet). Each chair requires 4 cubic feet; each sideboard, 6 cubic feet; and each table, 5 cubic feet. The importer anticipates profits of $40 per chair, $70 per sideboard, and $50 per table. How many of each should be imported for maximum profit? (*Reminder:* Each possible trio of constraints must be considered. There are 10 such trios.)

5

Linear Programming:
The Simplex Method

INTRODUCTION In Chapter 4 you were introduced to linear programming as a way of maximizing or minimizing a linear function subject to constraints. The methods we developed are based on being able to graph the feasible region. When there are more than two decision variables, or when the number of constraints is large, this geometric approach becomes difficult.

In this chapter we present the simplex method, an **algebraic** (no graphing required) **algorithm** (an orderly, repetitive procedure) for finding solutions to complicated linear programming problems. Though many of today's mathematical tools were developed in the sixteenth and seventeenth centuries, the simplex method was not devised until the 1940's by George Dantzig. Professor Dantzig's original work concerned military problems in planning and scheduling. Initial nonmilitary applications were in the petroleum industry, where firms used linear programming to find optimum gasoline blends. Today the simplex method is routinely used to solve problems involving thousands of constraints and variables.

From Chapter 4, you know that optimal solution(s) occur at corner points of the feasible region. With today's computers, it may seem you need only to substitute corner-point coordinates into the objective function and choose the one(s) that optimize. In principle, this seems easy. In practice, it is sometimes impossible. Even with super computers, large problems might require years of computation.

The simplex method begins with one point in the feasible region and progresses selectively to another solution, at least as good, eventually leading to an optimal solution or to realization that there is no solution.

Feasible region
(edges included)

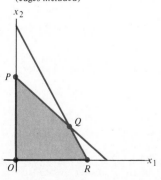

Linear objective function is
max. (or min.) at O, P, Q, or R.

5.1 THE SIMPLEX METHOD

The simplex method is algebraic, requiring no graphing, although we shall use graphing to illustrate the connection between the simplex method and the geometric methods of Chapter 4. The following example illustrates the simplex method. The discussion, while primarily intuitive, is thorough.

■ EXAMPLE 1

Jim Whitmore has received a $20,000 inheritance from his Great Aunt Alimony. Having an eye for investing, our young gentleman has identified two possibilities:

1. A junk bond that pays 14% annual interest.

2. A loan to cousin Drayno that pays 10% annual interest.

After much thought, Jim decides to invest no more than $14,000 in junk bonds, and he refuses to give Drayno more than $10,000. To maintain some semblance of investment balance, he decides that the amount invested in junk bonds should exceed the amount lent to Drayno by no more than $4,000. How should Jim allocate funds to maximize investment income?

SOLUTION

Let x_1 denote the amount to be invested in junk bonds, and x_2 the amount to be lent to Drayno. Our objective function here is the investment income, $Z = 0.14x_1 + 0.10x_2$. How should x_1 and x_2 be chosen to maximize Z?

As a "mathematical model" for Jim's investment options, we write the following, expressing $20,000 as simply "20," $14,000 as "14," etc. In assessing the solution, we will add back the "000."

Maximize $Z = 0.14x_1 + 0.10x_2$, subject to the following six constraints:

$$
\begin{array}{llll}
\textbf{(1)} & x_1 + x_2 \le 20 & \left.\rule{0pt}{1.6em}\right\} & \\
\textbf{(2)} & x_1 \quad\ \ \le 14 & & \text{Specific constraints} \\
\textbf{(3)} & \qquad x_2 \le 10 & & \text{imposed by problem—} \\
\textbf{(4)} & x_1 - x_2 \le\ \ 4 & & \text{"functional constraints"}
\end{array}
$$

$$
\begin{array}{lll}
\textbf{(5)} & x_1 \ge 0 & \left.\rule{0pt}{1.2em}\right\}\ \text{Nonnegativity} \\
\textbf{(6)} & x_2 \ge 0 & \quad\ \text{constraints}
\end{array}
$$

This formulation is known as a **standard maximization problem.**

STANDARD MAXIMIZATION PROBLEM

If the objective function is to be maximized, and each functional constraint is of the form "left side $\le b$," where b is a nonnegative number, then the linear programming problem is said to be a **standard maximization problem.**

When a constraint is not in standard maximization form, we can often rearrange it. For example, the constraint $x_1 + 2x_2 \geq -7$ can be multiplied by "-1" to produce $-x_1 - 2x_2 \leq 7$.

We now solve Jim's investment problem (a standard maximization problem), first with the graphical methods of Chapter 4, and then with the simplex method. There are six constraints in all, four of which are problem specific (the functional constraints), the other two being the usual nonnegativity constraints.

The feasible region is the set of points that satisfies all six constraints. Since each constraint determines a half-plane, the feasible region consists of points belonging to all six half-planes. Recall that the intersection of any two constraint equations determines a vertex, unless their two graphs are parallel. Solving for all vertices requires that we examine 15 different pairs of constraint equations; we show these 15 shortly. (In Chapter 7, we develop quicker ways of counting possibilities without enumeration.) Figure 5.1 shows the feasible region:

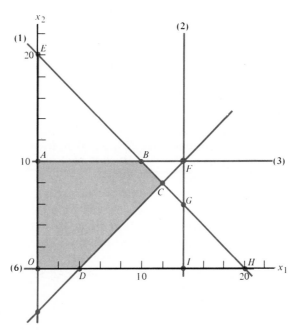

Figure 5.1
Graph of the feasible region for Example 1

The feasible region has vertices O, A, B, C, and D as corner points. The remaining 10 vertex possibilities are two inconsistent pairs and eight nonfeasible vertices. As graphs, constraint equations (2) and (5) are parallel and hence have no points in common; the same is true of (3) and (6). Point $H(20,0)$, for example, is not feasible because it does not satisfy constraints (2) and (4).

A convenient summary of the vertex solutions is shown in Table 5.1, along with the value of the objective function at each of the corner points of the feasible region.

Table 5.1
Vertex solutions for corner points of Example 1

Constraint Pair	Vertex	Feasible?	Objective Function Value
1 & 2	$G(14,6)$	No	
1 & 3	$B(10,10)$	Yes	2.40
1 & 4	$C(12,8)$	Yes	2.48
1 & 5	$E(0,20)$	No	
1 & 6	$H(20,0)$	No	
2 & 3	$F(14,10)$	No	
2 & 4	$F(14,10)$	No	
2 & 5	none; parallel	No	
2 & 6	$I(14,0)$	No	
3 & 4	$F(14,10)$	No	
3 & 5	$A(0,10)$	Yes	1.00
3 & 6	none; parallel	No	
4 & 5	$J(0,-4)$	No	
4 & 6	$D(4,0)$	Yes	0.84
5 & 6	$O(0,0)$	Yes	0

Vertex $C(12,8)$ produces the maximum objective function value. Jim's best investment course is to invest $12,000 in junk bonds, and to lend cousin Drayno $8,000. This gives an objective function value of 2.48, representing $2,480 interest he will earn on his $20,000 investment by investing optimally. As you will learn in Chapter 12, Jim will earn $2,480/20,000 = 0.124$, or 12.4% annual interest. This is reasonable, since his two investment alternatives yield 10% and 14%. The overall rate of 12.4% is higher than the arithmetic average of 10% and 14% because the optimal solution has Jim investing a greater proportion of his money in the higher yielding investment. All $20,000 gets invested.   ■

Terminology for Simplex Method

We now introduce terminology needed for the simplex method. We first convert each inequality in the system of "less than or equal" inequalities representing functional constraints to an equation. To illustrate, consider the simple linear inequality $x \leq 3$. For any $x \leq 3$, there is a nonnegative number s such that $x + s = 3$. For example, $x = 2$ is a solution to $x \leq 3$, and the value $s = 1$ "takes up the slack" between x and 3. For this reason we call s a **slack variable.** We add such a slack variable, denoted by s with an appropriate subscript, to each functional constraint inequality.

In **(a),** we show the original problem constraints from Example 1. In **(b),** we show the system of equations that results from adding nonnegative slack variables to each inequality. Refer to Figure 5.1 and observe that the lines drawn there are the equations of system **(b)** when all slack variables s_i are zero.

Functional constraints and resulting equations after addition of slack variables

$$\textbf{(a)} \quad \begin{aligned} x_1 + x_2 &\le 20 \\ x_1 \phantom{{}+x_2} &\le 14 \\ x_2 &\le 10 \\ x_1 - x_2 &\le 4 \end{aligned} \qquad \textbf{(b)} \quad \begin{aligned} x_1 + x_2 + s_1 &= 20 \\ x_1 \phantom{{}+x_2} + s_2 &= 14 \\ x_2 + s_3 &= 10 \\ x_1 - x_2 + s_4 &= 4 \end{aligned}$$

Any solution for x_1 and x_2 in system **(b)** having only nonnegative values for s_1, s_2, s_3, and s_4 will automatically satisfy system **(a),** and hence be a feasible solution.

To system **(b)** we now append the objective function as an equation in the variable Z. In particular, we rewrite the objective function $Z = 0.14x_1 + 0.10x_2$ in the form $-0.14x_1 - 0.10x_2 + Z = 0$, being sure to put the constant 0 on the right-hand side, and giving Z coefficient "1." The result is system **(5-1)**:

$$\begin{aligned} x_1 + x_2 + s_1 &= 20 \\ x_1 + s_2 &= 14 \\ x_2 + s_3 &= 10 \\ x_1 - x_2 + s_4 &= 4 \\ -0.14x_1 - 0.10x_2 + Z &= 0 \end{aligned} \qquad \textbf{(5-1)}$$

Basic Variables   System **(5-1)** has 7 unknowns but only 5 equations. In Chapter 1 we learned that if such a system has any solutions, it will have infinitely many. A convenient way of finding such solutions is to assign arbitrary values to $7 - 5 = 2$ of the variables (called **nonbasic variables**) and solve for the remaining 5 variables (called **basic variables**) in terms of the values assigned to the nonbasic variables. Such a solution is called a **basic solution.**

How do we decide which variables to make nonbasic and what values do we assign to them? In system **(5-1)**, note that variables s_1, s_2, s_3, s_4, and Z appear in one and only one equation (one variable per equation), and with a coefficient of plus 1. Let these five be the basic variables and arbitrarily assign zero to the other $7 - 5 = 2$ variables (variables x_1 and x_2), giving the system:

$$\begin{aligned} s_1 &= 20 \\ s_2 &= 14 \\ s_3 &= 10 \\ s_4 &= 4 \\ Z &= 0 \end{aligned} \qquad \textbf{(5-2)}$$

This system is already in reduced form, with (obvious) solutions given by the corresponding right-hand side entries. These values for s_1

through s_4, along with $x_1 = 0$ and $x_2 = 0$ provide a solution to system **(b)**. Since slack variables are nonnegative, the values $x_1 = 0$ and $x_2 = 0$ are a feasible solution to the standard maximization problem given by **(a)**. This full solution to system **(5-1)**, with $x_1 = 0$, $x_2 = 0$, $s_1 = 20$, $s_2 = 14$, $s_3 = 10$, $s_4 = 4$, and $Z = 0$, is called the **obvious basic feasible solution.** No other assignment of values to x_1 and x_2 yields such convenient values for Z and the slack variables. While convenient, there is nothing useful about this solution; we remedy this after making some comments about system **(5-1)**.

Write system **(5-1)** in the standard "augmented matrix" form of Chapter 1:

x_1	x_2	s_1	s_2	s_3	s_4	Z	
1	1	**1**	**0**	**0**	**0**	**0**	20
1	0	**0**	**1**	**0**	**0**	**0**	14
0	1	**0**	**0**	**1**	**0**	**0**	10
1	-1	**0**	**0**	**0**	**1**	**0**	4
-0.14	-0.10	**0**	**0**	**0**	**0**	**1**	0

Examine the structure of this system closely to determine which variables we can make nonbasic. For convenience we have added "column labels." Assigning the value 0 to x_1 and x_2 effectively removes these columns from consideration. Cover these columns with your hand, and observe that system **(5-2)** results. Further notice that the remaining five columns corresponding to s_1, s_2, s_3, s_4, and Z (shown in boldface and shaded) are the columns of the 5×5 identity matrix. This is precisely the form that identifies these five variables as basic variables: each equation contains one and only one basic variable, and that variable has a coefficient of $+1$; all other entries in any column containing a basic variable are zero.

Reading Solutions Cover (or mentally "tune out") the columns corresponding to the nonbasic variables (x_1 and x_2 here). For each of the remaining variables (all basic), go down the column for that variable until you locate the "1." The solution for that variable is the corresponding right-hand side entry. In the s_3 column, for example, the right-hand side entry corresponding to the "1" is 10, telling us that $s_3 = 10$ is part of the basic solution.

Try your luck in identifying the basic solution to the following practice problem.

PRACTICE PROBLEM 1 In the system below, identify basic and nonbasic variables and determine the obvious basic feasible solution.

$$x_1 + \quad\quad 5x_3 + x_4 = 6$$
$$2x_1 + x_2 - 4x_3 \quad\quad = 2$$

ANSWER(S) x_1, x_3 are nonbasic; basic variables are $x_2 = 2$, $x_4 = 6$.   □

An Intuitive Discussion of the Simplex Method

At this point, necessary terminology for using the simplex method is complete. In the remainder of this section, we continue Example 1, providing an intuitive but thorough discussion of ideas involved in using the simplex method and comparing it with the graphical method from Chapter 4.

Assigning zero to the nonbasic variables does more than make the solution simple. By limiting the nonbasic variables to the single value zero, we reduce the number of possible solutions to system **(5-1)** from an infinite number to a single solution! Furthermore, as we shall illustrate shortly, choosing two of the seven variables to be nonbasic, and hence zero, corresponds geometrically to finding the intersection of those two constraint equations. Speaking very intuitively, the simplex method is a clever way of identifying which variables are to be made 0!

> **In applying the simplex method to a standard maximization problem, decision variables will always start as nonbasic variables; slack variables and Z will be basic.**

This produces an immediate solution, the obvious basic feasible solution. While both obvious and feasible, this solution is of no use. The variables which are really important are x_1 and x_2, but we have called them nonbasic and set them equal to zero! While not "best," such a solution is a convenient starting place for the simplex method. We then use elementary row operations to produce another feasible solution in which one of the decision variables x_1 or x_2 becomes basic by changing places with one of the current five basic variables. The mechanics of the simplex are such that this exchange will make the objective function value at least as large as it was (typically larger).

Geometric Interpretion

Geometrically, the simplex method begins at one corner point of the feasible region (the "origin" with all decision variables zero), evaluates the objective function, and determines whether or not it can be improved. If improvement is possible, the simplex method takes us to an adjacent corner point where the value of the objective function is at least as high as it was. If the new corner point is optimal, the process stops. If not, the next iteration of the method identifies another nonbasic variable to be made basic, and takes us to another adjacent corner point with at least as large a value of the objective function. This process continues until the optimum solution is found or until it becomes clear that there is no solution.

We begin the simplex by constructing (in Table 5.2) the **initial tableau,** which is simply the augmented matrix for system **(5-1).**

Table 5.2
Initial simplex tableau

Row labels indicate the variables that are currently basic; new line above the Z-row helps to "spotlight" this row.

	x_1	x_2	s_1	s_2	s_3	s_4	Z	= RHS	
s_1	1	1	1	0	0	0	0	20	**(5-3)**
s_2	1	0	0	1	0	0	0	14	**(5-4)**
s_3	0	1	0	0	1	0	0	10	**(5-5)**
s_4	1	−1	0	0	0	1	0	4	**(5-6)**
Z	−0.14	−0.10	0	0	0	0	1	0	**(5-7)**

The basic variables, s_1, s_2, s_3, s_4, and Z are represented by the shaded, boldfaced "identity matrix" columns of the array.[1] We have now labeled the rows to indicate which variables are currently basic. By assigning x_1 and x_2 the value 0, we remove their columns from the picture, and the "obvious basic feasible solution" is given, along with $x_1 = x_2 = 0$, by $s_1 = 20$, $s_2 = 14$, $s_3 = 10$, $s_4 = 4$, and $Z = 0$. This solution, while obvious, is of no use since $x_1 = x_2 = 0$ has Jim keeping all his money under his mattress, making lumps rather than income. Can we improve matters? Consider the objective function row **(5-7)**, which reads $-0.14x_1 - 0.10x_2 + Z = 0$. Solve for Z:

$$Z = 0 + 0.14x_1 + 0.10x_2 \qquad \qquad \textbf{(5-8)}$$

When x_1 and x_2 are 0, as in the above tableau, Z is clearly 0. It should be apparent, though, that any positive value for either x_1 or x_2 would result in an improvement—a larger value of Z. The first iteration of the simplex method is designed to make one of the currently nonbasic variables, x_1 or x_2, positive, meaning that this variable will become basic. Since the number of basic variables must remain 5, a currently basic variable will leave to make room for the new, yet-to-be determined basic variable.

Since 0.14 (the multiplier of x_1) is larger than 0.10 (the multiplier of x_2), any change in x_1 will produce a larger increase in Z than the equivalent change in x_2. Thus, the first iteration of the simplex method will identify x_1 as the entering variable, and will make it as large as possible.

Just how large can x_1 be?

Since we are going to change only one variable at a time, we still have $x_2 = 0$. Substituting $x_2 = 0$ into equation **(5-3)** gives $x_1 + s_1 = 20$, or $s_1 = 20 - x_1$. But s_1 must be nonnegative, so $20 - x_1 \geq 0$, or $x_1 \leq 20$. Thus, we cannot make $x_1 > 20$ without violating equation **(5-3).**

---

[1] On rare occasions, a nonbasic variable also can have the structure of an identity matrix column. Exercise 50 illustrates this.

Now consider **(5-4)**. This reads $x_1 + s_2 = 14$, or, after solving for s_2, $s_2 = 14 - x_1$. Since s_2 must also be nonnegative, $x_1 \le 14$ or we will violate constraint equation **(5-4)**. Since equation **(5-5)** contains no x_1, we move to **(5-6)**. Substituting $x_2 = 0$ into **(5-6)**, we obtain $x_1 + s_4 = 4$, or $s_4 = 4 - x_1$. Since s_4 must be nonnegative, then $x_1 \le 4$ or else constraint equation **(5-6)** will be violated. Let us summarize:

To Keep from Violating Constraint Equation	The Value of x_1 Must Satisfy	
(5-3)	$x_1 \le 20$	
(5-4)	$x_1 \le 14$	**(5-9)**
(5-6)	$x_1 \le 4$	

To have a feasible solution, we cannot afford to violate any constraints. The only way to satisfy all three is to make $x_1 \le 4$. This answers the question of how large we can make x_1.

The Four Steps of the Simplex Method

We don't want to go through this lengthy analysis at every stage. The simplex method handles these thought processes as follows:

Step 1. **Determine the variable that will next become basic.** Locate the column containing the most negative entry (the negative value that is farthest from 0) on the left-hand side of the objective function row **(5-7)**. The most negative entry in **(5-7)** is -0.14, and this corresponds to the largest positive entry in **(5-8)**—that is, to x_1, the variable which when increased by one unit produces the largest change in Z. Thus, the "most negative" entry in the objective function row identifies the variable (x_1 here) which becomes basic on the next iteration of the simplex method.

Which one of the variables s_1, s_2, s_3, or s_4 will exit to make room for x_1?

Step 2. **Determine the variable that will exit to make room for the variable identified in Step 1.** Divide each *positive* entry in the column identified in Step 1 (x_1 in our example) into its corresponding right-hand side element. Record these values in the right margin of Table 5.2(a).

Table 5.2(a)
Initial simplex tableau

	x_1	x_2	s_1	s_2	s_3	s_4	Z	= RHS	Ratios
s_1	1	1	1	0	0	0	0	20	$\frac{20}{1} = 20$
s_2	1	0	0	1	0	0	0	14	$\frac{14}{1} = 14$
s_3	0	1	0	0	1	0	0	10	
s_4	1	-1	0	0	0	1	0	4	$\frac{4}{1} = \boxed{4}$
Z	-0.14	-0.10	0	0	0	0	1	0	

s_4 will exit the set of basic variables on the next iteration to be replaced by x_1

Note that the right-hand side ratios in Table 5.2(a) are the values we discovered in **(5-9)**. The minimum value of these ratios is "4." It is not the size of this number that determines the exiting variable, but the row location. The boxed entry is in the s_4 row, so s_4 is the variable that will exit to make room for new basic variable x_1.

The boxed "4" is the maximum amount to which we can increase x_1 without violating any constraints. On the first iteration of the simplex method, x_1 will replace s_4 as a basic variable. How will this be accomplished? Some terminology is needed.

PIVOT COLUMN, PIVOT ROW, AND PIVOT ELEMENT

The column containing the most negative element in the objective function row is the **pivot column.** The variable identified by this column will become basic during the following pivoting process. Divide each positive entry in the pivot column into the corresponding right-hand side (constant column) entry. The row that produces the smallest quotient is called the **pivot row.** The pivot row identifies the variable that will exit the set of basic variables during the next iteration, making room for the variable identified by the pivot column. The element that is in both the pivot row and the pivot column is called the **pivot element;** we circle this element.

Step 3. **Make basic the variable identified by the pivot column.** This is done by converting the pivot element to a "1" and performing elementary row operations to clear (make zero) all other entries in the pivot column. These operations produce an equivalent system having "1" in the pivot row and column and all other elements in the pivot column 0.

This clearing operation forces the pivot column variable to be in the solution, and the value of this variable becomes the corresponding right-hand side entry. We shall now demonstrate. Consider the initial simplex tableau for Example 1:

	x_1	x_2	s_1	s_2	s_3	s_4	Z	$=$	RHS	Ratios
s_1	1	1	1	0	0	0	0		20	$\frac{20}{1} = 20$
s_2	1	0	0	1	0	0	0		14	$\frac{14}{1} = 14$
s_3	0	1	0	0	1	0	0		10	
s_4	①	-1	0	0	0	1	0		4	$\frac{4}{1} = \boxed{4}$
Z	-0.14	-0.10	0	0	0	0	1		0	

The most negative entry in the Z-row is -0.14, which identifies x_1 as the pivot column and the variable that will become basic on the first iteration of the simplex method. The minimum right-hand side ratio in the x_1 column is 4, marking the pivot row and identifying s_4 as the variable that will exit the basic set to make room for x_1. We use the circled pivot element, 1, to clear the remainder of the first column including the -0.14 in the objective function row. The necessary operations are:

(a) Replace row s_1 by row s_1 minus row s_4.

(b) Replace row s_2 by row s_2 minus row s_4.

(c) Leave row s_3 alone, as it has a zero in the pivot column.

(d) Replace the Z row by row Z plus 0.14 times row s_4.

At the conclusion of the first iteration, the resulting tableau is shown in Table 5.3.

Table 5.3
Simplex tableau after first iteration (second tableau)

Note that x_1 has replaced s_4 as basic

		x_1	x_2	s_1	s_2	s_3	s_4	Z	=	RHS	
$s_1 - s_4$	s_1	0	2	1	0	0	-1	0		16	(5-10)
$s_2 - s_4$	s_2	0	1	0	1	0	-1	0		10	(5-11)
	s_3	0	1	0	0	1	0	0		10	(5-12)
	x_1	1	-1	0	0	0	1	0		4	(5-13)
$Z + 0.14 s_4$	Z	0	-0.24	0	0	0	0.14	1		0.56	(5-14)

The structure of the x_1 column indicates that x_1 is now a basic variable. The other basic variables, identified by their identity matrix column structures, are s_1, s_2, s_3, and Z. (We continue to show these shaded and in boldface.) Variable s_4, having been replaced by x_1, no longer has the necessary structure to be a basic variable. Covering the nonbasic variable columns x_2 and s_4, we read the following solution from the constant column: $x_1 = 4$, $s_1 = 16$, $s_2 = 10$, $s_3 = 10$, and $Z = 0.56$, and $x_2 = 0 = s_4$. This solution has Jim investing \$4,000 in junk bonds, while lending no money to Drayno. That $x_1 = 4$ is reasonable; as we determined in the system **(5-9)**, the largest that we could make x_1 is 4. The resulting investment income is $0.56 = 560—better than the first solution, but still leaving \$16,000 under Jim's mattress, where it earns no interest (causing Jim sleepless nights as the money is all in nickels). Is this solution the best Jim can do, or can he further improve matters?

Step 4. **Determine whether the current solution is optimal.** Check the equation given by the objective function row. If the solution is optimal, all elements on the left-hand side of the objective function row (the "Z-row") will be nonnegative.

To see why this criterion works, consider the objective function equation. It now reads $-0.24x_2 + 0.14s_4 + Z = 0.56$. Since $s_4 = 0$, we can rewrite this as $Z = 0.56 + 0.24x_2$. Clearly, we can increase the value of Z by making x_2 greater than zero. (If the coefficient of x_2 were negative, which would be the case if this same coefficient were positive on the left-hand side, then making x_2 anything other than zero would only reduce the value of Z.)

Since we do not have an optimal solution, we perform another iteration of the simplex method. Return to step 1. The entry -0.24 marks variable x_2 as the new pivot column, so x_2 now will become basic. To find the pivot row (to identify the current basic variable which will leave to make room for x_2), consider (5-10). Since $s_4 = 0$, we have $2x_2 + s_1 = 16$, or $s_1 = 16 - 2x_2$. Since s_1 must be nonnegative, this requires $x_2 \leq 8$. Similarly, from (5-11) we have that $x_2 + s_2 = 10$, or $s_2 = 10 - x_2$, requiring $x_2 \leq 10$. From (5-12), we see that $x_2 + s_3 = 10$, or $s_3 = 10 - x_2$, so that x_2 must also be less than or equal to 10. In order not to violate any constraints, we must be certain that x_2 satisfies all of these. Making another list like (5-9), we have

To Keep from Violating Constraint Equation	The Value of x_2 Must Satisfy	
(5-10)	$x_2 \leq 8$	
(5-11)	$x_2 \leq 10$	(5-15)
(5-12)	$x_2 \leq 10$	

Thus, by ensuring that $x_2 \leq 8$, all three requirements in (5-15) will be satisfied. We thus anticipate that the second iteration of the simplex method will cause x_2 to increase to 8, and send s_1 to 0, since (5-10), the equation that produced $x_2 \leq 8$, is associated with s_1.

Let's see if our expectations are realized. As in the first iteration, we locate the most negative entry in the objective function row (5-14). Since -0.24 is the only negative in the Z-row, we identify x_2 as the new pivot column and the variable that will become basic after this iteration. What variable will it replace? Anticipating that the exiting variable should be s_1, we divide each positive entry "above the line" in the x_2 column into the corresponding right-hand side, obtaining Table 5.3(a).

Table 5.3(a)
Second tableau

	x_1	x_2	s_1	s_2	s_3	s_4	Z	$=$	RHS	Ratios
s_1	0	②	1	0	0	-1	0		16	$\frac{16}{2} = \boxed{8}$
s_2	0	1	0	1	0	-1	0		10	$\frac{10}{1} = 10$
s_3	0	1	0	0	1	0	0		10	$\frac{10}{1} = 10$
x_1	1	-1	0	0	0	1	0		4	
Z	0	-0.24	0	0	0	0.14	1		0.56	

The division of each positive[2] entry above the line in the pivot column into its corresponding right-hand side entry fixes s_1 as the pivot row; s_1 will leave on the next iteration, to be replaced by x_2. The circled "2" is the pivot element. In order to make x_2 basic, we convert the pivot element to "1" by replacing the current s_1 row by 1/2 of s_1 in Table 5.3(b).

Table 5.3(b)
Beginning second iteration

		x_1	x_2	s_1	s_2	s_3	s_4	Z =	RHS
$(1/2)s_1$	s_1	0	①	$\frac{1}{2}$	0	0	$-\frac{1}{2}$	0	8
	s_2	0	1	0	1	0	-1	0	10
	s_3	0	1	0	0	1	0	0	10
	x_1	1	-1	0	0	0	1	0	4
	Z	0	-0.24	0	0	0	0.14	1	0.56

Using the circled "1" in the pivot position, we make x_2 basic by performing the following sequence of elementary row operations:

(a) Replace row s_2 by $s_2 - s_1$.

(b) Replace row s_3 by $s_3 - s_1$.

(c) Replace row x_1 by $x_1 + s_1$.

(d) Replace row Z by $Z + 0.24s_1$.

These operations complete iteration 2, producing tableau 3 (Table 5.4).

Table 5.4
Third tableau

x_2 has now replaced s_1 as a basic variable

		x_1	x_2	s_1	s_2	s_3	s_4	Z =	RHS
	x_2	0	1	$\frac{1}{2}$	0	0	$-\frac{1}{2}$	0	8
$s_2 - s_1$	s_2	0	0	$-\frac{1}{2}$	1	0	$-\frac{1}{2}$	0	2
$s_3 - s_1$	s_3	0	0	$-\frac{1}{2}$	0	1	$\frac{1}{2}$	0	2
$x_1 + s_1$	x_1	1	0	$\frac{1}{2}$	0	0	$\frac{1}{2}$	0	12
$Z + 0.24s_1$	Z	0	0	0.12	0	0	.02	1	2.48

As anticipated, x_2 has replaced s_1 as a basic variable. Letting nonbasic variables s_1 and s_4 be zero, we read the solution: $x_1 = 12$, $x_2 = 8$, $s_2 = 2$, $s_3 = 2$, $Z = 2.48$. Study the objective function row. As an equation, it now reads $Z = 2.48 - 0.12s_1 - 0.02s_4$. If we were to proceed, one of the current nonbasic (with value 0) variables, s_1 or s_4, would have to become basic. With minus signs in front of s_1 and s_4, this could only reduce Z from its current value of 2.48. Thus, **we are at an optimum: the left-hand**

---

[2] When all entries above the line in the pivot column are either zero or negative, a special situation holds. We discuss this situation in Example 6.

side of the Z row has only nonnegative coefficients, indicating we can-not increase Z by proceeding further. Jim's dilemma is solved: he should invest $x_1 = \$12{,}000$ into junk bonds, and lend $x_2 = \$8{,}000$ to cousin Drayno. His investment income will then be 2.48 (\$2,480), and presum-ably he will sleep better without the 400,000 nickels under his mattress. Note that $x_2 = 8$, as anticipated.

The Simplex Method: Pictorially

To see pictorially how the simplex method works, we trace the neces-sary moves in relation to our graphical solution. This may help you to understand how we are able to solve five equations in seven unknowns by using a two-dimensional picture! For convenience, we reproduce the feasible region from Figure 5.1 in Figure 5.2. Refer to Figure 5.2 in the following discussion.

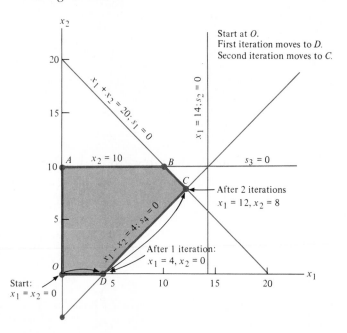

Figure 5.2
Progress of simplex method

We have indicated how slack variables are included on each boundary equation. For example, the first constraint equation is $x_1 + x_2 + s_1 = 20$. Therefore, on the line $x_1 + x_2 = 20$, s_1 must be 0. Similar reasoning shows the line segments where the other slack variables are zero. In Table 5.5 we show all feasible vertices, along with the variables that are basic at that vertex, as well as the basic feasible solution at that vertex.

We shall illustrate the solution at B; you should check the others. Since point B lies on the line $x_2 = 10$, we have $x_2 = 10$. But B is also on the line $x_1 + x_2 = 20$, which gives $x_1 = 10$. From the second equation in **(5-1)**, we have $x_1 + s_2 = 14$. But $x_1 = 10$, so $s_2 = 4$. Upon substituting $x_1 = x_2 = 10$ into $x_1 - x_2 + s_4 = 4$, we get $s_4 = 4$.

Table 5.5
All feasible vertices

Feasible Vertex	Nonbasic Variables at That Vertex	Basic Variables and Their Values	Z
O	$x_1 = 0,\ x_2 = 0$	$s_1 = 20,\ s_2 = 14$ $s_3 = 10,\ s_4 = 4$	0
A	$x_2 = 0,\ s_3 = 0$	$s_1 = 16,\ x_1 = 4$ $s_2 = 10,\ s_3 = 10$	1
B	$s_1 = 0,\ s_3 = 0$	$x_2 = 10,\ x_1 = 10$ $s_2 = 4,\ s_4 = 4$	2.40
C	$s_1 = 0,\ s_4 = 0$	$x_1 = 12,\ x_2 = 8$ $s_1 = 2,\ s_3 = 2$	2.48
D	$s_4 = 0,\ x_2 = 0$	$x_1 = 4,\ s_2 = 10$ $s_3 = 10,\ s_1 = 16$	0.56

The optimal solution is at C, where the value of Z is 2.48. Geometrically the simplex method commences at the origin, with decision variables x_1 and x_2 being zero. The first iteration takes us to a value of $Z = 0.56$. This occurs at point D, a feasible vertex adjacent to O. The value of Z definitely improved in going from O to D. Also note that we could have done even better by going to A, which is also adjacent to O. The simplex method does not guarantee that we go to the neighboring vertex having the highest value of Z—it does, however, guarantee that we will *not* go to an adjacent vertex with a smaller value of Z.

The second iteration begins at D. The only choices for adjacent vertex are C and O. O will not be chosen as it would reduce the value of Z to zero. Hence, the second iteration of the simplex takes us to C, which is optimal. If, initially, we had proceeded to A (which gives a larger value of Z than vertex D), we would have needed a total of *three* iterations, O to A, A to B, and B to C to reach an optimum solution.

The intuitive discussion of Example 1 illustrates the mathematical trappings involved in the simplex method. If you apply the simplex method, you will probably use a computer, but no one should use a "canned program" without first having some idea of what it does.

5.2 THE SIMPLEX ALGORITHM—THE MOVES WITHOUT THE JUSTIFICATION

Having developed an intuitive understanding of how the simplex method works, we summarize what we learned in the last section, and then concentrate on applying the simplex method. First, we define the **Initial Simplex Tableau**.

THE INITIAL SIMPLEX TABLEAU

To form the **Initial Simplex Tableau** for a standard maximization problem, proceed as follows:

1. Add nonnegative slack variables to the left-hand side of each "≤" constraint, making each one an equation.

2. Append the objective function as an equation in the form "decision variables + Z = 0."

3. Write the augmented matrix for the entire system, being sure to put the Z equation as the last equation. Separate the objective function equation from the rest of the system by drawing a horizontal line above it. The initial simplex tableau is composed of the objective function row and the part "above the line."

■ EXAMPLE 2

Find the initial simplex tableau for the following standard maximization problem.

$$x_1 - x_2 \leq 5$$

Maximize $Z = 4x_1 - 6x_2$,   subject to: $x_1 + x_2 \leq 8$

$$x_1 \geq 0, \quad x_2 \geq 0$$

SOLUTION   We add two slack variables, one for each functional constraint. The constraint $x_1 - x_2 \leq 5$ becomes the equation $x_1 - x_2 + s_1 = 5$, and the constraint $x_1 + x_2 \leq 8$ becomes $x_1 + x_2 + s_2 = 8$. We rewrite the objective function as an equation with Z as a variable and 0 on the right-hand side. This gives us $-4x_1 + 6x_2 + Z = 0$. Picking off the appropriate coefficients to form the augmented matrix, we have the initial simplex tableau:

Initial tableau for Example 2

	x_1	x_2	s_1	s_2	Z	=	RHS
s_1	1	−1	1	0	0		5
s_2	1	1	0	1	0		8
Z	−4	6	0	0	1		0

PRACTICE PROBLEM 2   Find the initial simplex tableau for the following standard maximization problem: maximize $Z = 12x_1 + 5x_2 + 3x_3$, subject to:

$$3x_1 + 4x_2 - 3x_3 \le 24$$

$$4x_1 - 6x_2 + 2x_3 \le 14$$

$$3x_2 - 4x_3 \le 6$$

$$x_1, x_2, x_3 \ge 0$$

ANSWER(S)   The initial simplex tableau is:

	x_1	x_2	x_3	s_1	s_2	s_3	Z =	RHS
s_1	3	4	−3	1	0	0	0	24
s_2	4	−6	2	0	1	0	0	14
s_3	0	3	−4	0	0	1	0	6
Z	−12	−5	−3	0	0	0	1	0

We now list the details of the simplex method, the algorithm that converts the initial simplex tableau into an optimal feasible solution or shows that there is no optimal solution.

THE SIMPLEX METHOD

1. Form the initial simplex tableau.

2. Check the objective function row for optimality by seeing if all coefficients on the left-hand side are nonnegative; if so, you have an optimal solution. If not, proceed to step 3.

3. Determine the pivot column by locating the most negative element on the left-hand side of the objective function row. Take your pick if there are "ties." Divide each positive element above the line in the pivot column into its corresponding right-hand side entry. The row that produces the smallest quotient is the pivot row, and the element at the intersection of the pivot row and column is called the pivot element. If there is a tie for the smallest quotient, choose any of the rows that are tied.

4. Using elementary row operations, convert the pivot element to a "1," and then obtain zeros in the remainder of the pivot column (above and below the line). This completes one iteration of the simplex method. Return to step 2.

Note 1: Do not be tempted to simplify rows by multiplication. Multiplying any row *other than* the pivot row by a constant can lead to some difficulties in interpreting solutions.

Note 2: In step 3 of the simplex method, we divide each right-hand side entry by the corresponding positive entry in the pivot column. What if there are no positive entries in the pivot column? In this case the solution is unbounded. (See Example 6, Chapter 4.) We illustrate in Example 6 of this chapter, too, but for now try Example 3.

■ EXAMPLE 3

Maximize $Z = 8x_1 + 12x_2$, subject to:

$$5x_1 + 4x_2 \leq 40$$

$$2x_1 + x_2 \leq 6$$

$$x_1 + x_2 \leq 4$$

$$x_1, x_2 \geq 0$$

SOLUTION   We first form the initial simplex tableau:

	x_1	x_2	s_1	s_2	s_3	Z =	RHS	Ratios
s_1	5	4	1	0	0	0	40	$\frac{40}{4} = 10$
s_2	2	1	0	1	0	0	6	$\frac{6}{1} = 6$
s_3	1	①	0	0	1	0	4	$\frac{4}{1} = \boxed{4}$
Z	−8	−12	0	0	0	1	0	

Smallest right-hand side ratio

The negatives in the Z-row indicate we do not yet have an optimum solution—very seldom would we have at the initial simplex tableau. The entry "−12" is clearly the most negative entry in the Z-row, earmarking x_2 as pivot column. Divisions into the right-hand side produce the quotients shown above. Since "4" is the smallest, row s_3 is identified as the pivot row and the circled "1" in the x_2 column is the pivot element. We have now determined that on the first iteration of the simplex method, variable x_2 will become basic, replacing s_3.

Now we "zero out" other entries in the x_2 column. Apply the following sequence of elementary row operations:

(a) Replace row s_1 by row s_1 minus 4 times row s_3.

(b) Replace row s_2 by row s_2 minus row s_3.

(c) Replace row Z by row Z plus 12 times row s_3.

The resulting simplex tableau is shown below:

		x_1	x_2	s_1	s_2	s_3	Z =	RHS
$s_1 - 4s_3$	s_1	1	0	1	0	-4	0	24
$s_2 - s_3$	s_2	1	0	0	1	-1	0	2
	x_2	1	1	0	0	1	0	4
$Z + 12s_3$	Z	4	0	0	0	12	1	48

x_2 is now basic (left of table, row x_2)

all nonnegative; optimum (right of Z row)

Because the objective function row contains only nonnegative entries on the left-hand side, we have an optimum solution. To read the solution, cover the columns corresponding to the nonbasic variables x_1 and s_3. Covering these columns is equivalent to assigning these variables the value 0. For each of the basic variables (x_2, s_1, s_2, and Z here, corresponding to columns of an identity matrix), go down the column for that variable until you locate the "1." The solution for that variable is the corresponding right-hand side entry. In the x_2 column, for example, the right-hand side entry corresponding to the "1" is 4, signifying that $x_2 = 4$ is part of the optimum solution. Continuing, we have $x_2 = 4$, $s_1 = 24$, $s_2 = 2$, and $Z = 48$. Observe that one of the decision variables, x_1, is nonbasic in our optimal solution, taking the value 0. In a given problem, x_1 will usually represent the quantity of some item. The solution $x_1 = 0$ would tell us that economically it is better not to produce any of this item. You should verify the slack variable figures 24 and 4 by substituting $x_1 = 0$ and $x_2 = 4$ into the first two constraint equations. ∎

PRACTICE PROBLEM 3   Maximize $Z = x_1 + x_2$ subject to

$$2x_1 + 3x_2 \le 14$$
$$3x_1 + x_2 \le 14$$
$$x_1, x_2 \ge 0$$

ANSWER(S)   Maximum value of Z is 6 when $x_1 = 4$ and $x_2 = 2$. ☐

Being able to properly perform the simplex method is necessary but not nearly as important as being able to set up properly a problem so that the simplex method can be employed, and then to interpret the results. Try Example 4.

■ **EXAMPLE 4**

A manufacturer of add-on memory boards for IBM compatible computers makes two models. Model 1 uses 1 special "S" chip and 72 ordinary dynamic ram chips (DRAMS). Model 2 uses 4 of the "S" chips and 18 DRAMS. Profits on each Model board are $200 and $300, respectively. The company currently has available 420 "S" chips and 5940 DRAMS. How should these chips be apportioned between Models 1 and 2 to maximize profit?

SOLUTION   Table 5.6, which summarizes the chip situation, will be helpful in establishing the necessary constraints.

Table 5.6

	S-Chips	DRAMS
Model 1	1	72
Model 2	4	18
# Available:	420	5940

Let x_1 and x_2 denote the number of Model 1 and Model 2 boards to be made. In addition to nonnegativity, there are two functional constraints: we only have so many chips of each kind. We use "1" S-chip in each Model 1 board and 4 S-chips in each Model 2 board. If we make x_1 of Model 1 and x_2 of Model 2, we will then use $1 \cdot x_1 + 4 \cdot x_2$ S-chips. Since we have only 420 of these available, we must be sure that $1 \cdot x_1 + 4 \cdot x_2 \le 420$. Similarly, the total number of DRAMS used in making x_1 of Model 1 and x_2 of Model 2 is $72 \cdot x_1 + 18 \cdot x_2$, and this must be at most 5940. These are the functional constraints:

$$1x_1 + 4x_2 \le 420 \quad \text{S-chip availability}$$

$$72x_1 + 18x_2 \le 5940 \quad \text{DRAMS availability}$$

The objective function is profit: $Z = 200x_1 + 300x_2$. The initial simplex tableau is Table 5.7.

Table 5.7
Initial simplex tableau for Example 4

	x_1	x_2	s_1	s_2	Z	=	RHS	Ratios
s_1	1	④	1	0	0		420	$\frac{420}{4} = 105$
s_2	72	18	0	1	0		5940	$\frac{5940}{18} = 330$
Z	-200	-300	0	0	1		0	

The "-300" in the Z-row marks x_2 as pivot column, and the smaller ratio is in row s_1, making s_1 the pivot row and the variable that will exit to make room for x_2; "4" is the pivot element. Multiplying row s_1 by 1/4 to get a "1" in the pivot position gives:

	x_1	x_2	s_1	s_2	Z	=	RHS
s_1	$\frac{1}{4}$	①	$\frac{1}{4}$	0	0		105
s_2	72	18	0	1	0		5940
Z	-200	-300	0	0	1		0

We clear the x_2 column with 2 operations:

(a) Replace s_2 by $s_2 - 18s_1$

(b) Replace Z by $Z + 300s_1$

These produce Tableau 1.

Tableau 1 for Example 4

x_2 is now a basic variable

	x_1	x_2	s_1	s_2	$Z =$	RHS	Ratios
x_2	$\frac{1}{4}$	1	$\frac{1}{4}$	0	0	105	$105 \div (\frac{1}{4}) = 420$
s_2	$\frac{270}{4}$	0	$-\frac{18}{4}$	1	0	4050	$4050 \div (\frac{270}{4}) = \boxed{60}$
Z	-125	0	75	0	1	31500	

This solution is not optimal because there is a negative on the left-hand side of the Z-row. Let us proceed with the second iteration of the simplex method. The smaller right-hand side ratio is 60 in the x_1 column and the s_2 row, indicating that the next iteration will move x_1 into the solution, replacing s_2. Multiplying the s_2 row by 4/270 to convert the pivot element to "1" gives us Tableau 2.

Tableau 2 for Example 4

	x_1	x_2	s_1	s_2	$Z =$	RHS
x_2	$\frac{1}{4}$	1	$\frac{1}{4}$	0	0	105
s_2	①	0	$-\frac{1}{15}$	$\frac{4}{270}$	0	60
Z	-125	0	75	0	1	31,500

The remainder of the pivot (x_1) column is cleared with the following two operations:

(a) Replace row x_2 by $x_2 - (1/4)s_2$

(b) Replace row Z by $Z + 125s_2$

These operations lead to Tableau 3.

Tableau 3 for Example 4

x_1 joins x_2 as a basic variable

		x_1	x_2	s_1	s_2	$Z =$	RHS
$x_2 - (\frac{1}{4})s_2$	x_2	0	1	$\frac{1}{15}$	$-\frac{1}{270}$	0	90
	x_1	1	0	$-\frac{1}{15}$	$\frac{1}{270}$	0	60
$Z + 125s_2$	Z	0	0	$66\frac{2}{3}$	$\frac{50}{27}$	1	39,000

This solution is optimal; we read $x_1 = 60$ Model 1 boards to be made and $x_2 = 90$ Model 2 boards to be made. The profit from making this mix of boards is $Z = \$39,000$. ◼

In examples of the simplex we have seen so far, all basic variables except Z have had a zero in the objective function row, and nonbasic variables have all had nonzero values in the Z row. In the next example we discover what it means to have a nonbasic variable with a zero in the Z row of the final simplex tableau.

◼ EXAMPLE 5

Maximize $Z = 3x_1 + 2x_2$ subject to

$$x_1 + x_2 \le 12 \qquad x_1 + 2x_2/3 \le 8$$

and the usual nonnegativity constraints.

SOLUTION

After adding a slack variable for each constraint, and expressing the objective function as an equation whose right-hand side is zero, we arrive at the following initial simplex tableau:

Initial Tableau for Example 5

	x_1	x_2	s_1	s_2	Z =	RHS	Ratios
s_1	1	1	1	0	0	12	$\frac{12}{1} = 12$
s_2	①	$\frac{2}{3}$	0	1	0	8	$\frac{8}{1} = \boxed{8}$
Z	-3	-2	0	0	1	0	

The most negative element in the objective function row is -3, and the right-hand side ratios are "12" and "8," which identifies the "1" in the row s_2 and column x_1 as the pivot element. Two operations complete the first iteration of the simplex:

1. multiply the s_2 row by "-1" and add it to the s_1 row.

2. multiply the s_2 row by "3" and add it to the Z row.

This gives

Tableau for Example 5 after one iteration

	x_1	x_2	s_1	s_2	Z =	RHS
s_1	0	$\frac{1}{3}$	1	-1	0	4
x_1	1	$\frac{2}{3}$	0	1	0	8
Z	0	0	0	3	1	24

We have reached an optimum in one iteration: $x_1 = 8$, $s_1 = 4$, and an objective function maximum of 24. Variable x_2 is nonbasic, indicating its value in the optimum solution is zero. Since x_1 and x_2 usually represent quantities or amounts of certain items, this would say (as in Example 3) that it is better not to produce any of item x_2. Note that the objective function entry for the nonbasic variable x_2 is 0. We shall not go into details, but *if there is a zero entry in the objective function row under a variable which is nonbasic in the final tableau, then there is more than one optimal solution.* To find another optimal solution, use the column containing that nonbasic variable as pivot column. (There are no more negatives on the left-hand side of the objective function row, so we can no longer look for the most negative entry.) Then, perform a typical iteration of the simplex. In this case there is a tie for the smallest ratio as both $4 \div (1/3)$ and $8 \div (2/3) = 12$. Because we can take our pick when there are ties, we shall use the "1/3" in the s_1 row as a pivot element since it is more convenient than "2/3." This leads to the following simplex tableau:

	x_1	x_2	s_1	s_2	Z	$=$	RHS
x_2	0	1	3	-3	0		12
x_1	1	0	-2	3	0		0
Z	0	0	0	3	1		24

This tableau is also optimal as there are no negatives on the left-hand side of the objective function row. The solution is $x_1 = 0$, $x_2 = 12$, and $Z = 24$. Thus we have discovered that $(8,0)$ and $(0,12)$ *both* produce $Z = 24$. To illustrate exactly what is happening here, we work the problem geometrically, using the methods of Chapter 4. The feasible region is shaded in Figure 5.3.

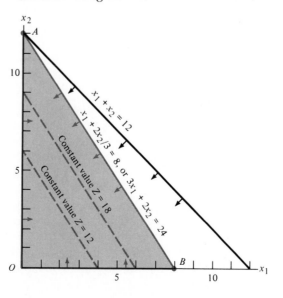

Figure 5.3
Feasible region for Example 5

For any value of Z, the objective function $Z = 3x_1 + 2x_2$ is parallel to the line $3x_1 + 2x_2 = 24$. Therefore, as lines of constant objective function value march upward from the origin in search of a maximum, they will last encounter the feasible region on this boundary line. Thus, the objective function will have the optimal value 24 not only at vertices A and B, but *also at any point on the line segment joining those vertices*. The point $(6,3)$, for example, is also on this line, producing $3 \cdot 6 + 2 \cdot 3 = 24$. In objective function value, there is no difference between any of these points producing the optimal value of 24. In a given situation, however, there may be compelling reasons for choosing one (x_1, x_2) combination over another. The size of packing cases for instance may dictate that multiples of 12 should be manufactured. ■

The following example, while not terribly typical, is important, illustraing what happens when there are no positive entries above the line in the pivot column.

■ EXAMPLE 6 _____

Maximize $3x_1 + 4x_2$ subject to $x_2 \geq x_1$ and the usual nonnegativity constraints.

SOLUTION

The initial simplex tableau is given by

	x_1	x_2	s_1	$Z\ =$	RHS
s_1	1	-1	1	0	0
Z	-3	-4	0	1	0

The most negative element on the left-hand side of the objective function row is -4, which identifies column x_2 as pivot column. The only possible pivot element is the -1 in row s_1, but the simplex method identifies a pivot element by looking for the *positive* entry in the pivot column with the smallest right-hand side quotient. As an equation, row s_1 reads $x_1 - x_2 + s_1 = 0$, but $x_1 = 0$ in this tableau since, at the moment, both x_1 and x_2 are nonbasic. If we substitute $x_1 = 0$ into this equation, we get $s_1 = x_2$. The next iteration of the simplex is designed to bring x_2 into the solution without violating any nonnegativity constraints. Since s_1 must be nonnegative, and $s_1 = x_2$, then there is no limit to how large x_2 can be. Thus, there is also no limit to how large the objective function can be. ■

Whenever there are only negatives and zeros above the line in the pivot column, the solution is said to be **unbounded**. Such solutions are not applicable in the real world as even the most skillful mathematics cannot produce infinite profits! When an unbounded solution is encountered in the real world, the most likely explanation is that an important constraint has been overlooked or some other error has been made.

Shadow Prices In the next example, we shall discover that the simplex method provides us with considerably more than just solutions for the decision variables.

■ EXAMPLE 7

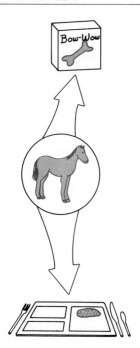

The OGM (Old Gray Mare prior to a corporate takeover) Packing Company grinds up leftover raw materials and markets them in one of two mixes: **(1)** dog food, or **(2)** salisbury steaks used by major airlines as dinner entrees for their First Class passengers. A case of dog food takes 4 hours of packing house labor and requires 30 pounds of ground raw materials. A case of salisbury steaks takes 6 hours of labor and requires 25 pounds of ground raw materials. The packing company makes a profit of $8 on each case of dog food and $10 on each case of salisbury steaks. The packing company work force consists of 55 people, each of whom works an 8 hour day. There are 2500 pounds of ground raw materials available each day. To maximize profit, how many cases of each mix should the packing company make?

SOLUTION

The objective function is profit $= Z = 8x_1 + 10x_2$, where x_1 and x_2 are the number of cases of dog food and salisbury steak, respectively, to be made daily. There is a total of $55 \cdot 8 = 440$ hours of labor. The specific problem constraints are then

$$4x_1 + 6x_2 \leq 440 \quad \text{Labor constraint}$$

$$30x_1 + 25x_2 \leq 2500 \quad \text{Raw materials constraint}$$

We want to maximize $Z = 8x_1 + 10x_2$ subject to these constraints and the usual nonnegativity constraints. The initial simplex tableau is:

Initial tableau for Example 7

	x_1	x_2	s_1	s_2	Z	= RHS	Ratios
s_1	4	⑥	1	0	0	440	$\frac{440}{6} = 73\frac{1}{3}$
s_2	30	25	0	1	0	2500	$\frac{2500}{25} = 100$
Z	−8	−10	0	0	1	0	

The −10 in the x_2 column locates the pivot column, and the minimum ratio is in the first row, identifying "6" as the pivot element. Dividing the first row by 6 to produce a "1" in the pivot position and clearing the remainder of the pivot column gives:

Tableau after one iteration

	x_1	x_2	s_1	s_2	Z	= RHS	Ratios
x_2	$\frac{2}{3}$	1	$\frac{1}{6}$	0	0	$\frac{220}{3}$	$\left(\frac{220}{3}\right) \div \left(\frac{2}{3}\right) = 110$
s_2	$\frac{40}{3}$	0	$-\frac{25}{6}$	1	0	$\frac{2000}{3}$	$\left(\frac{2000}{3}\right) \div \left(\frac{40}{3}\right) = \boxed{50}$
Z	$\left(-\frac{4}{3}\right)$	0	$\frac{5}{3}$	0	1	$\frac{2200}{3}$	

Because there still is a negative entry on the left-hand side of the Z-row, we perform another iteration. The pivot column is x_1, and the pivot element is 40/3. Dividing the second row by the pivot element produces a "1" in the pivot position, which can then be used to clear the remainder of the pivot column, giving

Tableau after two iterations

	x_1	x_2	s_1	s_2	Z	= RHS
x_2	0	1	$\frac{3}{8}$	$-\frac{1}{20}$	0	40
x_1	1	0	$-\frac{5}{16}$	$\frac{3}{40}$	0	50
Z	0	0	1.25	.1	1	800

We have an optimum; the solution is $x_2 = 40$ cases of salisbury steak and $x_1 = 50$ cases of dog food. The optimum profit is \$800. Substitute $x_1 = 50$ and $x_2 = 40$ into the two specific constraints:

$$4 \cdot (50) + 6 \cdot (40) = 440 \qquad \text{Labor constraint}$$

$$30 \cdot (50) + 25 \cdot (40) = 2500 \qquad \text{Raw materials constraint}$$

This shows that s_1 and s_2 are zero and hence nonbasic in the final solution. But, what do the entries in the Z-row of the s_1 and s_2 columns (1.25 and 0.1) tell us? These are important numbers. To see what they represent, we rework this example with one small change: we increase the available labor from 440 person-hours to 441 hours. (We add one person-hour of labor.) The initial simplex tableau has but one change: the 440 becomes $440 + 1$.

Initial tableau for Example 7, with one more hour of labor available

	x_1	x_2	s_1	s_2	Z	= RHS
s_1	4	6	1	0	0	$440 + 1$
s_2	30	25	0	1	0	$2500 + 0$
Z	-8	-10	0	0	1	$0 + 0$

Observe that the right-hand side changes only through addition of the column $[1 \ \ 0 \ \ 0]^{\mathrm{T}}$. This column is the same as the s_1 column. If we capitalize on this fact, we can save ourselves a lot of work. Whatever the original sequence of simplex iterations did to the s_1 column, it will also do to this tacked-on column. Thus, the final tableau in the simplex should become:

	x_1	x_2	s_1	s_2	Z	$=$	RHS
x_2	0	1	$\frac{3}{8}$	$-\frac{1}{20}$	0		$40 + \frac{3}{8}$
x_1	1	0	$-\frac{5}{16}$	$\frac{3}{40}$	0		$50 - \frac{5}{16}$
Z	0	0	1.25	.1	1		$800 + 1.25$

The important thing to note is this: increasing labor by one unit increased the objective function by 1.25 units. Thus, the slack variable entries in the Z-row of the final tableau determine what happens if resource amounts were to increase or decrease. The final Z-row slack variable entries are called **shadow prices**.

SHADOW PRICES

> **Shadow prices** are the entries in the slack variable columns of the objective function row in the final simplex tableau. A shadow price represents the change in the objective function that accompanies a one-unit increase in the corresponding resource.

Shadow price interpretations apply to decreases, too. Thus, if labor capacity were to decrease from 440 hours to 439 hours, the optimum Z would become $800 - 1.25 = \$798.75$. These results generalize, up to a point, when resource amounts change by k units. Consequently, if labor were to increase from 440 to $440 + k$ hours, the optimum value of Z would become $800 + k(1.25)$: each additional hour of labor translates into \$1.25 of additional profit—provided k is not too large. It is usually safe to make these marginal interpretations for small changes in available resources.

In Section 5.4, we show how the popular software package LINDO enables you to determine how much a given resource can vary and still preserve our shadow price interpretation.

We have interpreted the 1.25 corresponding to labor; what about the 0.10 under raw materials? This indicates that each additional pound of raw materials will increase profit by \$0.10—a dime a pound. Thus, if daily available raw materials were to increase to 2600 pounds, profit would increase to $\$800 + 100(0.10) = \$810$. Note that an extra hour of labor is worth far more than an additional pound of raw materials. ∎

One final note on the subject of shadow prices: if an optimum solution leaves some slack (not all of that resource gets used), then the shadow price for that resource will be zero—it does no good to have extra quantities of a resource that is not fully utilized. Thus, *if the slack is nonzero, the shadow price will be zero; if the slack is zero, then the shadow price will be nonzero.*

PRACTICE PROBLEM 4   In Example 7, if the amount of labor available were to become 460 hours, and if the amount of raw materials available were to drop to 2,000 pounds daily, find the optimum daily profit.

ANSWER(S) $800 + 20 \cdot (1.25) - 500(0.1) = \$775$ □

■ EXAMPLE 8

In Example 4, a memory-board manufacturer for computers was attempting to determine the appropriate mix of Model 1 and Model 2 boards to manufacture in order to maximize profit. Variables x_1 and x_2 were the number of boards of Model 1 and Model 2, respectively. The functional constraint equations

$$1x_1 + 4x_2 \le 420 \qquad \text{S-chip availability}$$

$$72x_1 + 18x_2 \le 5940 \qquad \text{DRAMS availability}$$

detail available quantities of S-chips (slack variable s_1) and DRAM chips (slack variable s_2). The final (optimal) simplex tableau was:

	x_1	x_2	s_1	s_2	Z	=	RHS
x_2	0	1	$\frac{4}{15}$	$-\frac{1}{270}$	0		90
x_1	1	0	$-\frac{1}{15}$	$\frac{4}{270}$	0		60
Z	0	0	$66\frac{2}{3}$	$\frac{50}{27}$	1		39,000

Interpret the shadow price entries.

SOLUTION   The $66\frac{2}{3}$ figure under s_1 says that if one more S-chip were available, making a total of 421 S-chips, profit would increase by \$66.67 to \$39,066.67. Similarly, if one more DRAM chip were available, then profit would increase by $\frac{50}{27} \approx \$1.85$. Having one more of each chip would increase the profit by \$66.67 + \$1.85 = \$68.52. Having 10 more of each chip, however, may not increase the profit by $10 \cdot \$68.52 = \$685.20$. These shadow prices have marginal interpretations and they may not hold for large changes in available resources.   ■

PRACTICE PROBLEM 5   Use the simplex method to maximize $Z = 4x_1 + x_2$ subject to the following: $x_1 + 2x_2 \leq 12$, $-2x_1 + 3x_2 \leq 20$, and $x_1, x_2 \geq 0$.

ANSWER(S) $x_1 = 12$, $x_2 = 0$, and $Z = 48$ ☐

PRACTICE PROBLEM 6   In Practice Problem 5, find and interpret the shadow prices.

ANSWER(S)   The shadow price for the first resource is 4. We estimate that increasing the right-hand side from 12 to 13, for example, will increase the optimum value of Z from 48 to 52. The shadow price associated with the second resource is 0. Small changes in the right-hand side of the second constraint will not alter the objective function optimum.   ☐

EXERCISES 5.2

PRACTICING THE MOVES AND MANEUVERS

Exercises 1–3: Express each constraint inequality in standard maximization form.

1. $4x_1 + x_2 \leq 9$ 2. $3x_1 + 5x_2 \geq -5$ 3. $-4x_1 + 6x_2 \leq 8$

Exercises 4–7: Determine if the given problem is a standard maximization problem. For those that aren't, convert them, if possible. If not, so indicate.

4. Maximize $Z = x_1 + x_2$, subject to:

$$x_1 + 4x_2 \geq 5$$
$$x_1 - 3x_2 \leq 4$$
$$x_1, x_2 \geq 0$$

5. Maximize $Z = 3x_1 + 5x_2 - 9x_3$, subject to:

$$5x_1 + 3x_2 + 7x_3 \leq 12$$
$$6x_1 + 4x_2 + 5x_3 \leq -4$$
$$-3x_1 + 5x_2 - 2x_3 \leq 6$$
$$x_1, x_2, x_3 \geq 0$$

6. Maximize $Z = -2x_1 + 3x_2$, subject to:

$$3x_1 + 2x_2 \leq 4$$
$$-2x_1 - 3x_2 \leq 5$$
$$x_1, x_2 \geq 0$$

7. Maximize $Z = 2x_1 - 4x_2$, subject to:

$$3x_1 + 6x_2 \geq 7$$
$$x_1 - x_2 \geq 5$$
$$x_1, x_2 \geq 0$$

Exercises 8–10: Introduce nonnegative slack variables and write the given set of constraints as a system of equations.

8. $4x_1 + 5x_2 \leq 8$
$3x_1 - 6x_2 \geq -4$
$x_2 \leq 5$

9. $x_1 - 2x_2 \leq 8$
$2x_1 + 4x_2 \leq 5$
$3x_1 - 2x_2 \leq 2$

10. $5x_1 + 2x_2 - 3x_3 \leq 6$
$3x_1 - 4x_2 + 2x_3 \geq -4$
$x_2 - 3x_3 \leq 2$

Exercises 11–14:   Find the initial simplex tableau for the given system.

11.   Maximize $Z = 4x_1 + 6x_2$, subject to:

$$4x_1 + 2x_2 \le 8$$
$$x_1 - 4x_2 \le 2$$
$$2x_1 + 4x_2 \le 12$$
$$x_1, x_2 \ge 0$$

13.   Maximize $Z = 2x_1 + 5x_2$, subject to:

$$x_1 + 2x_2 \le 8$$
$$2x_1 + 8x_2 \le 14$$
$$3x_1 - 2x_2 \le 10$$
$$x_1, x_2 \ge 0$$

12.   Maximize $Z = x_1 - 5x_2$, subject to:

$$2x_1 + x_2 \le 6$$
$$3x_1 - 2x_2 \le 5$$
$$x_1, x_2 \ge 0$$

14.   Maximize $Z = x_1 - x_2$, subject to:

$$4x_1 - 3x_2 \le 12$$
$$x_1 + 2x_2 \le 10$$
$$x_1, x_2 \ge 0$$

Exercises 15 and 16:   Identify the basic variables and the nonbasic variables and read the solution from the simplex tableau in final form.

15.

x_1	x_2	s_1	s_2	Z	=	RHS
1	0	2	-3	0		7
0	1	-2	2	0		5
0	0	4	5	1		14

16.

x_1	x_2	x_3	s_1	s_2	s_3	Z	=	RHS
2	1	0	-4	-3	0	0		24
-1	0	1	-4	1	0	0		16
2	0	0	3	0	1	0		8
7	0	0	5	1	0	1		64

Exercises 17–20:   Answer each of the following for the given simplex tableau.

(a) Which of the variables are basic? Which are nonbasic?

(b) Assuming a standard maximization problem, determine the obvious basic feasible solution.

(c) Is the solution in (b) optimal? If not, find the optimal solution, or show that none exists.

17.

x_1	x_2	s_1	s_2	s_3	s_4	Z	=	RHS
1	4	1	0	0	0	0		10
3	1	0	1	0	0	0		6
-1	-2	0	0	0	1	0		2
1	1	0	0	1	0	0		6
-2	1	0	0	0	0	1		44

18.

x_1	x_2	s_1	s_2	Z	=	RHS
1	1	1	0	0		5
1	0	2	1	0		8
5	0	3	0	1		24

19.

x_1	x_2	x_3	s_1	s_2	s_3	Z	=	RHS
3	4	-3	1	0	0	0		24
4	-6	2	0	1	0	0		14
0	3	-4	0	0	1	0		6
-12	-5	3	0	0	0	1		0

20.

x_1	x_2	s_1	s_2	s_3	s_4	Z	=	RHS
1	0	1	0	0	3	0		14
0	0	-1	0	1	3	0		1
0	1	-1	0	0	0	0		4
0	0	2	1	0	5	0		20
0	0	3	0	0	8	1		52

Exercises 21–24: Locate the pivot element, and clear the pivot column (that is, perform one iteration of the simplex method).

21.

x_1	x_2	s_1	s_2	Z	=	RHS
1	-2	1	0	0		8
0	2	0	1	0		3
-4	-1	0	0	1		15

22.

x_1	x_2	s_1	s_2	s_3	s_4	Z	=	RHS
2	3	1	0	0	0	0		4
1	-2	0	1	0	0	0		5
2	-3	0	0	1	0	0		2
3	2	0	0	0	1	0		8
-1	-3	0	0	0	0	1		0

23.

x_1	x_2	x_3	s_1	s_2	s_3	Z	=	RHS
2	2	-2	1	0	0	0		6
4	-3	1	0	1	0	0		4
0	2	-3	0	0	1	0		16
-4	-2	-3	0	0	0	1		0

24.

x_1	x_2	s_1	s_2	s_3	Z	=	RHS
-2	4	1	0	0	0		15
-4	2	0	1	0	0		6
2	4	0	0	1	0		8
-4	2	0	0	0	1		0

Exercises 25–50: Use the simplex method to find the optimum solution.

Exercises 25–27: Maximize the given Z subject to the following constraints:

$$2x_1 + 3x_2 \le 24 \qquad 3x_1 + 4x_2 \le 30 \qquad x_1 \ge 0, \quad x_2 \ge 0$$

25. $Z = 4x_1 + 3x_2$ 26. $Z = 2x_1 + 5x_2$ 27. $Z = -4x_1 + 2x_2$

Exercises 28–30: Maximize the given Z subject to the following constraints:

$$-3x_1 + 2x_2 \le 12 \qquad 2x_1 - 4x_2 \le 8 \qquad x_1 \ge 0, \quad x_2 \ge 0$$

28. $Z = 2x_1 - 4x_2$ 29. $Z = -2x_1 + 5x_2$ 30. $Z = 4x_1 + 2x_2$

Exercises 31–33: Maximize the given Z subject to the following constraints:

$$x_1 + x_2 \le 9 \qquad x_1 + 4x_2 \le 30 \qquad x_1 + 2x_2 \le 20 \qquad x_1 \ge 0, \quad x_2 \ge 0$$

31. $Z = 12x_1 + 16x_2$ 32. $Z = 8x_1 + 2x_2$ 33. $Z = 4x_1 - 2x_2$

Exercises 34–36: Maximize the given Z subject to the following constraints:

$$6x_1 + 4x_2 \le 8 \qquad x_1 + x_2 \le 2 \qquad 2x_1 - 5x_2 \le 12 \qquad x_1 \ge 0, \quad x_2 \ge 0$$

34. $Z = 8x_1 + 5x_2$ 35. $Z = -4x_1 + 2x_2$ 36. $Z = x_1 + 4x_2$

Exercises 37–40: Maximize the given Z subject to the following constraints:

$$x_1 - x_2 \le 4, \qquad 2x_1 + 4x_2 \le 20 \qquad x_1, x_2 \ge 0$$

37. $Z = 2x_1 + x_2$ 38. $Z = 4x_1 + 2x_2$ 39. $Z = 2x_1 - x_2$
40. $Z = x_1 - 3x_2$

Exercises 41–44: Maximize the given Z subject to the following constraints:

$$x_1 + 4x_2 \le 12 \qquad x_1 \le 6 \qquad x_1, x_2 \ge 0$$

41. $Z = x_1 + x_2$ 42. $Z = x_1 + 2x_2$ 43. $Z = x_1 + 4x_2$
44. $Z = x_1 - x_2$

Exercises 45–49: Maximize the given Z subject to the following constraints:

$$x_1 + 3x_2 - 4x_3 \le 40 \qquad 4x_1 + 2x_2 + x_3 \le 50 \qquad x_1, \quad x_2, \quad x_3 \ge 0$$

45. $Z = 12x_1 + 4x_2 - 3x_3$ 46. $Z = -12x_1 - 4x_2 + 3x_3$ 47. $Z = x_1$
48. $Z = x_1 - x_2$ 49. $Z = x_3$

Exercises 50–52: Maximize the given Z subject to the following constraints:

$$x_1 - 4x_3 \le 1 \qquad 2x_1 - 2x_3 \le 8 \qquad x_1, \quad x_2 \ge 0$$

50. $Z = x_1 - x_2 - x_3$ 51. $Z = x_1 - x_2$ 52. $Z = x_1 - x_3$

APPLYING THE CONCEPTS

Exercises 53–57: A candy company specializes in chocolate covered candies with caramel, nut, or creme-filled centers. These candies are marketed in two mixes: Mix I, with 4 of each kind, sells for $3.50. Mix II, which contains 8 caramel, 4 nut, and 12 creme-filled, sells for $6.00. Manufacturing caramel, nut, and creme-filled centers costs the manufacturer $0.15, $0.20, and $0.10, respectively. Facilities allow up to 2200 caramel centers, 2000 nut centers, and 4000 creme-filled centers to be produced weekly.

53. Using graphical methods, determine how many boxes of Mix I and Mix II should be made each week in order to maximize the company's profits (profits = revenue − costs). What is this maximum profit?
54. Using the simplex method, rework Exercise 53.
55. A change in the production of creme-filled centers allows only 3500 creme-filled centers to be produced. Redo Exercise 54 *without using the simplex method.*
56. The production of nut centers is changed to allow a weekly maximum of 2100. Redo Exercise 54 with only this change. Do not use the simplex method.
*57. New facilities allow 3000 caramel centers per week. Making only this change, use the shadow price for caramels from Exercise 54 to estimate profit. Then redo the simplex method from scratch and check your estimate. Comment.

Exercises 58–63: A cassette tape manufacturer makes two cassette tapes, C-60 and C-90, containing sixty or ninety minutes of recording time, respectively. The cost of manufacturing a C-60 is $0.60, and the cost of manufacturing a C-90 is $0.70. These tapes are sold in three-pack assortments to distributors: three-pack A contains 2 C-60 tapes and 1 C-90, while three-pack B contains 1 C-60 and 2 C-90. Three-pack C has all C-90 tapes. The cost to distributors is $2.50, $3.00, and $3.30, respectively. The tape manufacturer can produce up to 10,000 C-60 tapes and 8000 C-90 tapes in a month.

*58. How many three-packs of types A, B, and C should be produced in a month in order to maximize the tape manufacturer's profits? What is the maximum monthly profit?

*59. Redo Exercise 58 with only the following change: at most 6600 C-90 tapes can be made in a month. Use the shadow price for C-90 tapes to estimate the effect this change will have on monthly profit. Then redo the simplex and compare the profit with the shadow price estimate. Comment.

*60. Redo Exercise 58 with the following changes: at most, 8000 C-60 tapes and at most 6600 C-90 tapes can be manufactured in a month. Use shadow prices from Exercise 58 to estimate the change in profit, and then repeat with the simplex. Comment.

61. Rework Exercise 58 with only the following change: the price for three-pack A is lowered to $2.20.

62. Rework Exercise 58 with the following changes: the prices to distributors for three-packs A, B, C are $2.50, $3.40, and $3.50, respectively.

*63. Rework Exercise 58 with only the following change: up to 9000 C-90 tapes can be produced monthly.

Exercises 64–67: A manufacturer makes three bookshelf speakers—Model 40, Model 60, and Model 70. Readying these speakers for shipment to the company's dealers is a 3-stage process. At stage 1, cabinets are assembled and finished. At stage 2, speaker drivers and crossover network are installed, and at stage 3, the completed unit is tested and packed. Each Model 40 requires 1 hour of wood-working, $\frac{1}{2}$ hour of driver/crossover installation, and $\frac{1}{2}$ hour of testing and packing. Each Model 60 requires $1\frac{1}{2}$ hours of woodworking, 1 hour of driver/crossover installation, and 1 hour of testing and packing. Each Model 70 requires 2 hours of woodworking, 2 hours of driver/crossover work, and one hour of testing and packing. The company has the following weekly amounts of labor available: 120 hours of woodworking, 60 hours of crossover/driver installation, and 60 hours of testing and packing. Profits are $20, $30, and $40, respectively, on each Model 40, 60, and 70.

64. How many of each model speaker should the company make weekly to maximize profits? What is the maximum weekly profit?

65. Suppose the half-time (20 hours a week) speaker tester and packer goes on vacation for a week, and there is no suitable substitute. If this is the only change, what should the company's strategy be for that week? How much profit will the company make by employing its optimum strategy?

66. Suppose the company has just hired an additional 40-hour-a-week person to do cabinet work. If this is the only change from the original, what is their best strategy now? What maximum profit will be made?

67. Suppose the company has added a full-time (40 hours weekly) person for crossover/driver installation. If this is the only change from the original, what is the company's best strategy now? What is the maximum profit?

5.3 MINIMIZATION PROBLEMS: THE DUAL

If we have a standard maximization problem except that we want to minimize the objective function, we can still use the simplex method after making one change. In Chapter 4, we noted that minimizing a function can be accomplished by maximizing its opposite. Consider A = {4,5,6,7}. "Four" is clearly the minimum. Now consider B = {-4, -5,-6,-7}, obtained by taking the opposite of each number in A. In set B, "-4" is the maximum. What does this tell us in the context of linear programming? To *minimize an objective function, we find the maximum for the opposite of the objective function and then change its sign.* (The minimum in set A is 4, and not -4.) This approach works when all functional constraints are in "standard maximization form," or can be so restated.

■ EXAMPLE 9

Find the minimum value of $Z = -4x_1 + 2x_2 - 3x_3$, subject to the following constraints:

$$4x_1 - x_2 - x_3 \leq 20 \qquad 2x_1 + 4x_2 + x_3 \leq 15$$

$$x_1 + 2x_2 \leq 10 \qquad x_1, x_2, x_3 \geq 0$$

SOLUTION

Observing that all functional constraints are in standard maximization form, we need only to replace the objective function Z by its opposite, maximizing $Z^* = -Z = 4x_1 - 2x_2 + 3x_3$. When we find the maximum value of Z^*, we shall change its sign to give the minimum value of Z. The initial simplex tableau is:

	x_1	x_2	x_3	s_1	s_2	s_3	Z^*	= RHS	Ratios
s_1	④	-1	-1	1	0	0	0	20	$\frac{20}{4} = \boxed{5}$
s_2	1	2	0	0	1	0	0	10	$\frac{10}{1} = 10$
s_3	2	4	1	0	0	1	0	15	$\frac{15}{2} = 7.5$
Z^*	-4	2	-3	0	0	0	1	0	

The pivot element is "4" in the s_1 row. Multiplying the s_1 row by (1/4) to get "1" in the pivot position and then performing the simplex algorithm produces the following optimal tableau:

	x_1	x_2	x_3	s_1	s_2	s_3	Z^*	= RHS
s_1	6	3	0	1	0	1	0	35
s_2	1	2	0	0	1	0	0	10
x_3	2	4	1	0	0	1	0	15
Z^*	2	14	0	0	0	3	1	45

The maximum value of Z^* is 45, so the minimum value of Z (what we want) is -45 when $x_1 = 0$, $x_2 = 0$, and $x_3 = 15$.   ∎

PRACTICE PROBLEM 7   Using the simplex method, minimize $Z = -2x_1 - 3x_2$ subject to the following constraints:

$$4x_1 + 2x_2 \leq 12 \qquad -2x_1 + 3x_2 \leq 20 \qquad x_1 \geq 0, \quad x_2 \geq 0$$

ANSWER(S)   Minimum Z is -18, when $x_1 = 0$ and $x_2 = 6$.   □

Unfortunately, many real-world minimization problems do not have constraints of the $\leq$ (less than or equal to) variety. Consider the following example.

■ **EXAMPLE 10**   A retail sales organization hires two types of employees—floor salespeople and clerks. Salespeople make $6 per hour while clerks make $5. To adequately staff the sales area, prevent shoplifting, and service the customers, management has decided that there needs to be at least four people working. Further, because salespeople have such a strong influence in this organization, it is decided that there should be at least two more salespeople than clerks. At any given time, however, there should be at least one clerk. The objective is to minimize total hourly labor costs while satisfying these constraints. Set up the problem. Is this linear program a standard maximization problem?

SOLUTION   Let $x_1 =$ number of salespeople and $x_2 =$ number of clerks. The hourly labor cost is given by $Z = 6x_1 + 5x_2$, and this is to be minimized subject to the following constraints:

$$x_1 + x_2 \geq 4 \qquad \text{at least four people working}$$

$$x_1 - x_2 \geq 2 \qquad \text{at least two more sales people than clerks}$$

$$x_2 \geq 1 \qquad \text{at least one clerk}$$

$$x_1, x_2 \geq 0$$

This is clearly not a standard maximum problem for two reasons: we are not maximizing, and the constraints are "going the wrong way." We shall call this setup a **standard minimization problem**.   ∎

STANDARD MINIMIZATION PROBLEM

> If the objective function is to be minimized, and each functional constraint is of the form "left side $\geq b$," where b is a nonnegative number, then the problem is said to be a **standard minimization problem**.

PRACTICE PROBLEM 8   Which of the following formulations are in standard minimization form or can be converted to this form?

(a) Minimize $Z = 4x_1 - 2x_2$ subject to

$$3x_1 + 2x_2 \geq 5$$

$$x_1 - x_2 \leq 4$$

$$x_1, x_2 \geq 0$$

(b) Maximize $Z = 2x_1 + 3x_2$ subject to

$$x_1 - x_2 \leq -4$$

$$2x_1 + x_2 \geq 6$$

$$x_1, x_2 \geq 0$$

(c) Minimize $Z = 5x_1 - 2x_2$ subject to

$$x_1 + x_2 \geq 3$$

$$5x_1 \leq 4$$

$$x_1, x_2 \geq 0$$

ANSWER(S)   **(a)** no;   **(b)** yes (Minimize $Z^* = -Z$);   **(c)** no   □

Standard Minimization Problems and the Dual

In our development of the simplex method, we learned how to solve only standard maximization problems. What can we do with standard minimization problems? Associated with every standard minimization problem like the one we have just stated is another linear programming problem called **the dual problem.** The original linear program for Example 10 and its dual are:

Dual Problem for Example 10

Original Program	Dual Program
Minimize $Z = 6x_1 + 5x_2$ subject to:	Maximize $Z^* = 4y_1 + 2y_2 + y_3$ subject to:
$x_1 + x_2 \geq 4$ $x_1 - x_2 \geq 2$ $x_2 \geq 1$ $x_1, x_2 \geq 0$	$y_1 + y_2 \leq 6$ $y_1 - y_2 + y_3 \leq 5$ $y_1, y_2, y_3 \geq 0$

What is the connection between the original minimization problem (called **the primal problem**) and its dual? The original problem has two decision variables (x_1, x_2) and three functional constraints, while the dual problem reverses these: there are three decision varibles (y_1, y_2, y_3) and only two functional constraints. Further, note that the constraint right-hand side values (4, 2, and 1) in the original problem become *coefficients* of the new decision variables in the objective function for the dual problem. Also, the coefficients (1, 1, and 0) of x_1 in the three constraint equations of the original problem become the coefficients for constraint 1 in the dual problem ($y_1 + y_2 \le 6$). Similarly, coefficients of x_2 in the original problem (1, −1, and 1) become coefficients in the second constraint equation for the dual. This sounds complicated! By using matrices, however, we can determine the dual problem without having to remember these rules. To see how, write the original problem inequalities, all in standard minimization form, and below these tack on the objective function, *letting Z be the right-hand side.* Pick off coefficients of x_1 and x_2 just as you did in Chapter 2 when solving systems of equations. Append the right-hand side as a third column, and label this matrix A:

$$
\begin{array}{rl}
x_1 + x_2 \ge 4 \\
x_1 - x_2 \ge 2 \\
x_2 \ge 1 \\
6x_1 + 5x_2 = Z
\end{array}
\qquad
A =
\begin{array}{c}
\begin{array}{ccc} x_1 & x_2 & \text{RHS} \end{array} \\
\left[
\begin{array}{cc|c}
1 & 1 & 4 \\
1 & -1 & 2 \\
0 & 1 & 1 \\
6 & 5 & Z
\end{array}
\right]
\end{array}
$$

Next, form the transpose of matrix A (using a superscript T notation, A^{T}), and name its variable columns with y's:

$$
A^{T} =
\begin{array}{c}
\begin{array}{cccc} y_1 & y_2 & y_3 & \text{RHS} \end{array} \\
\left[
\begin{array}{ccc|c}
1 & 1 & 0 & 6 \\
1 & -1 & 1 & 5 \\
4 & 2 & 1 & Z
\end{array}
\right]
\end{array}
$$

To state the dual problem, simply undo the process that produced matrix A, but replace $\ge$-inequalities by $\le$-inequalities, name the decision

FORMING THE DUAL FOR A STANDARD MINIMIZATION PROBLEM

When the original (primal) problem is in standard minimization form, the dual is formed as follows:

1. Write the coefficients of the constraint inequalities as rows of a matrix A, using the objective function as the last row. Use the right-hand sides of the constraint inequalities, along with Z, to form the last column of this matrix.

2. Find the matrix A^{T}. Form a standard maximization problem by using the numbers in each row, except the last, as the coefficients for a $\le$ constraint in the dual problem. Use the numbers in the last row as objective function coefficients for the dual.

variables y_1, y_2, y_3, and replace Z by Z^*. The dual problem is:

Maximize $Z^* = 4y_1 + 2y_2 + y_3$ subject to:

$$y_1 + y_2 \quad\quad \leq 6$$
$$y_1 - y_2 + y_3 \leq 5$$

We summarize the formulation of the dual problem when the primal is a standard minimization problem in the box at the bottom of page 189.

PRACTICE PROBLEM 9   Find the dual problem for the following standard minimization problem: Minimize $Z = 2x_1 + 4x_2$ subject to the following constraints:

$$2x_1 + 3x_2 \geq 20$$
$$x_1 + 4x_2 \geq 14 \quad x_1 \geq 15$$
$$x_1 \geq 0, \quad x_2 \geq 0$$

ANSWER(S)   The dual to the above formulation is given by: Maximize $Z^* = 20y_1 + 14y_2 + 15y_3$ subject to the constraints:

$$2y_1 + \quad y_2 + y_3 \leq 2$$
$$3y_1 + 4y_2 \quad\quad \leq 4$$
$$y_1 \geq 0, \quad y_2 \geq 0, \quad y_3 \geq 0$$ $\square$

Once a standard minimization problem is converted to its dual, the solution can be obtained with the simplex method. The solution to this dual problem, however, will be of no use unless it is related to the primal solution, which, after all, is what we are seeking. The connection between the dual and primal is:

CONNECTION BETWEEN THE PRIMAL AND ITS DUAL

> There is a solution to a standard minimization problem if and only if there is a solution to its dual. *When a solution exists, the maximum value of the objective function in the dual is the same as the minimum value of the objective function in the primal problem.*

Knowing the optimum value of the objective function is important, but it is of little use unless you also know the values of the decision variables that produce the optimum. How do we determine these from the dual solution? There are as many problem constraints in the dual as decision variables in the primal problem. Associated with each problem constraint is a slack variable. Hence, there are as many slack variables in the dual as decision variables in the primal. It is the slack variable entries in the final tableau of the dual—we have called these **shadow prices**—that provide solutions for decision variables in the primal problem. This is summarized below.

SOLUTION TO STANDARD MINIMIZATION PROBLEM

> To obtain values of decision variables that minimize the objective function in a standard minimization problem, first solve the dual problem. Identify slack variable entries (shadow prices) in the objective function row of the final dual tableau. These shadow price values are the decision variable solutions in the primal problem.

Using the Dual to Solve Example 10

The initial simplex tableau for the dual in Example 10 is given by

	y_1	y_2	y_3	s_1	s_2	Z^*	=	RHS	Ratios
s_1	1	1	0	1	0	0		6	$\frac{6}{1} = 6$
s_2	①	−1	1	0	1	0		5	$\frac{5}{1} = \boxed{5}$
Z^*	−4	−2	−1	0	0	1		0	

This is not optimal, so we perform the first iteration of the simplex method, pivoting about the "1" in the s_2 row and y_1 column. This has the effect of bringing y_1 into the set of basic variables, replacing s_2:

		y_1	y_2	y_3	s_1	s_2	Z^*	=	RHS
$s_1 - s_2$	s_1	0	2	−1	1	−1	0		1
	y_1	1	−1	1	0	1	0		5
$Z^* + 4s_2$	Z^*	0	−6	3	0	4	1		20

One more iteration (with the "2" in the s_1 row and y_2 column as pivot) produces the following tableau, which is optimal:

	y_1	y_2	y_3	s_1	s_2	Z^*	=	RHS
y_2	0	1	−0.5	0.5	−0.5	0		0.5
y_1	1	0	0.5	0.5	0.5	0		5.5
Z^*	0	0	0	3	1	1		23

Because this is the dual problem, the solutions for the original decision variables are given by the shadow prices: $x_1 = 3$, $x_2 = 1$. To minimize labor costs, the retail outlet should hire 3 floor salespeople and 1 clerk. Minimal hourly labor cost will be $23.

Though we did not work it as such, Example 10 is in reality an **integer programming problem,** requiring that the solutions for number of clerks and floor salespeople be positive integers. Our solutions (fortunately) were integers. Such is not always the case. Using the simplex method and then hunting for the "closest" integer solution is not always productive. (See Chapter 4, Example 12.)

We end this section with a concrete standard minimization problem and its dual, solving by both the simplex method and the geometric approach in hopes of cementing concepts.

■ EXAMPLE 11

Find the minimum of $Z = 8x_1 + 3x_2$ subject to

$$x_1 + 2x_2 \geq 6 \qquad x_1, \quad x_2 \geq 0$$
$$4x_1 + \quad x_2 \geq 10$$

SOLUTION

We first form the dual. Writing the original problem in matrix form and transposing leads to:

$$A = \begin{bmatrix} 1 & 2 & 6 \\ 4 & 1 & 10 \\ 8 & 3 & Z \end{bmatrix} \qquad A^T = \begin{bmatrix} 1 & 4 & 8 \\ 2 & 1 & 3 \\ 6 & 10 & Z \end{bmatrix}$$

Hence the dual problem is to maximize $Z^* = 6y_1 + 10y_2$ subject to

$$y_1 + 4y_2 \leq 8 \qquad y_1, \quad y_2 \geq 0$$
$$2y_1 + \quad y_2 \leq 3$$

In Figure 5.4 we show feasible regions for the original standard minimization problem and its dual, a standard maximization problem.

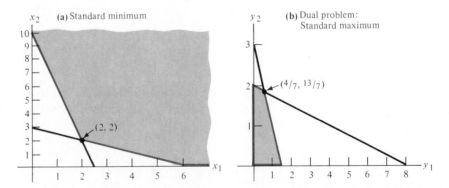

Figure 5.4
Feasible regions for Example 11

We now evaluate the original objective function (standard minimization problem) and its dual objective function (standard maximization problem) at corner points of the feasible regions.

Primal Problem: Standard Minimum Corner Point $Z = 8x_1 + 3x_2$		Dual Problem: Standard Maximum Corner Point $Z^* = 6y_1 + 10y_2$	
$(0,10)$	30	$(0,2)$	20
$(2,2)$	22	$(4/7, 13/7)$	22
$(6,0)$	48	$(3/2,0)$	9
		$(0,0)$	0

The minimum of 22 in the original problem agrees with the maximum of 22 in the dual problem. Now observe how the simplex works on the dual problem. The initial simplex tableau for the dual is given by:

	y_1	y_2	s_1	s_2	Z^*	=	RHS	Ratios
s_1	1	④	1	0	0		8	$\frac{8}{4} = \boxed{2}$
s_2	2	1	0	1	0		3	$\frac{3}{1} = 3$
Z^*	-6	-10	0	0	1		0	

The "-10" identifies y_2 as pivot column, and the smallest right-hand side ratio is in the s_1 row, making "4" the pivot element. A simplex iteration, in which y_2 enters and s_1 exits, gives:

		y_1	y_2	s_1	s_2	Z^*	=	RHS	Ratios
	y_2	$\frac{1}{4}$	1	$\frac{1}{4}$	0	0		2	$2 \div \left(\frac{1}{4}\right) = 8$
$s_2 - s_1$	s_2	⑦/④	0	$-\frac{1}{4}$	1	0		1	$1 \div \left(\frac{7}{4}\right) = \boxed{\frac{4}{7}}$
$Z^* + 10s_1$	Z^*	$-\frac{14}{4}$	0	$\frac{10}{4}$	0	1		20	$-\frac{14}{4}$ indicates no optimum yet

With the negative in the Z^* row, we need to continue the simplex method. The new pivot element is $\frac{7}{4}$. Another simplex iteration, with y_1 entering, replacing s_2, yields the tableau:

		y_1	y_2	s_1	s_2	Z^*	=	RHS	
$y_2 - \left(\frac{1}{4}\right)s_2$	y_2	0	1	$\frac{2}{7}$	$-\frac{1}{7}$	0		$\frac{13}{7}$	
	y_1	1	0	$-\frac{1}{7}$	$\frac{4}{7}$	0		$\frac{4}{7}$	
$Z^* + \left(\frac{14}{4}\right)s_2$	Z^*	0	0	2	2	1		22	We have an optimum

Looking under the slack variables in the objective function row, we find that both dual variables (shadow prices) have value 2, which indicates that the original minimum problem has solution $x_1 = 2$ and $x_2 = 2$. The minimum value of the objective function $8x_1 + 3x_2$ is 22, which agrees with the maximum value of the dual objective function $6y_1 + 10y_2$. Note that the values of y_1 and y_2 are $\frac{4}{7}$ and $\frac{13}{7}$, respectively, agreeing with what we determined geometrically in Figure 5.4.   ■

EXERCISES 5.3

PRACTICING THE MOVES AND MANEUVERS

Exercises 68–71: Find, if possible, the minimum of the given objective function by maximizing its opposite.

68. $Z = -6x_1 + 4x_2$ subject to:

$$2x_1 + 3x_2 \le 12$$
$$5x_1 + 2x_2 \le 16$$
$$x_1, x_2 \ge 0$$

69. $Z = -4x_1 - 6x_2$ subject to:

$$x_1 - 4x_2 \le 16$$
$$2x_1 + x_2 \le 40$$
$$x_1, x_2 \ge 0$$

70. $Z = -4x_1 - 2x_2$ subject to:

$$3x_1 + 2x_2 \le 10$$
$$5x_1 + x_2 \le 18$$
$$x_1, x_2 \ge 0$$

71. $Z = 2x_1 - 4x_2 - 2x_3$ subject to:

$$x_1 + 4x_2 - 2x_3 \le 20$$
$$3x_1 + 2x_2 + x_3 \le 24$$
$$x_1, x_2, x_3 \ge 0$$

Exercises 72–77: Find the dual problem for the given primal problem.

72. Minimize $4x_1 + 6x_2$ subject to:

$$4x_1 + 2x_2 \ge 16$$
$$5x_1 + 3x_2 \ge 24$$
$$x_1, x_2 \ge 0$$

73. Minimize $5x_1 + 3x_2$ subject to:

$$5x_1 + 7x_2 \ge 40$$
$$3x_1 - 5x_2 \ge 20$$
$$x_1, x_2 \ge 0$$

74. Minimize $3x_1 + 6x_2$ subject to:

$$2x_1 + 5x_2 \ge 20$$
$$x_1 + 3x_2 \ge 14$$
$$x_1, x_2 \ge 0$$

75. Minimize $7x_1 + 5x_2$ subject to:

$$x_2 \ge 10$$
$$6x_1 + 4x_2 \ge 30$$
$$x_1, x_2 \ge 0$$

76. Minimize $x_1 + 2x_2$ subject to:

$$5x_1 + 4x_2 \ge 16$$
$$3x_1 + 6x_2 \ge 12$$
$$x_1, x_2 \ge 0$$

77. Minimize $5x_1 + 2x_2$ subject to:

$$x_1 \ge 10$$
$$2x_1 - 5x_2 \ge 12$$
$$x_1, x_2 \ge 0$$

APPLYING THE CONCEPTS

Exercises 78–81:   A retailer in a small market has a limited advertising budget. The costs for radio, TV, and newspaper ads are $9, $25, and $8, respectively. She estimates that each radio, TV, and print ad will bring 50, 200, and 30 people into the store each month. (*Note:* In these Exercises, the optimal numbers may not be integers. Round to the nearest integer without violating constraints.)

78. How should the retailer allocate ads if she wants to minimize monthly ad costs and **(1)** if she needs at least 117 ad appearances of one form or another each month and **(2)** if the total number of radio and TV ads should be at least as large as the number of newspaper ads? What will the minimum cost be?

79. This month only the price of newspaper ads is $7. What is the appropriate mix now, and what will it cost if everything else stays the same?

80. Determine the optimal mix and the minimum ad costs if the conditions of Exercise 78 hold except that the retailer wants at least 140 ads monthly.

81. Do Exercise 78 with the additional restriction that the total number of radio and TV ads should be at most twice as large as the number of newspaper ads.

Exercises 82–84:   Consider a computer manufacturer that buys hard drives for installation in its microcomputers. The manufacturer buys either 40 or 80MB drives at costs of $200 and $240, respectively. (Pick nearest integer solutions that satisfy all constraints.)

82. How many drives of each type should the manufacturer purchase monthly if the only restriction is that total drive capacity should exceed 10,000MB? What will the minimum monthly hard drive expense be?

83. In Exercise 82, suppose the manufacturer wants to buy at least as many 40MB drives as 80MB drives. How many drives of each type should be bought to minimize hard drive costs? What is the minimum hard drive cost?

84. In Exercise 82, suppose the manufacturer wants to buy at least twice as many 40MB drives as 80MB drives. How many drives of each type should he buy to minimize hard drive costs? What is the minimum hard drive cost?

5.4 SOLVING LINEAR PROGRAMMING PROBLEMS BY COMPUTER

In this section we illustrate the popular and powerful Student Edition[3] of LINDO, developed by Professor Linus Schrage from the University of Chicago Graduate School of Business. LINDO is an acronym for **L**inear, **IN**teractive, and **D**iscrete **O**ptimizer. We shall use LINDO only for linear programming, although it will do much more. Rather than developing cumbersome special methods for handling nonstandard problems (for example, those that are a mixture of standard maximum and standard minimum problems), we recommend you input them into LINDO and solve them by computer. (*Note:* Even if you do not have LINDO available, the examples we work and discuss will be instructive. You can ignore the brief discussion of the necessary LINDO commands and go right to

[3] The Student Edition of LINDO is published by The Scientific Press, Redwood City, CA, and retails for $27.50 in either the Apple Macintosh or MS-DOS version.

interpretation of the solutions.) We begin with an example taken from Exercises 5.2.

■ EXAMPLE 12

A candy company specializes in chocolate-covered candies with caramel, nut, or creme-filled centers. These candies are marketed in two mixes: Mix I, with 4 of each kind, sells for $3.50. Mix II, which contains 8 caramel, 4 nut, and 12 creme-filled, sells for $6.00. Manufacturing caramel, nut, and creme-filled centers costs the manufacturer $0.15, $0.20, and $0.10, respectively. Production facilities allow 2200 caramel centers, 2000 nut centers, or 4000 creme-filled centers to be produced weekly. Use LINDO to find the mix that maximizes profit.

SOLUTION

We first state the problem. The simple table arrangement below summarizes required numbers of each candy in the two mixes:

	Mix I	Mix II
Caramel	4	8
Nut	4	4
Creme	4	12

The cost of manufacturing one box of Mix I is $1.80; a box of Mix II costs $8 \cdot (0.15) + 4(0.20) + 12(0.10) = \$3.20$. The two mixes sell to merchants for $3.50 and $6.00, so respective profits per box are $1.70 and $2.80. Let x_1 and x_2 represent the number of boxes of each mix to be made. The objective function is $Z = 1.70x_1 + 2.80x_2$. We want to maximize Z subject to tacitly assumed nonnegativity constraints and the following specific problem constraints:

$4x_1 + 8x_2 \leq 2200$ at most 2200 carmel centers made daily

$4x_1 + 4x_2 \leq 2000$ at most 2000 nut centers made daily

$4x_1 + 12x_2 \leq 4000$ at most 4000 creme centers made daily

Here is the problem in LINDO: (Input you supply to LINDO is shown in boldfaced type and LINDO output is shown in a box. Pushing the "Return" or "Enter" is symbolized by <CR>.)

Max 1.70x1 + 2.80x2 <CR>

ST <CR>   abbreviation for "subject to"

4x1 + 8x2 < 2200   ≤ is entered simply as <; subscripts are
4x1 + 4x2 < 2000   not necessary on the x variables.
4x1 + 12x2 < 4000   Nonnegativity constraints are built-in

If you type **Look all,** LINDO will show you the model you've entered. You get the solution by typing **GO.** LINDO responds:

```
LP OPTIMUM FOUND AT STEP 2
    OBJECTIVE FUNCTION VALUE
    1) 905.00000
    VARIABLE          VALUE            REDUCED COST
       X1           450.000000           .000000
       X2            50.000000           .000000
    ROW            SLACK OR SURPLUS      DUAL PRICES
    2)                 .000000           .275000
    3)                 .000000           .150000
    4)             1600.000000           .000000
    :DO RANGE(SENSITIVITY) ANALYSIS?
    ? N <CR>
```

LINDO calls the objective function row (1); the first problem constraint is row (2), etc. Study the solution. To maximize profit, we should make 450 boxes of Mix I and 50 of Mix II. If we substitute $x_1 = 450$ and $x_2 = 50$ into each of the constraints, we will find there is no slack except in constraint equation 4—just as LINDO indicates. Similarly, the value of the objective function is $905, which is $450 \cdot \$1.70 + 50 \cdot \$2.80$. The important information is given in the "DUAL PRICES" column. Recall that dual prices are the slack variable entries in the objective function row of the final tableau. We have called these shadow prices in a standard maximization problem. The 0.275000 in the DUAL PRICE column of ROW (2) indicates each additional caramel center beyond the fully utilized daily capacity of 2200 would increase profit by $0.275. Also, decreases in available daily capacity would reduce profits by 27.5 cents per caramel center. The 0.150000 indicates that each additional nut center beyond 2000 would result in $0.15 additional profit; having fewer would decrease the profit by the same amount. As yet there is no indication how far we can "push" these increases or decreases without fundamentally changing the solution. The dual price of 0.000000 in row (4) is testimony to the fact that having more of an unused resource (creme centers) does no good. We shall check these interpretations by capitalizing on the *interactive* nature of LINDO to investigate sensitivity analysis.

Sensitivity Analysis   Let us change the right-hand side of constraint 2 (caramel centers) from 2200 to 2400. If our interpretation is correct, we should expect the optimum objective function value to increase to $905 + 200 \cdot (0.275) = 960$. To change any element in a constraint, we issue the command **alter #,** and replace the **#** by the specific row number LINDO has attached. LINDO then prompts us for the variable to be altered. The variable is the right-hand side, written RHS. LINDO then asks for the new value. Here we go:

```
:alter 2 <CR>
VAR:
rhs <CR>
NEW COEFFICIENT:
? 2400 <CR>
:go <CR>
LP OPTIMUM FOUND AT STEP 2
      OBJECTIVE FUNCTION VALUE
    1) 960.00000
VARIABLE          VALUE              REDUCED COST
    X1          400.000000             .000000
    X2          100.000000             .000000
ROW            SLACK OR SURPLUS      DUAL PRICES
2)                .000000             .275000
3)                .000000             .150000
4)             1200.000000            .000000
```

This time we answer "Y" to the request for "Range Analysis," but first we study the solution. Note that our dual (shadow price) interpretation for caramels was correct: increasing daily available supply by 200 resulted in an objective function increase of $200(0.275) = \$55$ from \$905 to \$960. This increase changed the optimal solution to 400 boxes of Mix I (down from 450) and 100 boxes of Mix II (up from 50). We have only 1200 (down from 1600) unused creme centers. The DUAL PRICE (shadow price) column suggests we could increase daily capacity of caramel centers still more and achieve the same 27.5 cents-per-caramel benefit. Nut centers could also be increased at a gain of 15 cents each, but increasing creme centers would still do us no good. How far could we increase caramel and nut centers and continue to improve our profits by 27.5 and 15 cents each? The answer to this question is found by using the "RANGE ANALYSIS" feature of LINDO:

RANGES IN WHICH THE BASIS IS UNCHANGED:

	OBJ COEFFICIENT RANGES		
VARIABLE	CURRENT COEFF	ALLOWABLE INCREASE	ALLOWABLE DECREASE
X1	1.700000	1.100000	.300000
X2	2.800000	.600000	1.100000

		RIGHTHAND SIDE RANGES		
ROW	CURRENT RHS	ALLOWABLE INCREASE	ALLOWABLE DECREASE
2	2400.00000	600.00000	400.00000
3	2000.00000	400.00000	800.00000
4	4000.00000	INFINITY	1200.00000

In the heading "RANGES IN WHICH THE BASIS IS UNCHANGED," "basis" refers to the fact that both x_1 and x_2 are now nonzero—the optimal solution requires production of both mixes. A change in the basis would mean that only one mix should be made. Let's discuss the "RIGHTHAND SIDE RANGES" first. The 600 in row 2 (caramel centers) indicates that we could move the right-hand side from 2400 to 3000 without changing the basis (solution that has both x_1 and x_2 included). Similarly, we could decrease the daily available supply from 2400 to 2000 without changing the basis. Checking row 3 (nut centers) we find that the daily available supply of 2000 could be increased to 2400 or decreased to 1200 without changing the solution that requires both mixes to be made. In row 3 (those none-too-popular creme centers!) we find that any increase would leave the basis unchanged. Further increases in creme centers would just result in more slack (and less warehouse space!). We could decrease the amount of creme centers from 4000 to 2800 without changing the basis.

"OBJECTIVE COEFFICIENT RANGES" tell us that if everything else were unchanged, the $1.70 per box profit made on Mix I could be increased to $2.80 or lowered to $1.40 without changing the x_1, x_2 solution (the objective function value would change however). If we left profit per box on Mix I at $1.70, profits per box for Mix II could be anything from $1.70 to $3.40 without changing the solution, except for the objective function value. ∎

■ EXAMPLE 13

In Example 4 a computer manufacturer made two models of memory boards, Models 1 and 2. The optimal solution had the manufacturer making 60 boards of Model 1 and 90 Model 2. The final tableau was

	x_1	x_2	s_1	s_2	$Z =$	RHS
x_2	0	1	$\frac{4}{15}$	$-\frac{1}{270}$	0	90
x_1	1	0	$-\frac{1}{15}$	$\frac{4}{270}$	0	60
Z	0	0	$66\frac{2}{3}$	$\frac{50}{27}$	1	39,000

In Example 8, we interpreted the shadow prices of \$66.67 for S-chips and $\frac{50}{27} \approx \$1.85$ for DRAM chips. One more of each chip would increase profits by the indicated shadow price amounts. Just how far can we "push" these amounts? Would it be worth our while to have 200 more of each chip for example? LINDO can provide us with the answers. The original problem was formulated as follows:

maximize $Z = 200x_1 + 300x_2$ subject to

$$x_1 + 4x_2 \leq 420$$

$$72x_1 + 18x_2 \leq 5940$$

Entering this into LINDO and asking for "Sensitivity Analysis" gives the following:

```
           OBJECTIVE FUNCTION VALUE
    1)    39000.0000
VARIABLE        VALUE           REDUCED COST
    X1        60.000000            .000000
    X2        90.000000            .000000
  ROW     SLACK OR SURPLUS        DUAL PRICES
    2)        .000000             66.666660
    3)        .000000              1.851852
NO. ITERATIONS=          2
RANGES IN WHICH THE BASIS IS UNCHANGED:
                    OBJ COEFFICIENT RANGES
VARIABLE       CURRENT       ALLOWABLE       ALLOWABLE
                COEF         INCREASE        DECREASE
    X1      200.000000     1000.000000     125.000000
    X2      300.000000      500.000000     250.000000
                    RIGHTHAND SIDE RANGES
  ROW        CURRENT        ALLOWABLE       ALLOWABLE
              RHS           INCREASE        DECREASE
    2       420.000000      899.999900     337.500000
    3      5940.000000    24300.000000    4050.000000
```

Under "RIGHTHAND SIDE RANGES" we note that the manufacturer could utilize 899 more S-chips, and 24,300 DRAM chips without changing the basis—that is, the solution that requires making both Models 1 and 2 boards, and while still increasing profit by \$66.67 for each additional S-chip and \$1.85 for each additional DRAM. If, however, you increase the number of S-chips from 420 to 420 + 900 = 1320 (going beyond the maximum allowable increase that LINDO shows us), you will find that the solution basis changes. We show this.

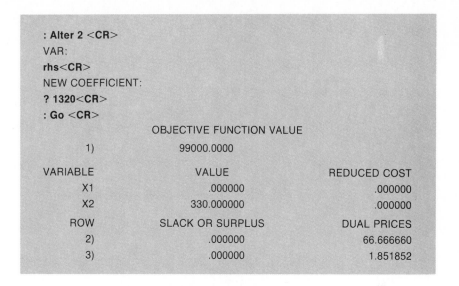

```
: Alter 2 <CR>
VAR:
rhs<CR>
NEW COEFFICIENT:
? 1320<CR>
: Go <CR>
```

	OBJECTIVE FUNCTION VALUE	
1)	99000.0000	
VARIABLE	VALUE	REDUCED COST
X1	.000000	.000000
X2	330.000000	.000000
ROW	SLACK OR SURPLUS	DUAL PRICES
2)	.000000	66.666660
3)	.000000	1.851852

Note that the optimum solution is now changed to where it is best to manufacture *all* Model 2 boards and *none* of Model 1.

In the next example we illustrate how LINDO handles a problem with mixed constraints—some inequalities of the standard ≤ variety and some ≥. ■

■ EXAMPLE 14

A manufacturer of laser printers makes two models—a Model I, which has only 0.5MB (Megabytes) of RAM (random access memory), and thus prints graphics rather slowly, and a Model II, which prints text twice as fast as a Model I and also has 1.5MB of RAM for faster graphics printing. The available labor force consists of 37 employees who work standard 40 hour weeks. The company budget officer allows purchases of up to $146,000 weekly in materials needed to manufacture these two printer models. In addition, to obtain good prices on RAM chips, the company has agreed to purchase a minimum of 425MB of RAM chips each week from their supplier. After manufacture, these printers are sold to distributors at an average profit of $500 for each Model I and $700 for each Model II. A summary of these material and purchase requirements is given in Table 5.8.

Table 5.8

	Model I	Model II	Resources
Labor	4 hours	5 hours	≤1480 hours/wk
Materials	$300	$500	≤$146,000/wk
RAM	0.5MB	1.5MB	≥425MB/wk
Profit	$500	$700	

How many printers of each model should the company manufacture each week in order to maximize profits without exceeding available labor and materials but still meeting RAM-purchase needs?

SOLUTION   **Labor.**   Let $X1$ and $X2$ represent the number of Models I and II printers, respectively, to be made each week. To make $X1$ printers of Model I and $X2$ of Model II requires $4X1 + 5X2$ hours of labor. Thus,

$$4X1 + 5X2 \leq 1480$$

Materials.   Making $X1$ printers of Model I and $X2$ of Model 2 requires $300X1 + 500X2$ dollars in material. Thus,

$$300X1 + 500X2 \leq 146{,}000$$

RAM.   Making $X1$ printers of Model I and $X2$ of Model 2 requires $0.5X1 + 1.5X2$ MB of RAM, and minimum purchase requirements dictate that

$$0.5X1 + 1.5X2 \geq 425$$

Profit.   The profit from making $X1$ of Model I and $X2$ of Model II is $Z = 500X1 + 700X2$. Putting these altogether, we arrive at the following formulation for the laser printer company:

Maximize $Z = 500X1 + 700X2$ subject to:

$$4X1 + \quad 5X2 \leq 1480$$
$$300X1 + 500X2 \leq 146{,}000$$
$$0.5X1 + 1.5X2 \geq 425$$
$$X_1 \geq 0, \quad X_2 \geq 0$$

Entering these constraints into LINDO, typing **Go,** and requesting RANGE ANALYSIS produces the following:

	OBJECTIVE FUNCTION VALUE	
1)	206000.000	
VARIABLE	VALUE	REDUCED COST
X1	20.000000	.000000
X2	280.000000	.000000
ROW	SLACK OR SURPLUS	DUAL PRICES
2)	.000000	80.000000
3)	.000000	.600000
4)	5.000000	.000000
NO. ITERATIONS=	3	

RANGES IN WHICH THE BASIS IS UNCHANGED:

OBJ COEFFICIENT RANGES

VARIABLE	CURRENT COEF	ALLOWABLE INCREASE	ALLOWABLE DECREASE
X1	500.000000	60.000000	80.000000
X2	700.000000	133.333300	75.000000

RIGHTHAND SIDE RANGES

ROW	CURRENT RHS	ALLOWABLE INCREASE	ALLOWABLE DECREASE
2	1480.000000	12.500000	20.000000
3	146000.000000	2000.000000	714.285700
4	425.000000	5.000000	INFINITY

The optimum solution has the printer company manufacturing 20 Model I printers and 280 Model II printers weekly for a total profit of $206,000. The only slack is in the RAM chip constraint, where 20 Model I and 280 Model II printers utilize 430MB of RAM—five more than our purchase minimums require. The DUAL PRICES (shadow prices) column indicates that each hour of additional labor would increase profits by $80, while each $1 increase in materials would increase profits by $0.60. There is no guarantee that these increases will hold if we increase labor and materials by more than a small amount, however. Checking the RANGE (SENSITIVITY) ANALYSIS reveals that we gain these shadow price benefits, without changing our solution basis, if we increase labor availability by no more than 12.5 hours, and purchase amounts by no more than $2000. To see the effects of such a change, we shall change the right-hand side of the labor constraint to 1490 hours (an increase of 10 hours—less than the 12.5 allowable) and also increase the weekly purchase budget by $2000 (the maximum allowable). We then resolve the problem, expecting that the current profit of $206,000 will increase by $10 \cdot (\$80) + 2000(\$0.60) = \$2000$. The LINDO commands and the resulting output are:

```
: Alter 2 <CR>
VAR:
rhs <CR>
NEW COEFFICIENT:
? 1490 <CR>
: Alter 3 <CR>
VAR:
rhs <CR>
NEW COEFFICIENT:
? 148000 <CR>
: go <CR>
```

OBJECTIVE FUNCTION VALUE

1)	208000.000	

VARIABLE	VALUE	REDUCED COST
X1	10.000000	.000000
X2	290.000000	.000000

ROW	SLACK OR SURPLUS	DUAL PRICES
2)	.000000	80.000000
3)	.000000	.600000
4)	15.000000	.000000

NO. ITERATIONS= 3

RANGES IN WHICH THE BASIS IS UNCHANGED:

OBJ COEFFICIENT RANGES

VARIABLE	CURRENT COEF	ALLOWABLE INCREASE	ALLOWABLE DECREASE
X1	500.000000	60.000000	80.000000
X2	700.000000	133.333300	75.000000

RIGHTHAND SIDE RANGES

ROW	CURRENT RHS	ALLOWABLE INCREASE	ALLOWABLE DECREASE
2	1490.000000	37.500000	10.000000
3	148000.000000	1000.000000	2142.857000
4	425.000000	15.000000	INFINITY

As anticipated, the profit has risen to $208,000. Observe that the optimum solution still has both models being manufactured, but the mix has changed from 20 Model I and 280 Model II printers to only 10 Model I and 290 Model II printers. Having made simultaneous changes in the right-hand sides of both the labor and materials constraints, the SENSITIVITY ANALYSIS shows that further increases are now possible. The slack in the RAM chip constraint has gone up to 15, indicating we are using 15 more MB than the required minimum purchase of 425MB. ∎

Some Additional Features of LINDO

In our examples with LINDO, we have used the GO command, which produces the solution directly. Should you wish to see how the solution progresses from the origin to successive corner points of the feasible region, you can issue the command PIVOT and then TABLEAU. This pair of commands steps you through the solution, tableau by tableau. You should note, however, that LINDO prefers to put the objective function row on the top of the array rather than the bottom, where we have placed it. At the final tableau, you will automatically get the same output as with the GO command.

There are numerous other features of LINDO, including easy solution to problems with mixed constraints and special integer programming capabilities. The ability to easily alter constraints, investigate shadow prices, and handle all kinds of linear programming problems are features that make LINDO highly recommended!

A Brief Summary of Important Ideas

When there are more than two decision variables or when there is a large number of constraints, the geometric method of linear programming is of little use. In this chapter we have developed the **simplex method,** an algorithm for solving **standard maximum problems** where the objective function is to be maximized, and all functional constraints are of the $\leq$ variety.

After finishing the simplex algorithm, special care should be paid to the **shadow price** entries, which are found in the slack-variable columns of the objective function row in the optimal tableau. These entries indicate the change in the objective function that would accompany a one-unit increase in the corresponding resource—provided there is no slack in that resource. Shadow prices help decision makers to decide whether it is worthwhile to obtain more of a fully utilized resource.

The simplex method also works for **standard minimization problems** where the objective function is to be minimized and all functional constraints are of the form $\geq$. Associated with every standard minimization problem (called the "primal" problem) is a **dual problem,** which is a standard maximization problem. The dual problem has a solution if and only if the primal problem does, and fortunately these solutions are related: the maximum value of the objective function in the dual problem is the same as the minimum value of the objective function in the primal problem. Thus, to solve a standard minimization problem, we simply form its dual (a standard maximization problem) and then solve the dual problem with the simplex method. The values of the decision variables that provide the required minimum solution to the primal problem are located in the slack variable positions of the objective function row in the dual solution.

REVIEW EXERCISES

PRACTICING THE MOVES AND MANEUVERS

85. Maximize $Z = 2x_1 + x_2$ subject to the following constraints:

$$4x_1 - 2x_2 \le 4 \qquad x_1 + 2x_2 \le 8 \qquad x_1, x_2 \ge 0$$

86. Maximize $Z = x_1 + x_2 + x_3$ subject to the following constraints:

$$2x_1 + 4x_2 + 2x_3 \le 24 \qquad 4x_1 + 2x_2 + 4x_3 \le 24 \qquad x_1, x_2, x_3 \ge 0$$

87. Maximize $Z = 3x_1 + 4x_2$ subject to the following constraints:

$$2x_1 + x_2 \le 12 \qquad x_1 + 2x_2 \le 18 \qquad x_1, x_2 \ge 0$$

88. Minimize $Z = 4x_1 + 2x_2$ subject to the following constraints:

$$x_1 - 2x_2 \ge 1 \qquad 2x_1 + 4x_2 \ge 2 \qquad x_1 \ge 0, x_2 \ge 0$$

89. Minimize $Z = -2x_1 - 3x_2$ subject to the following constraints:

$$2x_1 + 3x_2 \le 8 \qquad x_1 + 2x_2 \le 5 \qquad x_1 \ge 0, x_2 \ge 0$$

APPLYING THE CONCEPTS

Exercises 90–92: A tape manufacturer produces standard and high-grade videotape at three different plants. In the plant at Bucolic Bend, hourly production is 200 standard and 100 high-grade videotapes. In the plant at Femur Falls, hourly production is 400 standard and 300 high-grade videotapes. At Clavicle Center, hourly production is 500 standard tapes and 250 high-grade tapes. Hourly operating expenses are $400, $800, and $900, respectively, at the plants in Bucolic Bend, Femur Falls, and Clavicle Center. The tape manufacturer needs production of at least 5000 standard videotapes per day and at least 3000 high-grade tapes per day.

90. How many hours per day should each plant operate to produce necessary minimums and to minimize production costs? What is the minimum cost? Which plant might the manufacturer consider closing?
91. Suppose the Clavicle Center high-grade tape production drops to only 200 tapes per hour, but standard tape production is increased to 600. Redo Exercise 90.
92. Plant efficiency at Bucolic Bend has been improved: the hourly operating expense has dropped to $350. With this the only change from Exercise 90, determine the hours per day that each plant should operate in order to minimize production costs. What is the minimum production cost? Do you foresee any problems with implementing the optimal solution?

Exercises 93 and 94: A manufacturer of frozen yogurt bars makes two types of yogurt bars: low-calorie (LowCal) and a creamy, rich version (YumYum). To make these two models, ingredients A, B, and C are blended in varying proportions. Each LowCal bar contains 0.2 ounce of A, 0.3 ounce of B, and 0.15 ounce of C. Each YumYum bar contains

0.1 ounce of A, 0.4 ounce of B, and 0.3 ounce of C. The profits made on each LowCal and YumYum bar sold are 3 cents and 4 cents, respectively. Available to the manufacturer on a daily basis are the following quantities: 100 pounds of A, 80 pounds of B, and 120 pounds of C. (Write 3 cents as "3" and not ".03.")

93. How many bars of each should the manufacturer make to maximize profit?
94. Work Exercise 93 if the profit on each LowCal bar is 3.2 cents.

Exercises 95–97: Mike Williams has decided to invest $50,000 in CD's, money market mutual funds, or treasury bills. Current yields are, respectively, 9%, 11%, and 8.8%. For security, Mike wishes to put no more in money market funds than in CD's, and further wishes to limit the amount put in CD's to at most half that of the treasury bills.

*95. How much should Mike invest in each to maximize his investment income?
*96. How much should Mike invest to maximize his investment income if he changes his original stance and can invest up to the same amount in CD's as in treasury bills?
97. How much should Mike invest to maximize investment income if the only specific restriction on his investments is that the amount in money market mutual funds should be at least as large as the amount in treasury bills?
98. Exercises 78–83 were concerned with a retailer having a limited advertising budget. The costs for radio, TV, and newspaper ads are $9, $25, and $8, respectively. She estimates that each radio, TV, and print ad will bring 50, 200, and 30 people into the store each month. Furthermore, she needs (1) at most 100 ad appearances of one form or another each month and (2) the total number of radio and TV ads should be no more than the number of newspaper ads.
    (a) How should she allocate funds to the various media if she wants to maximize the number of people who enter the store each month due to advertising?
    (b) What is the maximum number of people who enter the store due to advertising each month?

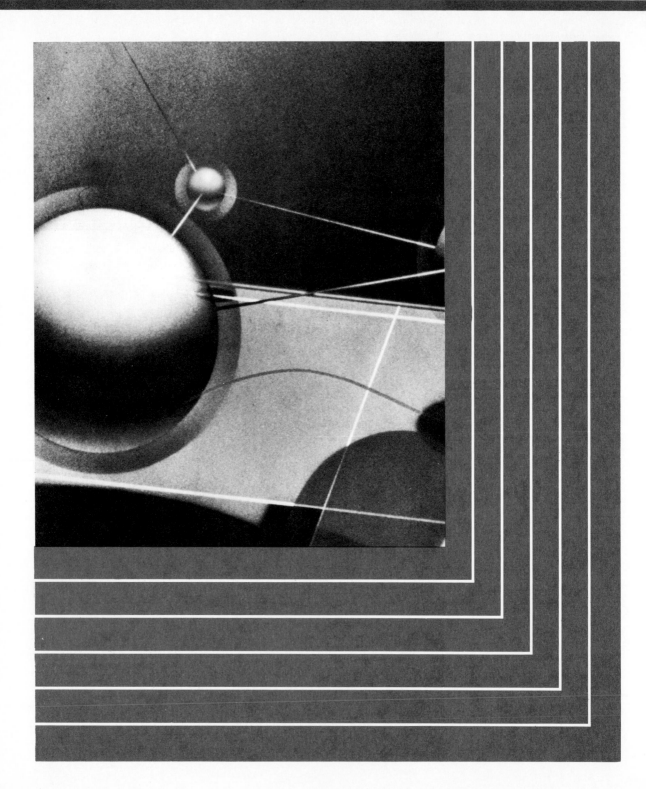

6 *Introductory Counting and Probability*

INTRODUCTION

How many arrangements of four competing airline ticket counters in four locations in the new terminal building are possible? You need a list of the possible three-person committees from your class of 28 students. How long will the list be? You are dealt three aces, a five, and a nine; if you lay aside the five and nine and draw two more cards, how likely are you to get the fourth ace (an outcome to be hoped for in a certain card game!)?

You can easily answer questions like these using elementary probability and combinatorics (streamlined counting procedures). The mathematics of counting began long ago. Examples appear in the Old Testament and in children's verses ("As I was going to St. Ives, I met a man with seven wives . . ."). Modern applications abound. Biologists use combinatorial counting methods to determine possible gene arrangements on a chromosome. Engineers use combinatorics for routing long-distance telephone calls, and probability for scheduling operators to handle traffic.

We now introduce you to some of these elementary but powerful tools of counting and probability. Much information is intentionally built into examples and problems. You thus encounter new ideas when you are in an actively thinking, rather than passively reading, mode. When questions arise during your study, make a note in the margin area; and, when you clear up that question, note your answer nearby. The result will be a "personalized" text useful for review and reference much later.

6.1 SORTING A POPULATION

Information about "populations" can be displayed in various ways. We will, in the context of several examples, explore two ways: display in table form, or display using a Venn diagram.

209

■ EXAMPLE 1

Twenty-eight people (19 Democrats, the rest Republicans) occupy a meeting room. Show this assortment in table and Venn diagram form.

SOLUTION   See Figure 6.1.

Classification by Political Party

Table Form

Rep.	Dem.	Total
9	19	28

19 and 28 were given; 9 was derived.

Figure 6.1
Classifying in table and Venn diagram

Venn Diagram Form

28 people, by party

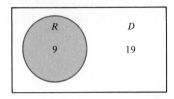

Several ideas in Example 1 are worth noting: further information can sometimes be derived from given information; the total number of items (people, in this case) is easily displayed within the table, but must explicitly be stated outside the Venn diagram. A circle in the diagram for "Democrats" was not necessary, since everyone outside the "Republican" circle is a Democrat.

■ EXAMPLE 2

Again: 28 people in a room, this time including 19 Democrats, 6 Republicans, and the rest "Independents." Classify this population by table and Venn diagram methods.

SOLUTION   See Figure 6.2.

Classification by Political Party

Rep.	Dem.	Ind.	Total
6	19	3	28

Figure 6.2
Table and Venn diagram classification by party

28 People Classified by Political Party

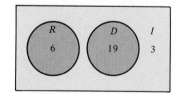

The region outside both circles is nonempty; this is the region corresponding to the third possible party affiliation. Also, the two circles do not overlap; this displays graphically that no one belongs to both the Republican and Democratic parties.   ■

In Examples 1 and 2 we sorted a population according to one criterion: political party affiliation. Similar techniques may be used to classify a population according to two or more criteria.

■ EXAMPLE 3

The 28 voters in Example 2 include 13 women. All 28 voted "yes" or "no" on Washington state becoming a nuclear waste repository. Nine women voted "no," and 7 men voted "yes." Classify all 28 voters according to their gender and vote.

SOLUTION

Finish the incomplete table and diagram; compare with classmate.

	Gender Male	Female	Totals
Yes	7		
No		9	
Totals		13	28

Vote (label at left of Yes/No rows)

28 Voters, Classified by Gender and Vote

Note the correspondences between table and diagram entries. Note that, in the diagram, separate circles were not needed for Male and Female, nor for Yes and No. Why not? ■

Sets, Elements, Subsets

Words like *class*, *category*, *group*, *herd*, *bunch*, and *gathering* denote collections of objects. All convey one simple idea: that of a **set**. The objects in (members of) a set are called its **elements**. We could refer to the set of voters in Example 2, the set of Democrats among them, etc. In general, we will use the word *set* rather than one of its more colorful synonyms.

SETS AND ELEMENTS

A group or collection of objects, clearly described so that any particular object is clearly in or not in the collection, is called a **set**. Each object in a set is called an **element** of that set.

It is customary to use capital letters such as A, B, and T to name sets, and small letters like x, y, and c to name elements. Finally, the symbol $\in$ means "is an element of," and $\notin$ means "is not an element of." Thus,

$c \in A$ means c is an element of set A

and

$c \notin A$ means c is not an element of set A

Sometimes one set is entirely included within another. For example, the set of male Republicans in Example 3 is included in the set of Republicans. Whenever any set A is entirely included within any other set B, we say that A is a **subset** of B.

> If A and B are sets, A is a subset of B, written "$A \subset B$," if A is entirely included within B, that is, *if every element of A is an element of B.*

The nonempty sets Republican and Democrat in Example 1 did not overlap (no one could belong to both), and completely accounted for the entire group. Such sets are **mutually exclusive** (no overlap) and **exhaustive** (account for entire population). In any population, subsets that are nonempty, mutually exclusive, and exhaustive are said to **partition** (or to form a partition of) the population. In Example 2 the classes Republican, Democrat, and Independent partition the group of voters.

PRACTICE PROBLEM 1   (a) In Example 2, why do the groups Republican and Democrat not partition the gathering of voters?

(b) In Example 3, do the classes Male, Female, and Yes partition the voters? Explain.

(c) Give two ways of partitioning the voters in Example 3.

ANSWER(S)   **(a)** Republican and Democrat are not exhaustive; Independents are omitted; **(b)** The three classes do exhaust the entire gathering of voters; however, they are not mutually exclusive; some male voters, for example, said "yes"; **(c)** One partition: Male, Female; another: Yes, No.   □

PRACTICE PROBLEM 2   Twelve students cram for exams in a library study area. Math and English books litter the table. "How many of you are taking math?" asks a professor, and seven arms are proudly raised. "Who among you is taking English?" she queries, and three hands eagerly go up. Four students responded to neither question. Show this information in a Venn diagram.

Discussion: A student may be enrolled in neither subject, English only, math only, or both. To classify the students relative to math and English, we need math (M) and English (E) circles that allow for "one only," "neither," and "both." We enter the only count we are sure of: "4," for "students in *neither* M nor E."

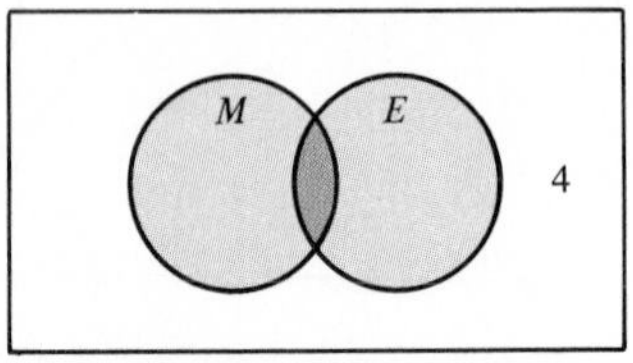

Figure 6.3
12 students, classed by English or math enrollment

We must account for a total of 8 students in the M and E circles, with 7 in M and 3 in E. A person in the darker region common to the two circles (called **the intersection of M and E,** written "$M \cap E$," and pronounced "*M* intersect *E*") is counted as a math student and as an English student. Such a person is in both math and English. The seven math students may be split up between the region of the math circle outside the English circle and the region inside the English circle in many ways (2 and 5, 4 and 3, etc.). Complete the diagram; try various apportionments (using pencil is a good idea!) until the numbers come out correctly. Make sure your final diagram and the narrative agree in every detail.

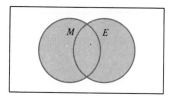

All space in the diagram but outside set *M* is the **complement** of *M*, written "M^c." The entire diagram (rectangle) depicts the **universe,** or set of all objects under discussion. Thus, M^c is the set of all items, or elements, in the universe but outside *M*. In Example 3 the elements are voters; in the present practice problem, the elements are students. Thus, we now seek to write in each region of the Venn diagram a number which tells how many elements are in that region.

ANSWER(S)   The space outside *M* and inside *E* contains elements in M^c and in *E* (that is, common to M^c and *E*, hence in $M^c \cap E$). Your final diagram should show two elements in $M \cap E$, five in $M \cap E^c$, one in $M^c \cap E$, and four in $M^c \cap E^c$. How did you do?   □

Union, Intersection, and Complement

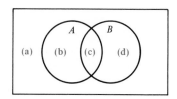

We often need to refer to the items included in one or more of several sets. For example, we might wish to refer to all people in Practice Problem 2 who are taking either of the two subjects. Such people might be taking math only (five people), or English only (one person), or both math and English (two people). These eight people are in math or English (or both). "Or both" is redundant, since any person taking both subjects would respond "Yes" to the question "Are you taking math or English?" The entire set formed by lumping together sets *M* and *E* is the union of *M* and *E*, written "$M \cup E$" and pronounced "*M* union *E*."

The same region may be named in several ways. We called that part of the universe outside both *M* and *E* "$M^c \cap E^c$." This region is also outside $M \cup E$; that is, the region is also $(M \cup E)^c$.

PRACTICE PROBLEM 3   In the Venn diagram below are regions **(a)–(d)**. Use appropriate notation to name each region in terms of its relationship to *A* and *B*.

ANSWER(S)   **(a)** $A^c \cap B^c$ or $(A \cup B)^c$;   **(b)** $A \cap B^c$;   **(c)** $A \cap B$;   **(d)** $A^c \cap B$.   □

We now have language to use in describing operations on or relation-ships among sets. In the next practice problem, we define a universe U and some sets within that universe, and ask you to describe other sets by using the given ones.

PRACTICE PROBLEM 4   Consider the universe $U = \{a,b,c,d,e,f,g,h\}$, which includes the sets $A = \{a,b,c,d\}$, $B = \{c,d,e\}$, $C = \{b,c,d,e\}$, $D = \{e,f,g,h\}$. (We use capital letters to name sets, and lowercase letters as elements.) Describe each set in parts **(a)** through **(d)** by listing its elements, separated by commas, within braces { }.

(a) $A \cap B$; (b) $A \cup C$; (c) B^c; (d) $A \cap D$; (e) $A \cap C \cup D$ (*Hint for Part* (e): In the absence of grouping symbols to indicate whether to form $A \cap C$ or $C \cup D$ first, group from left to right: $(A \cap C) \cup D$. First form $A \cap C$, then the union of the result with D.) (f) $A \cap (C \cup D)$; (g) Compare answers to (e) and (f). Conclusion?

ANSWER(S)   **(a)** $\{c,d\}$;   **(b)** $\{a,b,c,d,e\}$;   **(c)** $\{a,b,f,g,h\}$;   **(d)** { }, an "empty" set! See note below;   **(e)** $\{b,c,d\} \cup \{e,f,g,h\} = \{b,c,d,e,f,g,h\}$;   **(f)** $\{a,b,c,d\}$ $\cap \{b,c,d,e,f,g,h\} = \{b,c,d\}$.   **(g)** The order in which parts of a "set" expression are formed may alter the outcome. Obey grouping symbols when given; otherwise, work from left to right.   □

Special Notes Concerning Empty Sets   In Practice Problem 4 the set $A \cap D$ was empty. Could two empty sets be "different"? Not really; there is no detectable difference. Thus, there is only one empty set. We call it **the empty set** or **the null set**. The standard symbol for the empty set is "∅." Also, if A is any set, then every element of ∅ is an element of A. (There are certainly no exceptions!) Thus, the empty set, ∅, is a subset of every set.

■ EXAMPLE 4   A Venn diagram of two sets A and B must allow for all possible locations of an element x relative to the two sets. Imagine locating x by asking two questions: "Is x in A? Is x in B?" and recording the pair of answers. There are four possible answer pairs (more on this in Section 6.2), shown in Table 6.1, and four corresponding Venn diagram regions, shown in Figure 6.4(a).

Table 6.1
The four possible regions of a two-set Venn diagram

$x \in A$?	$x \in B$?	Word Description of Venn Diagram Region	"Set Notation" Label of Region
Yes	Yes	Inside A and inside B	$A \cap B$
Yes	No	Inside A and outside B	$A \cap B^c$
No	Yes	Outside A and inside B	$A^c \cap B$
No	No	Outside A and outside B	$A^c \cap B^c$

Four diagram regions are needed, to account for possibilities ranging from x in neither set to x in both sets. The result is the now-familiar diagram **(a)**, resembling a well-known credit card:

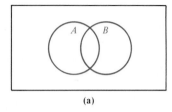
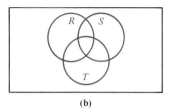

Figure 6.4
General two-set and three-set Venn diagrams

(a)   (b)

Similarly, when showing possible interrelationships among three sets in a Venn diagram, one must allow for all possibilities: overlap of all three, overlap of any two, regions found in only one of the sets, and finally a region outside all three sets. The result: diagram **(b)** above, with sets R, S, and T shown. Prepare a "three-set" table showing that eight regions are required. (*Hint:* For each "answer line" of the two-set table, two new lines for answers to "$x \in C$?" will be required.)   ◼

A word of caution: Mathematical language (as contrasted with everyday conversation) means *exactly* what it says. In Figure 6.4(a), an item "in A or in B" may lie in either set singly or in the common (intersection) area of the diagram. In Figure 6.4(b), an item in R and S may lie anywhere in the intersection of R with S—inside or outside T. Thus, three elements in $R \cap S$ may be distributed in several ways, from none inside T to all inside T.

Some phrases are used so often that we devise shorthand ways of saying them. (Being appropriately lazy is one characteristic of a mathematician!) One such phrase is "the number of elements in"—as, for example, in "the number of elements in set A" or, alternately, "the count of A." We shall use "$n(A)$" to stand for "the count of A." [What, then, does "n(Monte Cristo)" denote?]

Sorting with Tables   Sorting a collection of objects according to two questions or criteria is especially easy using a table. Answers to one question are assigned to the top edge, and answers to the other to the left edge, of the table. Each cell of the table corresponds to a pair of answers to the two questions. If each question has two possible answers, it is easy to construct a corresponding Venn diagram. However, if any question has more than two answers, a Venn diagram is not possible: for each set (circle, rectangle, or other boundary) in a Venn diagram, an object must be either inside or outside the set; no third response can be shown.

◼ EXAMPLE 5   Set up a table for categorizing a population relative to two sets A and B in a universal set U. Describe each of the four cells in the table, and each marginal total (right-hand edge, bottom edge, lower right corner), using set notation.

SOLUTION

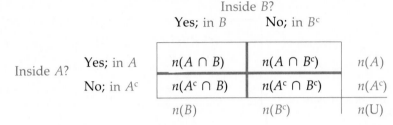

	Inside B?		
	Yes; in B	No; in B^c	
Yes; in A	$n(A \cap B)$	$n(A \cap B^c)$	$n(A)$
No; in A^c	$n(A^c \cap B)$	$n(A^c \cap B^c)$	$n(A^c)$
	$n(B)$	$n(B^c)$	$n(U)$

(Inside A?)

Each marginal total is easily explained. "$n(A)$" accounts for all objects in A. Every object in A is either inside B (in $A \cap B$) or outside B (in $A \cap B^c$). Thus, $n(A) = n(A \cap B) + n(A \cap B^c)$. The marginal sum $n(A) + n(A^c)$ is $n(U)$, since every object in U is either inside A or outside A. Likewise, $n(U) = n(B) + n(B^c)$.   ∎

PRACTICE PROBLEM 5   Complete the table. Then use the table entries to construct a Venn diagram showing the counts of all regions in the diagram.

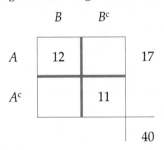

	B	B^c	
A	12		17
A^c		11	
			40

ANSWER(S)

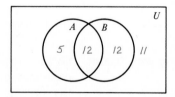

	B	B^c	
A	12	5	17
A^c	12	11	23
	24	16	40

PRACTICE PROBLEM 6   Use region counts from the Venn diagram to supply the following counts: **(a)** $n(A)$; **(b)** $n(B)$; **(c)** $n(A \cup B)$; **(d)** $n(U)$; **(e)** $n(B^c)$; **(f)** $n(A \cap B)$; **(g)** $n(A^c \cap B)$; **(h)** $n(A^c \cup B)$. (The next two parts are based on your answers to **(a)**, **(b)**, and **(c)**, so examine these before proceeding.)
   (i) Why, in this instance, is $n(A \cup B)$ not just $n(A) + n(B)$? **(j)** Could "$n(A \cup B) = n(A) + n(B)$" ever be true? Explain.

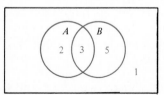

ANSWER(S)   **(a)** 5;   **(b)** 8;   **(c)** 10;   **(d)** 11;   **(e)** 3;   **(f)** 3;   **(g)** 5;   **(h)** 9.

(i) $A \cup B$ consists of three regions: $A \cap B^c$, $A \cap B$, and $A^c \cap B$. The sum $n(A) + n(B)$ counts the region $A \cap B$ twice!

(j) The only way for $n(A \cup B)$ to exactly equal $n(A) + n(B)$ is for the inclusion of twice the count of region $A \cap B$ to make no difference—that is, for $n(A \cap B)$ to be 0. This happens only if $A \cap B$ is empty! Otherwise (in fact, always), $n(A \cup B) = n(A) + n(B) - n(A \cap B)$ remedies any possible error resulting from counting $A \cap B$ twice.   ☐

Our discussion in Practice Problem 6, part **(j)**, contained several significant observations that can help us avoid serious and common errors:

COUNTING THE UNION OF TWO SETS

For any sets A and B, $n(A \cup B) = n(A) + n(B) - n(A \cap B)$. This is true whether or not $A \cap B$ is empty.

If $A \cap B = \emptyset$ (that is, if A and B are disjoint sets), then in that case, and that case only, $n(A \cap B) = n(A) + n(B)$. "The count of the union of disjoint sets is the sum of their separate counts."

EXERCISES 6.1

PRACTICING THE MOVES AND MANEUVERS

Exercises 1–4:   Show the given information in table and Venn diagram form.

1. Nineteen items are categorized: 5 in A but outside B, 4 in B but outside A, and 7 outside both A and B.
2. In a universal set of 80 elements, 17 are in C, 28 in D, and 39 in $C \cup D$.
3. Of 26 elements, 5 are in both R and S, 9 are in S, and 3 are in neither.
*4. Of 22 elements, 6 are in V but outside W, 7 are in W but outside V, and 8 are in neither W nor V.

5. $U = \{h,i,j,k,l,m,n,p,r\}$, $G = \{h,i,j,k,l\}$, $H = \{j,k,l,m\}$, $K = \{l,m,n,p\}$.

    (a) Arrange all elements of U in a 3-set Venn diagram. Then complete the statements in parts **(b)–(g)**.
    (b) $G \cap K =$ _____;   **(c)** $n(H) =$ _____;   **(d)** $n(G \cup H) =$ _____;
    (e) $n(G \cap H) =$ _____;   **(f)** $H^c \cap K =$ _____;   **(g)** $G \cup (H \cap K) =$ _____.

Exercises 6–7: Complete Venn diagrams using the given information.

6. $n(U) = 35$; $n(A \cap B \cap C) = 1$; $n(A \cap B) = 5$; $n(A \cap C) = 6$; $n(B \cap C) = 4$; $n(A) = 12$; $n(B) = 12$; $n(C) = 16$.

7. $n(U) = 32$; $n(R) = 8$; $n(S) = 22$; $n(T) = 12$; $n(R \cap S) = 7$; $n(R \cap T) = 4$; $n(S \cap T) = 10$; $n(R \cup S \cup T)^c = 7$.

APPLYING THE CONCEPTS

*8. Thirty-two students (18 of them boys) set forth on a field trip. Seven boys and 11 girls brought lunches. Show this information in **(a)** a table and **(b)** a Venn diagram.

9. Among 60 homes, 40 receive at least one of two local papers (the *Morning Sun* and the *Evening Bugle*). Thirty-three homes receive the *Sun*; 17 receive the *Bugle*. Show this information in a Venn diagram by guessing a number for the common area of the two circles, filling in the remaining regions in the diagram, checking the completed diagram, and then correcting your guess if necessary (a perfectly honorable problem-solving method!).

10. Use the given information in Exercise 9 to complete a table, without referring to your Venn diagram. Note that no guessing is required. (However, a table is not easy to do when sorting according to more than two criteria.)

*11. The pizza problem! Thirty-one pizza eaters reveal their topping preferences. Sixteen like strawberries; 16 like liver; 12 like anchovies. Ten like strawberries and liver; four enjoy liver and anchovies; five like strawberries and anchovies. Three like none of these toppings, preferring something bizarre. Do a Venn diagram. (*Hint:* Start with a three-set Venn diagram, as in Figure 6.4. Use the fact that exactly four people like both liver and anchovies to "guess" a count for the region common to all three circles. Then proceed as in Exercise 9.)

*12. Refer to Exercise 11. How many customers liked, among the three toppings considered, **(a)** all three? **(b)** exactly two? **(c)** at least one? **(d)** at most two?

*13. Cable TV subscribers may choose among three extra-cost services: Showtime, Bravo, and Play-

boy. Of 200 viewers surveyed, 80 subscribe to Showtime, 60 to Bravo, 25 to Playboy, 4 to both Bravo and Playboy, 40 to Showtime and Bravo, 10 to Showtime and Playboy, and 87 to none of the three. How many subscribed to all three? (Approach the problem using a Venn diagram, as in Exercise 11.)

14. One hundred voters in a small community responded "yes," "no," or "undecided" when asked their views concerning a proposed statue for the town square. In the 18–25 year old group, 9 said "yes," and 12 said "no." Of 55 people in the 26–30 age group, 42 were against the proposal. Eight people in the over-30 age group were undecided. In all, 17 people favored the proposal and 23 were undecided. The 18–25 group contained 30 people. Summarize in table form. Then answer the following:
   (a) How many of ages 30 and under were undecided?
   (b) How many were over 30 or in favor of the statue?
   (c) How many were in favor of the statue or undecided?
   (d) How many were under 31 and for the statue?

15. A survey of 100 freshmen at East Overshoe State University revealed 55 taking history, 45 psychology, 25 sociology, 12 both history and psychology, 10 taking history and sociology, 8 both psychology and sociology, and 5 taking all three courses. Summarize in a Venn diagram, and tell how many are:
   (a) in at least one of the subjects;
   (b) in exactly one of the three subjects;
   (c) in at most two of the three subjects;
   (d) in none of the three subjects.

6.2 THE FUNDAMENTAL COUNTING PRINCIPLE

In Section 6.1 we built a vocabulary for operations on, and relationships among, sets. We explored problems within the general theme "classifying a collection of objects." We needed and acquired some skill in the careful use of language. All of this was done in a context where counts of various sets were already established, and were either given to us explicitly or available to us through relationships among given counts.

Tree Diagrams and Fundamental Counting Principle (FCP)

In this section we shall acquire a powerful basic tool—the Fundamental Counting Principle. The "FCP" plays a key role in developing other important counting ideas. Let us begin with:

■ EXAMPLE 6

Joe Futz has two pairs of pants (one plaid, one striped) and three shirts (one red, one yellow, and one green with large orange spots). An outfit is one pair of pants and one shirt. If Joe has absolutely no sense of what looks well together (a safe assumption, in view of his wardrobe!), how many outfits has he?

SOLUTION

We could list all possibilities: (P,R), meaning "plaid with red," (P,Y), (P,G), (S,R), (S,Y), (S,G). To avoid missing possibilities, we select a pants type, exhaust the shirt options, then move to the second pants type and repeat. The same process for Joe's rich cousin (14 pairs of pants, 37 shirts) is not appealing!

To tell Joe how to pick an outfit, we might say "First, select pants. Then, select a shirt." We attach to each pants choice the possible shirt choices and display the possibilities in a tree diagram (Fig. 6.5).

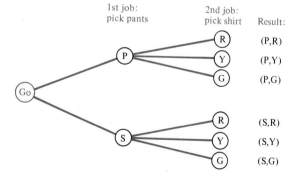

Figure 6.5
Tree diagram showing Joe's possible outfits

This two-stage (two-job) tree reads from left to right. Go, P, Y, etc., mark **nodes** of the diagram. "Go" is the **starting node;** R, Y, G are **ending (terminal) nodes.** The lines from Go to P, P to R, S to Y, etc. (linking consecutive nodes) are **branches.** A sequence of branches from Go to an ending node is a **path.** Each path shows one of Joe's six possible outfits.   ■

A tree diagram, drawn or merely visualized, helps one list or count the number of different ways to complete a sequence of tasks. The order of the tasks may or may not be significant. In Example 6, Joe could have chosen a shirt first, then pants.

PRACTICE PROBLEM 7   Suppose Joe (see Example 6) chooses a shirt first, then pants. Construct a tree diagram and list the set of possible outcomes.

ANSWER(S)   {(R,P), (R,S), (Y,P), (Y,S), (G,P), (G,S)}. Each possible outcome is an **ordered pair** where the first entry is "shirt" and the second "pants." Again, the count is six: three branches at the first tree stage ("pick shirt"), each followed by two branches at the second stage ("pick pants"). $3 \cdot 2 = 6$ □

PRACTICE PROBLEM 8   Joe's wealthy cousin Plato has 14 pairs of pants, 37 shirts, and an incredible collection of 118 caps, no two alike. Just think about the tree diagrams (sketching a bit of each if you wish), and determine the number of Plato's possible outfits if an outfit consists of the following items, chosen in the order named:

     (a) pants and shirt

     (b) shirt, pants, and cap (for formal occasions)

     (c) cap and pants

     (d) shirt and pants

ANSWER(S)   **(a)** $14 \cdot 37$;   **(b)** $37 \cdot 14 \cdot 118$;   **(c)** $118 \cdot 14$;   **(d)** $37 \cdot 14$. Compare parts **(a)** and **(d)**: order of choices makes no difference, so long as both tasks are completed.   □

PRACTICE PROBLEM 9   You must design the "standard office electronic workstation" for your company. Each station consists of a microcomputer, a keyboard, a video monitor, a printer, and a modem (device for communicating over a telephone line). You are considering two computers, three keyboards, three monitors, four printers, and two modems. How many workstation designs are possible?

ANSWER(S)   144   □

PRACTICE PROBLEM 10   A cafeteria offers three salads, four main dishes, two desserts, and five beverages.

(a) If you must make one choice from each category, how many distinct (nonidentical) meal choices are possible?

(b) If you may make at most one choice from each category (and choosing "nothing" is a possibility in each case), how many nonidentical meal choices are possible?

ANSWER(S)   **(a)** $3 \cdot 4 \cdot 2 \cdot 5 = 120$;   **(b)** $4 \cdot 5 \cdot 3 \cdot 6 = 360$.   □

A pattern has emerged: If, to accomplish some task (such as "choosing a meal" in Practice Problem 10) we must complete a sequence of small tasks, the number of possible ways to complete the large task is the product of the numbers of ways to complete the small tasks. Once we see a pattern such as this, we try to express it in general terms. We make such a statement (or write a "formula") only after we understand the concept it embodies. Formulas are not knowledge; they summarize what we know.

THE FUNDAMENTAL COUNTING PRINCIPLE (FCP)

> If a first task has m possible completions, a second has n possible completions (no matter how the first task is completed), . . ., and a final task has q possible completions (no matter how earlier tasks are completed), then the number of possible combined completions for all the tasks is $m \cdot n \cdot \ldots \cdot q$.

To use the Fundamental Counting Principle (FCP), we break down the large task into a sequence of smaller tasks so that no possible path to completion is omitted or duplicated. One good habit is writing a "job description": imagine doing the task, list the steps, and count the number of ways to perform each step.

■ EXAMPLE 7

A license plate consists of three alphabet letters followed by three digits (no spaces). How many plates are possible?

SOLUTION   Think of the plate as having six blanks to be filled. Write a six-step job description, and count the ways to do each step:

Step 1. Fill blank #1: 26 choices.

Step 2. Fill blank #2: 26 choices. (Repeats permitted!)

Step 3. Fill blank #3: 26 choices.

Step 4. Fill blank #4: 10 choices. (Why?)

Step 5. Fill blank #5: 10 choices. (Why?)

Step 6. Fill blank #6: 10 choices.

Number of ways to complete task: $26^3 \cdot 10^3 = 17,576,000$. Astonishing!

∎

PRACTICE PROBLEM 11   Solve Example 7 if repeats are not permitted.

ANSWER(S) $26 \cdot 25 \cdot 24 \cdot 10 \cdot 9 \cdot 8 = 11,232,000$—still impressive!   □

EXERCISES 6.2

PRACTICING THE MOVES AND MANEUVERS

16. A complex task consists of three steps. Step 1 may be completed in any of six ways; Step 2, five ways; Step 3, ten ways. How many paths to completion are possible?
17. A complex four-step task has 288 distinct possible completions. If Steps 1 and 2 each have three possible completions and Step 4 can be done in four ways, in how many ways can Step 3 be completed?
18. In how many ways can one pick a single vowel from {a, e, i, o, u} and a single digit from {1, 2, 3, 4, 5, 6, 7}?

APPLYING THE CONCEPTS

19. A license plate consists of two letters followed by three digits with the first digit nonzero. How many such plates are possible?
20. Margo wants a basic stereo system: a receiver, speakers, and a compact disc (CD) player. In her price range are three receivers, four kinds of speakers, and three CD players. How many different complete-system options has she?
21. Burger Bar's bare burger costs 99¢. The customer may add any of: lettuce, tomato, pickle, onion, cheese. How many burger variations are possible?
22. Five people are to line up for a photograph. How many lineups are possible? (*Hint:* Draw five blanks, and imagine filling each in turn with a person.)
*23. In Exercise 22, how many lineups are possible, if two of the people insist upon being together? (*First job:* count ways to select two blanks in the line for the two people who wish to be adjacent. Then count ways to fill each blank.)
*24. There are 4 roads from town A to town B, and 3 roads from town B to town C. In how many ways could a person travel
   (a) from A to C, passing through B?
   (b) round trip from A to C and back, by way of B?
   (c) round trip from A to C, by way of B, without using any road twice?
25. In how many ways can a 28-member class elect a president, vice president, and entertainment chairperson?
26. A Scrabble® player has seven different letters. She wants to consider all possible 5-letter sequences before playing. If she were able to test one sequence per second, how many minutes would elapse before she could play?
27. In Exercise 26, how many 4-letter sequences are possible? How many sequences of either 4 or 5 letters are possible?
28. A test consists of five true-false questions. How many different answer keys are possible? (*Job description:* Answer question #1; then answer #2; etc.)

29. How many answer keys to a 10-question true-false test are possible?

30. An exam consists of 5 multiple-choice items (each with four choices) and 5 true-false items. How many different sets of answers are possible?

Exercises 31–34: Form a 3-digit numeral using digits from {2, 4, 5, 7, 9}, with repeated digits permitted.

*31. How many such numerals are possible?

*32. How many are of numbers less than 500?

*33. How many are of even numbers?

*34. How many are of multiples of 5?

Exercises 35–38: Form a 3-digit numeral using digits from {2, 4, 5, 7, 9}, with no digit being repeated.

*35. How many such numerals are possible?

*36. How many are of numbers less than 500?

*37. How many are of even numbers?

*38. How many are of multiples of 5?

6.3 WHAT IS PROBABILITY?

Most of us have some intuitive notion of probability. We use the word to indicate "how likely" something is. Our everyday conversations include such statements as "The Seattle Seahawks will probably run the ball on first down," or "It's quite likely that the wind will blow tomorrow in Chicago." In this chapter we explain more precisely the meaning of such phrases. When finished, we will be able to analyze situations like the following: Trent Thomas and Malcolm McCurdy are spectators at a craps table in a Las Vegas casino. Trent offers to liven things up with the following private bet with Malcolm: When the dice are next tossed, Trent will pay Malcolm $5 if the two-dice sum is 6, 7, 8, or 9, while Trent will win $6 from Malcolm if the sum is 2, 3, 4, 5, 10, 11, or 12. Trent reasons:

> "He has only four winning sums, while I have 7; and I win $1 more when I win. This bet is a sure thing!"

It may surprise you that a majority of commonfolk would reason like Trent—and lose their shirts! Such "intuitive" wagers led to the beginnings of modern probability. Here is the story of the gambling game that started it all.

A certain seventeenth century French nobleman, gambler, and general rogue enjoyed dice games. Game 1 involved rolling a die four times. If a six ever appeared, he won the bet; if not, he lost. He lost frequently, but seemed to come out ahead in the long run. For variety, he often changed the game to one where two dice were tossed 24 times. In this version (Game 2), he won if a two-dice sum of 12 ever happened. He thought Game 2 was exactly equivalent to Game 1, reasoning as follows:

> When one die is tossed, the chance of a win is 1/6. When two dice are rolled, however, there are 36 possible outcomes (six times six, by the FCP). Only one of these 36 is a sum of 12. Hence, with one roll, there is a 1/6 = 6/36 chance of a win in Game 1, but only a 1/36 chance of a win in Game 2. To correct for this six-to-one disparity between one-roll win probabilities, he felt that he needed to toss the two dice six times as often as the one die. Since the one die was rolled four times, the two dice then needed to be rolled 24 times.

The logic is reasonably convincing—it's just not correct! He observed that he seemed to lose small but regular amounts during extended play of Game 2, while the opposite occurred at Game 1. Perplexed, he enlisted the aid of one of the great mathematicians of the time, Pierre de Fermat. Why, he asked Fermat, should there be a difference? Fermat's response (Fermat is said to have conferred with Pascal, another notable mathematician of that time) was the beginning of modern probability. This problem challenged the greatest minds of the seventeenth century. You will soon be able to solve it! (We will do so in an example.)

6.4 EXPERIMENTS, SAMPLE SPACES, AND EVENTS

Much new knowledge in science is due to observing experimentation, the results of which are usually unpredictable. When a couple has a child, for example, they cannot be sure before birth of the sex, hair color, eye color, or other characteristics. Before a high school student takes the SAT, there is no way of knowing what his/her scores will be. An investor buying a stock hopes that the price will go up, but cannot be certain. When a physician treats a cancer patient with radiation, she knows that some cancerous cells and some good cells will be destroyed, but she cannot predict the exact number of each. A farmer planting a corn field cannot predict the exact yield in bushels per acre. Even when the last place team plays baseball, you cannot be certain of the outcome.

All the above are examples of **random experiments.** Intuitively, a random experiment is a repeatable process whose outcomes depend on chance; the word "random" serves only to indicate the unpredictability of the outcome. Henceforth, the word random will be omitted, and we shall define an experiment as follows:

EXPERIMENT

> An **experiment** is a repeatable process with more than one possible outcome. The actual outcome of any one trial (performance of the experiment) is determined by chance.

Here are some examples of experiments:

1. Tossing a coin.

2. Rolling an ordinary die (one from a pair of dice).

3. Choosing a card at random from a deck of 52 cards.

4. Picking two of the six spark plugs at random from a car.

5. Measuring dissolved oxygen in a sample of river water.

6. Recording how long a light bulb burns until it fails.

7. Counting people in the "9-item" line at a grocery store.

In all these experiments, note that you cannot predict exactly what will happen. You can, however, list the possibilities. The set containing all possible outcomes is called the sample space.

SAMPLE SPACE

> A **sample space,** denoted by S, is a set whose elements describe all possible outcomes in an experiment.

■ EXAMPLE 8

List sample spaces for the first three experiments listed above.

SOLUTION

For Experiment 1, tossing a coin, a reasonable choice would be $S = \{H, T\}$. Here there are two outcomes: H and T. If you think anything is possible, you might choose $S = \{H, T, E\}$, where outcome E represents an "edgie!"

In Experiment 2, use $S = \{1, 2, 3, 4, 5, 6\}$, where outcomes represent possible numbers showing on the top face of the die.

In Experiment 3, familiarity with a deck of cards is necessary. We shall frequently use dice and cards to illustrate counting techniques or pose counting problems. Fortunately, there are still a few people in the world (including the authors!) who are innocent enough to need a review of card-deck details. (We refer here to a "bridge" or standard deck, and will consistently refer to this type, rather than a "pinochle" or other style deck.) A deck of 52 cards consists of four suits: hearts (♥) and diamonds (♦) (both red suits), and clubs (♣) and spades (♠) (both black). Each suit is further subdivided into 13 denominations: Ace (A), 2,

3, 4, 5, 6, 7, 8, 9, 10, jack (J), queen (Q), king (K). Finally, the jack, queen, and king are called face cards.

For some card games (for example, poker) each player is dealt a hand, or set, of 5 cards. (What happens after that is subject to considerable variation!) We will frequently structure illustrations and problems about 5-card poker hands. For Experiment 4 we list four plausible sample spaces (you may think of others):

S_1 = {club, diamond, heart, spade}

S_2 = {black card, red card}

S_3 = {2, 3, 4, . . ., J, Q, K, A}

S_4 = {club 2, club 3, . . ., club A, . . ., spade 2, . . ., spade A}

Which sample space is best for Experiment 3? One would be considered better than another only if it enabled us to describe the experimental outcomes more accurately for our purposes. To illustrate: If our interest lies in the suit, then S_2 and S_3 would be of no use. In S_2, for example, outcomes give color; knowing a card's color does not enable us to determine suit. If, however, we are interested in whether the outcome is a face card, only S_3 or S_4 would be helpful. The message is that the choice of a sample space is not unique; there are many ways to describe the outcomes. Generally, it is best to pick a sample space whose elements are sufficiently detailed to handle all conceivable questions of interest. In Experiment 3, S_4 is a good choice; its 52 elements cover all possible experimental observations. ∎

The sample spaces in Experiments 1–3 are **finite sample spaces,** since each has a definite number of elements. The same is true for Experiments 4 and 7. Since this is a finite mathematics book, you might suppose we would deal only with finite sample spaces. For the most part this is true. Experiments 5 and 6, however, lead to infinitely many possible outcomes. In Experiment 6, recording the time a light bulb burns before failing, S is the set of all possible burning times (numbers greater than or equal to zero). There are infinitely many values in S, so S is an **infinite sample space.** In Chapter 9, we consider infinite sample spaces and study two special cases. Until then, we consider only finite sample spaces.

Note well: In any experiment, even one with many possible outcomes, each trial (performance of the experiment) results in one and only one outcome.

■ EXAMPLE 9

List a sample space for Experiment 4, selecting two spark plugs at random from a car having six spark plugs.

SOLUTION

Suppose the six spark plugs are numbered from one to six, from the front toward the rear of the engine. The first plug chosen can be any one of six, and the second can be any one of the remaining five. Thus, by the FCP, there are $6 \cdot 5 = 30$ "ordered" ways of selecting two plugs. These 30 outcomes, obtained from a tree diagram or by simply listing possible orderings of two digits from {1, 2, 3, 4, 5, 6}, are:

1,2   1,3   1,4   1,5   1,6   2,1   2,3   2,4   2,5   2,6

3,1   3,2   3,4   3,5   3,6   4,1   4,2   4,3   4,5   4,6

5,1   5,2   5,3   5,4   5,6   6,1   6,2   6,3   6,4   6,5

Let's modify the problem slightly by supposing that our interest lies only in whether each plug is good or defective. The Figure 6.6 tree diagram easily produces a convenient sample space. Each outcome indicates whether or not each selected plug is defective.

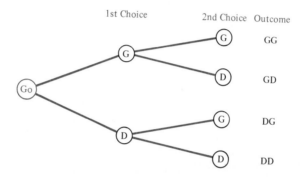

Figure 6.6
Tree diagram for selection of two spark plugs

Here G and D indicate "good plug" and "defective plug," respectively, and outcome GD signifies "first plug good, second defective." The "outcomes" column lists all elements of the sample space: $S = \{GG, GD, DG, DD\}$. Even if we were interested only in the number of defective plugs chosen, sample space S would be convenient, as its outcomes are readily classified according to the number of defective plugs in each. See Example 10. ■

Tree Diagrams and Events

Students sometimes have difficulty in listing the sample space for a given problem. A sample space will often reveal itself if you can carefully describe one outcome. One outcome will usually suggest others that are similar, and eventually you should get them all. A tree diagram helps keep track of what is happening, especially in experiments where steps occur in sequence. Note well the benefits of using a tree diagram in constructing a sample space:

Each path on the tree represents one outcome and the sample space is the collection of all possible paths on the tree.

In most experiments, it is not usually individual outcomes that are of interest, but some subset of these outcomes having certain features.

For example, when tossing a die, "1," "3," and "5" are odd numbers. If any one of these is the outcome, we would say the event of observing an odd number has occurred.

EVENTS

> Any collection of outcomes (subset of the sample space) is called an **event.** An event with only one outcome is called a **simple event.** An event containing two or more outcomes is called a **compound event.**

Events (sets of outcomes) are represented by italic capital letters A, B, C, etc. Speaking precisely, the simple event $B = \{b\}$ is *not* the same as the outcome b, but this mathematical distinction is not terribly important in this book. You can view a simple event as just an individual outcome written in set form.

■ EXAMPLE 10

From Example 9 (spark plugs), we describe certain events in ordinary English, and list the subsets of S that form those events. (Recall: $S = \{GG, GD, DG, DD\}$.) Note carefully the distinctions among "exactly one," "at least one," and "at most one." These are important and should be clearly understood!! Furthermore, "one" and "two" mean "exactly one" and "exactly two," respectively.

Event	Subset of S
A: Exactly one defective plug.	$\{DG, GD\}$
B: At least one defective plug.	$\{DG, GD, DD\}$
C: At most one defective plug.	$\{DG, GD, GG\}$
F: The plugs test the same.	$\{DD, GG\}$
H: The second plug is defective.	$\{GD, DD\}$
J: One plug is good.	$\{GD, DG\}$

When an experiment is performed and its outcome is observed, it is important to know whether a particular event has occurred. If a 1, 3, or 5 occurred on a die toss, we could say that the event of observing an odd number has occurred. In general: If the observed outcome is an element of a particular event K, then we say event K has occurred. A *compound event occurs if any element in that event is the observed outcome.*

Thus, if DG is the observed outcome, we say that events A, B, C, and J have occurred, while F and H have not. If we observe GG, then C and F have occurred, but A, B, H, and J have not.   ■

In Example 10 note that the result of the experiment is a single outcome, but that one outcome may "trigger" (indicate) the occurrence of more than one event.

A sample space is just a specialized universal set. Since events are sets (subsets of the sample space), everything we know about sets applies equally well to events. Thus, we may picture sample spaces and events with Venn diagrams. We show sample space S of Example 10 in the Figure 6.7 Venn diagram, with the four individual outcomes shown as "sample points" (elements) inside sample space S. We show events A, F, and H by enclosing appropriate sample points within loops.

Events A and F, with no points in common, are mutually exclusive. Knowing what it means for an event to occur (one of its elements must be the observed experimental outcome), we can say that if either one of a pair of mutually exclusive events occurs, the other cannot. Events H and A, however, are not mutually exclusive: the outcome GD results in the occurrence of both A and H.

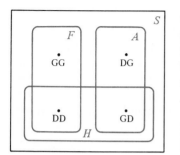

Figure 6.7
Events A, F, and H of Example 10

PRACTICE PROBLEM 12   In Example 10, list the subset that defines the event:

(a) "The number of defective plugs is one more than the number of good plugs."

(b) "The second plug is defective."

(c) "The first plug is good."

ANSWER(S)   (a) $\emptyset$;   (b) {GD, DD};   (c) {GG, GD}.   □

PRACTICE PROBLEM 13   Matt and Donna Slavich, an hour's drive from home on their vacation trip, cannot remember whether they locked all the doors. The house has three doors (front, side, and back). They telephone a neighbor to ask that she check all the doors.

(a) List a sample space for the experiment of the neighbor trying all the doors. Use L for locked, and O for open; list doors in the order front, side, back.

(b) Using your sample space, list the following events:

   A: One (door) is locked.

   B: At least one is locked.

   C: Two doors are locked.

   D: At least two are locked.

   E: The back door is locked.

   F: The side door is open.

> *G:* At most two are locked.
>
> *H:* At most one is open.
>
> *I:* All three are open.

(c) If LLO is observed, which events in part **(b)** have occurred?

ANSWER(S)

(a) $S = \{OOO,OOL,OLO,OLL,LOO,LOL,LLO,LLL\}$. The FCP assures us of exactly eight simple events: the front door has two possible states; regardless of the state of the front door, the side door has two possible states. Finally, regardless of the states of front and side doors, the back door has two possible states. Choosing one condition for each door yields $2 \cdot 2 \cdot 2 = 8$ descriptions for the three doors.

(b) $A = \{LOO,OLO,OOL\}$
$B = \{OOL,OLO,OLL,LOO,LOL,LLO,LLL\}$, or $\{OOO\}^c$
$C = \{OLL,LOL,LLO\}$
$D = \{LLO,OLL,LOL,LLL\}$
$E = \{OOL,OLL,LOL,LLL\}$
$F = \{OOO,OOL,LOL,LOO\}$
$G = \{OOO,OOL,OLO,OLL,LOO,LOL,LLO\}$, or $\{LLL\}^c$
$H = \{OLL,LOL,LLO,LLL\}$

(c) Events, B, C, D, G, and H have all occurred if LLO is observed.

□

In Practice Problem 13, events D and H are identical, even though their descriptions sound different. Compare them!

PRACTICE PROBLEM 14   In Practice Problem 13, find the following events:
(a) $A \cup B$;   **(b)** $A \cap B$;   **(c)** $(A \cup B)^c$;   **(d)** $A^c \cap B^c$;   **(e)** A^c.

ANSWER(S)   **(a)** $A \cup B = B$;   **(b)** $A \cap B = \{LOO,OLO,OOL\}$;   **(c)** $(A \cup B)^c = \{OOO\}$;   **(d)** $A^c \cap B^c = \{OOO\}$;   **(e)** $A^c = \{OOO,OLL,LOL,LLO, LLL\}$.

□

EXERCISES 6.4

PRACTICING THE MOVES AND MANEUVERS

Exercises 39–46: Refer to sample space $S = \{1a, 1b, 1c, 2a, 2d, 3b, 3e, 3f, 4a, 4g, 5b, 5e, 6a, 6f\}$. Each outcome (sample point) is an ordered pair consisting of a digit and a letter. Using appropriate notation, show the given event by listing its sample points.

39. *A:* the digit is even.
40. *B:* the letter is a vowel.
41. *C:* the digit is odd.
42. *D:* the letter is not a vowel.
43. *E:* 3 divides the digit evenly.
44. *F:* the letter is a consonant.
45. *G:* 3 divides the digit and the letter is a consonant.
46. *H:* 3 divides the digit or the letter is a consonant.

47. Express event *G* (Exercise 45) in terms of events *E* and *F*.
48. Express event *H* (Exercise 46) in terms of events *E* and *F*.

Exercises 49–54:   For the given outcome, tell which events A through H in Exercises 39–46 have occurred.

49. 2a
52. 5b

50. 6f
53. 3e

51. 1c
54. 4g

APPLYING THE CONCEPTS

55. An experiment consists of asking three male golf professionals whether they use Titleist brand golf balls in tournaments. Let U stand for *use*, N for *not use*, and list a suitable sample space for the responses of the three pros.

Exercises 56–61:   Use the sample space of Exercise 55 to list the sample points in the given event.

56. *A:* At most two use Titleist.
57. *B:* At least one uses Titleist.
58. *C:* Exactly one uses Titleist.

59. *D:* At most one uses Titleist.
60. *F:* Second man uses Titleist.
61. *G:* Last two don't use Titleist.

62. An experiment consists of throwing a coin and tossing a die. List a sample space for this experiment that will enable you to determine the specific number on the die or the specific outcome of the coin.

Exercises 63–66:   Use the sample space of Exercise 62 to list the sample points in the given event.

63. *A:* The die shows an odd number.
64. *B:* The coin shows a head.
65. *C:* The die shows a number greater than four.
66. *D:* The coin shows a head or the die shows a number greater than 4.

67. A judge ranks three platform divers *A*, *B*, and *C* by their performance on a particular dive. Give a sample space *S* for this experiment that will enable you to answer all questions about the rank orders of the three divers.

Exercises 68–73:   Use the sample space of Exercise 67 to list the sample points in the given event.

68. *A:* *A* is the best diver.
69. *B:* *A* does not end up last.
70. *C:* Either *A* or *B* takes first.

71. *D:* *A* is first and *C* is last.
72. *F:* *B* does not win.
73. *G:* *A* wins or *B* is not last.

74. Two dice, one red and the other green, are tossed. List the logical 36-event sample space describing in detail all possible observed outcomes.

Exercises 75–79: Use the sample space of Exercise 74 to list the sample points in the given event.

75. *A:* The sum of the numbers on the dice is 8.
76. *B:* The sum of the numbers is ten or more.
77. *C:* The number on the red die is a 5.
78. *D:* The number on the red die is two more than the number on the green.
*79. *E:* The green die shows a number which is at least four.

80. Shotgun shells are packed in boxes of 25. A quality control inspector follows this procedure: a box is chosen. One shell is drawn from the box and fired. If the shell is good, production continues uninterrupted. If it is bad, two more shells are drawn from the box and fired, one after the other. If either is bad, production stops until the difficulty is corrected. A box containing two bad shells is tested. List a sample space *S* describing the possible outcomes of the shell firings.

Exercises 81–84: Use the sample space of Exercise 80 to list the sample points in the given event.

81. *A:* One defective is found.
82. *B:* More than one defective is found.
83. *C:* The test discovers more good shells than bad.
*84. *D:* The second shell tested is defective.

85. When Sammy Suave returns Pam Proper to the sorority house, he either kisses her goodnight (K) or shakes her hand (H). She responds by blushing (B), fainting (F), or sighing (S). With the given letters, construct a sample space for the experiment of Sammy taking Pam home.

Exercises 86 and 87: Use the sample space of Exercise 85 to list the sample points in the given event.

86. *A:* Pam did not faint.
87. *B:* Sammy was rewarded with a blush or a sigh.

6.5 PROBABILITY BEGINNINGS, THE ADDITIVE LAW, AND THE COMPLEMENT RULE

When an experiment is to be performed, our real interest is in whether certain events occur. When a die is tossed, will we observe an odd number? We don't know! For an event to occur, the observed outcome must be an element of that event. But the outcome we observe depends on chance. We can say only that:

1. The observed outcome must belong to S, so the sample space S is an event that always happens. We call S a **certain event**—it happens 100% of the time.

2. The null set $\emptyset$ will never occur[1]; it is said to be an **impossible event**—it occurs 0% of the time.

Before the experiment is performed, the occurrence or nonoccurrence of any event other than S and $\emptyset$ is uncertain. The best possible information would be to know how likely the event is. Based on the two comments above, it appears that a typical event has somewhere between 0% and 100% chance of occurring.

How many events are possible within a given sample space? In Example 11, we investigate this question for a relatively small sample space S.

■ EXAMPLE 11

In a sample space S having 3 outcomes, determine how many different events may be identified.

SOLUTION

If $S = \{a,b,c\}$, the smallest event in S is the empty event, $\emptyset$. Next in size are the simple events $\{a\}$, $\{b\}$, and $\{c\}$. Events of size two, formed by omitting one outcome from S, are $\{a,b\}$, $\{a,c\}$, and $\{b,c\}$. Finally, $S = \{a,b,c\}$ is itself an event. Thus, from only 3 outcomes, 8 different events are possible.   ■

We will soon see that in a sample space of 10 outcomes, there are more than 1000 events. A sample space with 20 outcomes leads to over a million events. Fortunately, if we know a "probability" (a number expressing its "likelihood") for each simple event in S, then we may obtain the probability of any event, large or small, in S.

PROBABILITY OF AN EVENT

> In a finite sample space, the probability of any event A, written $P[A]$, is found by adding the probabilities of the individual outcomes (simple events) in A.

This makes probability easy! All we need to do is determine probabilities for simple events; the probability of any event of interest is found by summing its simple event probabilities.

---

[1] The null set $\emptyset$ is a subset of every set. Hence, it is an event (subset of any sample space). Since $\emptyset$ has no elements, the observed simple event cannot belong to $\emptyset$, and thus $\emptyset$ can never occur.

■ EXAMPLE 12

An experiment consists of tossing an unbalanced die and observing the "up" face. The sample space is $S = \{1,2,3,4,5,6\}$. The simple event probabilities are:

$$P[1] = 0.20, \quad P[2] = 0.05, \quad P[3] = 0.30, \quad P[4] = 0.10,$$
$$P[5] = 0.25, \quad P[6] = 0.10$$

Find the probabilities for the following events:

A: An odd number occurs.

B: An even number less than 4 occurs.

C: A number greater than 2 occurs.

D: An odd number less than 5 occurs.

SOLUTION

We express each event as a collection of outcomes, then sum the outcome probabilities.

$A = \{1,3,5\}$ $P[A] = 0.20 + 0.30 + 0.25 = 0.75$ This is a crooked die!

$B = \{2\}$ $P[B] = 0.05$

$C = \{3,4,5,6\}$ $P[C] = 0.30 + 0.10 + 0.25 + 0.10 = 0.75$

$D = \{1,3\}$ $P[D] = 0.20 + 0.30 = 0.50$ ■

■ EXAMPLE 13

Referring to the events of Example 12, express the following events as collections of outcomes, and find their probabilities. *Note:* Be sure to work this example. Though elementary, it illustrates important ideas.

(a) $A \cap C$;   **(b)** $A \cap B$;   **(c)** $B \cap C$;   **(d)** $A \cup B$;
(e) $A \cup C$;   **(f)** $B \cup C$;   **(g)** $A \cup B \cup C$;   **(h)** A^c;   **(i)** B^c

SOLUTION

All events, including unions, intersections, and complements, are just collections of outcomes. To find probabilities for these seemingly difficult events, we follow our basic rule: List the outcomes in the event, then sum their corresponding probabilities. Trace the solutions using the Venn diagram at left.

(a) $A \cap C = \{3,5\}$, so $P[A \cap C] = 0.30 + 0.25 = 0.55$

(b) $A \cap B = \emptyset$, and thus $P[A \cap B] = 0$

(c) $B \cap C = \emptyset$, and thus $P[B \cap C] = 0$

(d) $A \cup B = \{1,3,5,2\}$;
$P[A \cup B] = 0.20 + 0.30 + 0.25 + 0.05 = 0.80$

(e) $A \cup C = \{1,3,5,4,6\}$;
$P[A \cup C] = 0.20 + 0.30 + 0.25 + 0.10 + 0.10 = 0.95$

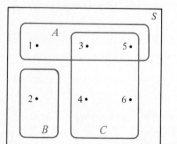

(f) $B \cup C = \{3,5,4,6,2\}$;
$P[B \cup C] = 0.30 + 0.25 + 0.10 + 0.10 + 0.05 = 0.80$

(g) $A \cup B \cup C = S$. Since S is a certain event, it occurs 100% of the time. If we follow our rule that says event probability is found by adding the appropriate outcome probabilities, we find that $P[A \cup B \cup C] = 0.20 + 0.05 + 0.30 + 0.10 + 0.25 + 0.10 = 1$; this illustrates that a certain event, one which occurs 100% of the time, has probability 1.

(h) $A^c = \{4,6,2\}$, so $P[A^c] = 0.10 + 0.10 + 0.05 = 0.25$

(i) $B^c = \{1,3,5,4,6\}$; $P[B^c] = 0.20 + 0.30 + 0.25 + 0.10 + 0.10 = 0.95$; or, we could have recognized that event B^c is the same as $A \cup C$, whose probability we found in part **(e)**.   ■

The Additive Law of Probability

We have answered the questions asked in Example 13. Let's study these results; several important facts will surface.

1. In part **(b)** we found that $A \cap B = \emptyset$, so that $P[A \cap B] = 0$ (no simple event probabilities to add). This shows that an impossible event has probability 0, and also illustrates that the probability of the intersection of mutually exclusive events is 0. Part **(c)** illustrates these ideas as well.

2. In Example 12, we found that $P[A] = 0.75$ and $P[B] = 0.05$. In Example 13, part **(d)**, we found that $P[A \cup B] = 0.80$. In this case, $P[A \cup B] = P[A] + P[B]$. Since forming a union of sets resembles "adding" sets, we may be tempted to generalize that, for any events A and B, $P[A \cup B] = P[A] + P[B]$. This is a trap! Observe from part **(e)** that $P[A \cup C] = 0.95$, while $P[A] + P[C] = 0.75 + 0.75 = 1.50 \neq 0.95$; thus, our theory is shot!

   What happened? Study the Example 13 Venn diagram. To find $P[A]$ we added probabilities of the simple events 1,3,5. To find $P[C]$, we added the probabilities of simple events 3,5,4,6. We included 3 and 5 twice—once in event A and once in event C! In part **(a)**, we found that $A \cap C = \{3,5\}$. Thus, in adding $P[A]$ to $P[C]$ to get $P[A \cup C]$, we included the probability of the intersection of A and C twice. To amend this, we need to subtract the intersection probability once.

We have discovered a truly important connection between the probability of the union of two events and the sum of their separate probabilities: $P[A \cup C] = P[A] + P[C] - P[A \cap C]$. This useful result is called **The Additive Law of Probability**.

THE ADDITIVE LAW OF PROBABILITY FOR TWO EVENTS

> If A and B are any two events in the same sample space S, then it is always true that
>
> $$P[A \cup B] = P[A] + P[B] - P[A \cap B].$$

When two events are mutually exclusive, $P[A \cap B]$ is 0. In that case, and that case only, $P[A \cup B] = P[A] + P[B]$. This is why things "worked" with events A and B (and B and C) in Example 13. Note the similarity of the Additive Law of Probability to the fact that $n(A \cup B) = n(A) + n(B) - n(A \cap B)$, noted in Section 6.1.

PRACTICE PROBLEM 15   In Example 12, find $P[C \cup D]$ in the following two ways:

(a) by summing simple event probabilities, and

(b) by using The Additive Law of Probability.

ANSWER(S)   (a) $C \cup D = \{3,5,4,6,1\}$, so $P[C \cup D] = 0.30 + 0.25 + 0.10 + 0.10 + 0.20 = 0.95$;   (b) $P[C] = 0.75$, $P[D] = 0.50$, and $P[C \cap D] = 0.30$, so $P[C] + P[D] - P[C \cap D] = 0.75 + 0.50 - 0.30 = 0.95$.   □

Assigning Simple Event Probabilities

Recent examples have been easy because the simple event probabilities were given. But you may have a searching question:

Where do simple event probabilities come from?

In this book we discuss three ways of assigning probabilities to simple events: (1) the "equally likely" approach; (2) the relative frequency approach; and (3) the subjective method. Regardless of which of these three you use to assign probabilities to simple events (individual outcomes), certain rules must be followed in order that probabilities calculated for compound events give consistent results. These rules, the **axioms of probability,** are:

RULES FOR ASSIGNING SIMPLE EVENT PROBABILITIES

> 1. The probability attached to any simple event must be at least 0 and no more than 1.
>
> 2. The sum of the probabilities of all simple events in a sample space must be one.

A choice of sample space along with an assignment of probabilities to the simple events that satisfies the above two rules is said to be a **probability model** for the experiment.

Adherence to these two rules does not guarantee a good probability model. These rules would allow you to say, when tossing a fair coin, "$P[\text{head}] = 1/1000$ and $P[\text{tail}] = 999/1000$." This would be an atrocious probability model. Does this mean the two probability rules are bad? Of course not! These rules merely limit the ways of assigning probabilities by ruling out assignments that do not meet certain minimum standards.

The situation is analogous to that of hiring a person for a specific job; you list a set of minimum requirements and then look for someone having special qualities beyond the minimum. The two probability axioms are comparable to the minimum job requirements. In the following sections, we search for the best way of attaching probabilities to the simple events.

The Complement Rule

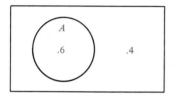

According to Rule 2 for assigning simple event probabilities, the sum of all simple event probabilities in a given sample space is 1. Since every outcome is either in B or in B^c, the probabilities of simple events in B plus the probabilities of simple events in B^c must be exactly 1. That is, $P[B] + P[B^c] = 1$. By knowing $P[B]$, we get $P[B^c]$ with very little effort. Likewise, knowing $P[B^c]$ makes it easy to find $P[B]$, using the **Complement Rule.**

COMPLEMENT RULE

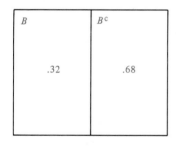

> The probability of any event A can be found by finding the probability that A does not occur and subtracting the result from one:
>
> $$P[A] = 1 - P[A^c]$$

The Complement Rule is elementary—and incredibly useful. Any time you encounter a probability problem that appears really difficult, look at the complement of the desired event and find its probability. This will often make an apparently difficult problem much easier.

Odds and Odds-Making

The Complement Rule is closely related to odds-making. The odds in favor of a win compare the likelihood of a team's winning to the likelihood of its losing. For example, if Jimmy the Greek gives odds of 7 to 1 that the Seattle Seahawks will win the AFC West Division, this is his way of saying that the Hawks have 7 chances of winning, compared to only 1 chance of losing, out of a total of 8 chances. In other words, their probability of winning is 7/8; of losing, 1/8. (A perfect example of subjective probability.)

Likewise, if the Raiders' winning probability is 0.40, Jimmy might say that the Raiders have 40 chances (out of 100) to win and 60 chances to lose. Therefore the odds in favor of the Raiders winning are 40 to 60, or 4 to 6, or 2 to 3, and the odds against the Raiders are 3 to 2. (Odds are usually expressed as a ratio of the smallest possible whole numbers.)

EXERCISES 6.5

PRACTICING THE MOVES AND MANEUVERS

Exercises 88–96: Supply the missing probability, if possible. If not possible, write "not possible." (When simple events are listed, assume none are omitted.)

88. $P[x] = 0.10$, $P[y] = 0.25$; $P[z] = ?$
89. $P[A] = 0.35$; $P[A \cap B] = 0.18$; $P[A \cap B^c] = ?$
90. $P[r] = 0.28$; $P[s] = ?$; $P[t] = 0.77$.
91. $P[x] = 0.55$; $P[y] = 0.45$; $P[z] = ?$
92. $P[M] = 0.6$; $P[M \cup N] = 0.8$; $P[N] = ?$
93. $P[t] = ?$
94. $P[a] = 0.65$, $P[b] = 0.20$, $P[c] = 0.05$; $P[d] = ?$
95. $P[A] = 0.19$; $P[A^c] = ?$
96. $P[(J \cup K)^c] = 0.6$; $P[J \cap K] = 0.1$; $P[K] = 0.3$; $P[J] = ?$

97.   In the Venn diagram below are outcomes a, b, . . ., g. Some individual outcome probabilities are: $P[a] = 0.10$, $P[b] = P[c] = P[d] = 0.15$, $P[e] = 0.20$, and $P[f] = 0.20$. Find the probabilities for the events in **(a–h)**: **(a)** $\{g\}$; **(b)** A; **(c)** B; **(d)** C; **(e)** $A \cap B$; **(f)** $A \cap C$; **(g)** $B \cap C$; **(h)** $A \cup B$. (Do this by using both available methods.)

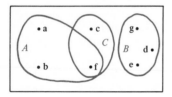

98.   In Exercise 97, identify which pairs of the compound events A, B, and C are mutually exclusive.
99.   A sample space consists of simple events E_1, . . ., E_5. (Remember: A simple event contains exactly one outcome.) $P[E_5] = 0.4$. For the remaining simple events, $P[E_1] = P[E_2] = P[E_3] = P[E_4]$. Events A and B are defined by $A = E_1 \cup E_3 \cup E_4$ and $B = E_2 \cup E_4 \cup E_5$. Find:

   (a) $P[E_1]$. **(b)** $P[A \cup B]$, by adding simple event probabilities. **(c)** $P[A]$. **(d)** $P[B]$. **(e)** $P[A \cup B]$, using The Additive Law of Probability.

APPLYING THE CONCEPTS

100. An unfair coin is twice as likely to produce a head as it is a tail. Find the simple event probabilities for the experiment of tossing the coin once.

Exercises 101–105: The probabilities that two famous movie reviewers will rate a new movie as poor, average, above average, very good, or excellent are, respectively, 0.14, 0.37, 0.24, 0.18, and 0.07. Find the probability that they rate a randomly selected movie:

101. very good or excellent;   102. at most average;   103. at least average;
104. neither poor nor average;   105. not excellent, but not poor.

Exercises 106–109: Basketball star Felmo Fahrquar is a good free-throw shooter. Records for his two-shot situations show the following simple event probabilities:

Event	Shot 1	Shot 2	Prob.
a	Make	Make	0.64
b	Make	Miss	0.16
c	Miss	Make	*
d	Miss	Miss	0.04

106. Fill in the correct probability to replace the *. (The team statistician spilled coffee and we can't read it!)
107. Find the probability that Felmo makes at least one free throw on his next two-shot opportunity.
108. Find the probability that Felmo makes at most one shot on his next two-shot situation.
109. Find the probability Felmo makes one of his next two shots.

Exercises 110–113: Felmo's sister, Feldspar, has a coin purse with her lunch money inside: a penny, a nickel, a dime, and a quarter. She selects two coins at random to pay for a Twinkie. As you will learn in Section 6.6, the phrase *at random* means that all outcomes have the same probability.

110. List the outcomes for her experiment.
111. Find the probability that she selects the quarter.
112. Find the probability that she gets at least 15 cents.
113. Find the probability that she gets no more than 20 cents.

Exercises 114–126: Two weird coins are tossed. Outcomes HH and TT are just as likely as one another. Also, $P[HT] = P[TH]$; but $P[HH] = 3 \cdot P[HT]$. Events *A–D* are defined as follows: *A:* one head occurs. *B:* At least one head occurs. *C:* Coins match. *D:* At most one tail occurs or the coins match. Find the following probabilities:

114. $P[HH]$;   115. $P[HT]$;   116. $P[A]$;   117. $P[B]$;
118. $P[C]$;   119. $P[D]$;   120. $P[A \cap B]$;   121. $P[A \cap C]$;
122. $P[B \cap C]$;   123. $P[A \cup B]$;   124. $P[A \cup C]$;   125. $P[B \cup C]$.
126. Which pairs of events among *A, B, C,* and *D* are mutually exclusive?

Exercises 127–130: Product consultant Penrose Prynne must rank three brands of carbonated prune juice—Brighter Day (B), Sunlight (S), New Dawn (N)—from best to worst flavor. Penrose detects absolutely no differences among the three brands. Therefore, all possible rankings will have the same probability.

127. List an appropriate sample space for the experiment of ranking the brands.
128. What is the probability he ranks B first?
129. What is the probability he ranks S last?
130. What is the probability he ranks N first and S not last?

*131.   A high school senior seeks admission to two colleges, A and B. He estimates that his probability of admission to college A is 0.8, and that his probability of admission to college B is 0.5. He also thinks his probability of rejection by at least one of the two colleges is 0.6. What is the probability that he will be admitted by at least one of the two colleges?

132.   Consider the Venn diagram. The regions represented by lowercase letters are all mutually exclusive, and their union is S. (They are a partition of S.) In this section we developed The Additive Law of Probability for two events A and B. Using the lettered regions as an aid, see if you can develop a similar law for $P[A \cup B \cup C]$. (We know that we can find $P[A \cup B \cup C]$ by adding the simple event probabilities for regions **a** through **g**; the idea here is to express the probability in terms of the probabilities for A, B, C, and suitable intersections of these three sets.)

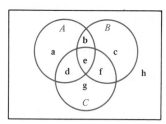

Exercises 133 and 134:   The probability that a rock concert at Dolt State University will sell out is 0.85.

133.   What are the odds on (that is, in favor of) the concert selling out?
134.   What are the odds on the concert not selling out?

Exercises 135 and 136:   Boris Becker has won 175 of his last 184 tennis matches.

135.   With this information only, and without knowing who his next opponent is, what is the estimated probability that Boris will win his next match?

136.   What are the odds in favor of Boris winning his next match?

137.   Your "passing math" probability is 0.94; what are the odds against your passing?

6.6 EQUALLY LIKELY PROBABILITY

The Equally Likely Method

The study of probability originated in games of chance. In most such games, including all popular casino games like blackjack, craps, roulette, keno, and baccarat, it is possible to describe the outcomes as *equally likely*. The same is true when a fair coin is tossed or a fair die is rolled. In these cases, it is convenient to attach probabilities to simple events by using the following logic: when a fair coin is tossed, there are two possible simple events—head and tail. One of the two is head, and thus the probability of a head should be "one out of two," or 1/2. The same is true for "tail." (Fortunately, assigning probability 1/2 to each of these two simple events also meets the requirement that "the sum of all simple event probabilities in a sample space must be 1.")

Likewise, when a fair die is tossed, there are six simple events ("up faces"), one of which is a two. Thus the probability of a two should be "one out of six," or 1/6. The following example shows how easy it is to use *equally likely* probability.

■ EXAMPLE 14

An American roulette wheel has its circumference divided into 38 equal-length slots: 18 black, 18 red, and 2 green. Red and black slots are numbered from 1 through 36 with these numbers situated among colors as follows:

Red: 1,3,5,7,9,12,14,16,18,19,21,23,25,27,30,32,34,36

Black: 2,4,6,8,10,11,13,15,17,20,22,24,26,28,29,31,33,35

Green: 0,00

The game is played by spinning the wheel in one direction and a small ball in the other; the slot where the ball stops is the outcome. Many different bets are available, including bets on color, bets on odd or even, bets on a specific number, and a variety of others. Find the probabilities of the following events:

A: The ball stops in an odd-numbered slot.

B: The ball stops in a slot which is a red, odd number.

SOLUTION

The balanced construction of the wheel suggests that any one of these 38 slots is just as likely as any other to capture the ball when the wheel is spun. Hence, all simple events (the 38 numbered slots) have probability 1/38. To calculate probability for an event requires that we list the event and sum its associated simple event probabilities. For event A, we have

$$A = \{1,3,5, \ldots, 35\} \quad \text{and thus} \quad P[A] = 1/38 + 1/38 + \cdots + 1/38$$

where we add as many fractions 1/38 as there are odd numbers in A. Since there are 18 odd numbers, we add 18 fractions 1/38. This is a tedious task, but primitive mathematicians devised a clever way of doing repeated addition—multiplication. Thus, the probability of A is $P[A] = 18(1/38) = 18/38$. Likewise, we obtain $B = \{1,3,5,7,9,19,21,23,25,27\}$, and $P[B] = 10/38$. ■

The purposely cumbersome way we arrived at probabilities in Example 14 suggests an easier way. In finding $P[A]$, "18" represents the number of outcomes in A, the event of interest, and "38" is the total number of outcomes in S. Thus, determining probabilities in an equally likely sample space requires that we count the number of elements in two sets—the sample space S and the event of interest. In summary:

EQUALLY LIKELY PROBABILITY

> In a sample space having $n(S)$ equally likely simple events, the probability of any event A is $n(A)/n(S)$. In words, the probability of any event is the ratio of the number of simple events in that event to the total number of simple events in the sample space.

Assigning equally likely probabilities automatically satisfies the two probability rules given earlier. Since a probability is a ratio of counts, it is greater than or equal to zero. Also, since an event A is a subset of S, $n(A)$ is less than or equal to $n(S)$, and hence the ratio $n(A)/n(S)$ is at most 1. The first rule is thus satisfied. You should convince yourself that rule 2 is also satisfied by reasoning that the sum of all simple event probabilities assigned in this way is one.

■ EXAMPLE 15

A card is selected at random from a well-shuffled standard deck of 52 cards. Find the probabilities of the following three events:

A: Black card B: Face card C: Red jack

SOLUTION

(If necessary, review the makeup of a standard deck.) Since the deck is shuffled (mixed), an equally likely approach is justified, with the 52 cards representing 52 equally likely simple events. Since $n(A) = 26$, and $n(S) = 52$, then $P[A] = 26/52 = 1/2$. Similarly, $n(B) = 12$, so that $P[B] = 12/52 = 3/13$. Finally, since there are two red jacks, $n(C) = 2$, and $P[C] = 2/52 = 1/26$.   ■

Recommendations on Rounding

You may prefer decimals to fractions, but you should be careful of how and when you round your answers. Carry as much accuracy as possible in your decimal arithmetic, and then round your probabilities to three decimal places in the final answer—or more to get a nonzero digit if your answer begins with 0.000. For example, if you add 1/3 and 1/3, and you first round 1/3 to 0.33, you will get $0.33 + 0.33 = 0.66$. If you maintain three or more digits after the decimal, then add and round to two decimal places, you will get 0.67, more accurate than 0.66. Above all, *do not* round 1/3 to 0.3. That is simply too inaccurate.

Sometimes a bit of imagination is required in order to see the equally likely sample space that underlies a given experiment.

■ EXAMPLE 16

Two fair coins are to be tossed, and the number of heads that results is to be reported. Devise an equally likely sample space for this experiment, and use it to assign probabilities to the various numbers of heads which might occur.

SOLUTION

The possible outcomes (numbers of heads) are 0, 1, and 2. Thus a first guess at the sample space might be $S_1 = \{0,1,2\}$. This is not incorrect, but it is not valid to assign probability 1/3 to each of the three. If we instead think of the coins as "first coin, second coin" and list possible outcomes, we arrive at sample space $S_2 = \{HH,HT,TH,TT\}$. The simple events associated with S_2 are equally likely. Of the four ways two coins can land, only one has "two heads"; so the simple event "2" in sample space S_1 has probability 1/4. Similarly, $P[0] = 1/4$ and $P[1] = 2/4 = 1/2$. ■

■ EXAMPLE 17

Two fair dice, one red and the other green (just to enable us to describe outcomes), are tossed. Find probabilities of these events:

A: The sum is seven.   B: The sum is less than six.
C: The numbers on the two dice match.

SOLUTION

For present and future reference, we first show in table form all distinct outcomes which the dice might display. The use of dice of two colors enables us to distinguish between outcomes we might otherwise overlook. For example, the outcome (red 2, green 3) is distinct from (red 3, green 2).

Table 6.2
Separate values and (total) of two dice

GREEN DIE

	1	2	3	4	5	6
1	1 ,1; (2)	1 ,2; (3)	1 ,3; (4)	1 ,4; (5)	1 ,5; (6)	1 ,6; (7)
2	2 ,1; (3)	2 ,2; (4)	2 ,3; (5)	2 ,4; (6)	2 ,5; (7)	2 ,6; (8)
3	3 ,1; (4)	3 ,2; (5)	3 ,3; (6)	3 ,4; (7)	3 ,5; (8)	3 ,6; (9)
4	4 ,1; (5)	4 ,2; (6)	4 ,3; (7)	4 ,4; (8)	4 ,5; (9)	4 ,6; (10)
5	5 ,1; (6)	5 ,2; (7)	5 ,3; (8)	5 ,4; (9)	5 ,5; (10)	5 ,6; (11)
6	6 ,1; (7)	6 ,2; (8)	6 ,3; (9)	6 ,4; (10)	6 ,5; (11)	6 ,6; (12)

Since the dice are fair, it is reasonable to assume the $6 \cdot 6 = 36$ outcomes or simple events are equally likely. Thus, $n(S) = 36$. To find $n(A)$, we simply count the occurrences of "(7)" (a sum of seven) in the table. A 1 on the red die and a 6 on the green is clearly an outcome different from a 6 on the red and a 1 on the green. By ordinary counting (no special formula needed), we see $n(A) = 6$ ways of obtaining the sum of seven. Thus, $P[A] = P[\text{Sum of seven}] = n(A)/n(S) = 6/36$.

To find $P[B]$, we need to count the outcomes in S that produce a sum less than six. A quick survey of our table for sums (2), (3), (4), and (5) reveals ten such occurrences. Thus, $n(B) = 10$, and $P[B] = 10/36 \approx 0.278$.

To find $P[C] = P$[two dice match], we count the ways that two dice can match. They can both show a one, or they can both show a two, and so on, so that $n(C) = 6$. Hence, $P[C] = 6/36 = 1/6 \approx 0.167$. ■

PRACTICE PROBLEM 16   In Example 17, find the probability that the number on the red die exceeds the number on the green die.

ANSWER(S) $15/36 \approx 0.417$ ☐

■ EXAMPLE 18

Two fair dice are tossed. Find the probability that the sum of the numbers on the two dice is four or more.

SOLUTION   An equally likely model is appropriate. We need only count, among the 36 possible outcomes of Table 6.2, those with sum four or more. There are 33 such outcomes. Thus, P[sum is 4 or more] = 33/36. This is easy, but yet much harder than necessary. Let's do the problem by using the Complement Rule. Let A be the event of interest: "The sum is four or more." Then A^c is the event: "Sum is three or less." $P[A^c] = 3/36$ (it's easy to count the three ways to get a sum of two or three), and thus $P[A] = 1 - 3/36 = 33/36$. ■

EXERCISES 6.6

APPLYING THE CONCEPTS

138. Find the probability of a green number at roulette.

139. At roulette, find the probability that the ball is captured by an odd-numbered slot or by a black slot.

Exercises 140–145:   One card is drawn at random from an ordinary deck of 52 cards. Find the probability that it is:

140. a spade

141. a jack

142. the jack of spades

143. a red card

144. a black face card

145. a black card or a spade

Exercises 146–150:   Three fair coins are tossed. List the following events as subsets of the sample space, and find their probabilities:

146. *A:* At least one head   147. *B:* More heads than tails   148. *C:* Two tails
149. *D:* At most two tails   150. *E:* Exactly one head or at least one tail

Exercises 151–153: When two fair dice are tossed, find the probability of:

151. *A:* Sum is more than six   152. *B:* Sum is odd   153. *C:* Sum is negative

Exercises 154–159: For the events of Exercises 151–153, find the probability of:

154. $A \cap B$ 155. $A \cap C$ 156. $B \cap C$
157. $A \cup B$ 158. $A \cup C$ 159. $B \cup C$

Exercises 160–163: One card is selected at random from a deck of 52. Find the probability that it is:

160. a face card   161. an ace or a king   162. an ace and a king   163. a heart or a jack

164. When an ordinary pair of dice is tossed, find the probability that the sum is at most 10. (In this exercise, one tempting sample space contains the various sums which might occur. You must use the underlying equally likely sample space containing the 36 pairs of values two dice might produce.)

165. When an ordinary pair of dice is tossed, find the probability that the two dice do not show the same number.

*166. When six fair coins are tossed, find the probability that there will be at least two heads. (In this exercise, both an equally likely sample space and the Complement Rule will be useful.)

*167. When three fair dice are tossed, find the probability that the sum of the three dice is between 5 and 17, inclusive. (Include the "endpoints" 5 and 17.)

Exercises 168–170: A single die is weighted so that $P[5] = 0.2$ and $P[6] = 0.25$. What is the probability that a toss of this die will produce a number:

168. other than 5?   169. less than 6?   170. less than 5?

Exercises 171 and 172: A card is drawn from a well-shuffled deck, examined, and returned to the deck. The deck is shuffled again, and a second card is drawn. (*Suggestion:* Imagine listing all possible outcomes as pairs of the form "first card, second card.") What is the probability that:

171. both cards are threes?   172. exactly one card is a three?

6.7 RELATIVE FREQUENCY AND SUBJECTIVE PROBABILITY

The Relative Frequency Approach

In many problems, an equally likely sample space is not reasonable, and using the probability methods we have been discussing would lead to disastrous results. What do we do then? If it is possible to perform the experiment many times, or to observe the results of experimentation, we can use the concept of **relative frequency** as a means of assigning probabilities to simple events.

■ EXAMPLE 19

Suppose you have thrown a dart 1000 times at a target. Summarizing and recording your scores after 10, 100, 200, 500, and 1000 throws gives the results shown in table form.

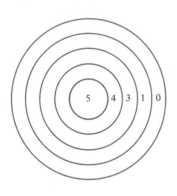

	# Times Achieved in n Throws				
Score	$n = 10$	$n = 100$	$n = 200$	$n = 500$	$n = 1000$
0	1	6	11	27	55
1	1	5	14	37	74
3	4	41	86	206	410
4	4	46	82	215	426
5	0	2	7	15	35
Total # throws	10	100	200	500	1000

A relative frequency is simply a proportion of the total. Consider the simple event of getting a 0 score. After 10 throws, the relative frequency of 0 is $1/10 = 0.100$. After 100 throws, the relative frequency of 0 is $6/100 = 0.060$. After 200 throws, the relative frequency is $11/200 = 0.055$. After 500 throws, the relative frequency is $27/500 = 0.054$, and after 1000 throws it is $55/1000 = 0.055$.

As you can see, the relative frequency is changing,[2] but as the number of experimental trials increases, the relative frequency is beginning to stabilize. It is this long-run stabilization that justifies relative frequency as an approximation to probabilities.

RELATIVE FREQUENCY PROBABILITY

The **relative frequency** of event A is found by performing an experiment a large number of times and observing how many times event A occurs. The relative frequency of event A is the ratio

$$\frac{\text{\# times event } A \text{ occurs}}{\text{\# times experiment repeated}}$$

Note: Remember the crooked die in Example 12? Relative frequency was used to establish the simple event probabilities. The die was tossed a high number of times, and the number of occurrences of each face was

[2] The volatile nature of relative frequencies for small numbers of experiments is expected. There is, however, a second element at work during the early experimental results. You are learning about dart throwing, and presumably improving. The effects of learning should have stabilized after roughly 200 throws.

recorded. The proportion of times each face occurred supplied the probabilities that we used.   ■

■ EXAMPLE 20

Medical records of 140 deceased males revealed the following:

| | Age at Time of Death | | |
Cause of Death	Under 40	40–60	Over 60
Heart disease	6	14	26
Cancer	4	9	12
Stroke	2	4	7
Pneumonia	0	1	2
Diabetes	1	2	2
Tuberculosis	0	1	1
Other	15	11	20

Find the probability that a male randomly chosen from this group died of **(a)** heart disease; **(b)** heart disease or a stroke; **(c)** cancer. **(d)** Find the probability that one who lived to age 40 died of a stroke.

SOLUTION

(a) The number of deaths due to heart disease is $6 + 14 + 26 = 46$. The relative frequency of death due to heart disease is $46/140 \approx 0.329$; this approximates the probability of death due to heart disease.

(b) The number of deaths due to heart disease or stroke is $46 + 13 = 59$. Thus, the relative frequency of death due to heart disease or stroke is $59/140 \approx 0.421$.

(c) The number of deaths due to cancer is 25, and hence the relative frequency of cancer deaths is $25/140 \approx 0.179$.

(d) The relative frequency of stroke death in the 40 or over subpopulation is $11/112 \approx 0.0982$.   ■

Using relative frequency to assign probabilities guarantees that the two probability axioms are satisfied. Rule 1, for example, says that probabilities should be at least 0 but no more than 1. A relative frequency has to be at least zero since an event cannot happen a negative proportion of the time. Also, a relative frequency must be no more than one: an event cannot happen more than once per experiment. You should persuade yourself that Rule 2 is also satisfied.

Probability obtained using relative frequency is called **objective or empirical probability** because values are based on experimental results. Sometimes an equally likely approach is unwarranted, but the experiment cannot be repeated in order to use relative frequency.

For example, suppose you are the manager of a small business and want to know the probability that your sales will go up by at least ten percent if you replace John, the current manager, with Harold, a dynamic new employee. You cannot simply say, "sales will go up by ten percent or they won't; hence the probability is 1/2 that Harold will increase sales by at least 10 percent." This is a gross misapplication of equally likely probability. Nor can you use relative frequency. (John is liable to get tired of being replaced by Harold after 40 or 50 times!) What can you do?

Subjective Probability

A third method, **subjective or personal probability,** can be helpful in this situation. You use your best information, intuition—and a lot of thought—to arrive at what you think is a reasonable probability. If you were to ask ten other people in your organization to give you their personal probabilities, you would no doubt get ten different answers. For this reason, subjective probabilities are not as defensible as objective, relative frequency probabilities, where everyone with the same data would arrive at the same relative frequencies.

There are times, however, when relative frequency is not appropriate because of the "one-shot" nature of an experiment. For example, as this book goes to press, the United States has several hundred thousand military personnel in Saudi Arabia. There is much speclation about the probability of a general war, involving large numbers of American troops, in the region. Relative frequency and equally likely methods are inappropriate. Only subjective probability estimates are possible. Example 21 shows how you might use the subjective method even when relative frequency is appropriate.

■ EXAMPLE 21

Charles Novak, a college junior, hopes to borrow $4000 toward senior-year expenses. Mr. Spencer, the bank's loan officer, has just read a report that, of 1200 junior-year borrowers, 238 had failed to repay their loans within five years after graduation. How might Mr. Spencer respond to Charles' application?

SOLUTION

Using relative frequency, Mr. Spencer might reason as follows: "Since 238 out of 1200 students in Charles' situation have apparently defaulted on (abandoned) their loans, it is reasonable to think that the probability that Charles will default is $238/1200 \approx 0.198$. I have about a 20% chance of losing money lent to Charles; the probability that he will repay the loan is about 0.8." This relative frequency approach treats Charles as being essentially identical to the 1200 junior borrowers in the report.

However, if Charles and Mr. Spencer are both long-time residents of a small community, and Charles has repaid money borrowed from Mr. Spencer's bank on two other occasions to buy cars, Mr. Spencer might say, "I know what the report says; but this Charles is a good, solid young man, well on his way to a college degree, and I believe in him. Only some personal disaster would keep him from paying his debt. I think his probability of repaying is about 0.95." ◼

Care must be taken that probability axioms are satisfied when using subjective probability. We do little with subjective probability in this book. Our objective has been to make you aware of its existence.

Of the remaining two methods for assigning probabilities to simple events, which method is better: the equally likely method or the relative frequency method? In making your choice, you should be guided by the following thought.

The goodness of a probability model is dependent entirely upon its accuracy in predicting the outcomes of future experiments.

This statement suggests that relative frequency is certainly a safe approach for attaching probabilities. Even if an equally likely approach is justified, relative frequencies would lead to approximately the correct probabilities. Of course, if it is obvious that an equally likely approach is correct, then you save lots of experimentation by adopting this approach from the start.

A Final Note   We recommend you interpret probabilities, where possible, with relative frequency. In Example 12, where we tossed the unbalanced die, the probability of an odd number was 0.75. This is the proper way of explaining this result: "On any given toss, I don't know what's going to happen, but in the long run, about 75% of our die tosses would give odd numbers."

EXERCISES 6.7

APPLYING THE CONCEPTS

173. Of 947 visitors polled after leaving Mt. Rainier National Park, 887 say they would like to return. Estimate the probability that a randomly chosen visitor would like to return. What method of assigning probabilities are you using?

*174. A consumer testing organization is interested in just how many cashews a consumer can expect to find in a can of nuts labeled: "Cashews

and mixed nuts." ("And mixed nuts" is of course in very small print!) To that end, they select a sample of 500 cans of these nuts, and find that only 420 cans have any cashews at all. Estimate the probability that a randomly chosen can of nuts will have no cashews.

175. A sample of 186 new model cars in California revealed 65 that could not meet emission control standards. Estimate the probability that a

randomly chosen new model California car will not be able to pass emission control standards.

176. Passenger bus records show that over the last four years, 1,789 of 2,154 buses arrived on time in Pittsburgh after leaving Chicago on schedule. Estimate the probability that the next on-schedule departure from Chicago to Pittsburgh will arrive on time. Would you feel safe in using your answer for any bus trip from Chicago to Pittsburgh?

177. A sample of 88 new video recorders of the same make and model showed that 14 were "D.O.A."—dead (defective) on arrival. Estimate the probability that the next machine of this type is defective when opened.

Exercises 178–183: A school district special report claims that 20% of all "problem students" have bad eyesight and 12% have poor hearing. Use a Venn diagram to guide your thinking, and answer the following:

*178. What is the *largest* percentage of problem children who could have bad eyesight or poor hearing?

*179. What is the *smallest* percentage of problem children who could have bad eyesight or poor hearing?

If it is further known that 6% of the district's problem students have bad eyesight and poor hearing, what is the probability that a randomly chosen problem child from this district will have:

180. poor hearing or bad eyesight
181. bad eyesight but good hearing
182. poor hearing but acceptable eyesight
183. have one or the other of these two sensory disabilities, but not both

Exercises 184–186: The table below, excerpted from a standard "mortality" table, shows the number of survivors at ten-year intervals of 100,000 alive at age 10.

Age	Number Living	Age	Number Living	Age	Number Living
20	92,857	50	73,921	80	18,783
30	87,641	60	57,917	90	985
40	81,239	70	45,674	100	6

184. Find (estimate) the probability that a 20-year-old will still be alive at age 60.
185. Estimate the probability that a 10-year-old will reach 80.
186. Estimate the probability that a 40-year-old will reach 70.

Exercises 187–191: A survey of 100 television viewers revealed that 55 watch football, 41 watch basketball, and 27 watch both. Suppose we choose one person at random from these 100 people. Estimate the probability that the person watches:

187. only basketball
188. only football
189. basketball or football
190. basketball or football, but not both
191. at least one of the two sports

Exercises 192–195: All 600 Anemia Tech undergraduates were asked their opinions of changing to a four-day school week. Their responses, by class standings, were:

Class Standing	Favor Four Days	Do Not Favor Four Days
Freshmen	120	40
Sophomores	130	20
Juniors	95	65
Seniors	60	70

If one Anemia Tech student is chosen at random, estimate the probability that:

192. he/she is a freshman
193. he/she favors a four-day week
194. he/she is a sophomore or does not favor a four-day week
195. he/she is a junior and favors a four-day week

A Brief Summary of Important Ideas

Counting is of fundamental importance. In this chapter we learned methods for systematic counting and sorting of sets of objects. These methods ranged from primitive notions such as enumerating or "pointing and counting," to more powerful, organized methods using Venn diagrams and tables. "Set" language, introduced naturally where helpful, included such notions as union of two sets ($A \cup B$), intersection of two sets ($A \cap B$), and complement of a set (A^c). The Fundamental Counting Principle, motivated and illustrated using tree diagrams, completed our treatment of counting methods.

Even elementary counting methods found swift application to probability, the measuring of likelihood of events. The set of all possible outcomes of an experiment was defined to be the sample space for the experiment. An event was then seen to be any subset of a sample space. Rules for assigning probabilities to all outcomes in a sample space, and then to any event, were discussed. The additive law for probabilities and the complement rule were slight modifications of familiar counting rules.

Equally likely probability assignments were easy to accept, provided all outcomes in a given sample space were demonstrably equally likely to occur. Even nonequally likely sample spaces may sometimes be seen as overlying equally likely spaces.

Relative frequencies were used to assign probabilities using observed data, rather than by assumptions of equal likelihood. Using relative frequencies, we can estimate probabilities of outcomes which we cannot analyze by thought alone.

In order to be useful, a probability model (assignment of probabilities to all possible outcomes) of an experimental situation must have two qualities: it must agree with observations of experimental results up to the time of construction of the model, and it must accurately predict the likelihood of future experimental outcomes.

REVIEW EXERCISES

APPLYING THE CONCEPTS

Exercises 196–200: Give a suitable sample space for each experiment.

196. Ask an individual undergraduate student his/her class standing.
197. In the student cafeteria, where each table seats six, choose a table and find out how many seniors are seated thereat.
198. Record the gender and class standing of a randomly chosen undergraduate.

199. From a dozen light bulbs containing two defectives, test 3 bulbs in succession and record the individual outcomes.
200. In the light bulb testing of Exercise 199, record the number of defective bulbs.

Exercises 201–204: Show the given event as a set of simple events (outcomes):

201. *A:* the student in Exercise 196 is in his/her first or final year of college.
202. *B:* in Exercise 198, a male was chosen.

203. *C:* in Exercise 199, an odd number of good bulbs occurred.
204. *D:* in Exercise 200, an odd number of good bulbs occurred.

Exercises 205–213: Using digits from among 1, 2, 3, and 4, how many numerals can be formed consisting of the given number of digits:

205. one
206. two, without repeats
207. three, no repeats
208. four, no repeats
209. four or fewer, no repeats

210. two, repeats permitted
211. three, repeats permitted
212. four or fewer, repeats permitted
*213. four or fewer, repeats required (*Hint:* See Exercises 209 and 212.)

214. The Torus, a new world-class car, just hit the market. (The company used to make donuts, but found itself going into the hole because there was too little dough in that business.) Options include 5 colors, 3 engine choices, bucket or regular seats, and 3 decor groups—standard, deluxe, or ridiculously extravagant. How many cars must a dealer buy if the Torus maker, DM ("Donut Motors," of course!) insists that the dealer display every possible configuration?

Exercises 215 and 216: A secretary has typed five business letters to five different people, and addressed an envelope for each letter. He puts a letter in each envelope at random.

215. How many different assignments of letters to envelopes are possible?

*216. What is the probability that each person receives the correct letter?

217. The "Express: 9 Items or Less" checkout line in a supermarket is moving slowly. The previous hour, among 85 consecutive customers checked through this line, 17 actually presented 10 items or more to be checked. What is the probability that a randomly selected customer in the express line is in compliance with the "9 items or less" rule?

Exercises 218 and 219: Hoping to account for large increases in electricity and water consumption in an affluent 60-home suburb, the utility company conducted a door-to-door survey to find out how many homes had hot tubs and/or swimming pools. The pollster lost his notes, but remembered that he visited all 60 homes, discovered that 18 had pools, 20 had tubs, and 33 had neither.

218. How many homes had both pools and tubs?

219. What is the probability that a randomly selected home in this neighborhood has a pool or tub?

220. Every local telephone number consists of a three-digit prefix from among 925, 962, and 963, and a special suffix (last four digits). How many different telephone numbers are possible in that community?

221. When two fair dice are tossed, what is the probability that the bigger of the two numbers showing will be at least two more than the smaller number?

Exercises 222–224: If U is an equally likely sample space in which $n(U) = 20$, $n(A) = 12$, and $n(B) = 10$, find:

*222. the minimum and maximum possible values for $n(A \cup B)$

223. $P[A^c]$

*224. the minimum and maximum possible values for $P[A \cap B]$

Exercises 225–227: An energy survey of 60 randomly selected homes in West Hysteria (a community whose harsh winters require heating systems in all residences) revealed that 31 homes use electricity (E) or fossil fuels (F) but not wood (W), 30 use fossil fuels, 26 use electricity, 12 use fossil fuels and electricity, 10 use fossil fuels and wood, and 2 oddly structured homes use all three types.

225. Complete a Venn diagram of heating system types in the 60 homes.

226. What is the probability that a randomly chosen home from among the 60 surveyed uses two or more heating system types?

227. Based upon the survey, what is the estimated probability that a home randomly chosen in the community will use exactly one type of heating system?

Exercises 228 and 229: From a box containing 20 apples, a researcher tests two consecutive, randomly chosen apples for apple maggot larvae. Each apple is either infested (I) or free (F). Unknown to the researcher, 7 of the apples are infested.

228. Represent the possible outcomes of the two selections in a four-region Venn diagram, showing the number of outcomes in each region. (A tree may help.)

229. What is the probability that the researcher will discover some infested apples? Obtain this probability both directly and by using the complement rule.

Exercises 230–232: Arlo, Bjorn, and Cedric, good friends and very evenly matched tennis players, agree to play a tournament among themselves to determine the order in which they will play Darth, the awesome new invader of their racquet club.

230. List the simple events in the sample space showing the various orderings among the friends which their tournament might determine.

231. What is the probability that Arlo will rank first or last?

232. What is the probability that Cedric will rank higher than Arlo?

Exercises 233–237: Many factors affect home heating energy. Among these are type of structure and primary source of heat. A complete community survey produced the table shown. All questions refer only to this community.

Heat Source	Structure Type		
	Frame	Masonry	Dome
Wood	31	19	8
Fossil	44	27	2
Electric	23	35	11

233. How many homes are of masonry or frame construction?

234. How many are dome homes or use electric heat?

235. How many are frame homes and use electric heat?

236. What is the probability that a randomly chosen home will be heated by combustion (wood or fossil fuels)?

237. What is the probability that a randomly chosen home will be of frame construction or heated by wood?

Exercises 238–240: Andy McCarthy's newly opened printing and copy shop has (he thinks) 3 to 2 odds in favor of being successful. Based upon this assessment,

238. What is Andy's probability of success?

239. What is Andy's probability of failing?

240. What are the odds in favor of Andy's failure (that is, against success)?

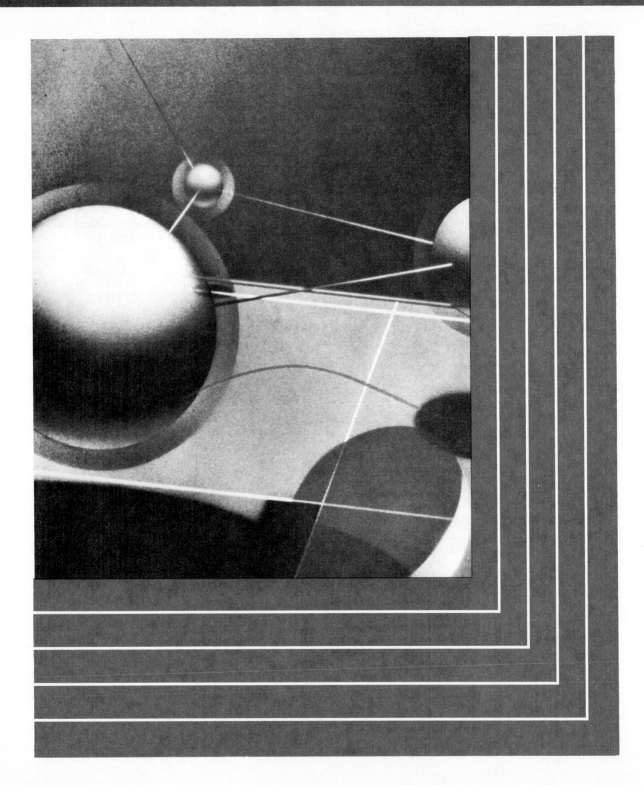

7 More Counting and Probability

Our goal in Chapter 6 was to become acquainted with basic ideas of counting and probability. In this chapter we will develop and use more powerful counting methods in computing probabilities. We will see a variety of applications—for example, to games of chance, quality control, and to sampling income tax returns in an effort to detect errors.

Merely being able to answer the question "What is the probability of event *A*?" has numerous applications. There are even more interesting questions. For example:

(a) **Application of independence.** Are having a high grade point average and a long commute to school independent?

(b) **Application of Bayes' Theorem.** If three machines manufacture identical articles, and a defective article is found in their collective output, which machine is most likely to need attention?

(c) **Application of conditional probability and Bayes' Theorem.** What is the probability that a person chosen at random will test positive for tuberculosis? If a person tests positive, how likely is it that he has the disease?

To see how rapidly we pass beyond our present ability to count, one example will suffice:

■ EXAMPLE 1

From a standard deck of cards, what is the probability that:

(a) a single card drawn will be an ace?

(b) a five-card hand will contain three aces?

SOLUTION

Part **(a)** is easy. Of the 52 equally likely outcomes, 4 are aces; so the probability of a single card being an ace is 4/52.

257

Part **(b)** *seems* easy. We need only to count the total number of (equally likely) five-card hands, then determine how many contain three aces and two non-aces. Then, because all hands are equally likely, the probability of a hand with three aces is just

$$P[\text{hand with 3 aces}] = \frac{\text{\# of 3-ace hands}}{\text{total \# of 5-card hands}}$$

In counting the total number of five-card hands, we could use the FCP: "Pick a first card, then a second card, . . ." yielding a count of $52 \cdot 51 \cdot 50 \cdot 49 \cdot 48$. However, this would count the hand 2♥, 4♣, 3♠, K♠, 8♦ and also the hand 3♠, 2♥, K♠, 8♦, 4♣. These are really two arrangements of the same hand, so the FCP has erred by counting rearrangements of identical hands. Our count is too large! How can we adjust it?

We face similar problems in counting 5-card hands with three aces. We could use the FCP and count the ways to draw three aces, the ways to draw two non-aces, and multiply. Counting the possible sets of three aces is not too difficult: there are four ways to omit one ace and select three. Counting the ways to select two non-aces from among the remaining 48 cards, however, is somewhat more difficult. We need to know more about counting. ■

7.1 COUNTS OF ARRANGEMENTS AND SETS

In Chapter 6 we counted orderings of all or part of a given set of objects. (*Example:* In how many ways can a class of 47 students choose a president, vice president, and party chairperson?) We also shall have frequent need to count the ways in which a subset of a certain size could be chosen from a given set. (*Example:* In how many ways could a class of size 47 choose a committee of three to plan a field trip?) Both types of questions yield easily to counting methods we will now develop.

■ EXAMPLE 2

Given a universe $U = \{a,b,c,d,e,f,g\}$ and sets $A = \{a,b,c,d,e\}$, $B = \{c,d\}$, $C = \{b,c,d,e\}$, draw a Venn diagram showing the elements in U, A, B, and C. Then specify which sets are subsets of other sets among these four named sets.

SOLUTION

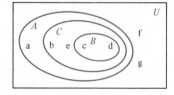

By examining the diagram or the listed elements of the given sets, it is clear that: A, B, and C are subsets of U; B and C are subsets of A; and B is a subset of C. What you may not have noticed is that U is a subset of U, A is a subset of A, B is a subset of B, and C is a subset of C. Remember, the only requirement for set R to be a subset of set S is that each element of R be an element of S. Thus, every set is automatically a subset of itself. ■

As we noted in Chapter 6, the empty set Ø is a subset of every set. With our Example 1 observation that any set S is a subset of itself, we are now absolutely certain of two subsets:

THE TRIVIAL SUBSETS OF S

> If S is any set, then S is a subset of S, and Ø is a subset of S. S and Ø are called the "trivial" subsets of S. They can be named without even examining S.

As noted in Chapter 6, these trivial subsets are the only ones whose probabilities are predictable. All other subsets of S (those of "in-between-size") are called **proper subsets** of S. Is there some way of predicting the number of possible proper subsets of a definite size one can find within a given set S? A good way to begin is with a rather small set S, enumerating all possibilities:

■ EXAMPLE 3

If $S = \{a,b,c\}$, and $n(S) = 3$, list all possible subsets of S of size 0, of size 1, of size 2, of size 3, and of size 4.

SOLUTION

Subsets of size 0: Ø; of size 1: $\{a\}$, $\{b\}$, $\{c\}$; of size 2: $\{a,b\}$, $\{a,c\}$, $\{b,c\}$; of size 3: $\{a,b,c\} = S$; of size 4: none. In table form:

# of Subsets in a Set of Size 3						
Subset sizes:	0	1	2	3	4	Total # of subsets:
# of subsets:	1	3	3	1	0	8

■

PRACTICE PROBLEM 1

Let's write a similar table for subsets of a set of size 5. Certain entries are easy; these are filled in. For example, there are 5 possible subsets of size 1, since we may choose one element from $S = \{a,b,c,d,e\}$ in any of five ways. Similarly, we may omit one element of S at a time to get five subsets of size 4. The table:

# of Subsets in a Set of Size 5								Total # of subsets:
Subset sizes:	0	1	2	3	4	5	6	
# of subsets:	1	5			5	1	0	

Fill in another table entry by first listing all possible subsets of size 2. Then fill in the remaining table entries and record the total number of subsets for a set of size 5. Do it!   ☐

We are now ready to establish quick, easy ways to count either orderings or subsets (disregarding order) of any size.

Orderings (Permutations)

We can solve problems like "In how many ways could a class of 47 students elect a president, vice president, and party chairperson?" Our "job description" might be "First: select a president; second: select a vice president; third: select a party chairperson." The corresponding counts are 47, 46, and 45. By the FCP, the total number of ways to choose the three officers is $47 \cdot 46 \cdot 45 = 97,290$.

Suppose we now wish to select and order a set of size 5 from among 47 objects. The logic used above is still appropriate, yielding a total count of $47 \cdot 46 \cdot 45 \cdot 44 \cdot 43$.

How many orderings within a set of five objects (arrangements using all five) are possible? We easily produce $5 \cdot 4 \cdot 3 \cdot 2 \cdot 1 = 120$.

Similarly, there are $4 \cdot 3 \cdot 2 \cdot 1$ possible orderings of a set of size 4, $6 \cdot 5 \cdot 4 \cdot 3 \cdot 2 \cdot 1$ possible orderings of a set of size 6, etc. How many orderings of an entire set of size 47 are possible? The total count is the product represented by $47 \cdot 46 \cdot 45 \cdot 44 \cdot \ldots \cdot 3 \cdot 2 \cdot 1$. Fortunately for mathematicians and other lazy people, there is a short way of writing "the product of all counting numbers from 47 down to 1;" it is "47!," spoken as "47 factorial" (not to be confused with exuberance over the number "47"). Thus, $5 \cdot 4 \cdot 3 \cdot 2 \cdot 1 = 5! = 120$, $6! = 6 \cdot 5 \cdot 4 \cdot 3 \cdot 2 \cdot 1 = 720$, etc. This gives us a convenient way to represent the number of possible orderings or permutations of a set of any size:

PERMUTATIONS OF A SET OF SIZE n

The number of possible orderings (permutations) of a set of any size n is $n! = n \cdot (n - 1) \cdot (n - 2) \cdot \ldots \cdot 3 \cdot 2 \cdot 1$.

This is an instance where the formula makes sense only after we have clearly understood the underlying ideas. Once an idea is captured (and killed, stuffed, and put into a box, as above), the formula is a useful reminder. Do not rely upon formulas in boxes for your understanding; they will desert you when you need them most. To own an idea, you must go through the effort, and experience the pleasure, of developing that idea.

■ EXAMPLE 4

A sales representative must visit 5 cities (A, B, C, D, E) in an attempt to increase business. He wants to choose a route through all five cities that minimizes his travel mileage. How many different possible routes must he consider?

SOLUTION

To complete a route, the salesman must visit all five cities. One possible route would be $ABCDE$, where he visits the cities in alphabetical order. The number of different routes is the same as the number of ways of arranging $n = 5$ items: $5! = 5 \cdot 4 \cdot 3 \cdot 2 \cdot 1 = 120$. ■

Now let's take a fresh look at counting the number of ways to produce an ordered list using elements from a larger set.

■ EXAMPLE 5

In how many ways could the editors of *Women's Wear Daily* produce a ranked list of the nation's 10 best-dressed women from a set of 25 nominees?

SOLUTION

The B.S. & A. (Brute Strength and Awkwardness) approach is to write down the product $25 \cdot 24 \cdot 23 \cdot 22 \cdot 21 \cdot 20 \cdot 19 \cdot 18 \cdot 17 \cdot 16$, corresponding to having 25 choices for #1, 24 for #2, etc. But wait—is there a better way? (Probably so, or we wouldn't string you along like this.) The above product starts out as if it's going to be 25!, but quits after just 10 factors. To put it another way, it looks like 25! with the final 15 factors removed.

We can get rid of the unwanted final fifteen factors (multipliers) by division: $25 \cdot 24 \cdot 23 \cdot 22 \cdot 21 \cdot 20 \cdot 19 \cdot 18 \cdot 17 \cdot 16 = 25!/15!$, a more compact and pleasing form than the string of 10 factors it replaces. ■

PRACTICE PROBLEM 2

Expand the following expressions into factored form, cancel all possible factors, and calculate:

(a) $7!/4!$; (b) $9!/5!$; (c) $112!/109!$

ANSWER(S)

(a) $7!/4! = (7 \cdot 6 \cdot 5 \cdot 4 \cdot 3 \cdot 2 \cdot 1)/(4 \cdot 3 \cdot 2 \cdot 1) = 7 \cdot 6 \cdot 5 = 210$

(b) Similarly, $9!/5! = 9 \cdot 8 \cdot 7 \cdot 6 = 3024$

(c) $1,367,520$ (Be sure you do it!) □

■ EXAMPLE 6

The top 32 NAIA basketball teams in the country assemble each year in Kansas City for a tournament. If there are 513 NAIA teams, in how many ways could a ranked list of 32 be prepared?

SOLUTION   We now know that we need the product of 32 factors, starting with 513 and decreasing by ones. We do not want all of the factors in 513!, but only the top (largest) 32 factors, omitting the bottom 481 factors. The number of possible lists is thus 513!/481!. The denominator, 481!, exactly wipes out those factors we wish to omit. Calculating the result is something else! ∎

PRACTICE PROBLEM 3   Give "factorial" expressions for the following counts:

(a) the number of ways one could choose an ordered set of size 7 from among a set of size 19;

(b) the number of possible orderings in which one could stack 11 ingredients on a sandwich;

(c) the number of possible orderings of 6 ingredients on a sandwich, if 11 are available;

(d) the number of possible arrangements of 20 of the 52 Miss America candidates for a publicity photograph.

ANSWER(S)   (a) 19!/12!;   (b) 11!;   (c) 11!/5!;   (d) 52!/32!   □

We are now ready to generalize: to count the possible orderings, or permutations, of size k from a set of n objects (where k is less than or equal to n), we multiply only the first k factors in the expansion of $n! = n(n-1)\ldots$, omitting the final $(n-k)$ factors. This is accomplished by dividing $n!$ by $(n-k)!$ This understanding is again captured in a pattern, or formula; make sure you understand the pattern.

PERMUTATIONS OF k OBJECTS CHOSEN FROM AMONG n OBJECTS ("PERMUTATIONS OF n THINGS TAKEN k AT A TIME")

> The number of possible permutations of k objects chosen from n objects is $n!/(n-k)!$, abbreviated $P(n,k)$.

■ EXAMPLE 7   Give factorial expressions for permutations of 12 objects taken

(a) 9 at a time;   (b) 4 at a time;

(c) 12 at a time;   (d) none at a time.

SOLUTION   (a) $12!/(12-9)! = 12!/3!$, since we wish to keep the 9 "large" factors in 12! and drop the 3 "small" factors; the "3!" in the denominator corresponds to the 3 objects we omit when choosing 9 objects from among 12;

(b) $12!/8!$;

(c) 12!/0!, if we follow our pattern. This makes us nervous; it looks suspiciously like a division by 0, which we know is not defined. Looking again at the question (taking an ordered set of size 12 from a set of size 12), and using the FCP, we must pick a first element (12 choices), a second element (11 choices), etc., until we pick a 12th element (1 choice). The resulting count: 12!. We know that "12!" is correct; our pattern yields "12!/0!." *Conclusion:* 12! = 12!/0!; thus 0! must be 1.

(d) Again following our pattern ("choosing an ordered set of size 0 from a set of size 12"), we are keeping none of the objects and omitting 12. The resulting expression: 12!/12!, or 1.

Although this problem asked specifically for factorial expressions, you should observe that each of these parts can be worked by simply applying the Fundamental Counting Principle. In part **(b)**, for example, we can arrange 4 of 12 in $12 \cdot 11 \cdot 10 \cdot 9 = 11{,}880$ ways. ∎

Counts Disregarding Order (Combinations)

A typical permutation question: "From five candidates, in how many ways can one prepare a ranked list of the top three?" Contrast this with a related "unordered" question: "From five candidates, in how many ways can one choose a committee of three?" Though three people are to be chosen in each case, order is important in the first instance, but not in the second.

To better understand the differing counts which answer these questions, consider a particular subset of three candidates {a,b,c}, chosen from a set of five: $S = \{a,b,c,d,e\}$. Subset {a,b,c} can be rearranged in 3! = $3 \cdot 2 \cdot 1 = 6$ ways: *abc, acb, bac, bca, cab, cba*. The same reasoning applies to any subset of three elements of S. Two of these possible subsets of S, and the corresponding possible orderings of their elements, are shown in table form:

Subset of S	Orderings of Subset
{a,b,c}	abc, acb, bac, bca, cab, cba
{a,b,d}	abd, adb, bad, bda, dab, dba

From the table, we see that each subset of size 3 produces six orderings or permutations. Equivalently, each group of six orderings of the same three elements yields only one subset of S. Since S has 5 elements, we know that the number of possible orderings of three elements from S is $P(5,3) = 5!/2!$; each subset of size three accounts for 3! of the orderings;

so the number of subsets is the number of orderings divided by 3!. That is, the number of possible subsets of three elements from among 5 elements is $(5!/2!) \div 3! = 60 \div 6 = 10$.

The easy way, then, to count subsets of a given size, disregarding order, is to first count orderings of that size, then divide by possible rearrangements of one set of that size. Such an "unordered" set is called a **combination.** Again, we generalize:

COMBINATIONS OF k OBJECTS CHOSEN FROM AMONG n OBJECTS ("COMBINATIONS OF n THINGS, TAKEN k AT A TIME")

The number of possible subsets of size k which could be chosen from a set of size n is the number of possible orderings of size k, divided by $k!$ The result: $(n!/(n - k)!) \div k!$, abbreviated $C(n,k)$, and written as follows:

$$C(n,k) = \frac{n!}{(n - k)!k!}$$

■ EXAMPLE 8

You have seven Rolls Royces and wish to give four to your hair stylist. How many different sets of four could you choose?

SOLUTION

Order is not important; count the number of combinations of four you could choose from among seven Rolls Royces:

$$C(7,4) = \frac{7!}{(7 - 4)!4!} = \frac{7 \cdot 6 \cdot 5 \cdot 4 \cdot 3 \cdot 2 \cdot 1}{(3 \cdot 2 \cdot 1) \cdot (4 \cdot 3 \cdot 2 \cdot 1)} = 35$$ ■

■ EXAMPLE 9

Bill and Shannon are planning a vacation, and wish to contact 8 travel agencies in search of good tour packages. Bill agrees to call 3 of them, and Shannon will call the other 5. How many different choices does Bill have?

SOLUTION

Since Bill plans on calling all 3, order makes no difference; the number of combinations he can choose is

$$C(8,3) = \frac{8!}{(8 - 3)!3!} = \frac{8 \cdot 7 \cdot 6 \cdot 5 \cdot 4 \cdot 3 \cdot 2 \cdot 1}{(5 \cdot 4 \cdot 3 \cdot 2 \cdot 1) \cdot (3 \cdot 2 \cdot 1)} = \frac{8 \cdot 7 \cdot 6}{3 \cdot 2 \cdot 1} = 56$$ ■

There is an interesting result concerning combinations that is worth mentioning. In Example 9, let the eight travel agencies be designated by the letters A,B,C,D,E,F,G, and H. Suppose Bill chooses the set $\{A,B,C\}$ to call. In choosing these three, he has also omitted a set of five; namely, $\{D,E,F,G,H\}$. Associated with any set of three that Bill chooses is a set of five that he has omitted. In other words, there are just as many subsets of size five, chosen from eight, as there are subsets of size three, chosen from eight. Thus, $C(8,3) = C(8,5)$. Similarly, $C(9,6) = C(9,3)$—each time you identify a subset of six to choose, you have also identified a subset of three that is excluded. In general, $C(n,k) = C(n,n - k)$, since each time you pick k elements from n you are automatically excluding $n - k$.

Being able to write an expression is of little use if you cannot evaluate it. An expression such as $C(8,3)$ can be swiftly simplified and made ready for calculation using even modest calculators with no special "factorial" (!) key. Consider, again, our calculation for $C(8,3)$:

$$C(8,3) = \frac{8!}{(8 - 3)!3!} = \frac{8!}{3!5!} = \frac{8 \cdot 7 \cdot 6 \cdot 5!}{3!5!} = \frac{8 \cdot 7 \cdot 6}{1 \cdot 2 \cdot 3} = 56$$

Pay special attention to the pattern that has resulted from our arithmetic. In the numerator of the final fraction representing $C(8,3)$ we begin with 8 and "move downward" 3 factors; in the denominator, we begin with 1 and move upward 3 factors. This pattern is appropriate for any "combination" calculation. Thus, for example, $C(9,4) = (9 \cdot 8 \cdot 7 \cdot 6)/(1 \cdot 2 \cdot 3 \cdot 4)$ and $C(14,2) = (14 \cdot 13)/(1 \cdot 2)$. In addition to being computationally convenient, this "form" is also a strong reminder of the connection between permutations and combinations: in $C(8,3)$, for example, the $8 \cdot 7 \cdot 6$ in the numerator represents the number of permutations of 3 items chosen from eight; the $1 \cdot 2 \cdot 3$ in the denominator is the number of different orderings or arrangements of any subset (combination) of 3. When order is not important, this denominator divides out the 6 permutations of any given combination of three.

With an expression like $C(21,18)$ you would not want to write 18 factors on the top and bottom; instead, use $C(21,18) = C(21,3)$, and write $C(21,18) = C(21,3) = (21 \cdot 20 \cdot 19)/(1 \cdot 2 \cdot 3)$. Further simplification is possible since the answer to any combination problem is a count, and hence must reduce to a whole number.

PRACTICE PROBLEM 4 Evaluate the following expressions.

(a) $\dfrac{13!}{(13 - 9)!9!}$ **(b)** $\dfrac{18!}{4!14!}$ **(c)** $C(19,3)$ **(d)** $P(19,3)$

ANSWER(S) **(a)** 715; **(b)** 3060; **(c)** 969; **(d)** 5814. (What should be the relationship between the answers to **(c)** and **(d)**? Do the answers verify this relationship?) ☐

An Important Message Regarding Calculators: "USE WITH CAUTION!" You should set up and carry out small-scale calculations as in Practice Problem 4, so that you will have a feel for how they are done. In general, be sure of your process, then use a calculator to speed up tedious arithmetic.

We have three basic counting patterns: **(1)** the FCP, **(2)** counting arrangements (permutations) from a given set, and **(3)** counting subsets (combinations) from a given set. These three patterns may now be combined in very useful and interesting ways!

■ EXAMPLE 10

A basketball coach has three centers, six forwards, and seven guards on his roster. His travel budget allows him to take only ten players on trips. If he wishes to take two centers, four forwards, and four guards, in how many ways can he pick a travel squad?

SOLUTION

First write a job description: **(1)** choose two centers from the three; order does not matter; **(2)** choose four forwards from the six; again, order does not matter; **(3)** choose four guards from the seven available; order is not important. Separate counts for jobs **(1)**, **(2)**, and **(3)** are $C(3,2)$, $C(6,4)$, and $C(7,4)$, respectively. By the FCP the total count of ways to do all three jobs is $C(3,2) \cdot C(6,4) \cdot C(7,4)$.

$$C(3,2) = C(3,1) = 3$$

$$C(6,4) = C(6,2) = (6 \cdot 5)/(1 \cdot 2) = 15$$

$$C(7,4) = C(7,3) = (7 \cdot 6 \cdot 5)/(1 \cdot 2 \cdot 3) = 35$$

Altogether, then, there are $3 \cdot 15 \cdot 35 = 1575$ different possible travel squads. A coach's job is not always easy! ■

■ EXAMPLE 11

Consider a standard 52-card deck.

(a) How many different five-card hands could be dealt from it?

(b) How many of these hands consist of only red cards?

(c) How many hands contain three aces and two kings?

(d) What is the probability of getting only red cards? of getting a hand containing three aces and two kings?

SOLUTION

Now we can deal with this! Since the order of the cards is not important, all questions involve choosing subsets, or combinations.

(a) The job description is very simple: "pick five cards from among the 52 available cards." $C(52,5) = 2,598,960$ is the count.

(b) Although there are 52 cards, all-red hands must be chosen from the 13 hearts and 13 diamonds. Since we do not care how the cards are assorted between hearts and diamonds, the count is $C(26,5) = 65,780$.

(c) A job description might be "1. Pick three aces; 2. Pick two kings." The counts for these two steps are $C(4,3)$ and $C(4,2)$, respectively, since the aces must be chosen from among the 4 available aces and the kings must be chosen from among the kings. The count for doing both jobs is thus $C(4,3) \cdot C(4,2)$. Verify that the result is 24.

(d) Using the counts in **(a)**, **(b)**, and **(c)**, we obtain:

$$P[\text{all red}] = \frac{65{,}780}{2{,}598{,}960} \approx 0.025$$

$$P[3A, 2K] = \frac{24}{2{,}598{,}960} \approx 0.0000092$$

■

■ EXAMPLE 12

In a preliminary audit, the Infernal Revenue Service has identified 12 suspicious tax returns. The I.R.S. plans to select three at random and subject them to thorough audits. Suppose, unknown to the I.R.S., five of the 12 contain illegal deductions. Find the probability that two of the chosen three will have illegal deductions.

SOLUTION

The order of returns is unimportant, and the selection is "at random," so all subsets (combinations) of size 3 are equally likely. The two quantities needed are:

$n(S)$ = the total number of subsets of 3 chosen from 12, and

$n(A)$ = the number of subsets of size 3 where 2 of the three contain illegal deductions.

Finding $n(S)$ is easy:

$$n(S) = C(12,3) = \frac{12 \cdot 11 \cdot 10}{3 \cdot 2 \cdot 1} = 220$$

Finding $n(A)$ requires two steps. If two of the three contain illegal deductions, then we must also have one legal return. The two illegal returns can be chosen from the five available in $C(5,2) = 10$ ways, and the one legal return can be chosen from the seven available in $C(7,1) = 7$ ways. By the FCP, the combined operation of choosing two illegal returns and one legal return can then be realized in $10 \cdot 7 = 70$ ways. Thus,

$$P[A] = \frac{C(5,2) \cdot C(7,1)}{C(12,3)} = \frac{10 \cdot 7}{220} \approx 0.318$$

■

PRACTICE PROBLEM 5

In Example 12, find the probability that the selection of three tax returns produces at least two with illegal deductions.

ANSWER(S)   0.364.

□

Fasten your seat belt! You are ready for some interesting and challenging problems! Some will be easy; others will have you talking to yourself as you walk about campus, filling paper napkins with scratchwork as you sit in the Student Union, drinking prune juice, and talking with other people about them. This is an important study technique (talking with other people—not drinking prune juice). A good way to learn is by trying to explain to another person what troubles you, or what you have tried that does not work. Genuine learning is not always easy!

EXERCISES 7.1

PRACTICING THE MOVES AND MANEUVERS

Exercises 1–13:   Evaluate the given expressions after first simplifying.

1. $C(8,5)$
2. $P(8,3)$
3. $P(8,5)$
4. $C(6,2)$
5. $C(23,19)$
6. $P(12,5)$
7. $P(11,5)$
8. $C(11,2)$
9. $C(11,5)$
10. $P(5,5)$
11. $C(8,4) \cdot C(6,2)$
12. $C(9,6) \cdot C(12,3)$

13. $\dfrac{C(8,2) \cdot C(4,3)}{C(12,5)}$

14. (*First review Example 3 and Practice Problem 1.*) We have developed methods for counting orderings (permutations) and subsets (combinations) chosen from a given set. Use these skills to fill in the missing entries in the following table:

Set Size, n (below)	Number of Subsets of Size k in Set of Size n								Total # Subsets
	Subset Sizes, k								
	0	1	2	3	4	5	6	7	
0	1	0	0	0	0	0	0	0	1
1									
2	1	2	1	0	0	0	0	0	4
3	1	3	3	1	0	0	0	0	8
4									
5	1	5			5	1	0	0	
6									
7	1	7					7	1	

Study the completed table, looking for patterns. Could you easily add lines for $n = 8, 9,$ etc? Can you predict, without filling in the body of the table, the total number of subsets possible from a set of size 10? 1? 50?

APPLYING THE CONCEPTS

15. A campus dining hall keeps eight kinds of vegetables on hand and will offer three of these vegetables at each evening meal. How many evening meals are possible without repeating a complete set of three vegetable offerings?

16. Of 12 faculty members in a mathematics department, five will teach finite mathematics (one section each) during the fall term. In how many ways could this choice of five be made?

17. The instructors in Exercise 16 must then be assigned to the five sections of finite mathematics. In how many ways could this assignment be made?

18. A designer's collection of golf shirts (the kind with a reptile embroidered on the pocket) is available in seven colors. Golf hats are available in five colors. Beau Dirk, a fashion-conscious golfer, wishes to buy three shirts and two different hats, with no two items alike. How many choices has he?

19. In how many ways can a committee of two men and three women be chosen from a group of seven men and five women?

20. The 12-person board of directors of Acme Widget Company must choose from its own members a president, a vice-president, and a secretary. From the remaining members of the board, a four-person policy study group is to be chosen. In how many ways can the required people be selected?

Exercises 21–27: A shipment of 24 imported coffee makers contains five defective units. An inspector chooses three units at random for testing.

21. How many different sets of size 3 might he select?

22. How many sets of three good (not defective) units could he choose?

23. How many of two good and one defective are possible?

24. How many sets contain exactly one good unit?

25. How many sets contain no good units?

26. How are the answers to 21 through 25 related?

27. Find the probability that the inspector chooses two good and 1 defective unit.

*28. In how many ways can a teacher select one or more students from among six? (Approach this problem in a manner resembling your use of the complement rule in Chapter 6. How many sets are possible? How many are empty?)

29. In how many ways can three or more people be selected from 12? (See hint in Exercise 28.)

Exercises 30–35: How many possible 5-card hands from a standard deck contain:

30. four aces?

31. at least three kings?

32. at most two face cards?

33. two aces and two kings?

34. four face cards?

35. three fives and two tens?

Exercises 36–39: Consider a set of letters (all different) consisting of four vowels (including "e") and 8 consonants (including "b"). From these letters, how many 5-letter sequences can be formed using two vowels and three consonants (all different) that:

*36. contain "b"?

*37. begin with "b"?

*38. begin with "e"?

*39. begin with "e" and contain "b"?

Exercises 40–48: A teacher plans to choose a committee of four from a class containing nine men and three women. How many possible committees of four are there:

40. altogether?

41. that contain exactly one woman?

42. that contain no women?

*43. with more men than women?

*44. that contain at least one woman? (*Hint:* How many are all male?)

Exercises 45–48: Find the probability that the Exercise 40 committee contains:

45. exactly one woman   46. at least one woman   47. no women   48. more men

Exercises 49–64: A poker player is to be dealt five cards from a 52-card deck. How many of her possible hands contain:

49. a spade flush (five spades)?
50. any flush (five of same suit)?
51. an ace-high spade flush (five spades with the ace)?
*52. a full house (three of one denomination, two of another)?
*53. an ace-high full house (three aces and another pair)?

The poker player's opponent is also to receive 5 cards. How many of his possible hands consist of:

54. three aces (without the fourth ace or another pair)?
*55. three of a kind (3 of one denomination, without the fourth or another pair)?
*56. two pairs (without the third card of either denomination)?

Exercises 57–64: What is the probability of the hand in:

57. Exercise 49?	58. Exercise 50?	59. Exercise 51?	60. Exercise 52?
61. Exercise 53?	62. Exercise 54?	63. Exercise 55?	64. Exercise 56?

*65. Seven people are to line up for a photograph. How many different lineups are possible if two of the people refuse to sit together?
66. In how many ways could five people be loaded on a toboggan if one of a certain set of three of them must be in front? (The three willing candidates are probably people who have never before steered a toboggan into a tree!)
67. If the toboggan in Exercise 66 is loaded in random order, what is the probability that the front person is *not* one of the three qualified drivers?

7.2 VARIATIONS ON COUNTING SCHEMES (OPTIONAL)

We have solved the elementary permutation problem: counting possible arrangements (orderings) of k objects chosen from n different objects. We have done the same for combinations (sets, disregarding order) of k objects chosen from n distinct objects. Finally, we have solved multi-step counting problems requiring a sequence of actions by counting possible ways to perform each step (using permutations, combinations, or list the possibilities), then using the FCP to reach a final count.

Not every counting problem is an elementary permutation, combination, or FCP type. We now look at some variations.

Permutations of Some "Alike" Objects

■ EXAMPLE 13

In how many different-looking ways could the letters in "PEPSI" be arranged (in a line, of course)?

SOLUTION

If the letters were all different, there would be 5! = 120 permutations. The problem is the repeated letter "P." Let us approach the problem in stages. Imagine filling five blanks

$$(\underline{\quad}_1\underline{\quad}_2\underline{\quad}_3\underline{\quad}_4\underline{\quad}_5)$$

using P, P, E, S, and I. One possible job description: Our steps then might be:

Step 1. Pick two of the five blanks to receive the two P's; then place the P's in the blanks chosen.

Step 2. Pick one of the remaining blanks to receive the E; fill it.

Step 3. Pick one of the remaining blanks to receive the S; fill it.

Step 4. Pick the remaining blank to receive the I; fill it.

The count for each step is unaffected by how preceding steps are completed. Using the FCP, we determine the possible permutations by multiplying the counts for Steps 1 through 4:

$$C(5,2) \cdot C(3,1) \cdot C(2,1) \cdot C(1,1) = \frac{5!}{3!2!} \cdot \frac{3!}{2!1!} \cdot \frac{2!}{1!1!} \cdot \frac{1!}{0!1!}$$

simplifying, and recalling that 0! = 1 and can hence be omitted

$$= \frac{5!}{2!1!1!1!0!} = \frac{5!}{2!1!1!1!}$$

a revealing form of the answer: The numerator, 5!, follows from there being five letters to arrange; the denominator shows the number of copies of each distinct letter. ■

■ EXAMPLE 14

Solve Example 13 by placing the E, then S, then I, then the P's.

SOLUTION

$$C(5,1) \cdot C(4,1) \cdot C(3,1) \cdot C(2,2) = \frac{5!}{4!1!} \cdot \frac{4!}{3!1!} \cdot \frac{3!}{2!1!} \cdot \frac{2!}{0!2!}$$

$$= \frac{5!}{1!1!1!2!} = 60 \quad ■$$

PRACTICE PROBLEM 6

Count the number of permutations of the letters in "TEPEE."

ANSWER(S)

5!/(1!1!3!), or 5!/(3!1!1!), or 5!/3!; all yield 20.   □

PRACTICE PROBLEM 7　Obtain the number of distinct permutations of the letters in: **(a)** GREETED;　**(b)** GREBE;　**(c)** TERRARIUM;　**(d)** ONOMATOPOEIC

ANSWER(S)　(Be sure you understand both the "factorial" expression and calculate the final result.)　**(a)** $7!/(3!1!1!1!1!) = 7!/3! = 840$;　**(b)** $5!/(2!1!1!1!) = 60$;　**(c)** $9!/3! = 60,480$;　**(d)** $12!/4! = 19,958,400$ ☐

PRACTICE PROBLEM 8　Count the permutations of the letters in "TERRORIST." (*Hint:* First place T's, then R's, then single letters.)

ANSWER(S)　30,240. ☐

PRACTICE PROBLEM 9　Count the possible arrangements of the letters in: **(a)** SCHEHERA-ZADE;　**(b)** ROTOTILLER;　**(c)** OTOLARYNGOLOGIST

ANSWER(S)　**(a)** 19,958,400;　**(b)** 226,800;　**(c)** 108,972,864,000 (a number that your calculator will represent as "1.0897 11"; if this occurs, and you don't understand it, ask your instructor!) ☐

Examples 13 and 14 and Practice Problems 6 through 9 lead to:

PERMUTATIONS OF "SOME ALIKE" OBJECTS

The number of permutations of a set of n objects, with n_1 of type #1, n_2 of type #2, . . ., n_k of type #k, is

$$\frac{n!}{n_1!n_2! \ldots n_k!}$$

Note that, if there is exactly one object of each type, the above counting pattern yields $n!$, as expected.

In solving the "some alike" problem, we have also solved another interesting problem: that of apportioning (or "partitioning"; see Section 6.1) a set of objects into "special-purpose" subsets.

■ **EXAMPLE 15**　Fifteen people are planning to prepare and serve a banquet. They set up three crews: six people cooking and serving, four washing dishes, and five setting up and taking down chairs and tables. In how many ways may people be assigned to tasks?

SOLUTION　Pick six people to cook and serve, then four to wash up, then five for chairs and tables. The total count: $C(15,6) \cdot C(9,4) \cdot C(5,5)$, yielding

$$\frac{15!}{6!4!5!}$$ ■

The counting method illustrated in Example 15 requires a caution: the subsets into which the whole group is to be apportioned must be of different sizes or have identifiably different roles. Otherwise, a corrective step is needed. If, for example, we sought to count ways in which 15 people could be split into three groups of five for the tasks of Example 15, the count would be

$$\frac{15!}{5!5!5!} = \frac{15 \cdot 14 \cdot 13 \cdot 12 \cdot 11 \cdot 10 \cdot 9 \cdot 8 \cdot 7 \cdot 6 \cdot 5!}{5 \cdot 4 \cdot 3 \cdot 2 \cdot 5 \cdot 4 \cdot 3 \cdot 2 \cdot 5!} = 756,756$$

In this instance, shifting an entire group of five people from one task (say, cooking) to another (say, cleanup) is a new assignment of people to tasks. Keeping groups of five intact, there are 3! possible work assignments for those particular groups.

If, however, we wanted to split 15 people into three discussion groups (all to discuss the same topic), then keeping groups of five intact and shuffling the groups among three meeting rooms does not result in new assignments. We would not want to count all of the 3! ways to assign the groups to meeting rooms; this is not a significant difference among the groups. The count of possible assignments to discussion groups would then be

$$\frac{15!}{5!5!5!} \div 3! = 756,756 \div 6 = 126,126$$

We divided by 3! in order to not count the ways that three groups, once established, can be interchanged.

PRACTICE PROBLEM 10   In how many ways could 15 different portraits be sorted into two groups of three, one group of four, and five "singles"?

ANSWER(S) $[15!/(3!3!4!1!1!1!1!1!)] \div 2! \div 5! = 6,306,300$ ☐

Counting Alternative Possibilities   It is sometimes helpful to break a counting problem into alternative cases, counting each case separately, then adding the separate counts.

■ EXAMPLE 16   Now that we've counted the five-letter permutations possible using letters in "PEPSI," let's count the four-letter arrangements.

SOLUTION   Which four letters we select from "PEPSI" clearly makes a difference in our count. Selecting both P's will give a different count than selecting one P, with {P,E,S,I} as our letter set. The possibilities, then, are: omit one P; omit E; omit S; omit I. Each of these will yield its own count. An abbreviated tree diagram helps:

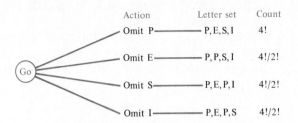

Since we have counted mutually exclusive alternatives ("omit a P or omit E or omit S or omit I"), and since these alternatives partition the set of possibilities, we must add the separate counts. The total count is 4! + 4!/2! + 4!2! + 4!/2! = 4! + 3 · (4!/2!) = 24 + 3 · (12) = 60. ∎

As you become more experienced, you will look for ways to count more efficiently. Then, discussing Example 16, you might say: "I can either select one P or two P's. If I select one P, the rest of the letter set is E, S, I; there are 4! permutations of this set. If I select two P's, I must choose two more letters from among E, S, and I; this can be done in C(3,2) ways, and each resulting set (with its two P's) yields 4!/2! permutations. A tree diagram:

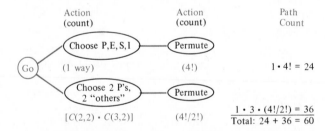

The moral: There's often more than one correct way to approach a counting problem. Be sure of your overall strategy, and be careful when formulating counts and doing arithmetic. Even if you tell yourself "I know what I'm doing—I just can't get the right answers," the fact remains: wrong answers are not worth much to anyone, and certainly not to your employer!

Tree Diagram Counting Methods

In some counting situations, it is necessary to examine information at a given step in the counting process in order to know whether to take another step or know possible outcomes to list at the next step.

■ EXAMPLE 17

Al, Bill, and Charlie are duck hunters of many years' acquaintance. Charlie is a superb shot, Bill is average, and Al "couldn't hit a bull's behind with a bass fiddle," as they say back on the farm. To keep hotshot Charlie from blasting all the ducks, the chums agree that Al will fire first at each duck. If Al misses, Bill may fire twice. If Bill misses, Charlie will fire once.

How many different and exciting experiences might occur to a duck who violates this trio's airspace?

SOLUTION We show the various possible developments in a tree diagram. A double slash (//) indicates a quitting point in the tree.

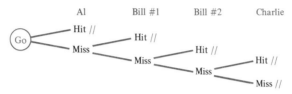

Five thrilling possibilities await the unsuspecting duck.

EXERCISES 7.2

APPLYING THE CONCEPTS

*68. In how many ways can five people line up for a picture if two of the five insist upon standing together?

69. How many permutations are possible of the letters in "BENZENE"?

70. How many permutations are possible of the letters in "MISSISSIPPI"?

71. How many permutations are possible of the letters in "TENNESSEE"?

72. The United States Supreme Court consists of nine judges. In how many different ways can the judges register a five-to-four decision in favor of an appeal?

73. In Exercise 72, in how many ways could they reach a majority decision in favor of an appeal (all nine judges vote)?

74. In how many ways could 12 different books be distributed equally among three people?

75. In how many ways could 12 different books be distributed, two per box, for mailing?

76. Twenty P.T.A. parents are to staff the school carnival. In how many ways can they be assigned to work teams, if eight must sell refreshments, eight must take tickets for games, two must check coats, and two must monitor hallways?

77. In Exercise 76, determine the number of ways the 20 parents can be allocated to four five-passenger cars to travel to the state convention.

*78. On a ten-question examination, you are required to answer *exactly* eight questions, including at least four of the first five questions. How many choices of question sets have you?

*79. On a ten-question examination, you are required to answer *at least* eight questions, including at least four of the first five questions. How many choices of question sets have you?

80. Bjorn and Helga agree to play a racquetball tournament, with the winner to be the first person to win two games. How many different paths might their tournament follow to completion?

7.3 CONDITIONAL PROBABILITY AND INDEPENDENCE

A life insurance company establishes premiums by considering the probability that a policyholder in a given class will die within a specified period of time. If, for example, 5% of a group dies in a given year, then the insurance company could charge all policyholders the same premium to pay the proceeds for the 5% who die, plus some amount for profit. Is this an equitable way? A 96-year-old may think so, but a 21-year-old surely wouldn't! The chances of a 96-year-old living an additional year are about 60%, while a 21-year-old has more than a 98% chance of living an additional year—a person's age definitely influences the chances of living an additional year.

Insurance companies are also concerned with the relationship between a person's health and smoking. Whether smoking "causes" cancer and heart disease is still hotly (sorry!) debated, but because of convincing evidence linking smoking to these diseases, most insurance companies offer discounts to nonsmokers. The reason is obvious: other things being equal, insurance companies have found a lower loss record among nonsmokers, and this is true not just for life insurance claims, but also for car insurance.

To further illustrate the effect of certain knowledge upon probability, let us consider a sweet and idealistic young coed named Debbie Dreme (one of Delmo Dweeb's girlfriends.) When Debbie gets a call from a blind date, she usually flips a coin and says "yes" if it comes up heads. If, however, she knows the fellow has excellent character (6'2" and 205 pounds), and is an intellectual type (drives a BMW), she will reevaluate the situation, flip five coins, and say "yes" if *any* heads show. In the former instance, her acceptance probability is 0.5; in the latter, it is nearly 0.97. (We shall soon see why.)

In the above examples, probabilities are reassessed in light of additional information. Sometimes, additional information has an influence on events under consideration, and probabilities change accordingly. This was true in the insurance examples and with Debbie. Other times, however, the additional information has no influence upon, or is independent of, the event being considered. Your intuition should tell you, for example, that the probability of rain tomorrow is not influenced by whether or not you go to bed before 10 P.M. tonight.

How do we decide whether additional information changes probability?

■ EXAMPLE 18

Five years after graduation, 1000 Dolt State University alumni were surveyed to see if a course in finite mathematics influenced one's fame and fortune. In terms of events *R:* "the graduate is now rich and famous" and *M:* "the graduate took finite mathematics," the study revealed the following:

	R: Rich and Famous	Rᶜ: Not Rich and Famous	Totals
M: Had Finite Mathematics	150	250	400
Mᶜ: No Finite Mathematics	20	580	600
Totals	170	830	1000

Using relative frequencies from the above table to form our probability model, we obtain:

$$P[M \cap R] = \frac{150}{1000} = 0.150 \qquad P[M \cap R^c] = \frac{250}{1000} = 0.250$$

$$P[M^c \cap R] = \frac{20}{1000} = 0.020 \qquad P[M^c \cap R^c] = \frac{580}{1000} = 0.580$$

$$P[M] = \frac{400}{1000} = 0.400 \qquad P[R] = \frac{170}{1000} = 0.170$$

A DSU graduate is chosen at random. Lacking additional information about the person chosen, these probabilities are appropriate. Suppose, however, that the person selected has taken finite mathematics. Given this information, what is the probability that the person is rich and famous?

SOLUTION   Since the person selected took finite mathematics, he/she could *not* have come from the bottom row of our table. Thus, the set of possible outcomes is now reduced to the 400 people who took finite. Within this "new" sample space, we look for the probability of being rich and famous. Since 150 of the 400 having finite are rich and famous, we could say the following:

Knowing that a person took finite mathematics, the probability that he/she is rich and famous is 150/400 = 0.375.

We are interested enough in this kind of problem to establish a special notation:

$$P[R|M] = 0.375$$

where you should read the vertical line as "knowing that," or "given that." Thus, $P[R|M]$ is read "Probability of a person being rich and famous, given that he or she has taken finite mathematics." This probability is called the **conditional probability** of event R occurring, given that event M is known to have occurred, or, in short form, "the probability of R, given M."

We did not need any special kind of formula to obtain this conditional probability. We used common sense and a little logic to see what effect the given information had on the sample space. If the given information reduced the sample space, then we worked the problem based on the new sample space. (If the given information did not reduce the sample space, the conditional probability we seek does not differ from the original, unconditional probability.) This technique of mentally "adjusting" the sample space can be done easily if the information is organized as in our table. Try it yourself in the following problem!   ◼

PRACTICE PROBLEM 11   In Example 18, find the following conditional probabilities: **(a)** $P[M|R^c]$;   **(b)** $P[R|M^c]$;   **(c)** $P[R^c|M]$;   **(d)** $P[M^c|R]$.

ANSWER(S)   **(a)** 250/830;   **(b)** 20/600;   **(c)** 250/400;   **(d)** 20/170   ☐

We worked the above problems without benefit of a formula, but there is a formula available for those times when you cannot use the intuitive, commonsense method. The formula is as follows:

CONDITIONAL PROBABILITY

> The conditional probability of event A happening, given that event B has occurred, written $P[A|B]$, is
>
> $$P[A|B] = \frac{P[A \cap B]}{P[B]} \quad \text{provided that } P[B] \neq 0$$
>
> If $P[B] = 0$, then $P[A|B]$ is undefined.

In Example 18 we intuitively found that $P[R|M] = 0.375$. Let's find $P[R|M]$ using the "definition" formula:

$$P[R \cap M] = \frac{150}{1000} \quad \text{and} \quad P[M] = \frac{400}{1000}, \quad \text{so that}$$

$$P[R|M] = \frac{150/1000}{400/1000} = \frac{150}{400} = 0.375$$

as in Example 18.

Most students find the formula is very nonintuitive—it doesn't seem to make a lot of sense at first (or even second) glance. Studying the

Venn diagram in Figure 7.1 will help you understand why the formula "works." Knowing event M has occurred tells us the outcome must be inside set M. We have reduced our sample space to set M. To be inside set M and also have R occur, the observed outcome must be in the set $R \cap M$. Thus, knowing that M has occurred, we are asking how likely the set of interest $R \cap M$ (the numerator of the formula) is, relative to (the phrase "relative to" is the division line in our formula) the new sample space M (the denominator of the formula).

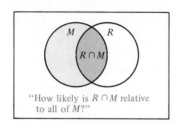

Figure 7.1
Components of the formula
$P[R|M] = P[R \cap M]/P[M]$

It is interesting to compare the conditional probability $P[R|M] = 0.375$ with the unconditional probability $P[R] = 0.170$. Having finite mathematics doesn't guarantee that you will be rich and famous, but for DSU grads, the chances of riches and fame for finite students are more than double those for graduates in general, and more than eleven times the chances for those without finite mathematics: $P[R|M^c] = 20/600 \approx 0.033$. (Go study!)

Since the probability of being rich and famous changes when you know that a person has finite mathematics, we shall say that the events "R" and "M" are **dependent**—knowledge about the occurrence or non-occurrence of one changes the probability of the other. If the conditional probability of event A occurring, given that event B has occurred, is equal to the unconditional probability of A, then events A and B are said to be **independent.**

INDEPENDENT EVENTS

> Events A and B are said to be *independent* if and only if at least one of the following equations is true:
>
> 1. $P[A|B] = P[A]$ or   2. $P[B|A] = P[B]$
>
> Events that are not independent are *dependent*.

We used our intuition to shape an algebraic definition of independent events. This algebraic definition suggests an extension of our intuitive understanding:

**INTUITIVE DEFINITION OF
INDEPENDENCE, AND
ALGEBRAIC INTERPRETATIONS**

Events A and B are independent *if and only if any knowledge about
either event does not affect the likelihood of the other.*

    Assuming A, A^c, B, and B^c all have nonzero probabilities, A
and B are independent if *any* equation in the following list is
satisfied:

$$P[A|B] = P[A] \qquad P[A^c|B] = P[A^c]$$
$$P[A|B^c] = P[A] \qquad P[A^c|B^c] = P[A^c]$$

$$P[B|A] = P[B] \qquad P[B^c|A] = P[B^c]$$
$$P[B|A^c] = P[B] \qquad P[B^c|A^c] = P[B^c]$$

To emphasize: If A and B are independent, and A, A^c, B, and B^c
have nonzero probabilities, *all* eight of the above equations are
satisfied, and any single equation is a sufficient test for independence. If A and B are dependent, then *none* of the above equations is satisfied, and any single equation failing to hold is a
sufficient test for dependence.

    Conditional probability appears to be quite simple. When a particu-
lar event has occurred, the sample space may change, and a conditional
probability is computed from this "new" sample space. Try another
example where we work the problem both by the "intuitive" method
and with use of the definition formula.

■ EXAMPLE 19

A card is drawn from a standard deck of 52 which has been appropriately shuffled. Given that the card is a face card (F), find the probability
that it is a jack (J).

SOLUTION

Our intuitive approach says that we can restrict attention to face cards.
Thus, our "new" sample space has 12 elements—three face cards for
each of the four suits. Since four of these 12 face cards are jacks, then
$P[\text{jack}|\text{face card}] = P[J|F] = 4/12 \approx 0.333$. The intuitive method works
fine because an equally likely model is appropriate. Alternatively, using
the formula gives:

$$P[J|F] = \frac{P[J \cap F]}{P[F]} = \frac{P[J]}{P[F]} = \frac{4/52}{12/52} = \frac{4}{12} = \frac{1}{3} \approx 0.333$$

    ■

■ EXAMPLE 20

In Example 19, determine whether the events "Jack" and "Face Card"
are independent.

SOLUTION

To check for independence, we compare $P[J|F]$ to $P[J]$. If they are the
same, the events J and F are independent. Since $P[J|F] = 1/3$ and $P[J] =$

1/13 are not the same, events J and F are not independent. This should agree with your intuition: knowing that a card is a face card makes it more likely to be a jack than if nothing is known about the card.

■

PRACTICE PROBLEM 12   In Example 20, check for independence by comparing $P[F \mid J]$ to $P[F]$.

ANSWER(S) $P[F \mid J] = 1$. $P[F] = 12/52$. These are not the same, so events F and J are not independent.

□

Note: It is not necessary to make both the check of Example 20 and Practice Problem 12. Either one is sufficient.

EXERCISES 7.3

PRACTICING THE MOVES AND MANEUVERS

Exercises 81–94: Sample space $S = \{a,b,c,d,e,f\}$, where $P[a] = 0.10$, $P[b] = 0.20$, $P[c] = 0.25$, $P[d] = 0.30$, $P[e] = 0.10$, $P[f] = 0.05$. Events A through D are defined as follows: $A = \{a,c,d\}$, $B = \{a,e,f\}$, $C = \{b,e,d,f\}$, $D = \{a,c,d,f\}$.

81. Find $P[A]$, $P[B]$, $P[C]$, and $P[D]$.
82. Find $P[A \cap B]$, $P[A \cap C]$, and $P[A \cap D]$.
83. Find $P[B \cap C]$, $P[B \cap D]$, and $P[C \cap D]$.
84. Find $P[A \mid B]$ and $P[B \mid A]$.
85. Find $P[A \mid C]$ and $P[C \mid A]$.
86. Find $P[A \mid D]$ and $P[D \mid A]$.
87. Find $P[B \mid C]$ and $P[C \mid B]$.

88. Find $P[B \mid D]$ and $P[D \mid B]$.
89. Find $P[C \mid D]$ and $P[D \mid C]$.
90. Are A and B independent? Explain.
91. Are A and C independent? Explain.
92. Are A and D independent? Explain.
93. Are B and C independent? Explain.
94. Are B and D independent? Explain.

APPLYING THE CONCEPTS

Exercises 95–105: Use the data from the following highly sophisticated study. One hundred students at Anemia Tech were asked the following questions: "Do you drink floor wax before an exam?" and "Does your mother wear overshoes?"

	Drinks Floor Wax	Doesn't Drink Wax
Mother Wears Overshoes	10	30
Mother Doesn't Wear Overshoes	15	45

Let event F be "Drinks Floor Wax," and event W "Mother Wears Overshoes." Find:

95. $P[F]$;   96. $P[W]$;   97. $P[F \cap W]$;   98. $P[F^c \cap W]$;
99. $P[F \cap W^c]$;   100. $P[F^c \cap W^c]$; 101. $P[F^c]$;   102. $P[W^c]$.
103. Find $P[F|W]$ and $P[F|W^c]$; compare with $P[F]$ and comment.
104. Are events F and W independent? Justify your answer.
105. Are events F and W mutually exclusive? Justify.

Exercises 106–132: Toss a well-balanced die, with the outcome being the "up" face. Consider the following events:

    A: Observe a number greater than two

    B: Observe an odd number

    C: Observe a number less than five

    D: Observe an even number less than six

List the outcomes in the following events and find their probabilities:

106. A 107. B 108. C 109. D
110. $A \cap B$ 111. $A \cap C$ 112. $B \cap C$ 113. $A \cap D$
114. $B \cap D$ 115. $C \cap D$ 116. $A \cup B$ 117. $A \cup C$
118. $A \cup D$ 119. $B \cup C$ 120. $B \cup D$

Find the following conditional probabilities:

121. $P[A|B]$ 122. $P[A|C]$ 123. $P[A|D]$ 124. $P[B|A]$
125. $P[B|C]$ 126. $P[B|D]$ 127. $P[C|B]$ 128. $P[C|A]$
129. $P[D|A]$ 130. $P[D|B]$
131. Which pairs of events are mutually exclusive?
132. Which pairs of events are independent?

Exercises 133–136: Two fair dice are thrown and the following events defined:

    A: The sum is odd   *B:* The sum is greater than eight

133. Find $P[A]$, $P[B]$, and $P[A \cap B]$.   135. Are A and B mutually exclusive?
134. Find $P[A|B]$.   136. Are A and B independent?

*137. A family has two children, and it is known that at least one of the two is a boy. Assuming that each child is just as likely to be a boy as a girl, find the probability that both are boys.
138. A fair coin is tossed until one of the following two events happens: a head shows, or the coin has been tossed three times. Find the probability that the coin was tossed three times given that there was no head on the first toss.

Exercises 139–145: Consider the following data from a random sample of 1000 Bachelor's degree graduates 15 years after their 1975 graduation. One person is to be selected at random from this group.

139. Find the probability that the person has an income of less than $25,000.
140. Find the probability that the person has at least a Master's degree.
141. If the person makes more than $50,000, what is the probability that person has a doctorate?

| | | Highest Degree Earned | |
	Bachelor's	Master's	Doctorate
Less than $25,000	390	20	5
$25,000–$50,000	210	80	60
More than $50,000	90	110	35

Current Annual Salary

142. If the person has a Master's degree, find the probability that the person makes more than $50,000.
143. If the person makes at least $25,000, find the probability that the person has a Master's degree or a doctorate.
144. Are the events "Makes less than $25,000" and "Highest degree is Bachelor's" independent? Explain with probability.
145. Are the events "Makes more than $50,000" and "Has a Doctorate" independent? Explain with probability.

7.4 THE MULTIPLICATIVE RULE, TREE DIAGRAMS, AND MORE ON INDEPENDENCE

An event is just a collection of outcomes, and thus the probability for that event can be found by adding its outcome probabilities. This approach works if it is easy to list the outcomes in that event. For certain kinds of compound events, however, we have developed quicker and better ways of obtaining probabilities. The Additive Law of Probability and the Complement Rule are two such instances that allow us to find probabilities by using special relationships (that is, unions and complements) among the events involved. Although we have developed special methods for unions and complements, we have ignored intersections. We will rectify that now.

Consider the formula for the conditional probability of event B occurring, given that event A is known to have occurred. (We have interchanged the left and right sides for convenience.)

$$\frac{P[A \cap B]}{P[A]} = P[B|A]$$

This formula contains three quantities; if any two are known, the third can be found. As presently written, the formula presumes we know $P[A \cap B]$ and $P[B]$ and want the conditional probability of A given B. We can also use the formula to find either of the other two quantities. In particular, we will often want to find the probability that both events happen. Multiply both sides by $P[B]$, and then simplify the left-hand side, obtaining:

$$P[A \cap B] = P[A] \cdot P[B|A]$$

In this form, we can find the probability of an intersection of two events—that is, the probability that both of the events occur. This result is known as the **Multiplicative Rule.**

THE MULTIPLICATIVE RULE

> If A and B are two events in the same sample space, and A is not an impossible event, then the probability that events A and B both occur is given by
>
> $$P[A \cap B] = P[A] \cdot P[B|A]$$

Note: In this form we must have information about A occurring prior to B. We could interchange the roles of A and B and, since event $B \cap A$ is the same as $A \cap B$, we would have $P[A \cap B] = P[B] \cdot P[A|B]$. This would be appropriate if B occurs prior to A.

Note: The conditional probability formula can be used to obtain one and only one of the three quantities. You cannot use the formula to obtain both conditional probability and the probability for an intersection.

The importance of the Multiplicative Rule stems from the fact that it is sometimes easy to obtain conditional probability without a formula, and thus you can use the Multiplicative Rule to find the probability that both A and B occur. We illustrate.

■ EXAMPLE 21

A pool of candidates for jury duty consists of seven women and two men. Two people will be picked at random from this pool to complete a jury. Find the probability that both will be women.

SOLUTION

The event of interest is an intersection—the first person must be a woman, and the second person must also be a woman. Let W_1 be the event "First person is a woman," and W_2 be the event "Second person is a woman." Our job is to find $P[W_1 \text{ and } W_2] = P[W_1 \cap W_2]$. The natural order of selection suggests we use $P[W_1] \cdot P[W_2|W_1]$. There are nine people available, and seven are women, so $P[W_1] = 7/9$. If the first person is given to be a woman, then the second pick comes from a reduced set of eight, six of whom are women. Thus, $P[W_2|W_1] = 6/8$, and $P[W_1 \cap W_2] = (7/9) \cdot (6/8) = 21/36 = 7/12 \approx 0.583$. ■

The Multiplicative Rule is best understood using a tree diagram. A tree diagram for Example 21 is shown in Figure 7.2.

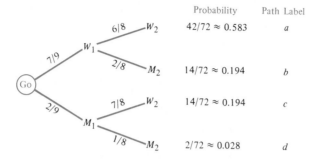

Figure 7.2
Tree diagram for selection of two jurors

When we use a tree diagram to develop a sample space, each path on the tree is a simple event. Imagine paths as being roads that we travel. Each path is composed of branches. To travel the top path, we must first select a woman juror, placing us at node W_1. Any branch probability proceeding from node W_1 is a conditional probability, the given condition being a woman selected first. To complete travel on the top path, we must select a woman second, knowing a woman was selected first. Hence, to travel path a, we must select a woman first *and* a woman second. Path a describes an intersection of two events. In fact, all four paths describe intersections. In "tree-diagram talk":

> **The probability of any path on the tree is found by multiplying the probabilities for all the branches on that path.**

Recall that events are just collections of outcomes. Since the outcomes on a tree diagram are its paths, it follows that any event can be viewed as a collection of paths. Since we find the probability of an event by adding its outcome probabilities, then the probability of an event is found by adding the probabilities of all its paths. This discussion suggests the following procedure for solving probability problems:

PROCEDURE FOR SOLVING PROBABILITY PROBLEMS IN TREE DIAGRAM FORM

1. Represent the sample space by drawing a tree diagram. Label each of the nodes and paths on the tree. Attach a probability to each branch.

2. Find the probability for each path by multiplying all the branch probabilities that lie on that path.

3. Express any event of interest as a collection of paths. The probability of that event is found by adding the probabilities of its paths.

This simple procedure is appropriate any time the outcomes of your experiment can be represented in tree diagram form. We recommend it strongly—using this procedure will enable you to work a great many of the probability problems, both in this course and in the real world. Try the example that follows.

■ EXAMPLE 22

Refer to Figure 7.2 to find the probabilities of the listed events.

A: Exactly one woman is chosen.

B: At least one woman is chosen.

C: The second person chosen is a woman.

D: The first person chosen is a man, or the second person chosen is a woman.

SOLUTION

To find $P[A]$, note that event A is the set of paths given by $\{b,c\}$. Thus, $P[A] = 7/36 + 7/36 = 14/36 \approx 0.389$.

To find $P[B]$, note that event B is given by $\{a,b,c\}$, and thus $P[B] = 21/36 + 7/36 + 7/36 = 35/36 \approx 0.972$. Observe that $C = \{a,c\}$, so $P[C] = 21/36 + 7/36 \approx 0.778$.

Finally, note that event D is given by the set $\{a,c,d\}$, and thus $P[D] = 21/36 + 7/36 + 1/36 \approx 0.806$.   ■

Finding Tree Probabilities

Here are some helpful comments about finding tree probabilities:

1. *The sum of all path probabilities must be one.* This is rule two for assigning simple event probabilities. (If path probabilities don't sum to one, you have an error. Typical causes: you have omitted paths, or have entered incorrect branch probabilities, or have multiplied incorrectly in finding a path probability.)

2. *The sum of probabilities for all branches emanating from the same node is one.* Branches ending in nodes W_1 and M_1 both come from the "Go" node; the sum of these branch probabilities is $7/9 + 2/9 = 1$. Two branches emanate from node W_1 (proceeding to W_2 and M_2); the sum of their probabilities is $7/8 + 1/8 = 1$.

3. *The sum of all path probabilities that branch from a given node should equal the probability of reaching that node.* Paths a and b, for example, come from node W_1. The sum of probabilities for paths a and b is $21/36 + 7/36 = 28/36 = 7/9$, which, as it should be, is the probability of reaching W_1.

Practice your tree diagrams on the following example.

■ EXAMPLE 23

Delmo has a cassette deck in his flatbed van. For trips to the dump (where he collects garbage) he randomly selects two tapes from his rock group cassette collection: four cassettes by "Conniption Fit" and one by "Old Men at the Home" (both male groups), and two by the female group "Bodacious Warlord."

List a sample space for his selection process, and find the probabilities of the following events:

A: There is at least one "Bodacious Warlord" tape.

B: There is at least one tape recorded by a male group.

C: The same group recorded both tapes.

D: There is at most one cassette from a male group.

SOLUTION Our first step is to build a tree diagram illustrating the experiment of selecting two cassette tapes at random. Figure 7.3 is the first stage of a suitable tree, showing the possible outcomes of the first selection and their probabilities.

The tree's second stage, shown appended to the first in Figure 7.4, accounts for all possible second tape selections, given the first selection, and thus second stage probabilities are conditional.

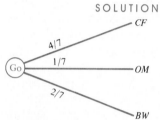

Figure 7.3
First stage for Delmo's experiment in Example 23

	Probability	Path Label
CF	$12/42 \approx 0.286$	a
OM	$4/42 \approx 0.095$	b
BW	$8/42 \approx 0.190$	c
CF	$4/42 \approx 0.095$	d
BW	$2/42 \approx 0.048$	e
CF	$8/42 \approx 0.190$	f
OM	$2/42 \approx 0.048$	g
BW	$2/42 \approx 0.048$	h

Figure 7.4
Complete tree for Delmo's experiment of selecting two cassettes from among seven

To find $P[A]$, note that $A = \{c,e,f,g,h\}$. Adding path probabilities for these simple events gives $22/42 \approx 0.524$.

Event B is $\{a,b,c,d,e,f,g\}$. Adding path probabilities, $P[B] = 40/42 \approx 0.952$. It is easier, however, to use the Complement Rule. Event B contains all paths except path h, so $P[B^c] = P[h] = 2/42$. Thus, $P[B] = 1 - 2/42 = 40/42$, as before.

Event C is the set $\{a,h\}$, so $P[C] = 14/42 \approx 0.333$.

Event D is the set $\{c,e,f,g,h\}$. Observe that this set is identical to event A: "At least one Bodacious Warlord tape." Hence, $P[D] \approx 0.524$. ∎

PRACTICE PROBLEM 13 In Example 23, find the probabilities of the following events:

E: There is at most one "Old Men at the Home" cassette.

F: There is at least one "Bodacious Warlord" cassette, but not more than one "Conniption Fit" cassette.

G: There is exactly one "Conniption Fit" cassette, or there are no "Bodacious Warlord" tapes.

ANSWER(S) $P[E] = 1$; $P[F] = 0.524$; $P[G] \approx 0.857$.   □

The preceding examples used the Multiplicative Rule to find the probability of a two-event intersection. This result generalizes, to any number of events. In Example 21, suppose we were to select three people from the jury pool of seven women and two men. What is the probability that the first two selected are women and the third is a man? The multiplicative rule for three events would go like this: The probability of a woman being selected first is (still) 7/9. Given that the first selection was a woman, the probability of the second being a woman is now 6/8 (still). Given that the first two were women, there are now seven potential jurors left, two of whom are men. Hence, the probability that the third is a man, given that the first two were women, is 2/7. The probability that all three happen in the sequence indicated is the product of these three probabilities, $(7/9) \cdot (6/8) \cdot (2/7) = 1/6$ (≈ 0.167).

The Multiplicative Rule for Independent Events

When two events are independent (knowledge of one provides no information about the other), the multiplicative rule becomes especially easy, because the *conditional* probability involved is the same as the *unconditional* probability. The Multiplicative Rule then becomes

$$P[A \cap B] = P[A] \cdot P[B|A] \qquad \text{always correct, if } P[A] \neq 0$$

$$= P[A] \cdot P[B] \qquad \text{with independence, } P[B|A] = P[B]$$

This is such an important and useful rule that we "box" it for emphasis. Learn this one well! It forms the basis for much of our future work, including the famous Binomial Distribution.

PROBABILITY FOR TWO INDEPENDENT EVENTS

> If events A and B are independent, then the probability that they both occur is given by the product of their separate probabilities:
>
> $P[A \cap B] = P[A] \cdot P[B]$

Note: This rule extends to any number of independent events. To find the probability that every one of several independent events happens, multiply the separate probabilities for each of them happening. We illustrate in the following example.

■ EXAMPLE 24

Elmo Dweeb (Delmo's brother who attends Follicle Institute of Technology and is thus a FIT student) is taking a six-question, multiple-choice exam, with four possible answers to each question. Since Elmo has not studied, he guesses at the answer to each question. Find the probability that he misses all six.

SOLUTION

Since Elmo is guessing, an equally likely model is appropriate: The probability that Elmo misses any one question is 3/4. Whatever he does on any one question has no bearing on the results of others. Hence, Elmo's answer choices for the six questions can be considered to be six mutually independent events. (The phrase *mutually independent* means that any two or more of the events are independent.)

To miss all six, he must miss the first *and* miss the second *and* miss the third *and* miss the fourth *and* miss the fifth *and* the sixth. The *ands* tell us we have an intersection. Since these events are independent, we find the probability that all six happen by multiplying the separate event probabilities:

$$(3/4) \cdot (3/4) \cdot (3/4) \cdot (3/4) \cdot (3/4) \cdot (3/4) \approx 0.178$$ ■

■ EXAMPLE 25

An air defense missile has a 0.7 chance of hitting its target. A test is performed with one missile of this type being fired at each of three targets. **(a)** Find the probability that all three missiles hit their targets; **(b)** find the probability that none of the three missiles hit their targets.

SOLUTION

Since the missiles are firing at different targets, it is reasonable that the outcome of any one firing is independent of the outcome of others. For part **(a)**, the probability that all three hit is $0.7^3 = 0.343$. For part **(b)**, the probability that all three miss is $0.3^3 = 0.027$. ■

PRACTICE PROBLEM 14

In Example 25, use a tree diagram to find the probability that exactly one missile hits its target.

ANSWER(S) 0.189. □

PRACTICE PROBLEM 15

You throw a fair die three times. What is the probability that

(a) you get numbers larger than four on all tosses?

(b) you never get a three?

ANSWER(S) **(a)** $(1/3)^3 \approx 0.037$; **(b)** $(5/6)^3 \approx 0.579$. □

Example 25 and Practice Problems 14 and 15 are examples of the binomial probability distribution, which we study in Chapter 8.

■ EXAMPLE 26

In Section 7.2 we introduced a problem encountered by a seventeenth-century gambler. It took the greatest minds of the day to solve this problem, but you can now do it easily. Here is a quick review of the two games involved:

Game 1: A single die is tossed four times. You win your bet if there is at least one six.

Game 2: Two dice are tossed 24 times. You win your bet if there is at least one sum of 12.

Find the probability of winning at each of these games.

SOLUTION

Game 1: We seek $P[A]$, where A is "at least one six in four rolls of a die." "At least one" means one, two, three, or four. By the FCP there are $6 \cdot 6 \cdot 6 \cdot 6 = 1296$ equally likely outcomes. Since the die is balanced we need only to determine how many of these 1296 outcomes have one or more sixes. This is an enormous undertaking, requiring that we calculate probabilities for "exactly one," "exactly two," "exactly three," and "exactly four."

Fortunately, there is a better way. Remember what we said previously: "When a probability problem looks tough, consider the Complement Rule." Let's try it. Event A is "at least one six." Thus, A^c is the event "no sixes." Since the outcome on one toss has no bearing on the outcome of others, the four tosses are independent. The probability of "no six" on one toss is 5/6. Hence, the probability of no sixes on four tosses is $(5/6) \cdot (5/6) \cdot (5/6) \cdot (5/6) = 625/1296 \approx 0.482$. Applying the Complement Rule, we obtain:

$P[\text{at least one six in 4 tosses of a die}] = 1 - 0.482 = 0.518$

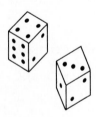

Game 2: The event whose probability we want is event B: "at least one sum of 12 in 24 tosses of two dice." B^c is the event "no sum of 12 in 24 tosses of two dice." On any one roll of two dice, $P[\text{no sum of 12}] = 35/36$, since (6,6) is the only one of 36 possibilities that gives a sum of 12. We want "no sum of 12" 24 times in a row; because the 24 tosses are independent, we have $P[\text{no sum of 12 on 24 tosses of two dice}] = (35/36)^{24} \approx 0.509$. From the Complement Rule, it follows that:

$P[\text{at least one sum of 12 in 24 rolls of two dice}] = 1 - 0.509 = 0.491$

You can see why the French nobleman was disturbed. He won about 52% of the time with Game 1 and about 49% of the time with Game 2. For a short history of plays, there may not be much difference in the outcomes of these two, but over the long haul, you would notice a considerable improvement in your fortune if you played Game 1, and a considerable loss if you played Game 2. Roughly speaking, after 1000 $1 bets you might expect to win 491 times with Game 2 and lose the other

509, for a net loss of about $18. With Game 1 you would win about 518 times while losing 482, giving net winnings of about $36.   ■

Mutually Exclusive Events and Independent Events

We have defined and used the terms "mutually exclusive" and "independent" on several occasions. People often confuse these terms, using them interchangeably. They are different concepts and should be considered separately. Independence tells us that a conditional probability is the same as an unconditional probability. That is, *independence* is a property of probabilities.

Mutually exclusive events are events whose intersection is empty. That is, *mutually exclusive* is a term applied to events. There is, however, a case when the two concepts are connected. If A and B are mutually exclusive events, then they cannot both happen on the same experiment. Thus, if one of the two occurs, the other cannot. In this case, the events are obviously *dependent*.

EXERCISES 7.4

APPLYING THE CONCEPTS

146. In Seattle, it only rains when it is cloudy. It is cloudy 40% of the time, and when it is cloudy, it rains 20% of the time. What proportion of days does it rain in Seattle?

147. When Delmo calls Debbie for a date, there is a 70% chance she will be available. Even if available, there is only a 30% chance she will agree to Delmo's request. When Delmo calls Debbie, find the probability that she agrees to go out with him.

Exercises 148–153: In the meat section of a supermarket, there are 30 chickens, of which 25 are fresh, and the other five are at least one week old. Delmo selects two chickens at random to use in making beef stew. What is the probability that:

148. both are fresh?

149. the first one is fresh?

150. the second one is fresh?

151. at least one chicken is fresh?

152. What is the probability that Delmo's second chicken is fresh, given that the first chicken is not fresh?

153. Are the events "first chicken fresh" and "second chicken fresh" independent? Justify your answer.

Exercises 154–156: An unbalanced coin shows heads 60% of the time.

154. If this coin is tossed six times, find the probability of heads on all tosses.

155. Find the probability of at least one head in six tosses.

*156. How many times should the coin be tossed in order that the probability of at least one head be 0.99 or higher? Find the smallest number of times.

157. An instructor in a finite math course estimates that a student who reads the text carefully has a probability of 90% of passing the course, while a student who does not read the text carefully has only a 20% chance of passing the course. If 25% of the students in a large class read their texts carefully, what percentage of all the students will pass?

158. A recent study reveals that half of all college seniors who apply for graduate school have IQs of 115 or more. Of these, 60% get admitted to graduate school, while only 20% of those with IQs less than or equal to 114 get admitted. Find the probability that a college senior selected at random from those who have applied for graduate school will be admitted.

159. A fair die is tossed three times. Find the probability that a number less than 5 occurs on the first two tosses and a 4 occurs on the third toss.

Exercises 160–163: Two fair dice are tossed.

160. Find the probability that the sum is seven or less on the first toss, while a sum of nine or more occurs on the second toss.

161. Find the probability that a sum of seven or less is observed on the first toss, or a sum of nine or more occurs on the second toss.

162. Consider the events "first toss produces a sum of seven or less" and "a sum of nine or more occurs on the second toss." Are these events independent?

163. Are the events in Exercise 162 mutually exclusive?

Exercises 164–166: Professor Plague can either drive his Edsel or take his bike to school. He takes the Edsel 40% of the time. When he drives the Edsel, he is late for school 10% of the time. When he takes his bike, he is late only 6% of the time.

164. In the long run, what proportion of the time is Professor Plague late?

165. Consider the events "Professor Plague late for school" and "Professor Plague took his bike." Are these events independent?

166. Are the events in Exercise 165 mutually exclusive?

7.5 BAYES' THEOREM (OPTIONAL)

The probability questions we have encountered have all been of a "forward-looking" nature. We have generally sought the probability of an event occuring (future tense) when an experiment is performed. In this section we look at Bayes' Theorem, a famous result that is particularly appropriate in multistage experiments where we know the outcome of a later stage of the experiment, but do not know exactly what happened at an earlier stage. Our interest will be in whether or not a certain event happened "along the way."

■ EXAMPLE 27

Cybil Ninjaneer is planning her trip home from Anemia Tech for Christmas vacation. She has her choice of traveling by bus, by plane, or by train. Unfortunately, Cybil frequently gets sick when she travels. When she takes the bus, there is a 40% chance she will get motion sickness. When flying there is a 30% chance, and when she takes to the rails, there is a 20% chance of getting sick. Having passed finite mathematics, she knows that probability is important. She decides to choose her mode of travel by tossing an ordinary die. If she gets an odd number, she will take the bus, while if she gets a two, she will fly; otherwise, she will take the train.

(a) Before Cybil flips her die, find the probability that she will get motion sickness on her trip.

(b) If upon completion of her trip Cybil reports that she became ill, find the probability that she traveled by bus.

SOLUTION   This is a multistage experiment where a tree diagram approach is bound to be helpful. Stage one is Cybil's selection of a mode of travel, and stage two should indicate whether or not she gets motion sickness. The tree diagram, with B, P, and T denoting the three modes of travel and S signifying the event "motion sickness occurs," is as follows:

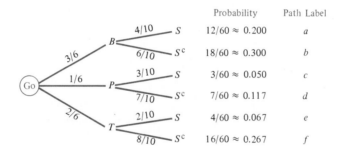

	Probability	Path Label
$B \xrightarrow{4/10} S$	$12/60 \approx 0.200$	a
$B \xrightarrow{6/10} S^c$	$18/60 \approx 0.300$	b
$P \xrightarrow{3/10} S$	$3/60 \approx 0.050$	c
$P \xrightarrow{7/10} S^c$	$7/60 \approx 0.117$	d
$T \xrightarrow{2/10} S$	$4/60 \approx 0.067$	e
$T \xrightarrow{8/10} S^c$	$16/60 \approx 0.267$	f

(a) The event "getting sick" is $\{a,c,e\}$. Thus, the probability of getting sick is found by adding these path probabilities, which total $19/60 \approx 0.317$. This is not a "new" kind of problem. Bayes' Theorem, the subject of this section, comes into play in part **(b)**.

(b) Do you see how this is a different kind of problem? We are given the outcome to the second stage (Cybil got sick), and asked to find the probability that something happened at an earlier stage (Cybil took the bus). This is clearly a "reverse" use of conditional probability. Using the tree diagram approach, however, makes it easy. Knowing Cybil got sick restricts the sample space to the set of paths which end in "sick," namely $\{a,c,e\}$. Path a is the only one where she traveled by bus. Hence, in terms of the tree, we are asking the following:

How likely is the path of interest (path a here) relative to the set of all possible paths $\{a,c,e\}$ that could have happened, given "Cybil got sick"?

Setting up the standard conditional probability format, with appropriate probabilities from the tree diagram, yields

$$P[\text{Cybil took the bus}|\text{Cybil got sick}] = \frac{P[a]}{P[a] + P[c] + P[e]}$$

$$= \frac{12/60}{19/60} = \frac{12}{19} \approx 0.632$$

Before Cybil chooses her mode of transportation, there is a 50% chance (probability = 0.50) that she will take the bus. Even after the trip, if we have no information about her health, the probability that she took the bus is 0.50 (paths a and b). However, if we know that she got sick, then it is much more likely that she took the bus—the probability has increased to 0.632. Prior to knowing she got sick, the probability of her taking the bus was 0.5. Knowing she got sick, the posterior (after the fact) probability is 0.632.

Study this example carefully, and be sure you understand the method we used: "Path(s) of interest relative to all possible paths." Try it on the practice problem that follows. ■

PRACTICE PROBLEM 16   In Example 27, find the following probabilities:

(a) that Cybil flew, given that she got sick

(b) that Cybil took the train, given that she got sick

(c) that Cybil did not fly, knowing that she did not get sick

(d) that Cybil gets sick, given that she takes the bus

ANSWER(S)   (a) $3/19 \approx 0.158$;   (b) $4/19 \approx 0.210$;   (c) $34/41 \approx 0.829$;   (d) $3/10$
    □

■ EXAMPLE 28
A rare and severe form of anemia occurs at a rate of one case per thousand people in the general population. A simple diagnostic test for this anemia has the following properties:

1. If the person tested actually has this anemia (A), then the probability of a positive test result (P) is 0.95.

2. If the person tested does not have this anemia (A^c), then the probability of a negative (N) test result is 0.98.

These two properties suggest this diagnostic test is exceedingly reliable, and thus anyone taking the test should have confidence in the outcome. Herby Hypochondriac, fearful of this particular anemia, has the test. The result? Positive! The doctor says he has anemia. Herby is extremely concerned. Should Herby be so worried? Let's check by finding the following probability:

> **Given that the test says Herby has anemia, what is the probability that he actually has anemia?**

SOLUTION   A tree diagram is clearly indicated in this case. We have a two-stage experiment where stage one describes probabilities of Herby having or not having anemia, and stage two describes the diagnostic test result possibilities. The tree, with branch and path probabilities both shown and named, is shown in Figure 7.5.

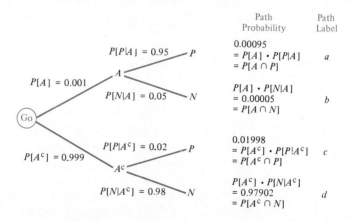

Figure 7.5
Tree diagram for anemia test

We know Herby has been diagnosed as having anemia. Hence, the only possible outcomes (our "new" sample space) are paths on the tree that end with a "positive" test—reporting that Herby has anemia. These paths are labeled a and c. The question is "How likely are the path(s) of interest (only path a here) relative to the reduced set of paths that end with a positive diagnosis (paths a and c)?" In terms of conditional probability, this translates to:

$$P[\text{anemia}|\text{positive test}] = \frac{P[a]}{P[a] + P[c]}$$

$$= \frac{0.00095}{0.00095 + 0.01998} \approx 0.045$$

Even though the test says he has the severe anemia, there is less than a one-in-twenty chance that he actually has it. This seemingly reliable test is not so reliable after all! ∎

PRACTICE PROBLEM 17   In Example 28, find the probability that Herby has anemia if the test says he does not.

ANSWER(S)   0.0000511. ☐

Example 28 and Practice Problem 17 are further examples of Bayes' Theorem—a result we have alluded to without stating. You will notice that we did not need any formula to find the probabilities required. Instead we phrased things in terms of the tree by asking "How likely are the path(s) of interest relative to all the paths that could have produced the given event?" We feel this is much easier than using a "formula." Indeed, for our purposes, the tree diagram approach is entirely sufficient, and you should thoroughly understand and use it.

However, Bayes' Theorem is an important formal result with many applications beyond the present course. For the sake of completeness, we shall state the theorem in formula form, first in a simple version related to the tree diagram of Example 28, then in its usual general form.

Bayes' Theorem as Illustrated in Example 28

Writing $P[\text{anemia}|\text{positive test}]$ as $P[A|P]$, and using the results of Example 28, we begin with:

$$P[A|P] = \frac{P[a]}{P[a] + P[c]} \qquad (7.1)$$

To develop Bayes' Formula, we shall replace $P[a]$ and $P[c]$ in Equation 7.1 with equivalent expressions obtained by using both the previous tree diagram and the Venn diagram of Figure 7.6 which provides an alternate but equivalent view of the tree. To aid in comparing the tree and Venn diagrams we show the tree paths a, b, c, and d in appropriate regions of the Venn diagram. To emphasize the two stages of the tree, we first split (partition) the Venn diagram into regions A and A^c (showing that all tree diagram paths first split between A and A^c). We then overlay the "indicator" event, a loop showing the region P of positive test results inside the loop and the region P^c of negative test results outside the loop. The regions P and P^c both overlap A and A^c.

From the Venn diagram it is easy to see that path a is the same as the set $A \cap P$, and thus $P[a]$ is the same as $P[A \cap P]$. Similarly, $P[c]$ is the same as $P[A^c \cap P]$. Referring to the tree and using the Multiplicative Rule for event intersections, we obtain:

$$P[a] = P[A \cap P] = P[A] \cdot P[P|A]$$

$$P[c] = P[A^c \cap P] = P[A^c] \cdot P[P|A^c]$$

Substituting these expressions for $P[a]$ and $P[c]$ into Equation 7.1 gives the following:

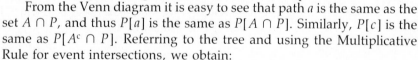

$$P[A|P] = \frac{P[A] \cdot P[P|A]}{P[A] \cdot P[P|A] + P[A^c] \cdot P[P|A^c]}$$

This is the specialized version of Bayes' Theorem used when there is a partition of the same space containing only two sets (sets A and A^c here). Bayes' Theorem allows us to find the probability of one partitioning set

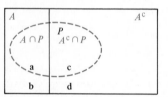

Figure 7.6
Venn diagram of Herby's possible conditions and test results

occurring when we know that another "indicator" event (event P here) has occurred.

In a general setting, there would be more than two sets in a partition of the sample space. In particular, suppose there are n sets B_1, B_2, . . ., B_n that partition the sample space S. (These would correspond to n first-stage options in the tree diagram.) The general form for Bayes' Theorem would then read as follows:

BAYES' THEOREM

If $B_1, B_2, \ldots, B_n$ form a partition of the sample space S, and if A is any event in S, then for any B_i,

$$P[B_i|A] = \frac{P[A|B_i] \cdot P[B_i]}{P[A|B_1] \cdot P[B_1] + \cdots + P[A|B_n] \cdot P[B_n]}$$

This looks unnecessarily complicated! (That's a polite way of putting what you must be feeling.) You can appreciate why we recommend viewing these kinds of problems in tree form and simply asking, "How likely is the path(s) of interest relative to all paths that could have produced the given result?"

We conclude this section with one more example.

EXAMPLE 29

A company uses computer diskettes from three different manufacturers: brands A, B, and C. Of the diskettes currently in use by the company, 60% are Brand A, 30% are brand B, and 10% are brand C. Experience with these brands has shown that brand A has a 2% defective rate, while brand B has a 5% defective rate. Brand C is the most reliable, having only a 1% defective rate. A computer operator discovers a diskette error at work. Find the probability that the diskette is brand B.

SOLUTION

Before knowing the diskette is defective, we would have answered 0.30, since 30% of the diskettes are of brand B. With this new information, however, we shall form a probability "update" by using Bayes' Theorem. We need $P[\text{brand } B|\text{defective}]$. A tree diagram is shown in Figure 7.7.

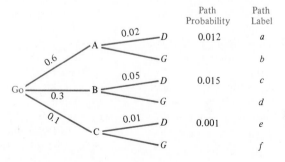

Figure 7.7
Tree diagram for Example 29

Using the tree, we find:

$$P[\text{brand } B | \text{defective}] = \frac{P[c]}{P[a,c,e]} = \frac{0.015}{0.012 + 0.015 + 0.001} = 0.536$$

Thus, even though brand B accounts for only 30% of the diskettes in use, there is a 53.6% chance that a known-to-be defective diskette is of brand B. ∎

PRACTICE PROBLEM 18   In Example 29, find the probability that the diskette is of brand A if it is known to be defective.

ANSWER(S)   0.429. ☐

EXERCISES 7.5

APPLYING THE CONCEPTS

Exercises 167–169: Refer to the following situation, first encountered in Exercise 157. A student who reads the text carefully has a probability of 90% of passing a course, while a student who does not read the text carefully has only a 20% chance of passing the course. Twenty-five percent of the students in a large class read their texts. One student is selected at random from this class. Find the probability that:

167. the student read the text carefully if he/she passed the course.
168. the student did not read the text carefully if he/she did not pass the course.
169. the student did not read the text carefully if he/she passed the course.

Exercises 170–172: In Exercise 158, we encountered the following situation: Half of all college seniors who apply for graduate school have IQs of 115 or more. Of these, 60% get admitted to graduate school, while only 20% of those with IQs less than or equal to 114 get admitted. Use this information to work Exercises 170–172.

170. Find the probability that a student has an IQ of 115 or more if we know that the student was admitted to graduate school.
171. Find the probability that a student has an IQ of 114 or less if we know that the student was not admitted to graduate school.
172. Find the probability that a student has an IQ of 115 or more if we know the student was not admitted to graduate school.

173. In Exercises 164–166, we learned that Professor Plague drives his Edsel or his bike to work, taking the Edsel 40% of the time. When he drives the Edsel, he is late for school 10% of the time. When he bikes, he is late only 6% of the time. Find the probability that Professor Plague took his bike if we learn that he was late to school.
174. In Exercise 173, suppose we learn that Professor Plague was on time. Find the probability that he drove the Edsel.

175. Dr. Anderson's gardener is not dependable. When Dr. Anderson is gone, there is only a 30% chance that he will water Dr. Anderson's begonias. When not watered, there is a 60% chance they will die. Even if watered, there is still a 10% chance that they will die. Dr. Anderson returns home one day to find a dead bego- nia. Should he fire the gardener? Explain with probability.

176. In Exercise 175, suppose Dr. Anderson comes home to healthy begonias. Does that mean that the gardener did his job? Justify your reply using probability.

Exercises 177–180: A large corporation manufacturers one type of item at plants in Atlanta, Boston, and Cincinnati. Atlanta, with new machinery, produces only 2% defective items. 5% of Boston's items are defective. In Cincinnati, things are even worse—10% of the items made there are defective. Of total production of this item, 40% comes from Atlanta, 50% from Boston, and 10% from Cincinnati. All production is sent to a common warehouse. Suppose we choose one item at random from this warehouse. Find the probability that:

177. the item is defective.
178. the part was manufactured in Atlanta, if you know it to be defective.
179. the part was manufactured in Cincinnati, if you know it to be defective.
180. the part was manufactured in Boston, given that it is not defective.

Exercises 181–183: Delmo's coin purse contains three coins. One is fair, one has two heads, and the third is unbalanced (like Delmo!), showing heads 65% of the time. Delmo grabs a coin at random and tosses it. Find the probability that:

181. the coin shows a head.
182. the coin is the two-headed one, given that the toss produced a head.
183. the coin is the unbalanced coin, given that a tail resulted.

Exercises 184–187: At Anemia Tech only 10% of the men and 4% of the women are taller than 5 feet. (Delmo is 4'10", and Debbie Dreme is 6'5".) In addition, 70% of the student body is female. One student is picked at random. Find:

184. the probability that the student selected is a woman.
185. the probability that the student selected is more than 5 feet tall.
186. the probability that the student was male, given the student is over 5 feet.
187. the probability that the student is female, given the student is at most 5 feet.

188. Three secretaries in the same office type many documents. A photocopy is always placed in the files. Secretaries 1, 2, and 3 type 1/6, 2/6, and 3/6 of the material, respectively. Probabilities that a given page of their output contains at least one error are, respectively, 0.03, 0.02, and 0.01. One page is selected at random from the files. Find the probability that it contains at least one error.

189. In Exercise 188, find the probability that the page selected is the work of secretary 2, if we know that it contains an error.

Exercises 190–192: Delmo has several dinner options. He may stay at home and fix himself fondued frog warts, he may go to Bertha's for frittered chicken toes, or he may go home to mother's for an Alpo and lobster casserole. If he stays home, he has a 30% chance of indigestion, while if he goes to Bertha's, there is only a 20% chance of indigestion. If, however, he goes to mother's house, there is a 40% chance of indigestion. As Delmo hates to cook, he stays home only 10% of the time. When he does go out, he is twice as likely to go to Bertha's as to mother's.

190. Before Delmo chooses a place to eat, find the probability that he will end up getting indigestion.

191. Knowing that he got indigestion, how likely is it that Delmo ate at Bertha's?

192. Knowing that he did not get indigestion, how likely is it that he cooked?

*193. A classic problem: "The Prisoner's Dilemma." Three prisoners, A, B, and C, are informed by their jailer that one of them has been chosen at random to be executed; the other two will go free. Prisoner A reasons to himself that he has a probability of 1/3 of being executed. He then asks the jailer to tell him privately the name of one prisoner, other than himself, who will be set free, claiming there would be no harm in divulging this information, since he (A), already knows that at least one will go free. The jailer, an ethical chap, refuses to answer, observing that if A knew which of his cellmates were to be set free, then the probability of A being executed would increase to 1/2 since he (A) would then be one of two prisoners, one of whom would be executed. Suppose the jailer does tell A that B will be released. Is it true that $P[A$ is executed | jailer says B will go free$] = 1/2$? Assume that in the event A has been chosen for execution, the jailer is just as likely to say B as C.

7.6 RELIABILITY OF SYSTEMS (OPTIONAL, BUT RECOMMENDED)

Many of today's complex electronic and/or mechanical systems are composed of smaller subsystems. Your stereo receiver consists of a preamplifier, an amplifier, and a tuner (radio) section. The microcomputer system that produced this manuscript is made up of several subsystems—a keyboard for inputting information, a microprocessor for analyzing and manipulating this information, a hard drive for storage, and a monitor or printer for displaying output. Even a device as simple as a flashlight may be viewed as a system composed of two subsystems—the electrical supply (batteries) and the light source (the bulb). In this section we illustrate how basic probability can be used to analyze such systems, and, in particular, to determine the reliability of a system. In everyday usage, the word *reliability* means dependability. We shall intend a more specific meaning.

SYSTEM RELIABILITY

> The **reliability** of a system, R_s, is the probability that the system functions properly for a given time under designated conditions.

Note 1: The reliability of a single component is the probability of that one component performing properly.

Note 2: The phrases "for a given time" and "under designated conditions" are necessarily ambiguous. The reliability of a 2000cc compact car engine is very nearly 1 for 50,000 miles of typical driving, but this engine would have a reliability near zero for 50,000 miles in a truck hauling 200,000-pound loads. Reliability depends upon time involved and conditions of operation. Thus, for example, the reliability of a standard videotape may be close to 1 for 100 hours of recording, but only 0.90 for a thousand hours of recording. For simplicity in our examples, we will assume an unspecified "usual" time. Thus, we can speak simply of "reliability" rather than "the reliability for 1000 hours."

Series Systems   All systems are ultimately composed of individual components (the batteries and the light bulb in the flashlight, for example). We shall use capital letters to represent system components, and display them graphically as boxes. A system composed of the four components *A, B, C,* and *D* is shown in Figure 7.8.

Figure 7.8
A four-component series system

Figure 7.8 is a *series system*. A series system functions properly only when all components perform as required. Alternately, a series system fails if any one component fails. Imagine this system as a road that begins with box A and ends with box D; each box is an obstacle that must be overcome if you are to complete your travels. We summarize this below.

SERIES SYSTEM

> An interconnected system of components is said to form a **series system** if the system fails whenever any one of its components fails.

You encountered a simple example of a two-component series system when you tested for your driver's license. You had to take a written examination and a behind-the-wheel test; if you failed either, you did not get your license. As another example of a series system, suppose the four-component diagram in Figure 7.8 represents a set of bridges, all of which must be crossed to reach your destination. If any bridge is impassable, then your journey cannot be completed—the series system will fail.

■ EXAMPLE 30

A series system with four components is shown below, with the reliability of each component shown below its box in the diagram.

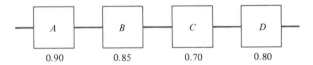

Find R_s, the reliability of this system, under the assumption that the four components operate independently.

SOLUTION

By definition, a series system will function properly only when all of its components function properly. Since the components operate independently, we find the probability that all work by simply multiplying the separate component reliabilities:

$$R_s = (0.90)(0.85)(0.70)(0.80) = 0.4284$$

Roughly speaking, only about 43% of such series systems will function properly for the required amount of time.   ■

Product Law of Reliability

The fact that a series system functions only when all of its components function leads us to state a general rule for the reliability of a series system.

RELIABILITY OF A SERIES SYSTEM

Suppose a series system contains k independent components with reliabilities given by $p_1, p_2, \ldots, p_k$. Then the reliability of the series system, denoted by R_s, is the product of the individual reliabilities:

$$R_s = p_1 \cdot p_2 \cdot \ldots \cdot p_k$$

This result for independent components in series is often known as the **product law of reliability**.

PRACTICE PROBLEM 19

Five components, A, B, C, D, and E operate independently of one another. Components A through D have reliability 0.999, while component E has reliability 0.05. **(a)** Find the system reliability if a series system contains one each of components A through D; **(b)** Find the system reliability if there is one of each of the five components operating independently in series.

ANSWER(S)   **(a)** 0.996006;   **(b)** 0.049800   □

PRACTICE PROBLEM
19 SYSTEM: Low
reliability due to poor
component *E*.

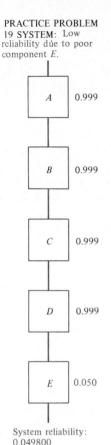

System reliability:
0.049800

Part **(b)** of Practice Problem 19 illustrates vividly the maxim that "A chain is only as strong as its weakest link." Equivalently, the reliability of a series system cannot exceed the reliability of its least reliable component. In spite of the extraordinarily high reliability of components *A* through *D*, the reliability of the system is limited by the (appallingly) low reliability of component *E*. How do we improve the reliability of this system? We could turn to our design engineers and say, "improve component *E*." Suppose they respond as follows: "For $25,000, we can increase the reliability of component *E* to 0.6." Deciding that this is a reasonable cost, we invest the $25,000 to get the improved *E*. (From now on, we use the letter *E* to mean only the improved version.) The reliability of series system *A–E* is now $R_s = (0.999)^4(0.6) \approx 0.597604$, a dramatic improvement, but still much too low. Suppose our engineers tell us they simply cannot further improve the reliability of component *E*, regardless of how much we spend. At the same time, our marketing people tell us that, to be competitive, our series system must have a reliability of at least 95%. To resolve this impasse, we turn to the notion of a parallel system.

Parallel Systems

A parallel system is configured in such a way that the system functions properly if any one of its components works, failing only if all components fail. A typical portrayal of a parallel system with two components of type *A* is shown in Figure 7.9.

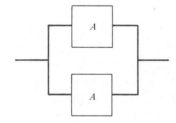

Figure 7.9
A parallel system with two components

A couple of nontechnical, sports-related examples of parallel systems are provided by (1) a baseball batter with three bats; as long as any one of the bats is not broken, he will be able to take his turn at the plate; and (2) a golfer with four golf balls. If he does not lose all four balls, he will be able to complete his round. A real-world instance of a parallel system is provided by the pilot-copilot combination found in every commercial airline; if something should happen to the pilot, his/her backup is readily available. We summarize the concept of a parallel system:

PARALLEL SYSTEM

> An interconnected system of components is said to form a **parallel system** if the system fails only when all components in the system fail.

Redundancy   In practice, parallel systems are used to provide backups in case of failure. In complex applications, where reliability is of utmost importance, two or more items are configured in an arrangement known as **standby redundancy:** the second item does not get switched on unless the first fails. A third item would not attempt to function unless both the first two had failed, and so on. The importance of backup systems is hard to overemphasize. A space shuttle mission was aborted simply because one of three identical on-board computers was not functioning; NASA felt that a single backup was simply not enough. Modern airliners are replete with backup systems. Even the best of intentions are not always enough. A freak accident in the summer of 1989 simultaneously disabled all three "independent" control systems for the tail assembly on a DC-10 that crashed in Iowa.

To illustrate the workings of a parallel subsystem, we continue our practice problem, concentrating on reducing the risk due to failure of component E by using standby redundancy—backups in parallel. Consider a parallel subsystem consisting of one E and a backup which switches on only if the main E component fails, as in the system shown.

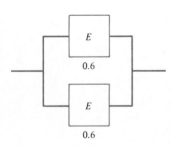

This E subsystem fails only when both components fail. The probability of both E's failing is $(0.4)(0.4) = 0.16$, so the reliability of the E subsystem is $1 - 0.4^2 = 0.84$. By using an extra E in backup, we have increased the reliability from 0.6 (for one E) to 0.84 (for two E's). We can do better yet. With three E's (two backups in parallel), the system fails only if all three E's fail. The probability of such a triple failure is $0.4^3 = 0.064$, making the system reliability $1 - 0.064 = 0.936$.

There is a similarity between failure of a parallel system and success of a series system. Recall the product law for reliability of a series system. For a parallel system with n identical components, each having reliability p, there is a corresponding product law for system unreliability: the probability that the system fails is $(1 - p)^n$. Thus, by using the Complement Rule, we find that the reliability of such a parallel system is $1 - (1 - p)^n$. We summarize below what we have learned about parallel systems.

**RELIABILITY OF AN
n-COMPONENT PARALLEL
SYSTEM**

> If a parallel system consists of *n* independent components, each having reliability *p*, then the parallel system reliability is given by:
>
> $$R_s = 1 - (1 - p)^n$$

With each *E* component having reliability 0.6, we have seen that the parallel subsystem reliability is 0.84 for two *E* components (one backup) and 0.936 for three *E* components (two backups). The reliability for several backup configurations is shown in the following table.

"IMPROVED" System for
Practice Problem 19:

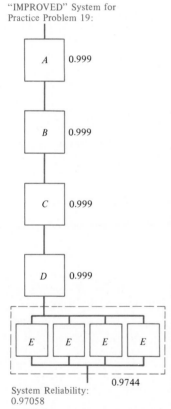

System Reliability:
0.97058

The Moral: "One *can* get reliable
performance from unreliable
components."

No. of *E* Components in Parallel	System Reliability
2	0.84
3	0.936
4	0.9744
5	0.98976
6	0.995904
7	0.9983616
8	0.99934464

If we are willing to use enough backups in parallel, we can make the parallel system reliability as close to one as we want. Now, back to the system in the Practice Problem 19 where components *A* through *D* have reliability 0.999 while component *E* has only a 0.6 reliability: To make our marketing people happy, we need a minimum system reliability of 0.95. With one each of the five components, the series system has reliability $(0.999)^4 \cdot (0.6) \approx 0.597604$. When we give *E* a single backup in parallel, our overall system reliability becomes $(0.999)^4 \cdot (0.84) \approx 0.836645$—not high enough. With three *E* components in parallel (two backups), we get $(0.999)^4 \cdot (0.936) \approx 0.932262$. We're getting closer. With four *E* components (three backups), we get an *E*-system reliability of $(0.999)^4 \cdot (0.9744) = 0.970508$, large enough (finally!) to satisfy the marketing director.

PRACTICE PROBLEM 20   A component of type *A* has reliability only 0.2. What is the minimum number of *A* components needed in a parallel subsystem in order that the subsystem have a reliability of at least 0.9?

ANSWER(S)   Using 10 *A* components gives a subsystem reliability of 0.89263, which is not enough since we want a minimum reliability of 0.9. With 11 *A* components, the parallel subsystem has reliability ≈ 0.9141.   □

Comment   In a sense, the effectiveness of a parallel subsystem goes against the grain of what most of us have heard for years: "Anything worth doing is worth doing well" have always been good words to live by. Our results for parallel systems suggest that *quantity is sometimes better than quality*. To illustrate, suppose we need an *A*-component subsystem reliability of 0.9 or better, and that a single, well-designed *A* component would have a reliability of 0.9—at a cost of $40 each. On the other hand, a shoddy, poorly made version, with a reliability of only 0.2, can be made for only $3. The results of Practice Problem 20 tell us that 11 of these ramshackle components, with a total cost of $33, will have a higher reliability of about 0.914.

■ EXAMPLE 31

A parallel subsystem is designed to have an *A* component and a single backup. There are only two *A* components available, and they are not equally reliable. One has reliability 0.7 (the last part available from an older design), and the other 0.8 (a new, improved version). Which should we make the primary and which the backup? Does it make any difference?

SOLUTION

Parallel subsystem problems we have worked have used components having identical reliabilities. Different reliabilities, however, do not alter our thinking. A parallel system of two components fails only when both components fail: probability of failure is $(0.3)(0.2) = 0.6$ *regardless of which component we designate as "primary."* System reliability is $1 - 0.06 = 0.94$ for either arrangement. Observe that the parallel subsystem reliability exceeds the reliability of the most reliable component in the system.

■

In the next example, we show how to use the results of this section to calculate the reliability of mixed systems, having both serial and parallel subsystems.

■ EXAMPLE 32

Consider the system diagrammed in Figure 7.10. Within this system is a parallel subsystem with two *C*'s. The reliability of this subsystem is $1 - 0.1^2 = 0.99$. Next, consider the parallel subsystem of three *D*'s. This subsystem has reliability $1 - 0.2^3 = 0.992$. If we replace the parallel

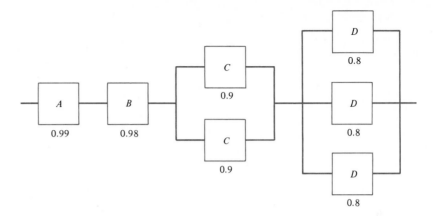

Figure 7.10
Combination series/parallel
system

subsystem of C's by a single component C' whose reliability is 0.99, and if we also replace the D subsystem by a single component D' with reliability 0.992, we can replace the system in Figure 7.10 with the following equivalent system:

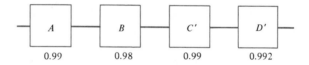

This is now an ordinary series system, and its reliability is found by using the product law: $(0.99) \cdot (0.98) \cdot (0.99) \cdot (0.992) = 0.952814$. ∎

■ EXAMPLE 33

A system requires at least one of each of components A, B, and C. Individual component reliabilities are given by $p_A = 0.8$, $p_B = 0.6$, and $p_c = 0.7$. Furthermore, the cost of an A component is $10, while B and C components cost $6 and $2, respectively. What is the least expensive system configuration that will have a minimum system reliability of 0.95? What is the cost of this system?

SOLUTION

Before proceeding, note that a series system having one of each component has reliability less than 0.60, the reliability of the least reliable component. Clearly, we need parallel subsystems for each component. In addition, each parallel subsystem will need a reliability exceeding 0.95 if overall system reliability is to exceed 0.95. Let's do a few calculations just for component A:

Number of A's in Subsystem	Subsystem Reliability	Cost
1	$1 - 0.2 = 0.8$	$10
2	$1 - (0.2)^2 = 0.96$	$20
3	$1 - (0.2)^3 = 0.992$	$30
4	$1 - (0.2)^4 = 0.9984$	$40
5	$1 - (0.2)^5 = 0.99968$	$50

Similar calculations for components B and C show:

Number of B's in Subsystem	Subsystem Reliability	Cost	Number of C's in Subsystem	Subsystem Reliability	Cost
1	$1 - 0.4 = 0.6$	$6	1	$1 - 0.3 = 0.7$	$2
2	$1 - (0.4)^2 = 0.84$	$12	2	$1 - (0.3)^2 = 0.91$	$4
3	$1 - (0.4)^3 = 0.936$	$18	3	$1 - (0.3)^3 = 0.973$	$6
4	$1 - (0.4)^4 = 0.9744$	$24	4	$1 - (0.3)^4 = 0.9919$	$8
5	$1 - (0.4)^5 = 0.98976$	$30	5	$1 - (0.3)^5 = 0.99757$	$10
6	$1 - (0.4)^6 = 0.99590$	$36	6	$1 - (0.3)^6 = 0.999271$	$12
			7	$1 - (0.3)^7 = 0.9997813$	$14
			8	$1 - (0.3)^8 = 0.99993439$	$16

We have done more calculations for C since, while it is the least expensive, it is not the least reliable, and hence should figure prominently in any economical solution.

Knowing that each subsystem must have reliability exceeding 0.95 in order for a series composed of these to have reliability at least 0.95, we observe that it will take at least 2 A's, at least 4 B's, and at least 3 C's. The reliability of the system containing these minimums (2, 4, and 3, respectively) is found by multiplying the separate reliabilities for each subsystem, giving:

$$(0.96)(0.9744)(0.973) \approx 0.91021$$

This particular arrangement is not good enough to reach the desired minimum of 0.95, and costs $50. Let's examine other series system configurations, checking the reliabilities and costs.

Component Configuration			System Reliability	System Cost
#A	#B	#C		
3	4	3	$(0.992)(0.9744)(0.973) \approx 0.9405$	$60
3	5	3	$(0.992)(0.98976)(0.973) \approx 0.9553$	$66
3	4	4	$(0.992)(0.9744)(0.9919) \approx 0.9588$	$62
2	6	5	$(0.96)(0.9959)(0.99757) \approx 0.9537$	$66
2	5	5	$(0.96)(0.98976)(0.99757) \approx 0.9478$	$60
2	5	6	$(0.96)(0.98976)(0.999271) \approx 0.9495$	$62
2	5	7	$(0.96)(0.98976)(0.9997813) \approx 0.94996$	$64
2	5	8	$(0.96)(0.98976)(0.99993439) \approx 0.9501$	$66
2	6	4	$(0.96)(0.9959)(0.9919) \approx 0.9483$	$64

Clearly, the 3-4-4 configuration is the least expensive (and, in this instance, most reliable!) among these arrangements having reliability exceeding 0.95. ■

EXERCISES 7.6

APPLYING THE CONCEPTS

194. Components A, B, and C, with individual reliabilities 0.8, 0.9, and 0.6, are arranged in series. Find the reliability of this series system.

195. Older Christmas tree lights used to be wired in series. If any one bulb failed, the entire string would not light; substituting good bulbs, one by one, until the culprit(s) was found, was an aggravating process!
   (a) Find the reliability of a 12-light series if each light has reliability 0.98.
   (b) To have a 12-light system with reliability 0.98, how reliable would each bulb have to be?

196. Component C works only 60% of the time. What is the minimum number of C components in parallel so that the parallel system has reliability
   (a) at least 0.9?   (b) at least 0.98?

197. Consider a system containing four identical components. If each has reliability 0.7, find the system reliability if the system is configured as a:
   (a) series system   (b) parallel system.

198. A series system consists of one item each of types A, B, and C. If the reliabilities of A and B are 0.90 and 0.95, respectively, what must the minimum reliability of C be in order that the series system have reliability at least 0.80?

199. Work Exercise 198 if A has reliability 0.80.

200. A system consists of five components as shown. Find the reliability of this system if the reliabilities of A, B, and C are 0.90, 0.95, and 0.80, respectively.

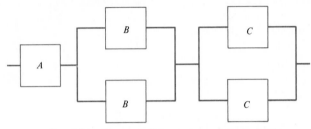

201. Consider the parallel system shown below, which is composed of two series subsystems. If reliabilities of A, B, C, and D are 0.90, 0.98, 0.99, and 0.95, respectively, find the reliability of the entire parallel subsystem.

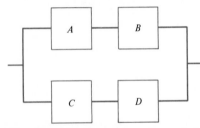

202. Consider the system shown below. The six different components in this system $A, \ldots, F$ have reliabilities given, respectively, by 0.90, 0.80, 0.70, 0.95, 0.70, and 0.99. Find the reliability of the entire system.

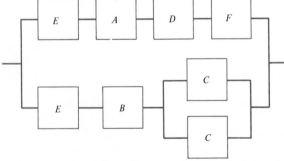

203. A series configuration requires at least one each of component types A, B, and C. Component A has reliability 0.80 and costs \$20. Component B has reliability 0.7 and costs \$10. Component C has reliability 0.90, and costs \$40. Using back-

ups in parallel, design the minimum cost series system having reliability of at least 0.97.

204. Find the minimum reliability for component C if the system below is to have reliability of at least 0.94.

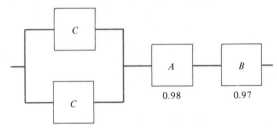

205. Consider the diagram in Exercise 204, and suppose A now has reliability 0.99 while B's reliability is unchanged. What is the minimum value for the reliability of C if the entire system is to have reliability 0.96?

206. Which of the two systems below has the better reliability? The individual component reliabilities are 0.85 for A, 0.75 for B, 0.60 for C, and 0.92 for D.

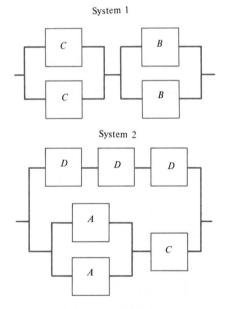

207. A series system requires that both an A component and a B component work. If A has reliability 0.9 and B has reliability 0.7,
   (a) determine the reliability of an A/B series system that has three B components in a

parallel arrangement and one *A* component.

(b) determine the reliability of an *A/B* series
system with four *B* components in parallel
and three *A* components in parallel.

208. A resistor has reliability 0.999. A specialized circuit utilizes eight of these resistors along with
two transistors, each having reliability 0.99. If
all ten components are in series, find the reliability of the entire series system.

209. Find the reliability of the system diagramed below. The reliabilities of components *A*, *B*, and *C*
are 0.86, 0.74, and 0.65, respectively.

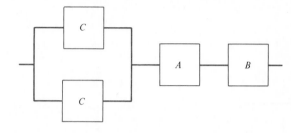

A Brief Summary of Important Ideas

In the present chapter we sharpened our focus on counting techniques,
and established patterns (formulas) for counting the ways to form a
permutation (arrangement) of some or all objects from a given set, and
ways to form a combination (set of objects, without regard to order)
chosen from a given set. The patterns were:

Permutations: The number of possible permutations or arrangements of *k* objects chosen from a set of *n* objects (all different) is:

$$P(n,k) = \frac{n!}{(n-k)!}$$

Combinations: The number of possible combinations (sets) of *k* objects chosen from a set of *n* objects (all different) is:

$$C(n,k) = \frac{n!}{(n-k)!\,k!}$$

Facility with these two counting patterns greatly simplified other, more
complex counting problems. We also learned to count arrangements of
objects, some of which were alike (Section 7.2). In the same section, we
observed that not every counting problem falls neatly into one of these
two standard types; sometimes, only enumeration (often assisted by
tree diagrams) of possibilities will do.

The principal purpose of all of this attention to counting is the assignment of probabilities to possible outcomes of an experiment. As
further applications of probability, we analyzed the **conditional probability** of an event *A*, given that event *B* has occurred:

$$\text{if} \quad P[B] \neq 0, \quad P[A|B] = \frac{P[A \cap B]}{P[B]}$$

Using this concept of conditional probability, we devised a test for **independence** of two events A and B: events A and B are independent if $P[A|B] = P[A]$.

An easy algebraic change in the definition of conditional probability led to the **Multiplicative Rule** for probability:

$$P[A \cap B] = P[A] \cdot P[B|A]$$

(For independent events A and B, $P[A \cap B] = P[A] \cdot P[B]$.)

The Multiplicative Rule meshed nicely with tree diagrams, providing a way to label separate branches and entire paths with their probabilities.

We emphasized the distinction between **mutually exclusive** events and independent events: A and B are mutually exclusive if and only if $A \cap B = \emptyset$.

Full path probabilities in a tree diagram gave us easy access to **Bayes' Theorem,** a result which uses information about outcomes at late stages of a multistep process to determine the probabilities of outcomes at earlier stages.

We concluded the chapter with a study of **reliability** of systems of components connected in series and/or parallel.

REVIEW EXERCISES

PRACTICING THE MOVES AND MANEUVERS

Exercises 210–218: Evaluate the given expressions after first simplifying.

210. $C(7,3)$

211. $P(14,4)$

212. $P(9,9)$

213. $C(14,4)$

214. $C(18,17)$

215. $P(7,3)$

216. $\dfrac{C(4,3) \cdot C(6,2)}{C(10,5)}$

217. $\dfrac{C(7,2) \cdot C(4,2)}{C(11,4)}$

218. $P(10,1)$

Exercises 219–229: Use the following information: Sample space $S = \{a,b,c,d,e\}$, where $P[a] = 0.15$, $P[b] = 0.20$, $P[c] = 0.25$, $P[d] = 0.30$, $P[e] = 0.10$. Events A, B, and C are given by: $A = \{c,d,e\}$, $B = \{a,d,e\}$, $C = \{b,e\}$.

219. Find $P[A]$, $P[B]$, and $P[C]$.

220. Find $P[A \cap B]$, $P[A \cap C]$, and $P[B \cap C]$.

221. Find $P[A \cup B]$, $P[A \cup C]$, and $P[B \cup C]$.

222. Find $P[A|B]$ and $P[A|C]$.

223. Find $P[B|C]$ and $P[B|A]$.

224. Are A and B independent? Explain.

225. Are A and C independent? Explain.

226. Are B and C independent? Explain.

227. Are A and B mutually exclusive? Explain.

228. Are A and C mutually exclusive? Explain.

229. Are B and C mutually exclusive? Explain.

Exercises 230–234: $P[A|B] = 0.4$, $P[B] = 0.3$, and $P[A \cup B] = 0.5$. Use this information to find the following:

230. $P[A \cap B]$ 231. $P[A]$ 232. $P[B|A]$
233. Are A and B independent? Justify!
234. Are A and B mutually exclusive? Justify your answer!

235. Events C and D are independent, $P[C] = 0.4$ and $P[C \cup D] = 0.6$. Find $P[D]$.

APPLYING THE CONCEPTS

Exercises 236–238: Seven Harvard graduates and four Yale graduates are applying for three ditchdigging jobs at the local employment office. If the three to be hired are selected at random, find the probability that:

236. two are from Harvard.   237. at least one is from Yale.   238. all three are from Harvard.

*239. There are two defectives in one package of six flashlight batteries and three defectives in the second package of six. If two batteries are selected at random from each package, find the probability that at least three of the four chosen batteries will work.

240. In Exercise 239, find the probability that all four selected batteries work.

241. In Exercise 239, find the probability of getting exactly one defective battery from each package.

242. A series system requires that both an A component and a B component work. If A and B have reliabilities 0.9 and 0.7, determine the reliability of an A/B series system that has three B's in a parallel arrangement, and one A.

243. In Exercise 242, determine the reliability of an A/B series system with four B components in parallel and three A components in parallel.

244. Delmo throws a balanced die, and Cousin Bertha tosses Delmo. (Assume that Delmo is like a fair coin—half the time he lands on his head and half on his tail.) Find the probability that Delmo gets a three or Delmo lands on his tail.

245. In Exercise 244, find the probability that Delmo gets a three and Delmo lands on his tail.

246. Component A has reliability 0.6. A specialized circuit uses four such components along with two transistors, each with reliability 0.9. If all six components are in parallel, find the reliability of the system.

247. In "Five-card Blotto," five cards are dealt at random to each player. The best hand in this game is a "Wounded Wombat," a hand consisting of three two's, the jack of hearts, and no other jacks or twos. Find the probability of getting a "Wounded Wombat."

248. In "Five-card Blotto (see Exercise 247), the second-best hand is called a "Shrdlu" (pronounced SHURD-lu). A Shrdlu is a hand having one three, two fours, and two red sevens. Find the probability of being dealt a Shrdlu.

249. A burglar is considering breaking into Delmo's house and stealing the valuables (last week's garbage) in Delmo's safe. Delmo, however, is ready. He has installed an alarm system. Define the following events:

   A: Burglar gets past alarm.

   B: Burglar opens the safe.

   The probability that the burglar gets past the alarm and opens the safe is 0.6. The probability of successfully opening the safe, if he gets past the alarm, is 0.8. Find the probability that the burglar gets past Delmo's alarm.

250. How many signals, each consisting of eight flags hung on a vertical rope and read from top to bottom, are possible using an assortment of four red flags, three green flags, and one white flag?

251. An army sergeant barks to a group of six recruits, "I need at least four of you to unload a truck." How many different groups of volunteers might she get?

Exercises 252–258: Use the results of a survey of 500 former finite mathematics students who gave the following information about studying for the first exam and consequent success (or lack thereof!) on the exam. The data are:

	Studied	Did not Study
Passed Exam	290	60
Did not Pass	40	110

One student is selected at random from this group of 500.

252. Find the probability that the student selected studied for the first exam.
253. Find the probability that the student selected passed the first exam.
254. Suppose we know the student selected passed the first exam. What is the probability that he/she studied?
255. If we know the student did not study, what is the probability that he/she passed the exam?
256. If we know the student studied for the first exam, find the probability that he/she passed.
257. Are the events "Student studied" and "Student passed exam" mutually exclusive? Justify your answer.
258. Are the events "Student studied" and "Student passed exam" independent? Justify your answer.

Exercises 259–261: When Delmo has a milk shake at bedtime, there is only a 50% chance of a good night's sleep. Even if he doesn't have a milk shake, there is only an 80% chance of a good night's sleep. (Delmo worries about burglars stealing his garbage.) Delmo has a milk shake 60% of the time before going to bed. Find the following probability that:

259. Delmo has a good night's sleep.
260. Delmo had a milk shake before bedtime if we know that he slept poorly.
261. Delmo did not have a milk shake, if he slept well the previous night.

262. Find the reliability of the system diagramed below. The reliabilities of components A, B, and C are 0.65, 0.92, and 0.84, respectively.

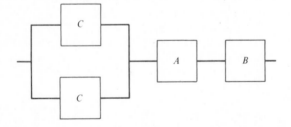

Exercises 263–269: Refer to the following situation: A store's owners have two monthly advertising budgets—large and small. If they use the small budget, there is a 40% chance of having large sales, a 30% chance of having average sales, and a 30% chance of poor

sales the following month. If they use the large advertising budget, there is a 65% chance of large sales, a 25% chance of average sales, and only a 10% chance of poor sales. As the owners have frequent cash-flow problems, they use a large advertising budget only 40% of the time. Find the following:

263. the percentage of the time that the store has a large sales month.
264. the percentage of the time that the store has an average sales month.
265. the percentage of the time that the store has a poor sales month.
266. the probability that the store used the large advertising budget if we learn they had a large sales month.
267. the probability that the store used the small advertising budget if we learn they had a poor sales month.
268. the probability that the store used the small advertising budget if we learn they had a large sales month.
269. the probability that the store used the small advertising budget if we learn they had an average sales month.

Exercises 270–273: Consider six couples lining up in a movie queue. How many single-file arrangements are possible with:

270. no restrictions?
*271. couples together, women preceding men in the line?
272. women first, in a group?
273. couples together?

Exercises 274–277: Consider a case of 12 cans of tuna, three of which are contaminated with dangerous bacteria. Five cans are to be opened and tested by an inspector who does not know of the contamination.

274. How many samples of size 5 are possible?
275. How many samples of size 5 contain only "good" cans?
276. How many samples will include at least one "bad" can?
277. Is the inspector more likely to discover or not discover that the case contains some contaminated tuna? Justify your answer.

*278. You have time for at most five plays of a casino game before your helicopter arrives to whisk you away to your yacht. You pay $3 to play each time; if you win, you get another dollar, and if you lose, you part with your $3. You start with $5, and will quit if you are ever $3 ahead, or you lack time or money to continue. How many different paths could your playing of this game follow to its conclusion?

279. In Exercise 278, how many paths are there, if you start with $4 instead of $5?
280. In how many ways could four math books, three chemistry books, and five biology books (all different) be arranged on a shelf, if books are to be grouped by subject?

Exercises 281–283: We consider a shipment of 12 television sets containing three that are defective. Delmo's brother Felmo will purchase four of these TV sets to put into the barn so that his milking machines (his four kids!) will have something to watch during chores. Find the probability that his purchase of four has:

281. no defectives.
282. at least one defective.
283. all three defectives.

Exercises 284 and 285: Eight students are eligible to go, and six will be sent, to the National Student Body Painting Convention held in East Doldrum, North Dakota. In how many ways may the six delegates be chosen if:

284. two of the students insist on not being separated?
285. two of the students quarrel and cannot both be sent?

Exercises 286–288: Two fair dice are tossed. Find the probability that:

286. both dice show even numbers.
287. at least one of the two dice shows an even number.
288. exactly one die shows an even number.

289. A basketball coach has three complimentary tickets. He decides to give these tickets to three players chosen at random from his starting five: Alpo (A), Bozo (B), Carp (C), Deltoid (D), and Enamel (E). Find the probability that Alpo and Bozo get tickets.
290. In Exercise 289, find the probability that Alpo and Bozo get tickets or Carp and Deltoid get tickets or Bozo, Carp, and Enamel get tickets.

291. Following a windstorm, five insurance adjustors (numbered 1 through 5 for our convenience) in Terre Haute, Indiana, have 27 wind-damage claims to settle. In how many different ways could the claims be distributed so that adjustors 1 and 2 take six claims each, the rest being distributed equally to the other adjustors?
292. In Exercise 291, in how many ways could the claims be grouped equally in three file folders?

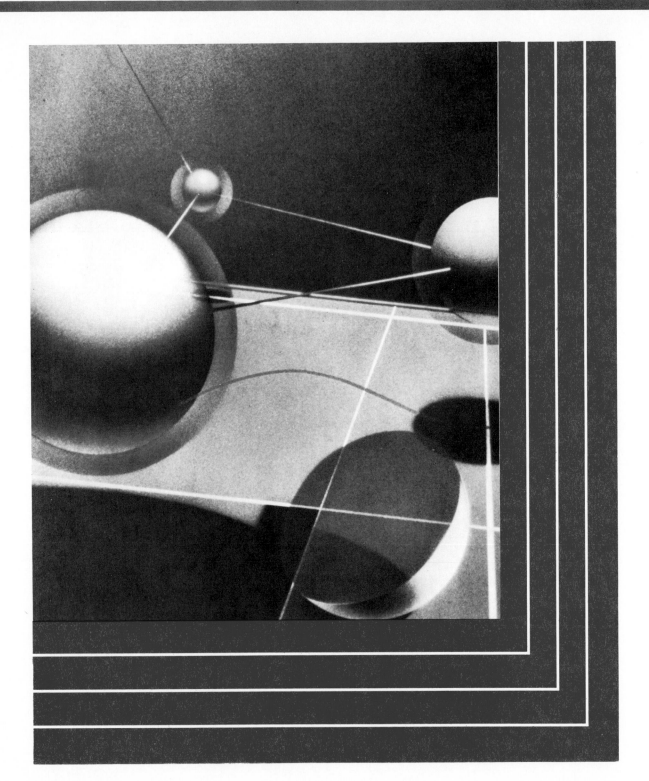

8 Random Variables and Probability Distributions

8.1 RANDOM VARIABLES

Discrete Random Variables

In most probability problems we have worked, outcomes were nonnumerical. In Example 21 of Chapter 7, two jurors were chosen from a pool of seven women and two men, and outcomes were W_1W_2, W_1M_2, M_1W_2, and M_1M_2. In experiments like this the outcome itself does not interest us as much as some number associated with the outcome. In the jury selection, for example, we might be more interested in the number of women in the outcome than in the outcome itself. Let X equal the number of women jurors. Notice that we cannot predict the value of X before the experiment, because the value of X depends on the outcome of our experiment. In particular, observe that

If W_1W_2 is the outcome, $X = 2$.

If W_1M_2 is the outcome, $X = 1$.

If M_1W_2 is the outcome, $X = 1$.

If M_1M_2 is the outcome, $X = 0$.

Since X varies and its value depends on the outcome of our random experiment, we shall say that X is a *random variable*.

RANDOM VARIABLE

> A **random variable** is a rule for assigning a unique real number to each outcome in an experiment. The number we assign is called the **value** of the random variable. We name random variables with capital letters like X, Y, Z, W, U, V and represent their numerical values by the corresponding lowercase letters x, y, z, etc.

To use statistics, we need numerical, rather than "descriptive," outcomes. A random variable converts a nonnumerical sample space into a numerical sample space whose outcomes are values of the random variable. Figure 8.1 abbreviates the tree diagram for Chapter 7, Example 21 (jury selection), with a new column showing the value of the random variable X (number of women) on each path.

Figure 8.1

Tree diagram for "number of women" in selection of two jurors

	Probability	Path Label	X-Value
$6/8$ W_2	$42/72 \approx 0.583$	a	2
$2/8$ M_2	$14/72 \approx 0.194$	b	1
$7/8$ W_2	$14/72 \approx 0.194$	c	1
$1/8$ M_2	$2/72 \approx 0.028$	d	0

Note that paths b and c are equivalent when our interest is in the number of women and not in which one of the jurors was a woman. When we introduce random variable X, we are essentially replacing the nonnumerical outcomes a, b, c, and d with three new simple events (0, 1, and 2) representing values of X. Since $X = 2$ only when the outcome is path a, then the probability that X takes the value 2, written $P[X = 2]$, should equal $P[a]$. This gives $P[X = 2] = 42/72 \approx 0.583$. The random variable X takes the value 1 when the outcome is either path b or c, and thus the event "$X = 1$" should have the same probability as event $\{b,c\}$. Therefore, $P[X = 1] = 14/72 + 14/72 = 28/72 \approx 0.389$. Finally, the event "$X = 0$" occurs when and only when the outcome is path d. It follows that $P[X = 0] = 2/72 \approx 0.028$. We summarize our findings concerning the random variable X by making the following table:

Value of X	Paths	Probability
0	d	$2/72 \approx 0.028$
1	b,c	$28/72 \approx 0.389$
2	a	$42/72 \approx 0.583$

This table, which lists values of the random variable X and their associated probabilities, is called the **probability distribution** for X. This is indeed an apt name; the total probability in any sample space is one, and we have spread or distributed this total probability over the possible values.

Sometimes it is convenient to express a probability distribution graphically by means of a **histogram,** as in Figure 8.2.

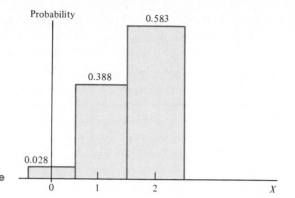

Figure 8.2
Histogram of probability
distribution for random variable
X: "number of women chosen"

The Figure 8.2 histogram is composed of three rectangles, each having a base one unit wide and height equal to the probability of the *x*-value over which the rectangle is centered. The area of each rectangle, "base times height," represents the probability that the random variable *X* takes the value in the base of that rectangle. The total area of all rectangles is one. Test your understanding of a random variable and its probability distribution in the following example.

■ EXAMPLE 1

Consider Example 23 from Chapter 7, where Delmo randomly picked two rock cassettes from his collection of seven, which included four by the all-male group "Conniption Fit," one by the all-male group "Old Men at the Home," and two by the female group "Bodacious Warlord." Find the probability distribution for the random variable

$$Y = \text{the number of tapes recorded by a male rock group}$$

SOLUTION   We reproduce Figure 7.4 from Example 23 of Chapter 7, adding a final column that records the value of *Y* for each path.

	Probability	Path Label	*Y*-Value
CF: 3|6 → CF	12/42 ≈ 0.286	*a*	2
CF: 1/6 → OM	4/42 ≈ 0.095	*b*	2
CF: 2/6 → BW	8/42 ≈ 0.190	*c*	1
OM: 4|6 → CF	4/42 ≈ 0.095	*d*	2
OM: 2/6 → BW	2/42 ≈ 0.048	*e*	1
BW: 4|6 → CF	8/42 ≈ 0.190	*f*	1
BW: 1/6 → OM	2/42 ≈ 0.048	*g*	1
BW: 1/6 → BW	2/42 ≈ 0.048	*h*	0

Tree: Go → 4/7 CF, 1/7 OM, 2/7 BW

Since our interest is centered in the random variable Y, we "summarize" the information on the tree, obtaining the following probability distribution:

Value of Y	Paths	Probability
0	h	$\dfrac{2}{42}$
1	c,e,f,g	$\dfrac{8 + 2 + 8 + 2}{42} = \dfrac{20}{42}$
2	a,b,d	$\dfrac{12 + 4 + 4}{42} = \dfrac{20}{42}$

Now that we have the idea, let's streamline the above table. Letting $p(y)$ be the probability associated with the value y, and omitting references to the tree, we can write:

y	$p(y)$
0	2/42
1	20/42
2	20/42

From now on we shall use this much "cleaner" form for our probability distributions. ■

The jury selection problem and Example 1 are alike in that the random variable has only a finite number of possible values. Some experiments have more than a finite number of outcomes (refer to Experiments 5 and 6 in Section 6.4). In the next example, we shall encounter an experiment with infinitely many outcomes that can still be analyzed with precisely the same techniques we have been using.

■ EXAMPLE 2

The famous golfer, Shankus Handmashie, is standing on the tee of a 194-yard par three hole hitting ball after ball, intending to keep hitting until he gets a hole-in-one. Find the probability distribution for the random variable W which represents the number of shots required to get the hole-in-one.

SOLUTION   Let H stand for "hole-in-one" and M stand for a "miss." A good sample space, with associated values of W listed below it, is:

$$S = \{H, MH, MMH, MMMH, MMMMH, \ldots\}$$

Values of W: 1,   2,   3,   4,   5, . . .

Since it is possible for Shankus to fire away forever, there is no definite number of elements in S; the random variable W has infinitely many possible values. It is thus impossible to construct a probability distribution in table form. Instead, we derive an expression, which, upon substitution of a possible value w, will yield $p(w)$, the probability of observing that value. To find an expression for $p(w)$, we shall make the following assumptions:

1. The results of any shot by Shankus are independent of the results of any other shot.

2. The probability of a hole-in-one on any shot is 1/10,000, an arbitrarily assigned but reasonable figure.

Using these assumptions, we shall evaluate a few values for $p(w)$. Since $W = 1$ occurs only when the observed simple event is H, then

$$p(1) = P[W = 1] = P[H] = \frac{1}{10,000} = 0.0001$$

The event $W = 2$ occurs only when MH is the observed simple event. Since repeated shots are independent, it is reasonable to view MH as the intersection of the two independent one-shot results M and H. The probability that the first shot misses and the second goes in is given by the product:

$$p(2) = P[W = 2] = P[MH] = P[M] \cdot P[H]$$
$$= (1 - 0.0001) \cdot 0.0001 = 0.00009999$$

Similarly,

$$p(3) = P[W = 3] = P[MMH] = P[M] \cdot P[M] \cdot P[H]$$
$$= (0.9999) \cdot (0.9999) \cdot (0.0001) \approx 0.00009998$$

There is little chance that Shankus will go home early! Finding probabilities for these three values of W suggest a pattern for finding $p(w)$, the probability of getting his hole-in-one for the first time on trial number w. To get the first hole-in-one on shot w requires that Shankus miss the first $w - 1$ shots and then score a hole-in-one on shot w. Since shots are independent, this probability is obtained by multiplying the probabilities at each shot. Thus,

$$p(w) = P[W = w] = \underbrace{(0.9999)^{w-1}}_{\substack{w - 1 \text{ misses} \\ \text{in a row}}} \cdot \underbrace{(0.0001)}_{\substack{\text{a hit on} \\ \text{shot } w}} \qquad \text{for} \quad w = 1, 2, \ldots$$

Although not in tabular form, this formula is the **probability distribution for *W***. Instead of an infinitely long table, we have a convenient expression that allows us to input a possible value for *w*, and the resulting output is the probability of that value. ∎

Example 2 was distinctive in that the random variable had infinitely many possible values, each with a probability greater than zero. Even so, there are definite gaps between any pair of possible values. Random variables like the ones in Examples 1 and 2 that have either a finite number of values, or an infinite number with definite gaps between any two distinct values, are called discrete random variables.

DISCRETE RANDOM VARIABLE

A random variable that has definite gaps between possible values is said to be a **discrete random variable**.

Here is an easy check: a variable whose values represent counts, whether finite or infinite, is discrete. Some examples:

1. The number of passes completed by the Seattle Seahawk starting quarterback in his next 10 attempts.

2. The number of defectives in a sample of 100 transistors.

3. The number of people in the "9 item" line at a supermarket.

Every discrete random variable has a probability distribution which describes how the one unit of total probability is spread (distributed) among the possible values of the random variable. Any probability distribution must satisfy the following properties:

REQUIREMENTS FOR A PROBABILITY DISTRIBUTION OF A DISCRETE RANDOM VARIABLE

1. The probability of any possible value of the random variable must be at least 0 and not more than one.

2. The sum of the probabilities attached to all possible values of the random variable must be one.

Convince yourself that the random variables in Examples 1 and 2 do indeed satisfy these two properties.

Continuous Random Variables

We shall study one other kind of random variable known as a *continuous random variable*. Whereas a discrete random variable has definite gaps between adjacent values, a continuous random variable has no such gaps, and can assume any value in some interval of real numbers.

CONTINUOUS RANDOM
VARIABLE

> A random variable that can take any possible value in some interval of numbers on the real number line is said to be a **continuous random variable**.

One way to think of continuous random variables is this: If, given precise measuring equipment, you could measure the value to more decimal places, then the value is continuous. (Extra decimal places would not help with a discrete random variable—a count is still a count.) The following are some examples of continuous random variables:

1. Weight of a person selected at random from your finite mathematics class.

2. Speed of a car passing a certain exit on a freeway.

3. Amount of alcohol in a bottle of wine.

4. Time required to complete an exam in your English class.

5. Distance a car takes to stop from a speed of 70 mph.

6. Length of a randomly sawed log.

Because continuous random variables have so many values, we run into trouble if we try to form a probability distribution by assigning a probability to each possible value. The probabilities so assigned would sum to "a lot more" than one. Instead, we describe continuous random variables with probability density curves. We discuss continuous random variables and special methods necessary for treating them in Section 8.5. Until then we concentrate on discrete random variables.

■ EXAMPLE 3

The famous basketball player Airebhall Netbender has a 60% chance of making any free throw, independently of what happens on any other free throw. Airebhall, having been fouled in the act of shooting his midcourt stuff shot, steps to the line for two shots. Let the random variable V be the number of free throws made. Find the probability distribution of V.

SOLUTION

A sample space for this experiment is illustrated by the tree diagram in Figure 8.3. G denotes a good free throw, while M represents a miss.

Figure 8.3
Airebhall's possibilities on next
two free throws

	Path Label	Probability	V-Value
G (0.6), G (0.6) → G	a	0.36	2
G (0.6), M (0.4) → M	b	0.24	1
M (0.4), G (0.6) → G	c	0.24	1
M (0.4), M (0.4) → M	d	0.16	0

Reading the tree and summarizing, we have:

v	$p(v)$
0	0.16
1	0.48
2	0.36

$$p(0) = P[V = 0] = P[d] \qquad\qquad = 0.16$$
$$p(1) = P[V = 1] = P[b] + P[c] = 0.48$$
$$p(2) = P[V = 2] = P[a] \qquad\qquad = 0.36$$

This is an example of a binomial probability distribution, which we will study in considerably more depth in Section 8.4.   ■

EXERCISES 8.1

PRACTICING THE MOVES AND MANEUVERS

Exercises 1–9: Determine whether the random variables are discrete or continuous.

1. Number of people waiting for service at the Premium Unleaded line at the Arco station nearest you.
2. Number of traffic accidents in a week at the busiest intersection in your town.
3. The time it takes to walk from finite math class to your school residence.
4. The number of fish you catch on your next fishing trip.
5. The length of the largest fish you catch on your next fishing trip.
6. The number of red lights you stop for on your next trip downtown.
7. The number of defective TV sets in a shipment of 200 received by a major department store.
8. The amount of snow that falls in Fairbanks, Alaska, during December.
9. The number of breakdowns of the campus computer during a one-week period.

Exercises 10–12: Use the following probability distribution, which describes random variable X = monthly demand for compact disc players in an audio specialty store.

x = # CD Players	$p(x)$
0	0.10
1	0.15
2	0.25
3	0.20
4	0.15
5	0.10
6 or more	?

10. What is the probability that the monthly demand is for 6 or more players?
11. Suppose the store orders 4 CD players at the start of the month. What is the probability of selling all 4?
12. Suppose the store stocks 5 CD players at the start of the month. Assuming they do not order any more, what is the probability that they have at least 2 in stock at the end of the month?

APPLYING THE CONCEPTS

Exercises 13–16: Toss two fair dice, one red and the other green.

13. Let random variable X be the sum of the numbers on the up faces. Find the probability distribution of X.
14. Express the probability distribution for X with a histogram.

15. Let the random variable Y be the number on the red die minus the number on the green die. Find the probability distribution of Y.
16. Draw a histogram representing the probability distribution of Y.

Exercises 17 and 18: Consider a box containing four green and two red balls. Two balls are drawn in succession, the first ball being replaced before the second is drawn.

17. Define random variable W to be the number of green balls drawn. Find the probability distribution of W.
18. Define the random variable V to be the number of red balls selected. Find the probability distribution of V.

Exercises 19 and 20: Consider a Senate committee which consists of four Republicans and three Democrats. A subcommittee of two is chosen at random.

19. Let the random variable X represent the number of Democrats on the subcommittee. Find the probability distribution for X.
20. Let the random variable Y be the number of Republicans selected on the subcommittee. Find the probability distribution for Y.

Exercises 21–23: Delmo is at the local supermarket buying pizza. He selects two pizzas at random from the freezer section which has eight pepperoni pizzas, four sausage pizzas, and three rutabaga pizzas.

21. Find the probability distribution for the random variable X, which counts the number of pepperoni pizzas Delmo buys.
22. Find the probability distribution for the random variable Y, which represents the number of rutabaga pizzas Delmo buys.

*23. Suppose Delmo is really hungry and decides to buy three pizzas. Find the probability distribution for random variable U, which counts the number of sausage pizzas Delmo buys. Express it with a histogram.

24. A shipment of 12 compact disc players contains nine good units and three defectives. A random sample of size three is selected and tested. Let random variable Y represent defective units found. Find the probability distribution for Y.
25. In Exercise 24, find the probability distribution for W = number of good units.
*26. A magazine subscriber takes both *Time* and *Newsweek*, each supposed to arrive in Wednesday's mail. Because of vagaries of the mail system, however, actual delivery can be on Wednesday, Thursday, Friday, or Saturday. Suppose the arrival of either magazine is independent of the arrival of the other, and that the probabilities of delivery are 0.5, 0.35, 0.1, 0.05 on Wednesday through Saturday, respectively,

for each magazine. Let the random variable X be the number of days beyond Wednesday until both magazines arrive. Find the probability distribution for X. *Hint:* the possible values of X are 0 (if both magazines arrive on Wednesday), 1, 2, 3 (if the last magazine arrives on Saturday).
*27. In Exercise 26, define random variable Y by the total number of days the two magazines are late. Thus, if *Time* arrives on Wednesday and *Newsweek* on Thursday, $Y = 1$; if both arrive on Friday, each is two days late, and $Y = 4$. Find the probability distribution for Y.
28. A coin is biased so that a head is twice as likely as a tail. Let Y be the number of heads when the coin is tossed twice. Find the probability distribution for Y.

29. Two cards are drawn at random without re-placement from a standard deck of 52 cards. Let the random variable Y be the number of clubs drawn. Find the probability distribution for Y.

30. Debbie has a set of 11 men that she asks for dates. Six are redheads, four are blonds, and one is bald. She picks two different names at random from her little black book. Let the random variable W represent the number of blond-haired men she selects. Find the probability distribution for W.

31. At a party, three dweebs leave their hats at the hatcheck counter. At the end of the evening, none is able to recognize his own hat. Their three hats are the only ones available, and the hatcheck person hands each dweeb a hat at random. Let the random variable V be the number of dweebs who get their own hats. Find the probability distribution for V.

*32. The contents of two ice chests filled with cola drinks are shown below:

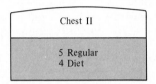

One beverage is selected at random from Chest I and put into Chest II. Two cans are then selected at random from Chest II. All cans have lost their labels, so that the selection is definitely "at random." Let the random variable X represent the number of cans of Regular (nondiet) cola obtained by the selection from Chest II. Find the probability distribution for X.

*33. In Exercise 32, let Y be the total number of cans of Regular selected, either from Chest I or Chest II. Find the probability distribution for Y.

*34. Every Tuesday Delmo gets up at 4 A.M. to attend the weekly meeting of SPURT (Society for Preservation of Used Rutabaga Tacos). He picks one sock at random from drawer I (which has six black and four red socks) and puts this sock into drawer II, which had four black and five red socks before Delmo's addition. He then picks two socks simultaneously and at random from drawer II. Since SPURT gives awards for those wearing red socks, Delmo hopes to get at least one red sock. Let the random variable X count red socks Delmo gets. Find the probability distribution of X.

8.2 DESCRIBING RANDOM VARIABLES

v	$p(v)$
0	0.16
1	0.48
2	0.36

Although we cannot predict the value of a random variable that results from an experiment, the probability distribution allows us to describe its long-range behavior. In particular, the probability distribution summarizes the population of values that would result from infinitely many repetitions of that experiment. To illustrate, consider Example 3, where random variable V records free throws made by Airebhall Netbender in his next two shots. The probability distribution for V is shown in the table. Suppose Airebhall's next 10 trips to the line for two shots spawn the following V values:

$$2, 1, 1, 1, 2, 2, 0, 2, 1, 1$$

These ten values are but a sample of size 10 from the infinite population of V values that would result from Airebhall shooting two foul shots forever and ever. The probability distribution summarizes this infinitely long string of population results by informing us that in the long run (that is, after many, many sets of two free throws), Airebhall would make none of his two free throws about 16% of the time, would make exactly one of the two about 48% of the time, and would make both about 36% of the time. It is in this sense that a probability distribution summarizes a population. Frequently, however, we are interested in an even more concise summary. Certain numbers, called *parameters*, provide useful information about probability distributions or their corresponding population of values.[1]

PARAMETER

> A **parameter** is a number that describes a probability distribution; to compute a parameter, you must know all values in the population or, equivalently, the probability distribution for these population values.

In describing a distribution it seems reasonable to pick a parameter that somehow measures the "center" of the population. One choice for describing a population of X values is the **mean** or the **expected value** of X. Consider a "perfect" sequence of 1,000,000 trips to the free throw line for two shots by our erstwhile roundballer Airebhall Netbender. Intuitively, we would expect him to make both free throws 360,000 times, one free throw 480,000 times, and to miss both shots 160,000 times. Thus, the average number of free throws made would be the sum of all 1,000,000 values divided by 1,000,000:

$$\frac{0 \cdot 160,000 + 1 \cdot 480,000 + 2 \cdot 360,000}{1,000,000}$$

$$= 0 \cdot \frac{160,000}{1,000,000} + 1 \cdot \frac{480,000}{1,000,000} + 2 \cdot \frac{360,000}{1,000,000}$$

$$= 0 \cdot (0.16) \quad + 1 \cdot (0.48) \quad + 2 \cdot (0.36)$$

$$= 1.2$$

This average, 1.2, is the sum of three products, each having the form "value of x · relative frequency of that value." Using the relative fre-

---

[1] From now on, when we speak of a distribution, keep these "population implications" in mind: each performance of an experiment produces one value of the random variable; repeating the experiment indefinitely generates a population of values of the random variable. The probability distribution summarizes this population.

quencies 0.16, 0.48, and 0.36 as suitable probabilities for the values 0, 1, and 2, we write this last expression as

$$0 \cdot p(0) + 1 \cdot p(1) + 2 \cdot p(2) = \sum v \cdot p(v) = 1.2$$

where the symbol "Σ" is read "sum of." Thus, $\Sigma v \cdot p(v)$ means "sum the products of the form value times probability." This thinking leads us to define the *mean* of a random variable by:

MEAN OF A PROBABILITY DISTRIBUTION

> When a population of values of a random variable X is given in summary form by a probability distribution, then the **mean** of X (or the mean of the probability distribution of X) is given by
>
> $$\mu_x = \sum x \cdot p(x)$$
>
> where the sum is taken over all possible values x.

Using subscripts allows us to talk about the means of several random variables by using only the symbol μ. If the random variables we are studying are Y and Z, then their means would be written μ_y (say "mew-sub-y") and μ_z.

The mean number of free throws made by Airebhall in two-shot opportunities is $\mu_v = \Sigma v \cdot p(v) = 0 \cdot (0.16) + 1 \cdot (0.48) + 2 \cdot (0.36) = 1.2$. Based on the "perfect sequence" of one million two-shot attempts discussed above, we have the rough idea that μ_v represents a "long-range average." To reinforce this idea, we now examine the 10 values of V we presented earlier.

The data are: 2, 1, 1, 1, 2, 2, 0, 2, 1, 1. We use these to compute the mean of V as each new value becomes available:

Trial #	Value of V	Average Value of All V's Through That Trial
1	2	$2/1 = 2$
2	1	$(2 + 1)/2 = 1.5$
3	1	$(2 + 1 + 1)/3 \approx 1.33$
4	1	$(2 + 1 + 1 + 1)/4 = 1.25$
5	2	$(2 + 1 + 1 + 1 + 2)/5 = 1.40$
6	2	$(2 + 1 + 1 + 1 + 2 + 2)/6 = 1.50$
7	0	$(2 + 1 + 1 + 1 + 2 + 2 + 0)/7 \approx 1.29$
8	2	$(2 + 1 + 1 + 1 + 2 + 2 + 0 + 2)/8 \approx 1.38$
9	1	$(2 + 1 + 1 + 1 + 2 + 2 + 0 + 2 + 1)/9 \approx 1.33$
10	1	$(2 + 1 + 1 + 1 + 2 + 2 + 0 + 2 + 1 + 1)/10 = 1.30$

Suppose we were to continue in this manner, recalculating the average as each new value of V becomes available. The average would change less and less as more and more data accumulate. The value 1.2, which represents μ_v, is the number toward which these numbers are tending (or "converging"). Speaking loosely, μ_v is the average of infinitely many V values. Intuitively, we consider the mean μ as being a "long-range average value."

Physical Interpretation of a Mean

Imagine a weightless rod engraved with a number scale. On this rod, locate each value of the random variable and place a weight there equal to the probability of that value. If you view this rod and its attached weights as a teeter-totter, the balance point for the teeter-totter would be the mean μ_v. This idea is illustrated for the Airebhall's free throw shots distribution in Figure 8.4.

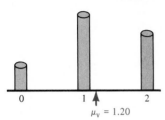

Figure 8.4
The mean as "balance point"

Expected Value

For historical reasons, the mean of a random variable X is also called the **expected value of X**, written $E(X)$. Henceforth, we shall use these two terms interchangeably, but be aware that the term "expected value" is extremely misleading, as the following example shows.

■ EXAMPLE 4

Consider the experiment of throwing a fair die. Let the random variable W denote the value on the up face. Find the probability distribution for W and also the expected value or mean of W.

SOLUTION

The probability distribution is shown in Figure 8.5. The mean of W, written either μ_w or $E(W)$, is $\mu_w = E(W) = 1 \cdot \frac{1}{6} + 2 \cdot \frac{1}{6} + 3 \cdot \frac{1}{6} + 4 \cdot \frac{1}{6} + 5 \cdot \frac{1}{6} + 6 \cdot \frac{1}{6} = 3.5$, a result that is definitely not "expected" when you toss a die. Though we frequently use the term expected value, be sure to interpret it as "long-range average." ■

W	$p(W)$
1	1/6
2	1/6
3	1/6
4	1/6
5	1/6
6	1/6

Figure 8.5

PRACTICE PROBLEM 1

In Example 1, find $E[Y]$.

ANSWER(S)

(a) $E[Y] = \mu_y \approx 1.43$.   □

Rather than finding $E(X)$, in some instances we shall want to find the average value of $g(X)$, a quantity which depends on X. For example, if random variable X represents number of tickets sold for a performance, and each ticket costs \$8.50, then "$g(X) = 8.5X$" is a quantity which depends on X, and which represents the revenue in dollars from ticket sales. To help us find a way of computing $E[g(X)]$, consider how we find $E[X]$; we multiply each value X can take by its corresponding probability; we then add the results. Thus, to find $E[g(X)]$, we could proceed in analogous fashion: Multiply the values of $g(X)$ by the probabilities associated with the corresponding values of X and then add.

EXPECTED VALUE OF A QUANTITY THAT DEPENDS ON X

If X is a random variable whose probability at x is given by $p(x)$, then the expected value of $g(X)$ is given by

$$E[g(X)] = \sum g(x) \cdot p(x)$$

where the sum is evaluated over all possible values x.

■ EXAMPLE 5

In Example 4, find the expected value of W^2.

SOLUTION

Following the boxed procedure, we should compute the following:

$$E[W^2] = \sum w^2 \cdot p(w)$$

where we evaluate $w^2 \cdot p(w)$ for all values w before adding:

$$E[W^2] = 1^2 \cdot p(1) + 2^2 \cdot p(2) + 3^2 \cdot p(3) + 4^2 \cdot p(4)$$
$$+ 5^2 \cdot p(5) + 6^2 \cdot p(6)$$
$$= 1 \cdot \frac{1}{6} + 4 \cdot \frac{1}{6} + 9 \cdot \frac{1}{6} + 16 \cdot \frac{1}{6} + 25 \cdot \frac{1}{6} + 36 \cdot \frac{1}{6}$$
$$= \frac{91}{6} \approx 15.167$$

Right now there is no apparent reason for wanting such a quantity as $E[W^2]$; in the next section, however, you will learn that $E[W^2]$ is helpful in finding an important quantity known as the standard deviation. The next example illustrates why you might be more interested in a quantity that depends on X rather than the random variable itself.

■ EXAMPLE 6

Your authors propose the following game: Two ordinary fair dice are tossed, and if the sum is either 7 or 11, we pay you a total of $8. If the sum is 6 or 8, we pay you a total of $12. On any other dice sum, you pay us $10. Is this a good game for you?

SOLUTION

We can let the random variable X represent the sum when the two dice are tossed. From Exercise 13 of this chapter, we know that the probability distribution for X is given by:

x	2	3	4	5	6	7	8	9	10	11	12
$p(x)$	$\dfrac{1}{36}$	$\dfrac{2}{36}$	$\dfrac{3}{36}$	$\dfrac{4}{36}$	$\dfrac{5}{36}$	$\dfrac{6}{36}$	$\dfrac{5}{36}$	$\dfrac{4}{36}$	$\dfrac{3}{36}$	$\dfrac{2}{36}$	$\dfrac{1}{36}$

This probability distribution for the dice sum X is important, but we are more interested in the payoffs associated with the dice sums. These payoffs depend on the value of X; in mathematical language, payoff is a function of (depends on) X. We indicate this by letting $g(X)$ represent the payoff to you when the dice sum is X. For example, if $x = 7$, then $g(7) = \$8$. If $x = 5$, then you pay us \$10, so $g(5) = -\$10$—note that since X has been defined as the amount you receive, then a payment to us is considered as a negative amount. We append to the above probability distribution a $g(x)$ row which describes the payoff for each dice sum.

x	2	3	4	5	6	7	8	9	10	11	12
$p(x)$	$\dfrac{1}{36}$	$\dfrac{2}{36}$	$\dfrac{3}{36}$	$\dfrac{4}{36}$	$\dfrac{5}{36}$	$\dfrac{6}{36}$	$\dfrac{5}{36}$	$\dfrac{4}{36}$	$\dfrac{3}{36}$	$\dfrac{2}{36}$	$\dfrac{1}{36}$
$g(x)$	-10	-10	-10	-10	12	8	12	-10	-10	8	-10

On one play of the game, possible payoffs are -10, 8, and 12. Thus, the expected payoff, $E[g(X)]$, is given by:

$$E[g(X)] = \sum g(x) \cdot p(x) = (-10)\left(\frac{18}{36}\right) + 8\left(\frac{8}{36}\right) + 12\left(\frac{10}{36}\right)$$

$$= \frac{4}{36} = \frac{1}{9} \quad (\text{about } \$0.11)$$

We simplified calculations by combining probabilities for dice sums 2, 3, 4, 5, 9, 10, and 12, since they all give -10 as payoff. Similarly, we combined probabilities for 6 and 8, and also for 7 and 11.

This game is one you might want to play because, in the long run, you would average 1/9 dollar (a little over 11 cents) per play. If we were able to play the game at the rate of once every 10 seconds, then, for five days of 8-hour play, your expected value would be $(1/9) \cdot 6 \cdot 60 \cdot 8 \cdot 5 = \$1600$. ∎

EXERCISES 8.2

PRACTICING THE MOVES AND MANEUVERS

Exercises 35–42: Find the mean of the given probability distribution.

35.

x	$p(x)$
2	0.6
3	0.4

36.

y	$p(y)$
1	0.3
2	0.4
3	0.3

37.

z	$p(z)$
3	0.1
5	0.5
6	0.4

38.

w	$p(w)$
0	0.4
1	0.6

39.

y	$p(y)$
−2	0.6
2	0.4

40.

v	$p(v)$
−2	0.5
2	0.5

41.

w	$p(w)$
0	0.5
4	0.3
6	0.2

42.

x	$p(x)$
2	0.1
6	0.5
10	0.4

APPLYING THE CONCEPTS

43. In Exercise 13, you found the probability distribution for the random variable X which represented the sum of the numbers on the faces when two dice were tossed. Now, find $E(X)$, μ_x, and $E(X^2)$.
44. In Exercise 15, you found the probability distribution for the random variable Y that represented the number on the red die minus the number on the green die. Now, find the mean of the random variable Y, and $E(Y^2)$.
45. In Exercise 17, two balls were drawn, with replacement, from a box containing four green balls and two red balls. You found the probability distribution for the random variable W, which counted the number of green balls obtained. Now, find the mean of random variable W, and $E(W^2)$.
46. In Exercise 18, you found the probability distribution for the random variable V, which counted the number of red balls when two balls were selected, with replacement, from a box having four green balls and two red balls. Find the expected value of the random variable V.

47. Two fair dice are tossed. The authors will pay you $8 if the dice differ; you must pay them (one payment of) $41 if the dice match. In the long run, how much do you expect to win per play of this game?
*48. In the game of Exercise 47, suppose the authors sweeten the deal by giving you an additional $3 when the dice sum is 5. Find your long run average winnings at this game.
49. In Exercise 19, two people were to be selected at random from a Senate committee consisting of four Republicans and three Democrats. In this exercise, you found the probability distribution for the random variable X = number of Democrats. Find $E(X)$ and $E(X^2)$.
50. In Exercise 20 (see Exercise 49 for description), you found the probability distribution for the random variable Y, the number of Republicans selected. Find $E(Y)$ and $E(Y^2)$.
51. In Exercise 23, Delmo chose three pizzas at random from a freezer compartment containing eight pepperoni, four sausage, and three rutabaga pizzas. The random variable whose proba-

bility distribution you found was U = number of sausage pizzas. Find the mean of this random variable.

52. In Exercise 22, Delmo chose two pizzas at random from an assortment of eight pepperoni, four sausage, and three rutabaga pizzas. The random variable whose probability distribution you found was Y = number of rutabaga pizzas chosen. Find the mean of the random variable Y.

53. In Exercise 24, a random sample of three com-

pact disc players was chosen from a shipment having nine good and three defective players. You found the probability distribution for the random variable Y = number of defective players. Find the expected value of random variable Y.

54. In Example 6, suppose we change the game. If the dice sum is any odd number, other than seven, you get $10. If a seven is thrown, you get $6. On any even number, you pay us $8. What is your expected payoff in this game?

8.3 MEASURING DISPERSION: THE VARIANCE AND THE STANDARD DEVIATION

How Well Does the Mean Work in Describing a Random Variable?

Would the mean be a good predictor for future values of that variable? Yes—if there is a reasonably high probability of observing a value close to the mean. This suggests that we need a way of measuring "closeness to the mean." In the next example, we look for a way of finding such a measure.

■ EXAMPLE 7

Consider two different populations, one associated with a random variable X and the other with a random variable Y. Each is summarized by a probability distribution, as shown below:

X:

x	$p(x)$
-100	7/16
0	2/16
100	7/16

Y:

y	$p(y)$
$-1/100$	1/16
0	14/16
1/100	1/16

Discuss "closeness to the mean" for each population.

SOLUTION Note that

$$E[X] = \mu_x = (-100) \cdot \left(\frac{7}{16}\right) + 0 \cdot \left(\frac{2}{16}\right) + 100 \cdot \left(\frac{7}{16}\right) = 0$$

Probability distribution for X

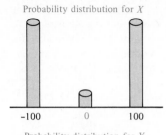

-100   0   100

Probability distribution for Y

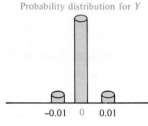

-0.01   0   0.01

and

$$E[Y] = \mu_y = \left(\frac{-1}{100}\right) \cdot \left(\frac{1}{16}\right) + 0 \cdot \left(\frac{14}{16}\right) + \left(\frac{1}{100}\right) \cdot \left(\frac{1}{16}\right) = 0$$

Both populations have mean 0, but the mean does a good job of describing only the Y population, failing miserably for X. The reason is clear: there is high probability that values of X will differ considerably from the mean—in fact, the probability that X will differ from its mean by 100, in either direction, is 14/16. On the other hand, values of Y *never* differ from the mean by more than 1/100, and thus μ_y would be a good predictor of Y.

How do we measure "closeness" to the mean μ_x? For any one value x, $x - \mu_x$ measures the difference between x and μ_x. We call this difference a "deviation from the mean." Since X_i is random, so is any deviation $X - \mu_x$. In measuring closeness of X to its mean, it seems reasonable to ask: "On the average, how far is X from μ_x?" This suggests computing the average deviation from the mean, $E[X - \mu_x]$. Since $g(X) = X - \mu_x$ is a quantity that depends on X, we know how to find $E[g(X)]$. We do this for both the X and Y populations above, in our attempt to establish a measure of "closeness" to the mean:

For X:

$$E[X - \mu_x] = \sum (x - \mu_x) \cdot p(x)$$

$$= (-100 - 0) \cdot p(-100) + (0 - 0) \cdot p(0)$$

$$+ (100 - 0) \cdot p(100)$$

$$= -\frac{700}{16} + 0 + \frac{700}{16} = 0$$

For Y:

$$E[Y - \mu_y] = \sum (y - \mu_y) \cdot p(y)$$

$$= \left(-\frac{1}{100}\right) \cdot p\left(-\frac{1}{100}\right) + (0 - 0) \cdot p(0)$$

$$+ \left(\frac{1}{100} - 0\right) \cdot p\left(\frac{1}{100}\right)$$

$$= -\frac{1}{1600} + 0 + \frac{1}{1600} = 0$$

Wait a minute! Values of Y are more concentrated around their mean than are values of X (Y tends to be "closer" to its mean than X)—but yet we get zero for *both* $E[X - \mu_x]$ and $E[Y - \mu_y]$! Nothing is wrong. What we have observed is a property of a mean: in *any* distribution it is *always true that the expected (long-range average) deviation from the mean is zero.* The mean is the only number possessing this feature—it is centrally located in such a way that "gaps" about the mean (positive and negative deviations) sum to zero and thus average 0.

A more suitable way of measuring spread is to square deviations first, and then take expectation. The quantity $(X - \mu_x)^2$ is always nonnegative, so its long-range average value (expected value) is surely greater than or equal to zero. In fact, $E[(X - \mu_x)^2]$ would be zero only if all X values were equal to the population mean—an unlikely (and uninteresting!) case. The quantity $E[(X - \mu_x)^2]$ is such a good way of measuring how well a population mean describes the population values that we give it a special name.

VARIANCE OF A PROBABILITY DISTRIBUTION

> The expected squared difference between the random variable X and its mean, μ_x, is called the **variance** of X (the variance of the population of values of X) and is represented by the square of the lower-case Greek letter σ_x, pronounced "sigma sub-x." That is,
>
> $$\sigma_x^2 = E[(X - \mu_x)^2]$$

Since the population variance σ_x^2 ("sigma sub-x, squared") is just the expectation of a quantity $g(X)$ that depends on X, we find $E[g(X)]$ by $\sigma_x^2 = \Sigma(x - \mu_x)^2 \cdot p(x)$, where summation is over all possible values of X. If there is no chance for confusion, we drop the subscript and write just σ^2. ∎

■ EXAMPLE 8

In this example we consider two finite populations:

$$X: 7, 7, 9, 5, 7, 6, 8, 7 \qquad Y: 9, 5, 5, 9, 9, 9, 5, 5$$

Summarize each population with a probability distribution, and then find the mean and variance of each population.

SOLUTION

The probability distributions summarizing these populations are:

x	$p(x)$
5	1/8
6	1/8
7	4/8
8	1/8
9	1/8

y	$p(y)$
5	4/8
9	4/8

Before finding the mean and variance of each of these random variables, we'll introduce yet another graphical summary device called a **dot diagram** that is especially helpful for small populations like these. One look at each of these dot diagrams is enough to explain the construction.

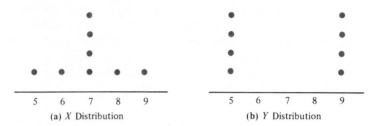

(a) *X* Distribution   (b) *Y* Distribution

The mean for *X* is

$$\mu_x = \sum x \cdot p(x)$$

$$= 5 \cdot \left(\frac{1}{8}\right) + 6 \cdot \left(\frac{1}{8}\right) + 7 \cdot \left(\frac{4}{8}\right) + 8 \cdot \left(\frac{1}{8}\right) + 9 \cdot \left(\frac{1}{8}\right) = \frac{56}{8} = 7$$

The mean for *Y* is

$$\mu_y = \sum y \cdot p(y) = 5 \cdot \left(\frac{4}{8}\right) + 9 \cdot \left(\frac{4}{8}\right) = \frac{56}{8} = 7$$

Though both populations have the same mean, it is clear from the dot diagram that the *X* distribution is more concentrated than is the *Y* distribution. That fact ought to be reflected in the variance for *X* being much smaller. Let's see.

The variance for *X* is

$$\sigma_x^2 = \sum (x - \mu_x)^2 \cdot p(x)$$

$$= (5 - 7)^2 \cdot \frac{1}{8} + (6 - 7)^2 \cdot \frac{1}{8} + (7 - 7)^2 \cdot \frac{4}{8} + (8 - 7)^2 \cdot \frac{1}{8}$$

$$+ (9 - 7)^2 \cdot \frac{1}{8}$$

$$= \frac{4}{8} + \frac{1}{8} + 0 + \frac{1}{8} + \frac{4}{8} = \frac{10}{8} = 1.25$$

The variance for *Y* is

$$\sigma_y^2 = \sum (y - \mu_y)^2 \cdot p(y)$$

$$= (5 - 7)^2 \cdot \frac{4}{8} + (9 - 7)^2 \cdot \frac{4}{8} = \frac{16}{8} + \frac{16}{8} = 4$$

Our supposition is verified: *Y* has a much larger variance than *X*.   ∎

Example 8 illustrates how the variance formula operates: If an x value differs considerably from μ_x, then $x - \mu_x$ will be large, and squaring a large deviation, positive or negative, produces a dramatically[4] larger number. If much probability is associated with a large deviation, that deviation will contribute considerably to the variance. For example, if a value of X having probability 0.4 deviates from the mean by 20 units, this value contributes $20^2 \cdot (0.4) = 160$ to σ^2! On the other hand, if this value occurred with probability 0.05, then the contribution to σ^2 would be only $20^2 \cdot (0.05) = 20$. The formula for σ^2 helps to understand what a variance does, but is not the best way to compute variance. The following "computing formula" makes calculation easier; we omit the straightforward derivation.

COMPUTING FORMULA FOR POPULATION VARIANCE

> The population variance σ^2 may be computed by finding $E[X^2] - \mu_x^2$. That is
>
> $$\sigma^2 = \sum x^2 \cdot p(x) - \mu_x^2$$

In words, the variance is "the mean of the squares minus the square of the mean." Try this formula on X from Example 8:

$$E[X^2] = \sum x^2 \cdot p(x)$$

$$= 5^2 \cdot \frac{1}{8} + 6^2 \cdot \frac{1}{8} + 7^2 \cdot \frac{4}{8} + 8^2 \cdot \frac{1}{8} + 9^2 \cdot \frac{1}{8}$$

$$= \frac{25}{8} + \frac{36}{8} + \frac{196}{8} + \frac{64}{8} + \frac{81}{8}$$

$$= \frac{402}{8}$$

We found earlier that $\mu_x = 7$, so $\sigma^2 = 402/8 - 7^2 = 1.25$, as before.

Use this formula for computing; the other formula (in the definition of σ^2) helps you to understand what a variance does.

■ EXAMPLE 9

In Example 7, use the computing formula to find the population variance σ^2 for both the X and the Y populations.

SOLUTION   **For X:** $\sigma_x^2 = \sum x^2 \cdot p(x) - \mu_x^2$. Here,

---

[4] The square of any number greater than one (or less than -1) produces a larger answer than the number itself. The increase due to squaring becomes even more dramatic as the deviation increases.

$$\sum x^2 \cdot p(x) = (-100)^2 \cdot \left(\frac{7}{16}\right) + 0^2 \cdot \left(\frac{2}{16}\right) + (100)^2 \cdot \left(\frac{7}{16}\right)$$

$$= \frac{70{,}000}{16} + 0 + \frac{70{,}000}{16} = \frac{140{,}000}{16} = 8{,}750$$

Thus, $\sigma_x^2 = 8{,}750 - 0^2 = 8{,}750$.

For Y: $\sigma_y^2 = \sum y^2 \cdot p(y) - \mu_y^2$

$$\sum y^2 \cdot p(y) = \left(-\frac{1}{100}\right)^2 \cdot \left(\frac{1}{16}\right) + 0^2 \cdot \left(\frac{14}{16}\right) + \left(\frac{1}{100}\right)^2 \cdot \left(\frac{1}{16}\right)$$

$$= \frac{1}{160{,}000} + 0 + \frac{1}{160{,}000} = \frac{1}{80{,}000} \approx 0.0000125$$

Hence, $\sigma_y^2 = 0.0000125 - 0^2 = 0.0000125$.

The sizes of these two variances confirm what we already know: "small" variance suggests the mean μ will be a suitable predictor of the random variable; "large" variance says just the opposite. ∎

Warning: In using the computing formula $\sigma_x^2 = \sum x^2 \cdot p(x) - \mu_x^2$, a common error (made by beginners and those who should know better!) is forgetting to subtract μ_x^2. Don't you do it!

PRACTICE PROBLEM 2   Find the mean and variance of the following probability distribution:

x	2	3	5	7	8
$p(x)$	$\frac{1}{8}$	$\frac{3}{8}$	$\frac{1}{4}$	$\frac{1}{8}$	$\frac{1}{8}$

ANSWER(S) $\mu = 4.5$; $\sigma^2 = 4$.   ☐

PRACTICE PROBLEM 3   In Example 1, find σ^2 for the Y distribution by using both the definition formula and the computing formula.

ANSWER(S) $\sigma^2 = 50/147 \approx 0.3401$.   ☐

The Standard Deviation   At the moment we know variance measures "closeness" to the mean μ, but we don't know what the size of a variance conveys. To give more precise meaning to the notion of variability, we introduce another parameter, called the *standard deviation*.

STANDARD DEVIATION OF A PROBABILITY DISTRIBUTION

> The positive square root of the population variance σ^2 is called the population **standard deviation**. We use the Greek letter σ to indicate population standard deviation:
>
> $$\sigma = \sqrt{\sigma^2}$$

We can also say that σ is the standard deviation of the distribution or the standard deviation of the random variable.

A good reason for taking the square root of the variance is to give us a measure of dispersion having the same units as the population values. If population units are in dollars, then a variance is in "dollars squared," making interpretation difficult. The standard deviation, however, is in dollars.

For the X and Y populations in Example 7, standard deviations are, respectively, $\sigma_x = \sqrt{8750} \approx 93.54$, and $\sigma_y = \sqrt{0.0000125} \approx 0.0035$. What do the sizes of these numbers indicate? As another example, suppose you read that "the average salary for plumbers is \$96,000 and the standard deviation is \$6,000." What does this tell you (other than that you wish you were a plumber!)? The standard deviation enables us to answer this question. To see how, we look to the great Russian mathematician Chebyshev for an answer. Chebyshev proved the following results, which allow us to interpret the size of the standard deviation.

CHEBYSHEV'S THEOREM

> Consider any population of values of a random variable X (discrete or continuous) having mean μ_x and standard deviation σ_x. All the following statements are true:
>
> **1.** *At least* 3/4 of the population values are within 2 standard deviations of the mean. Equivalently,
>
> $$P[\mu_x - 2 \cdot \sigma_x < X < \mu_x + 2 \cdot \sigma_x] \geq 0.75$$
>
> **2.** *At least* 8/9 of the population values are within 3 standard deviations of the mean. Equivalently,
>
> $$P[\mu_x - 3 \cdot \sigma_x < X < \mu_x + 3 \cdot \sigma_x] \geq \frac{8}{9} \approx 0.89$$
>
> **3.** In general, if k is any real number greater than 1, we can say that *at least* $1 - 1/k^2$ of the values in the population are within k standard deviations of the mean. Equivalently,
>
> $$P[\mu_x - k \cdot \sigma_x < X < \mu_x + k \cdot \sigma_x] \geq 1 - \frac{1}{k^2}$$

In statement 3, substitute $k = 2$; this gives

$$P[\mu_x - 2 \cdot \sigma_x < X < \mu_x + 2 \cdot \sigma_x] \geq 1 - \frac{1}{2^2} = 1 - \frac{1}{4} = \frac{3}{4} = 0.75$$

Thus, when $k = 2$, statement 3 is just a repeat of statement 1. Similarly, putting $k = 3$ into statement 3 duplicates statement 2. In other words, all we need is statement 3. Statements 1 and 2 are given separately because they represent two common applications.

A visual illustration is helpful in understanding Chebyshev's Theorem. Consider a population with mean $\mu = 10$ and standard deviation $\sigma = 2$.

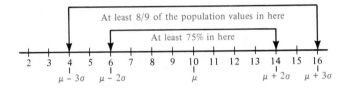

Knowing only the mean and standard deviation allows us to use Chebyshev's Theorem and state that certain minimum proportions in any distribution are within a specific number of standard deviations either side of the mean.

■ EXAMPLE 10

In the plumber example, where $\mu = \$96,000$ and $\sigma = \$6,000$, use Chebyshev's Theorem to describe plumbers' salaries.

SOLUTION

We shall use $k = 2$ and $k = 3$, and thus describe the minimum population proportions that fall within zones of width two, and three standard deviations, respectively, on each side of the mean.

1. At least 3/4 of the plumbers make between \$84,000 (which is $\mu - 2 \cdot \sigma$) and \$108,000 (which is $\mu + 2 \cdot \sigma$).

2. At least 8/9 of the plumbers make between \$78,000 (which is $\mu - 3 \cdot \sigma$) and \$114,000 (which is $\mu + 3 \cdot \sigma$).

An alternate way of viewing statement 2 would be to say that we are willing to give at least 8-to-1 odds that a plumber selected at random has an income between \$78,000 and \$114,000.   ■

It is truly remarkable that we can make such statements about an entire population, no matter what its probability distribution, by using only μ and σ.

■ EXAMPLE 11

A hamburger machine is set to produce 1-pound packages. With the consumer in mind, the machine is set to give an average fill of 16.4

ounces and a standard deviation of 0.2 ounce. Knowing nothing else about the packaging process, what can be said about the proportion of package weights that are between 15.9 and 16.9 ounces?

SOLUTION Note that $15.9 = 16.4 - 0.5$; i.e., 15.9 is 0.5 ounces below the mean. In standard deviations, 0.5 is $0.5/0.2 = 2.5$ standard deviations below the mean. Similarly, 16.9 is 0.5 ounces or 2.5 standard deviations above the mean. What can we say about the proportion of the population within 2.5 standard deviations of the mean? Using Chebyshev's Theorem, with $k = 2.5$, we can say that *at least* $1 - 1/(2.5)^2 = 1 - 1/6.25 = 0.84$ (that is, 84%) of the hamburger packages weigh between 15.9 and 16.9 ounces.

A final note: Chebyshev's Theorem is usually quite conservative. When we say "at least 84% of the values are between 15.9 and 16.9 ounces," the exact figure might well be 90%, 98%, or even 100%. If we are fortunate enough to *know* the probability distribution, we can almost always make a more informative statement than that provided by Chebyshev's Theorem.

■ EXAMPLE 12

In Example 11, what can be said about the proportion of package weights that are less than 15.9 ounces?

SOLUTION In Example 11, we noted that 15.9 ounces was 2.5 standard deviations below the mean. Also, *at least* 84% of all hamburger packages contained between 15.9 and 16.9 ounces. Equivalently, at most 16% of the packages contain values outside this range. Because of this, it is tempting to split 16% down the middle and say at most 8% weigh less than 15.9 ounces and at most 8% weigh more than 16.9 ounces. This would be incorrect! All we know is that at most 16% have either less than 15.9 or more than 16.9 ounces. We have no way of apportioning this maximum of 16% between the two "end zones." All we can say is that at most 16% of the packages weigh less than 15.9 ounces. The diagram that follows illustrates the situation:

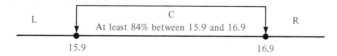

At least 84% of the values are in region C (between 15.9 and 16.9), while at most 16% of the values are either less than 15.9 (region L) or greater than 16.9 (region R); we cannot say, however, how the maximum possible 16% is distributed between the two tails (ends).

The next example should reinforce the idea that standard deviation measures concentration about the mean.

■ EXAMPLE 13

In Delmo's section of finite math at Anemia Tech, final exam scores averaged 75%—which, remarkably enough, was the same average earned by brother Elmo's section. What can you say about the proportion of scores between 60 and 90 in each section if the standard deviation for scores in Delmo's section was 1.5 while the standard deviation for scores in Elmo's section was 10?

SOLUTION

Delmo's section: A score of 60 is 15 units below the mean. These 15 units represent 15/1.5 = 10 standard deviations. A score of 90 is 10 standard deviations above the mean. Using $k = 10$ in Chebyshev's Theorem, we can say that at least $1 - 1/(10)^2 = 1 - 0.01 = 0.99$ of the scores were between 60 and 90.

Elmo's section: Since the standard deviation for his section was 10, then 60, which is 15 units below the mean, is 15/10 = 1.5 standard deviations below the mean. Similarly, 90 is 1.5 standard deviations above the mean. Using Chebyshev's Theorem, with $k = 1.5$, we can say that at least $1 - 1/(1.5)^2 \approx 0.556$ of the scores in his section were in the 60 to 90 range.   ■

The message here? The smaller the standard deviation, the greater the concentration of values near the mean. A rough graphical illustration, using histograms, is shown in Figure 8.6.

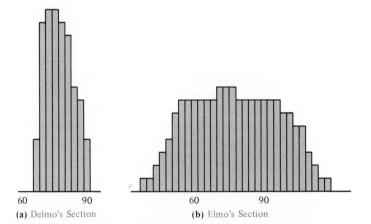

Figure 8.6
Histograms for Delmo's and Elmo's sections

60   90
(a) Delmo's Section

60   90
(b) Elmo's Section

EXERCISES 8.3

PRACTICING THE MOVES AND MANEUVERS

Exercises 55–62: Find the variance and standard deviation for the given probability distributions. (These are distributions of Exercises 35–42.)

55.

x	p(x)
2	0.6
3	0.4

59.

y	p(y)
-2	0.6
2	0.4

56.

y	p(y)
1	0.3
2	0.4
3	0.3

60.

v	p(v)
-2	0.5
2	0.5

61.

w	p(w)
0	0.5
4	0.3
6	0.2

57.

z	p(z)
3	0.1
5	0.5
6	0.4

62.

x	p(x)
2	0.1
6	0.5
10	0.4

58.

w	p(w)
0	0.4
1	0.6

63. Consider the following probability distribution for the random variable Y:

y	p(y)
0	0.20
1	0.25
2	0.30
3	0.15
4	0.10

(a) Find μ_y.   **(b)** Find σ^2 for Y.   **(c)** Find σ for Y.

64. A random variable Y has probability distribution given by the following:

y	$p(y)$
-3	0.10
-1	0.15
0	0.50
1	0.15
3	0.10

(a) Find μ_y, σ_y^2, and σ_y.

(b) Draw a probability histogram and locate μ_y, $\mu_y - 2 \cdot \sigma_y$ and $\mu_y + 2 \cdot \sigma_y$.

(c) What is the probability that Y is between $\mu_y - 2 \cdot \sigma_y$ and $\mu_y + 2 \cdot \sigma_y$?

Exercises 65–67: Use the two following probability distributions.

x	$p(x)$
2	0.4
3	0.2
4	0.4

y	$p(y)$
2	.05
3	.90
4	.05

65. Use your intuition and common sense to find the mean for each of the two probability distributions. Don't use a formula!
66. For which of the two populations would the mean be a better predictor?
67. Calculate μ (use the formula we did not want you to use in Exercise 65) and σ^2 for both distributions and verify your answers to Exercises 65 and 66.

*68. The probability distribution for the random variable X, which records the sum of the numbers when two fair dice are tossed, is shown below.

x	2	3	4	5	6	7	8	9	10	11	12
$p(x)$	$\dfrac{1}{36}$	$\dfrac{2}{36}$	$\dfrac{3}{36}$	$\dfrac{4}{36}$	$\dfrac{5}{36}$	$\dfrac{6}{36}$	$\dfrac{5}{36}$	$\dfrac{4}{36}$	$\dfrac{3}{36}$	$\dfrac{2}{36}$	$\dfrac{1}{36}$

Find the variance and standard deviation for the random variable X by using the definition formula.
*69. In Exercise 68, find the variance and standard deviation for X by using the computing formula.
70. Find the mean and variance for the following probability distribution

(a) by using the definition formula;   (b) by using the computing formula.

x	1	3	5	7
$p(x)$	$\dfrac{1}{16}$	$\dfrac{6}{16}$	$\dfrac{7}{16}$	$\dfrac{2}{16}$

71. Find the variance and standard deviation for the random variable X whose probability distribution is shown below:

   (a) by using the definition formula;

   (b) by using the computing formula.

x	0	1	2
$p(x)$	$\dfrac{1}{8}$	$\dfrac{5}{8}$	$\dfrac{2}{8}$

*72. The probability distribution for a random variable V is given below. Using the computing formula, find the variance and standard deviation of V.

v	10	15	20	25	30
$p(v)$	0.10	0.15	0.35	0.25	0.15

73. Find the variance and standard deviation for the random variable X whose probability distribution is given below by using the computing formula.

x	-5	-10	50	100
$p(x)$	0.20	0.50	0.25	0.05

*74. For each day during the last three school years, the number of people that passed the south entrance to the Student Union at Anemia Tech has been recorded. (Consider these data to be a population.) The objective was to determine in what percentage of school days more than 260 people went by this entrance. The original population data have been lost, but it is known that the population mean was 220 people and the population standard deviation was 30. What can you say about the percentage of school days in which more than 260 people passed by the south entrance?

75.   Medical research has shown that radiation treatment is 70% effective in treating one form of cancer. Suppose five patients with this cancer are selected at random and treated with radiation. Let random variable X be the number of cures recorded among the five. The probability distribution for X is shown below. (You will study this probability distribution in Section 8.4.)

x	$p(x)$
0	0.002
1	0.029
2	0.132
3	0.309
4	0.360
5	0.168

(a) Find μ_x. (b) Find σ_x^2. (c) Find σ_x.

(d) Draw a probability histogram for $p(x)$ and locate μ_x, $\mu_x - 2 \cdot \sigma_x$, and $\mu_x + 2 \cdot \sigma_x$ on this histogram.

(e) For any probability distribution, the guaranteed minimum probability that lies within two standard deviations of the mean is 0.75. Compare this amount with the actual probability within two standard deviations of the mean for this distribution.

8.4 THE BINOMIAL DISTRIBUTION

In this section we discuss an important and frequently occurring discrete probability distribution—the binomial distribution. "Bi" means two; there are many cases where we classify outcomes in one of two ways. We classify a newborn as male or female. We classify a coin toss as head or tail. A drug is either effective or it isn't. A manufactured item is either defective or nondefective; a phone call local or long distance. We do not, however, need to consider only two outcomes. With more than two, we can sometimes form two *groups* by combining outcomes. Outcomes to a die toss, for example, can be grouped into two classes (events!) "odd number" and "even number." TV viewers at 10 P.M. Thursday can be classified as watching "L.A. Law" or "something else." Scores on an exam can be classified as "passing" (all scores greater than 70, say) or "not passing." All these examples can be viewed as binomial experiments.

In a binomial experiment, our primary interest will be in the binomial random variable Y, which records the number of successes in the n trials. Y is a discrete random variable since its possible values are 0, 1, 2,

BINOMIAL EXPERIMENT

A **binomial experiment** has the following attributes:

1. The experiment has n identical trials.

2. The sample space for each trial is partitioned into two sets of outcomes: "success" and "failure." (These are merely labels; a success does not have to mean something good—a success could be a defective part.)

3. The probability of "success" on any trial is p. By the Complement Rule, the probability of "failure" is $q = 1 - p$.

4. The result of any one trial is independent of the result of all other trials.

. . ., n. In Example 14, we find the probability distribution of the binomial random variable Y.

■ EXAMPLE 14

The present treatment for a certain disease has only a 20% cure rate. A researcher claims to have developed a new drug with a higher cure rate. To test its effectiveness, the new drug is given to three diseased patients. Assume the new drug is equivalent to the present one (that is, the cure rate is 20%), and find the probability distribution for Y = number of cures among the three patients.

SOLUTION

Let's be sure conditions for a binomial experiment are met. We have three trials, where a trial is examining a patient to see if he/she recovers. Independent trials seems a plausible assumption—whether any one patient recovers should not have any bearing on the others. Further, the trials may be assumed identical in that the three patients receive the same treatment. In order that the probability of success remain constant for all trials (all people), we assume that the three patients are in equally good (or poor) health except for the disease. We proceed, beginning with a tree that represents possible outcomes:

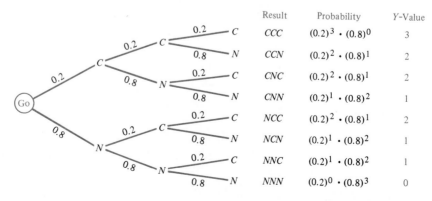

	Result	Probability	Y-Value
	CCC	$(0.2)^3 \cdot (0.8)^0$	3
	CCN	$(0.2)^2 \cdot (0.8)^1$	2
	CNC	$(0.2)^2 \cdot (0.8)^1$	2
	CNN	$(0.2)^1 \cdot (0.8)^2$	1
	NCC	$(0.2)^2 \cdot (0.8)^1$	2
	NCN	$(0.2)^1 \cdot (0.8)^2$	1
	NNC	$(0.2)^1 \cdot (0.8)^2$	1
	NNN	$(0.2)^0 \cdot (0.8)^3$	0

Pay careful attention to the form of the path probabilities. Observe that the value of Y is the same as the exponent on 0.2. Also, note that the sum of the two exponents is 3, the number of trials. The probability that $Y = 1$ can be found by adding probabilities for the three paths that end with $Y = 1$. These three paths all have the same probability. Hence:

$$p(1) = P[Y = 1] = \begin{pmatrix} \text{number of paths} \\ \text{on tree where} \\ Y = 1 \end{pmatrix} \begin{pmatrix} \text{probability of} \\ \text{any one path} \\ \text{with } Y = 1 \end{pmatrix}$$

$$= 3 \cdot (0.2)^1 \cdot (0.8)^2 = 0.384$$

Similarly, to find $p(2) = P[Y = 2]$, observe that all paths having $Y = 2$ have identical probability. Adding these is accomplished by multiplying the common path probability by the number of paths:

$$p(2) = P[Y = 2] = \begin{pmatrix} \text{number of paths} \\ \text{on tree where} \\ Y = 2 \end{pmatrix} \begin{pmatrix} \text{probability of} \\ \text{any one path} \\ \text{with } Y = 2 \end{pmatrix}$$

$$= 3 \cdot (0.2)^2 \cdot (0.8)^1 = 0.096$$

In like manner, the probability of three successes is:

$$p(3) = P[Y = 3] = \begin{pmatrix} \text{number of paths} \\ \text{on tree where} \\ Y = 3 \end{pmatrix} \begin{pmatrix} \text{probability of} \\ \text{any one path} \\ \text{with } Y = 3 \end{pmatrix}$$

$$= 1 \cdot (0.2)^3 \cdot (0.8)^0 = 0.008$$

and

$$p(0) = P[Y = 0] = \begin{pmatrix} \text{number of paths} \\ \text{on tree where} \\ Y = 0 \end{pmatrix} \begin{pmatrix} \text{probability of} \\ \text{any one path} \\ \text{with } Y = 0 \end{pmatrix}$$

$$= 1 \cdot (0.2)^0 \cdot (0.8)^3 = 0.512$$

Summarizing, we obtain the probability distribution of Y:

	0	1	2	3
	0.512	0.384	0.096	0.008

A histogram for this probability distribution—a binomial distribution with $n = 3$ trials and $p = 0.2$—is shown in Figure 8.7. This particular binomial distribution is highly "skewed" (that is, it lacks symmetry), with highest probability at $y = 0$ and each subsequent y-value having less probability than its predecessor. We soon see that not all binomial distributions behave like this.

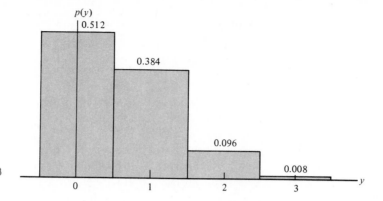

Figure 8.7
Binomial distribution with $n = 3$
and $p = 0.2$

The method we used in finding binomial probabilities will work for any binomial distribution. The key to using this method is being able to find the following two quantities:

1. The probability of any one path that contains y successes (and, as a result, $n - y$ failures).

2. The number of paths on the tree that contain y successes (and $n - y$ failures).

If n is larger than 4 or 5, we don't want to draw the tree, but thought processes we used in Example 14 enable us to find quantities 1 and 2 without drawing the tree.

To find quantity 1, observe that a path containing y successes and $n - y$ failures will have y branch probabilities of p and the remaining $n - y$ branch probabilities will be $(1 - p)$. The probability of such a path is found by multiplying its branch probabilities: $p^y \cdot (1 - p)^{n-y}$.

To find quantity 2, note that counting paths with y success branches (and thus $n - y$ failure branches) is like asking "In how many ways can I pick y of n branches to 'hold' successes?" (The rest will have failures.) From Chapter 7, we know the answer is $C(n, y)$. Hence, for any n and p,

$$p(y) = P[y \text{ successes in } n \text{ trials}] = C(n, y) \cdot p^y \cdot (1 - p)^{n-y}$$

This expression, which works for any of the possible values of y from 0 through n, is called the **binomial probability distribution**.

BINOMIAL PROBABILITY DISTRIBUTION

In a binomial experiment, the probability of exactly y successes in n independent trials is given by

$$p(y) = C(n, y) \cdot p^y \cdot (1 - p)^{n-y}$$

where p is the success probability on each trial, and y can be any of the possible values 0, 1, . . ., n.

■ EXAMPLE 15

Delmo is the captain of the coin-flipping team at Anemia Tech. Perseverance, dedication, and long hours of practice enable him to produce heads 50% of the time. Let Y be the number of heads on his next six flips. Find the probability distribution of Y.

SOLUTION

Conditions necessary to "model" the next six flips with a binomial distribution seem quite reasonable. If we were to draw the tree, the FCP tells us there would be $2 \cdot 2 \cdot 2 \cdot 2 \cdot 2 \cdot 2 = 64$ paths. Each path would consist of six branches—one per flip. To find the probability of four heads, we construct the probability for any one path having four heads. This is $(0.5)^4(0.5)^2$. Then we determine the number of paths (from the 64 possible) that have four branches with heads and two with tails. The ways of choosing four of the six branches to hold heads is $C(6,4)$. Thus,

$$p(4) = C(6,4) \cdot (0.5)^4(0.5)^2 = \frac{15}{64} \approx 0.234$$

The general formula for $p(y)$, the probability of y successes in six trials where $p = 0.5$ is the success probability at any trial, is

$$p(y) = C(6,y) \cdot (0.5)^y(0.5)^{6-y} \qquad \text{where} \quad y = 0, 1, 2, \ldots, 6$$

We complete the problem by substituting values of y, getting:

y	$p(y)$	# paths on tree with y heads
0	0.016	1
1	0.094	6
2	0.234	15
3	0.312	20
4	0.234	15
5	0.094	6
6	0.016	1

The "# paths" column is to help you check your work.

■

In Figure 8.8, we show a probability histogram for the number of heads when Delmo flips a coin six times.

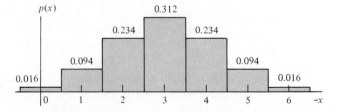

Figure 8.8
Binomial distribution with $n = 6$ and $p = 0.5$

Contrast the symmetry of Figure 8.8 histogram with Figure 8.7.

As a general rule, the closer p is to 0.5, the more symmetric the histogram.

The number of trials, n, has a dramatic influence upon symmetry as well. If we were to extend Example 14 to ten people rather than three, we would get Figure 8.9.

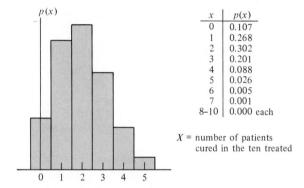

x	$p(x)$
0	0.107
1	0.268
2	0.302
3	0.201
4	0.088
5	0.026
6	0.005
7	0.001
8–10	0.000 each

X = number of patients cured in the ten treated

Figure 8.9
Binomial distribution with $n = 10$ and $p = 0.2$

Comparing the Figure 8.9 histogram to Figure 8.7, you can see that even though $p = 0.2$ for both, there is much less skewness (more symmetry) for the larger n. Knowing when a binomial distribution is nearly symmetric will be important in Section 8.8.

■ EXAMPLE 16

Find the mean and standard deviation for the random variable Y which records the number of cures when three patients are treated in Example 14. Assume that the new drug is no better than the old drug so that the probability of a cure is 0.2.

SOLUTION   The probability distribution from Example 14 is repeated below:

y	0	1	2	3
$p(y)$	0.512	0.384	0.096	0.008

As usual, to find a mean, we sum the $y \cdot p(y)$ terms:

$$\mu_y = \sum y \cdot p(y) = 0 \cdot (0.512) + 1 \cdot (0.384) + 2 \cdot (0.096)$$

$$+ 3 \cdot (0.008)$$

$$= 0 + 0.384 + 0.192 + 0.024$$

$$= 0.6$$

To find standard deviation, we first find the variance. Using the computing formula $\sigma_y^2 = \Sigma y^2 \cdot P(y) - \mu_y^2$, we compute $\Sigma y^2 \cdot p(y)$:

$$\Sigma y^2 \cdot p(y) = 0^2 \cdot (0.512) + 1^2 \cdot (0.384) + 2^2 \cdot (0.096) + 3^2 \cdot (0.008)$$
$$= 0.384 + 0.384 + 0.072 = 0.840$$

Thus, $\sigma_y^2 = \Sigma y^2 \cdot P(y) - \mu_y^2 = 0.840 - 0.6^2 = 0.48$. ∎

Mean, Variance, and Standard Deviation for a Binomial Distribution

The arithmetic in Example 15, though not difficult, is irritating! The result $\mu = 0.6$, obtained with our usual formula, just happens to be $3 \cdot (0.2)$, which is $n \cdot p$ (that is, the number of trials times the success probability at any trial). This is no accident!

The expected value of a binomial random variable is always $\mu = n \cdot p$.

This is intuitively reasonable: after all, when you flip a coin 100 times, the mean (long-range average) number of heads ought to be $100 \cdot (0.5) = 50 = n \cdot p$.

There is also a "special" formula for the variance of a binomial distribution. Our answer of 0.84 for σ^2 can be obtained as $3 \cdot (0.2) \cdot (0.8) = n \cdot p \cdot q$, where $q = (1 - p)$. (We often ignore the multiplication notation and write just "npq.") This result applies to any binomial distribution—the standard deviation is $\sqrt{npq}$. We summarize these special results for the binomial distribution:

BINOMIAL MEAN AND STANDARD DEVIATION

The mean and standard deviation for a binomial probability distribution with parameters n and p are:

$$\mu = n \cdot p \quad \text{and} \quad \sigma = \sqrt{npq}$$

Brief Review

The idea of drawing a tree to represent the n trials of a binomial experiment is helpful, though we may not actually draw the tree. Calculating $p(y)$, the probability of y successes, requires that we know **(1)** how many paths on the tree contain exactly y successes, and **(2)** the probability of any one such path.

The answer to **(1)** is $C(n,y)$, while the answer for **(2)** is $p^y \cdot (1 - p)^{n-y}$. Multiplying these gives

$$p(y) = C(n,y) \cdot p^y \cdot (1 - p)^{n-y}$$

Let's try the following example.

■ EXAMPLE 17

In the first edition of a book, each page has probability 0.4 of being error free. If we randomly select 20 pages from this book, find the probability of seven error-free pages.

SOLUTION Having randomly selected the 20 pages, it seems plausible that these 20 pages represent 20 independent and identical trials of a binomial experiment where "success" is a page with no errors. Thus, for this binomial distribution, $n = 20$ and $p = 0.4$. The answer to the probability problem posed above is:

$$p(7) = C(20,7) \cdot (0.4)^7 \cdot (0.6)^{13}$$

Remember that $C(20,7)$ counts how many paths on the tree would have 7 branches labeled "no errors" and 13 labeled "error." (Be thankful you don't have to draw this tree—there would be $2^{20} = 1,048,576$ paths!) Even without drawing the tree, the required arithmetic—large factorials and probabilities raised to large powers—begins to get exasperating. To avoid cumbersome arithmetic, we provide tables for various binomial distributions. (See Appendix, Table I.)

Using the Binomial Tables   Entries in Table I give cumulative, "less than or equal to" probabilities: $P[Y \le y]$, where y is a possible value of Y. In our current example, refer to the table for $n = 20$, and locate the $p = 0.4$ column. The entry in the $y = 7$ row and $p = 0.4$ column, 0.416 represents the probability of seven or fewer successes (error-free pages). We don't want probability of seven or fewer. We want just the "seven" part. The "seven or fewer" probability is $p(0) + p(1) + p(2) + p(3) + p(4) + p(5) + p(6) + p(7)$. We need to get rid of $p(0) + \cdots + p(6)$. But this is "six or fewer," a quantity tabled in the $y = 6$ row. Thus, the probability of exactly seven is found by subtracting the probability of six or fewer from the probability of seven or fewer. The result: $0.416 - 0.250 = 0.166$. ∎

■ EXAMPLE 18   In Example 17, use Table I to find the following:

    (a) the probability of at most nine error-free pages.

    (b) the probability of at least ten error-free pages.

    (c) the probability of no more than eight error-free pages.

    (d) the probability that there are at least seven pages with errors, but no more than ten pages having errors.

    (e) the expected number of error-free pages.

    (f) the standard deviation for the number of error-free pages.

SOLUTION For **(a)**, note that the event "at most nine" is precisely what the table gives. Hence, we need only to check the $n = 20$ table under the $p = 0.4$ column corresponding to $y = 9$. The answer is 0.755.

    For **(b)**, observe that the event "at least ten" is not directly obtainable from Table I. We need to express events whose probabilities we want in terms of equivalent "less than or equal" events. The Comple-

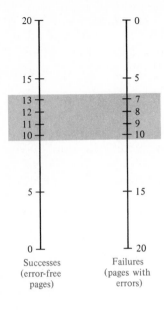

Successes (error-free pages)   Failures (pages with errors)

ment Rule saves us. The complement of "at least ten" is "at most nine," and hence $P[\text{at least ten}] = 1 - P[\text{at most nine}] = 1 - 0.755 = 0.245$.

In (c), the event "no more than eight" is just another way of saying "eight or fewer" or "at most eight." Thus, using Table I directly, we get $P[\text{no more than eight error-free pages}] = 0.596$.

In part (d), be careful! The problem is phrased in terms of "pages with errors" (failures) rather than error-free pages (successes). Careful thought shows that "at least seven but no more than ten failures" is the same as "at least ten but no more than thirteen successes" (see figure).

Subtract the "nine or fewer" entry from the "13 or fewer" entry under $p = 0.4$ to get the answer. Easier still is this reasoning: If the number of successes follows a binomial distribution with parameters $n = 20$ and $p = 0.4$, then number of failures also has a binomial distribution with parameters $n = 20$ and $p = 0.6$. This approach does not require that we convert from failures to successes. All we do is switch to the 0.6 column. Thus, the probability of "at least seven failures and no more than ten failures" is given by $p(7) + p(8) + p(9) + p(10)$. This sum can also be found from Table I by subtracting the "six or fewer" entry from the "ten or fewer" entry, both under $p = 0.6$, giving $0.245 - 0.006 = 0.239$.

For part (e): Since the number of error-free pages follows a binomial distribution, we use the special result "$\mu = n \cdot p$." For our example, we have $\mu = 20 \cdot (0.4) = 8$.

For part (f): Our special result for the binomial distribution gives $\sigma = \sqrt{npq} = \sqrt{20(0.4)(0.6)} \approx 2.191$. ∎

PRACTICE PROBLEM 4   In Example 17, find the following:

(a) the probability of at least eight error-free pages.

(b) the probability of at least six pages with errors, but no more than ten pages with errors.

(c) the expected value for the number of pages with errors.

(d) the standard deviation for number of pages with errors.

ANSWER(S) (a) 0.584; (b) 0.243; (c) 12; (d) 2.191. □

It is important to recognize whether the conditions necessary for applying the binomial distribution are met. Try the next example.

■ EXAMPLE 19

A quality control (QC) inspector tests newly manufactured items to determine if quality is "up to snuff." His testing procedure picks three items from a carton of 20: if all three are acceptable, then he "passes" the entire carton as acceptable. If there are one or more defectives, then he tests all remaining items in the carton. Suppose, unknown to him, that there are four defective items in a carton of 20. Find the probability that the inspector will need to go to "stage two" and inspect each item in the box.

SOLUTION   It might be tempting to reason as follow: four defectives in the box of 20 is 20%. With one or more defectives, the inspector will go to stage two. Since probability of "one or more" is $1 - p(0)$, we compute $1 - p(0) = 1 - C(3,0) \cdot (0.20)^0 \cdot (0.8)^3$. *This, however, would be incorrect!* One requirement of a binomial experiment is that the success probability p must be constant from trial to trial. That assumption is violated here. The probability of a success (a defective) is indeed 0.20 on the first trial, but it is $3/19 \approx 0.158$ on the second item if the first item selected was a defective. On the other hand, if the first item were good, then the probability that the second would be defective is $4/19 \approx 0.210$. The fact that these two numbers are not 0.20 indicates that the trials are not independent, since the probability of a defective on the second trial depends on the result of the first trial.

Although the binomial distribution is not appropriate, we know what to do. Since all possible samples of size three are equally likely:

$$P[0 \text{ defectives in 3}] = \frac{\begin{array}{c}\text{number of ways of selecting} \\ \text{3 items having no} \\ \text{defectives} \end{array}}{\begin{array}{c}\text{total number of subsets of} \\ \text{size 3 selected from 20} \end{array}} = \frac{C(4,0) \cdot C(16,3)}{C(20,3)}$$

This form should look familiar—we discussed it in Example 11 of Chapter 7, and you used it in solving "poker-hand" problems. The 20 items consist of 16 good and 4 defective, and our interest is in a sample of three, chosen without replacement, having 0 defectives (and 3 good items). Necessary arithmetic gives $P[0 \text{ defective items in sample}] = 0.491$. ■

Approximating Hypergeometric Probabilities with Binomial Probabilities   When sampling without replacement (as in Example 19), the "poker-hand" method (correct name is "hypergeometric" distribution) is proper, and the binomial distribution is not. In certain situations, however, it is advantageous to ignore the correct method and apply the binomial. Why? The correct hypergeometric method consists of three different combination calculations. These are troublesome with large numbers. The incorrect binomial distribution contains only one such calculation. Furthermore, tables of the binomial distribution are widely available, so no calculations may be required. We ought not use the incorrect binomial method to approximate the correct hypergeometric method, however, unless the resulting answer is close to the correct answer. This will be the case if probability of a success occurring at a later trial is much the same regardless of whether the previous trial was a success or not.

To illustrate, suppose 20 of 100 students in a classroom are seniors. We select five at random, and want the probability of getting 2 seniors. The probability that the first is a senior is 0.20, while the probability of the second being a senior, given the first was, is $19/99 \approx 0.192$. Similarly, the probability that the second is a senior, given that the first was not, is $20/99 \approx 0.202$. The numbers 0.20, 0.192, and 0.202, are not the same, but reasonably close. Using the binomial distribution should give an answer which is relatively close. For fun, we calculate the probability correctly (using "poker-hand" methods) and compare the answer with the binomial, which, although technically inappropriate, should give us a reasonably close answer.

Correct Method

$$P[2 \text{ seniors in a sample of } 5] = \frac{C(20,2) \cdot C(80,3)}{C(100,5)} = 0.207$$

Binomial Approximate Method

$$P[2 \text{ seniors in a sample of } 5] = C(5,2) \cdot (0.2)^2 \cdot (0.8)^3 = 0.205$$

Although not the same, the answers are close enough to where we would be willing to sacrifice a small amount of accuracy in order to gain the much easier computing afforded by the binomial.

EXERCISES 8.4

PRACTICING THE MOVES AND MANEUVERS

Exercises 76–85:   Find $p(0)$ and $p(1)$ for the binomial distributions having the given values of n and p.

76. $n = 5, p = 0.4$	77. $n = 6, p = 0.2$	78. $n = 8, p = 0.5$	79. $n = 10, p = 0.3$
80. $n = 4, p = 0.1$	81. $n = 8, p = 0.2$	82. $n = 3, p = 0.8$	83. $n = 7, p = 0.9$
84. $n = 12, p = 0.8$	85. $n = 2, p = 0.6$		

Exercises 86–90:   Find the probability of at least one success for a binomial distribution having the given values of n and p.

86. $n = 8, p = 0.5$	87. $n = 3, p = 0.8$	88. $n = 12, p = 0.8$	89. $n = 7, p = 0.9$
90. $n = 5, p = 0.4$			

Exercises 91–95:   Find the binomial probability distributions for the indicated values of n and p.

91. $n = 5, p = 0.4$ 92. $n = 3, p = 0.2$ *93. $n = 8, p = 0.2$ *94. $n = 8, p = 0.8$
95. $n = 3, p = 0.8$

Exercises 96–105: Let Y represent the number of successes in a binomial distribution with $n = 10$ and $p = 0.4$. Find the indicated probabilities by using Table I.

96. $P[Y \le 6]$ 97. $P[Y < 6]$ 98. $P[Y \le 8]$ 99. $P[Y \ge 5]$
100. $P[Y > 3]$ 101. $P[Y = 7]$ 102. $P[Y = 9]$ 103. $P[4 \le Y \le 6]$
104. $P[Y > 9]$ 105. $P[Y < 9]$

Exercises 106–115: Let Y represent the number of successes in a binomial distribution with $n = 15$ and $p = 0.6$. Find the indicated probabilities by using Table I.

106. $P[Y \le 9]$ 107. $P[Y > 8]$ 108. $P[Y \le 12]$ 109. $P[Y \ge 10]$
110. $P[Y > 13]$ 111. $P[9 < Y \le 12]$ 112. $P[Y < 9]$ 113. $P[8 \le Y \le 12]$
114. $P[Y > 9]$ 115. $P[Y < 7]$

Exercises 116–120: Find the mean and standard deviation for the binomial distributions having the indicated values of n and p.

116. $n = 20, p = 0.2$ 117. $n = 50, p = 0.6$ 118. $n = 25, p = 0.4$
119. $n = 15, p = 0.4$ 120. $n = 8, p = 0.5$

121. By actually drawing the necessary tree, find the probabilities for the binomial distribution having parameters $n = 5$ and $p = 0.8$.

APPLYING THE CONCEPTS

Exercises 122–126 use the following information: A study of bills issued by a certain repair company shows that 10% contain overcharges. Consider the next 15 bills sent out by this company. Find the following:

122. probability of at most three bills with overcharges.
123. probability of at least two bills with overcharges.
124. probability of at least one bill with an overcharge, but no more than four bills with overcharges.
125. the mean and standard deviation for the number of overcharges.
*126. the actual probability that the number of overcharges is within two standard deviations of the mean. Compare this answer with "Chebyshev's guarantee."

Exercises 127–130: A 1989 article by Jamie Diaz in *Sports Illustrated* magazine showed that PGA Tour golfers make 83% of their three-foot putts. Use this fact to find the probability that in the next ten such putts on the PGA Tour,

*127. at least seven will be made.   *128. at most eight will be made.
*129. at least five will be made.   *130. at least six but no more than eight will be made.

Exercises 131–133: Use the fact that PGA Tour pros make about 55% of their six foot putts. In a random selection of eight such putts, find the probability that

*131. at least four are made.   *132. at most six will be made.
*133. between three and six, inclusive, will be made.

Exercises 134–137 use the following information: Twenty percent of the VCR's made by a certain manufacturer will need warranty work during the 90-day warranty period. If a dealer has sold ten of these machines, find the following:

134. the probability that at most five will need warranty work.
135. the probability that at least two will need warranty work.

136. the expected number of warranty repairs.
137. the standard deviation for the number of repairs that will be made under warranty.

138. A vaccine has supposedly been developed for the common cold. With this vaccine, people in the over-50 age group are supposed to have an 80% chance of making it through a winter without a cold. If this conjecture (about the effectiveness of the vaccine) is correct, find the probability that at least 13 of 20 people who are vaccinated in this age group will not have a winter cold.

139. A quality control procedure consists of selecting five items from a box of 50 of these items. If there are two or more defectives in the sample of five, the lot of 50 is rejected. Suppose that a box of 50 has 12 defective items.
   (a) Find the probability that the lot will be rejected, using the (correct) hypergeometric method.
   (b) Find the probability that the lot will be rejected, using the binomial distribution (incorrect—but only slightly—and definitely much easier to use).

Exercises 140–143 use the following radon study: A study has shown that approximately 10% of a certain type of Pacific Northwest homes have unsafe levels of radon. If 15 homes of this type are selected at random, find the following:

140. the probability that exactly two of the homes have unsafe radon levels.
141. the probability that at least one home has unsafe radon levels.
142. the probability that no more than three homes have unsafe radon levels.
143. the mean and standard deviation for the number of homes with unsafe radon levels.

*144. The probability that an air defense warning station correctly detects an incoming enemy missile is only 0.4. How many of these warning stations, operating independently but in the same area, would be needed in order that the probability of at least one detecting an enemy missile is at least 0.99?

Exercises 145–148 use the following information: The probability that any one 75-watt light bulb from a certain manufacturer will last for at least 200 hours is 0.8. If ten of these light bulbs are selected at random, find the following:

145. the probability that at least eight will burn for at least 200 hours.
146. the probability that at most nine of the bulbs will burn for at least 200 hours.
147. the probability that between six and eight inclusive will last for 200 hours.
148. the mean and standard deviation for the number of bulbs among the ten that will last for at least 200 hours.

Exercises 149–152 use the following information: The power steering in a certain late model car has been found to be defective in 30% of a large number of cars tested. If we test five previously untested cars of this type, find the following:

149. the probability that at least two of them have defective power steering.
150. the probability that at most two of them have defective power steering.
151. the expected number having defective power steering.
152. the standard deviation for the number of cars having defective power steering.

153. See Exercise 75. Verify the probability distribution that was given there.
*154. In Exercise 75, find the mean and standard deviation by using formulas that work for any probability distribution. Verify by using $\mu = n \cdot p$ and $\sigma = \sqrt{n \cdot p \cdot q}$.

8.5 AN INTRODUCTION TO CONTINUOUS RANDOM VARIABLES

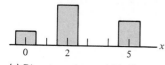

(a) Discrete random variable X
Possible x-values: 0, 2, 5.
Total area of bars: 1

You now have experience and ability in determining probability distributions for discrete random variables. The methods developed depend on being able to attach probabilities to the outcomes in a sample space so that these probabilities sum to one. This is possible whenever the sample space is finite, and even when there are infinitely many outcomes, provided there are distinct gaps between those outcomes. This was illustrated in Example 2 by Shankus's attempts to get a hole-in-one.

Continuous Random Variables and Probability Density Functions

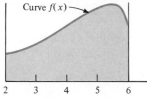

(b) Continuous random variable X
Possible x-values: Any number from 2 to 6.
Total area under curve: 1.

A continuous random variable can take any value in some interval of real numbers—there are no gaps between two possible values in that interval. With no gaps between values, attempting to list or count the number of possible values will surely omit certain numbers—there are simply too many values to be counted. As a result, it is not possible to attach a probability to every possible value in the interval and still have those probabilities sum to one. Thus, continuous random variables do not have probability distributions. Instead, for every continuous random variable X, there will always be a "curve," called the *probability density function*, having the following important properties:

PROBABILITY DENSITY FUNCTION FOR A CONTINUOUS RANDOM VARIABLE

> For any continuous random variable X, there is a smooth, non-negative curve $f(x)$, known as the **probability density function** of X. This curve has the following properties:
>
> **1.** The total area under this probability density curve is one.
>
> **2.** The probability that X takes a value in some interval is the area under the probability density curve over that interval.

Difference Between Discrete and Continuous Random Variables

With discrete random variables, we attach probabilities between 0 and 1 to all possible values, and these probabilities sum to one. With continuous random variables, however, we assign probabilities to intervals of values. As shown in Figure 8.10, probability is an area under the probability density curve:

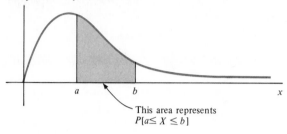

Figure 8.10

Probability for a continuous random variable X

This area represents
$P[a \leq X \leq b]$

In Section 8.6, we encounter the most useful of all continuous probability density curves—the normal density. We first look at a more easily understood continuous random variable having a probability density function known as the uniform density.

Intuitively, a "uniform" density is a smooth, level spreading of the one unit of probability over all the possible values of a random variable in some interval of numbers, as in Example 20.

Note: Balance of Section 8.5 is optional.

■ EXAMPLE 20

A statistician for the Department of Transportation wishes to study highway damage due to metal-studded snow tires. She selects a mile of typical highway and introduces a random variable X that represents *distance from the beginning of the mile to the location of the next damage spot*. She has a very accurate scale painted along the highway's edge, starting at 0, ending at 1. Using this scale, she records the *x*-value of each blemish. When she has located several million blemishes she makes a dot for each one on a drawing, looking for a pattern.

Not surprisingly, the dot pattern is smoothly scattered from 0 to 1 on her drawing. The number of dots between 0.00 miles and 0.01 miles is nearly the same as the number between 0.20 miles and 0.21 miles. Further checking reveals that all intervals of size 0.01 miles contain nearly the same number of dots. She concludes that each interval of size 0.01 mile is just as likely as any other such interval to receive the mile's next damage spot. Since there are 100 nonoverlapping intervals of width 0.01 in the mile, and since the total area under the curve must be one, then the area over each interval of width 0.01 mile should be 0.01. To make the area 0.01 for any interval of width 0.01 requires that we adopt the "curve" in Figure 8.11 as our probability density curve.

Since the range of possible values is one mile, then, to have the total area under our density curve (which is a rectangle here) be one, the height of the rectangle (the probability density) must be one. The area

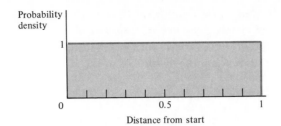

Figure 8.11
Uniform density

under this curve between any two *x*-values is just the area of a rectangle. Thus, for example, the probability that the next damage spot occurs somewhere between 0.017 and 0.024 mile is the area under the curve between 0.017 and 0.024, which is "base times height" or $(0.024 - 0.017) \cdot 1 = 0.007$. The same is true for every interval of width 0.007, *regardless of location*. Using this same logic, any interval of width 0.05 should have probability 0.05 of receiving the next damage spot. The probability that the next damage spot will fall within the first half-mile is 0.50; within the final one-tenth mile, 0.10. The fact that all intervals of the same length have the same probability leads us to say that we have a uniform density—or that probability is uniformly distributed.

Examine Figure 8.11 carefully. In particular, contrast this picture with the probability histogram for a discrete distribution. For a discrete random variable, there is a distinct, nonzero "lump" of probability at each possible value. Here, every value between 0 and 1 is possible, and we have simply spread the total probability of one smoothly and uniformly over all these possible values.

The probability of the next damage spot being exactly at 0.3 mile is the area trapped between vertical lines at 0.3 and 0.3. This area is zero! Conclusion: given a smooth, continuous distribution of probability, the probability of any single value is zero because there is zero area over any individual value.

Nonzero areas (and hence nonzero probabilities) are instead associated with intervals of values. Contrast these notions with the probability distribution for a discrete random variable, where there were few enough possible values so that each possible value had a nonzero probability.   ■

PRACTICE PROBLEM 5   A ten-year record of road-killed jackrabbits on a four-mile stretch of scenic highway near Flat Rock, North Dakota, revealed such kills to be uniformly distributed. What is the probability that the next kill will occur:

(a) between 0 and 2 miles?

(b) between 1.5 and 3 miles?

(c) between 3.2 and 4.0 miles?

(d) exactly at 0.6 mile?

Hint: Draw a picture of the probability density curve. Since the total area over this 4-mile stretch must be one, then the (uniform) height over that span must be one-fourth. Shade the region under the curve over each interval and then find its area.

ANSWER(S)   If X is the location of the next kill, then

(a) $P[0 \leq X \leq 2] = 2 \cdot (1/4) = 0.5$;

(b) $P[1.5 \leq X \leq 3] = 1.5 \cdot (1/4) = 0.375$;

(c) $P[3.2 \leq X \leq 4.0] = 0.8 \cdot (1/4) = 0.2$;

(d) $P[X = 0.6] = P[0.6 \leq X \leq 0.6] = 0$.   □

Did you draw your own pictures for the previous practice problem, study the answers, and make sure you understand how they were obtained? If not, do so now! The understanding gained here will pay off for the rest of this chapter, your life, and the future of the universe! (Is this important, or what?)

Though this section is concerned primarily with the Uniform Density, we now consider an example and practice problem of a slightly different type, to ease our transition into the "normal density," which will be our principal concern.

■ EXAMPLE 21

The route from the Rancid Creek Bridge to suburban East Overshoe consists of 4 miles of two-lane scenic road followed by 2 miles of freeway. Jackrabbit kills on the two-lane road are uniformly distributed; so are kills on the freeway, but freeway miles have twice the kills of two-lane miles. If the random variable X measures distance from the Rancid Creek Bridge, sketch a picture showing the probability density function for the next kill, and find the probability that the next kill occurs:

(a) on the two-lane.

(b) between 2 and 5 miles from the bridge.

SOLUTION

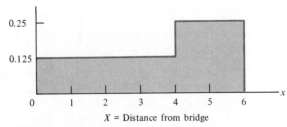

X = Distance from bridge

(a) $P[\text{kill occurs on two-lane}] = P[0 \leq X \leq 4] =$ area under probability density curve between 0 and 4 $= 4 \cdot (0.125) = 0.5$.

(b) $P[2 \leq X \leq 5]$ = area under the curve between 2 and 5, which is the area from 2 to 4 plus the area from 4 to 5 = $2 \cdot (0.125) + 1 \cdot (0.25)$ = 0.5.   ▮

PRACTICE PROBLEM 6   Find the probability that, in the situation described in Example 21, the next kill will occur:

(a) between 4.5 and 5.5 miles from the bridge.

(b) between 3 and 5 miles from the bridge.

(c) between 3.5 and 4.5 miles from the bridge.

(d) exactly 2 miles from the bridge.

ANSWER(S)   (a) 0.25;   (b) 0.375;   (c) 0.1875;   (d) 0.   □

EXERCISES 8.5

APPLYING THE CONCEPTS

Exercises 155–162 use the following information: Below is a plot of the probability density for spilled carrots along five miles of road from a farm near Walla Walla, Washington, toward the processing plant. The first mile of road is quite rough; the next two miles are better, and the final two miles are very good. (Also, trucks have spilled most of the easily dislodged carrots before reaching the better roads.)

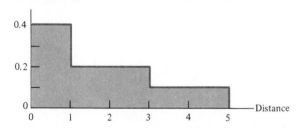

155. What is the probability that a randomly chosen spilled carrot was found in the first mile?

*156. What is the probability that a randomly chosen spilled carrot was found in the first two miles?

157. On the average, how many carrots out of 200 spilled from a truck would fall between two and four miles from the farm?

*158. On the average, how many of 200 spilled carrots would fall less than three miles from the farm?

In *Exercises 159–162,* if X is the random variable "distance from the farm" obtain the following:

159. $P[X \geq 2]$ 160. $P[1 \leq X \leq 4]$ 161. $P[X \geq 5]$

162. the percentage of spilled carrots found within three miles of the farm

Exercises 163–169: Use the probability density curve shown below.

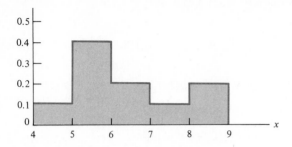

163. Find the total area under the curve.   164. Find $P[X \geq 6]$.
165. Find $P[5 \leq X \leq 8]$.   166. Find $P[X \leq 7]$.   167. Find $P[X > 5]$.
168. Find the percentage of the population with values between $x = 6$ and $x = 9$.
*169. In a sample of 300, find the expected number falling between $x = 5$ and $x = 7$.

8.6 THE NORMAL DISTRIBUTION: AN INTRODUCTION

We now consider the most celebrated of all continuous probability density functions: the **normal distribution**. (*Note:* The phrase "normal probability density" is correct, but in common usage most people say "normal distribution.") There is a mathematical equation describing the normal distribution, but it is sufficient to know that its shape is a "bell curve" as shown in Figure 8.12.

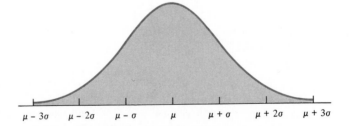

Figure 8.12
Normal distribution

There are actually infinitely many different normal distributions, but they all have the same basic shape, differing only in the mean (μ) and/or the standard deviation (σ). The mean μ is located underneath the "high point" of the curve, and the spread about the mean depends on the standard deviation σ. Two different normal curves are shown in Figure 8.13. Observe the symmetry.

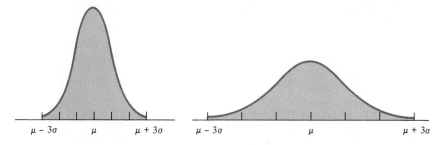

Figure 8.13
Two different normal
distributions

A theoretical normal distribution covers the range from minus infinity to plus infinity. Nothing we measure in the real world spans an infinite range. As we shall see, however, virtually all the area (probability) in any normal distribution lies within three standard deviations of the mean (that is, between $\mu - 3\sigma$ and $\mu + 3\sigma$) so the normal distribution, while a theoretical abstraction, can still serve as a suitable model for many real-world random variables. (The uniform probability density function of Example 20 is also a theoretical abstraction, but experience with actual data convinced the statistician that this density would provide a good model for the real-world situation. Examining data is generally a good way of deciding whether to adopt a particular probability density function as a suitable real-world model.)

Examples of Normal Distributions

What kinds of populations tend to have a normal distribution? Some examples: heights of adult Hispanic males; weights of Golden Delicious apples in a given year; diameters of steel ball bearings, if the intended diameter is 0.050 inch; IQ scores; heights cleared by 12th-grade high jumpers; daily sales of a business; and many other populations in which values of a random variable tend to cluster symmetrically about a "typical" (mean) value, tapering off rapidly as distance from the mean increases.

Properties of Normal Distributions

In Section 8.5 we saw that **(a)** the total area under any continuous probability density curve is one, **(b)** the probability of observing a value between two given numbers is precisely the area under the density curve between "cuts" made at those values, and **(c)** the probability of any single value is zero. These observations apply, of course, to the normal distribution. Due to its shape, areas in the normal distribution are not easy to find. However, because the normal distribution has so many applications, exhaustive efforts have gone into approximating these areas very closely. The results are available to us in table form. Here is a list of some of the important results that apply to every normally distributed random variable:

1. The area trapped between cuts at $\mu - \sigma$ and $\mu + \sigma$ is about 0.6826. "About 68% of a normal distribution falls within (a distance of) one standard deviation of the mean."

2. The area between cuts at $\mu - 2\sigma$ and $\mu + 2\sigma$ is about 0.9544. "About 95% of any normal distribution falls within two standard deviations of the mean."

3. The area between cuts at $\mu - 3\sigma$ and $\mu + 3\sigma$ is about 0.9974. "Virtually all of a normally distributed population falls within three standard deviations of the mean."

4. The normal distribution is symmetric about its mean (μ): the area "below" (to the left of) the mean is 0.5; the area "above" (to the right of) the mean is also 0.5.

Contrast statement 2, which applies only to normal distributions, with Chebyshev's Theorem, which says at least 75% of the probability in any distribution is within two standard deviations of the mean. By knowing that the population is normally distributed, we can replace the "at least 75%" figure with "about 95%." By knowing the form of the distribution, we are able to make more informative statements than if we know nothing about the distribution.

Using the above areas and the symmetry of a normal curve about its mean enables us to calculate the areas shown in Figure 8.14.

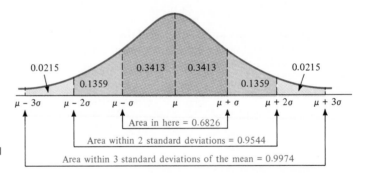

Figure 8.14

Normal curve areas in standard deviation units

Thus, only 0.0215 (2.15%) of any normal distribution has values that fall between $\mu - 3\sigma$ and $\mu - 2\sigma$. If scores on a nationwide test are normally distributed with mean 500 and standard deviation 100, then only 2.15% of the scores are between 200 and 300.

We illustrate how probabilities in Figure 8.14 were obtained by considering "0.1359." Observe that $0.9544 - 0.6826 = 0.2718$ is the total area that falls in the regions from $\mu - 2\sigma$ to $\mu - \sigma$ and from $\mu + \sigma$ to $\mu + 2\sigma$. From symmetry, it is apparent that half of 0.2718, or 0.1359, should fall in each zone. Other probabilities are figured similarly.

Knowing only the mean and standard deviation of a normally distributed random variable, along with the above chart, enables us to find probabilities about a normal distribution—provided those probabilities can be phrased in terms of one, two, or three standard deviations relative to the mean.

Practice Problem 7 contains most "normal distribution" ideas you will need. Make a sketch for each probability (area).

PRACTICE PROBLEM 7   Using only Figure 8.14, obtain the probability that a randomly chosen member of a normally distributed population is:

    (a) more than one standard deviation away from the mean (in either direction).

    (b) more than two standard deviations above the mean.

    (c) between two and three standard deviations away from the mean (in either direction).

    (d) below a cut-line at one standard deviation above the mean.

    (e) above a cut-line at two standard deviations below the mean.

    (f) between two standard deviations below the mean and one standard deviation above the mean.

ANSWER(S)   **(a)** 0.3174; **(b)** 0.0228; **(c)** 0.0430; **(d)** 0.8413; **(e)** 0.9772; **(f)** 0.8185.   □

Our discussion about normally distributed random variables has so far been in general terms—so many standard deviations above or below the mean. How can we make the connection with specific normal distributions?

■ EXAMPLE 22   A large population of male laboratory rats was given a high calorie diet with steroid supplements. At the end of one month, these rats could bench press, on average, 360 grams, with a standard deviation of 8 grams. Assuming that the bench press weights were approximately normally distributed,

    (a) What percentage of the rats could press 376 grams or more?

    (b) What is the probability that a randomly chosen rat from the group could press between 352 and 360 grams?

    (c) On average, how many out of 300 rats taken from this group could not bench press at least 368 grams?

SOLUTION   Using Figure 8.14 as a guide, we sketch (see Figure 8.15) the normal curve representing the X distribution. Beneath μ, write the mean (360); underneath $\mu + \sigma$, write 368 (8 grams, or one standard deviation, above the mean), etc. Underneath this x-scale, add another scale, representing departures from the mean measured in standard deviation units. One unit on this new scale corresponds to 8 units on the x-scale. At the mean value of 360, this new scale is labeled "0," since there is no difference between the value 360 and the mean. Underneath 368, write "1" be-

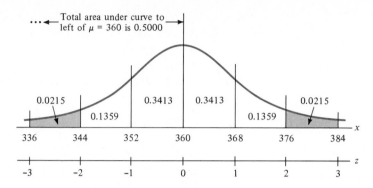

Figure 8.15
x- and z-scales for Example 22

cause 368 is one standard deviation above (to the right of, or greater than) the mean. Underneath 352, write "−1" to indicate that a value of 352 is one standard deviation below (to the left of, or less than) the mean. Numbers on this new scale are called z-*scores* or *standard scores* since they measure departures from the mean in standard deviation units.

z-SCORE

> The **z-score** (or **standard score**) for the value x measures how far x is from its mean in terms of standard deviations. Specifically:
>
> $$z = \frac{x - \mu}{\sigma}$$

A positive z-score indicates that x is above the mean; a negative z-score indicates x is below its mean. If $x = 376$, $z = (376 − 360)/8 = 2$; if $x = 352$, $z = (352 − 360)/8 = −1$, etc.

With sketches completed, follow all steps carefully:

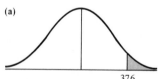

(a) $P[X \geq 376]$ = area under X curve to right of 376. This is the same as $P[Z \geq 2]$ = area to right of 2 on the z-scale. This area is 0.0228. About 2.28% of rats can press 376 grams or more.

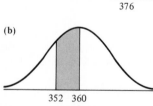

(b) $P[352 \leq X \leq 360]$ = area under X curve between 352 and 360. On the z-scale, this is the area between −1 and 0, which is 0.3413. The probability of a rat falling in this group is 0.3413.

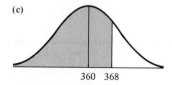

(c) $P[X \leq 368]$ = area under the X curve below 368. This is the same as $P[Z \leq 1]$ = area to left of 1 on z-scale, which is 0.5 + 0.3413 = 0.8413. Viewing each of the 300 rats as one trial of a binomial experiment with "success" (failing to press 368 grams or more) probability 0.8413, then the expected number of successes in these 300 trials is 300(0.8413) = 252.39. On the average, about 252 out of 300 would fail to press 368 grams or more.   ■

PRACTICE PROBLEM 8   Long-jump distances achieved during nationwide testing of eighth-grade girls were approximately normally distributed, with a mean of four meters and standard deviation 0.5 meter. What is the probability that a randomly selected girl from this group jumped

    (a) more than 5 meters?

    (b) between 2.5 and 3 meters?

What percentage of the girls jumped

    (c) more than 3 meters?

    (d) 4.5 meters or less?

On average, about how many girls out of 500 should be able to jump

    (e) more than 3 meters?

    (f) more than 2.5 meters but no more than 3.5 meters?

ANSWER(S)   **(a)** 0.0228;   **(b)** 0.0215;   **(c)** 97.72%;   **(d)** 84.13%;   **(e)** about 489;   **(f)** about 79.   ☐

The Importance of the Normal Distribution   The importance of the normal distribution can hardly be overestimated. Many variables in nature can be modeled by the normal distribution. This fact by itself is enough to justify study of the normal distribution, but there are other, equally compelling reasons. For example, the normal distribution will be used to approximate binomial probabilities in Section 8.8. In addition, when we discuss statistics in Chapter 9, we shall encounter possibly the most significant reason of all for studying the normal distribution: the Central Limit Theorem.

EXERCISES 8.6

PRACTICING THE MOVES AND MANEUVERS

Exercises 170–173:   Let X have a normal distribution with mean 80 and standard deviation 6. By using only Figure 8.14, determine the following probabilities:

170. $P[X \geq 92]$ 171. $P[X \leq 86]$ 172. $P[74 \leq X \leq 92]$ 173. $P[68 \leq X \leq 80]$

Exercises 174–177: Let X have a normal distribution with mean 100 and standard deviation 5. By using only Figure 8.14, determine the following probabilities:

174. $P[X \geq 95]$ 175. $P[X \leq 90]$ 176. $P[85 \leq X \leq 95]$ 177. $P[95 \leq X \leq 105]$

APPLYING THE CONCEPTS

Exercises 178–180 use the following information: The time it takes a student to walk from his mathematics class to his P.E. class follows a normal distribution with a mean of 8 minutes and a standard deviation of 0.5 minute.

178. Find the probability that it takes him more than 9 minutes on his next trip.
179. Find the probability that it takes him less then 8.5 minutes on his next trip.
180. Find the probability that his next trip takes between 7 and 9 minutes.

Exercises 181–183 use the following information: Yearly precipitation in Trepidation, Wyoming, is normally distributed about a mean of 8 inches, and the standard deviation is 1 inch. Find:

181. the probability that the precipitation in the next 12 months exceeds 9 inches.
182. the probability that next year's precipitation is at most 6 inches.
183. the probability that the precipitation next year is between 6 and 9 inches.

Exercises 184–188: Speed of cars passing a certain milepost on Interstate 90 follows a normal distribution with a mean of 70 miles an hour and a standard deviation of 4 miles an hour. Use this information to find the probability that:

184. the next car is driving more than 74 miles an hour.
185. the next car is driving less than 62 miles an hour.
186. the next car is driving more than 78 miles an hour.
187. at least 3 of the next 5 cars passing this milepost are traveling faster than 70.
188. at most 4 of the next 5 cars passing this milepost are traveling faster than 70.

8.7 APPLYING THE NORMAL DISTRIBUTION

We saw in Example 22 a connection between "raw" measurements and "z-scores" (positions relative to the population mean, measured in standard deviation-sized steps). We worked with convenient values: raw measurements differing from the mean by exaclty one, two, or three standard deviations. Not all measurements fall at such tidy distances from the population mean. In this section we explore further connections between raw measurements and z-scores, with a variety of applications.

■ EXAMPLE 23

Recall the long-jump distances for eighth-grade girls: normally distributed, with mean 4 meters and standard deviation 0.5 meter. Draw a sketch for each part, and solve.

(a) A jumper's z-score was 1.5. What was her jump distance?

(b) What jump distance produced a z-score of −2.2?

(c) One girl jumped 4.75 meters. What was her z-score?

(d) What z-score corresponds to a 2.94 meter jump?

SOLUTION

(a)

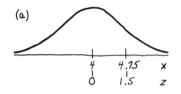

(a) A z-score of 1.5 means "1.5 standard deviations beyond the mean." 1.5(0.5 meter) = 0.75 meter above the mean; so the raw measurement is $\mu + 1.5\sigma = 4 + 0.75 = 4.75$ meters.

(b)

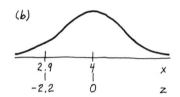

(b) When $z = -2.2$, x is 2.2 standard deviations less than the mean. $\mu - 2.2\sigma = 4 - (2.2)(0.5) = 4 - 1.1 = 2.9$ meters.

(c)

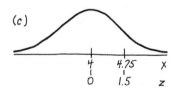

(c) A measurement of 4.75 meters is 0.75 meter beyond 4 meters (the mean). Measured in standard deviations, 0.75 meter is (0.75 ÷ 0.5 = 1.5) standard deviations above the mean: when $x = 4.75$ meters, $z = 1.5$.

(d)

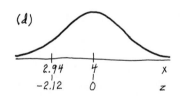

(d) When $x = 2.94$, x is $(4 - 2.94) \div 0.5$ standard deviations below the mean. On the z-scale, this is −2.12; so when $x = 2.94$ meters, $z = -2.12$.

PRACTICE PROBLEM 9 Kumquat seeds from Bosco Anchovy's orchard have mean diameter 0.6 inch, with standard deviation 0.12 inch. Draw pictures to help yourself, and fill in the blanks (**a–m**) in the following tables:

x-values	0.354	0.36	0.44	0.56	0.6	0.67	0.75
z-values	(a)	(b)	(c)	(d)	(e)	(f)	(g)

x-values	(h)	(i)	(j)	(k)	(l)	(m)
z-values	−3.6	−2.44	−1.5	0.0	1.72	4.14

ANSWER(S)   **(a)** −2.05; **(b)** −2; **(c)** −1.33; **(d)** −0.33; **(e)** 0; **(f)** 0.58; **(g)** 1.25; **(h)** 0.168; **(i)** 0.31; **(j)** 0.42; **(k)** 0.6; **(l)** 0.81; **(m)** 1.10.   ☐

The preceding practice problem was designed to encourage short cuts in performing tedious computations. Some patterns emerged:

Conversion of raw measurement (x-value) to standard score (z-score). Find distance of raw measurement from mean; divide by standard deviation. Proper sign results automatically if distance of raw measurement from mean is calculated as $x - \mu$. This process of converting from a raw x-measurement to its standard score (z-score) is called **standardizing**.

Conversion of z-score to raw measurement or x-value. Recall that "z-score" is "distance from mean, measured in standard deviations." Multiply z-score (including its sign) by standard deviation, then add result (including proper sign) to mean. We summarize this conversion process in tidy "box form," but as with all formulas, we remind you that the process should be understood and not simply memorized. We urge you to apply the above processes until you own them, and then practice creating the formulas on scrap paper.

CONVERTING BETWEEN RAW MEASUREMENTS AND z-SCORES

Given a set of values with mean μ and standard deviation σ, the z-score corresponding to the raw value x is:

$$z = \frac{x - \mu}{\sigma}$$

Given a set of values with mean μ and standard deviation σ, the raw score x corresponding to a given z-score is:

$$x = \mu + z \cdot \sigma$$

Now we make the crucial connections allowing application of the normal distribution to a wide variety of problems:

1. "The" normal distribution, which we have informally introduced, with mean 0 and standard deviation 1 on the z-score scale, is called the **standard normal distribution**.

2. The correspondence between values in any normal distribution and the standard normal distribution can be worked out using the conversion processes discussed above.

Since raw measurements and z-scores do not usually fall into patterns of whole standard deviations, there is a need to be able to "read between" the whole standard deviations of the standard normal distribution. The Standard Normal Distribution, a table at the end of this text, allows readings down to the nearest hundredth of a standard deviation. A small portion of the table follows.

The Standard Normal Distribution

A number in this table corresponding to z represents the area under the standard normal distribution between the mean 0 and the value z. The area between 0 and 0.95, for example, is 0.3289.

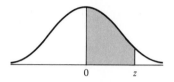

z	0.00	0.01	0.02	0.03	0.04	0.05	0.06	0.07	0.08	0.09
0.7	0.2580	0.2611	0.2642	0.2673	0.2704	0.2734	0.2764	0.2794	0.2823	0.2852
0.8	0.2881	0.2910	0.2939	0.2967	0.2995	0.3023	0.3051	0.3078	0.3106	0.3133
0.9	0.3159	0.3186	0.3212	0.3238	0.3264	0.3289	0.3315	0.3340	0.3365	0.3389
1.0	0.3413	0.3438	0.3461	0.3485	0.3508	0.3531	0.3554	0.3577	0.3599	0.3621
1.1	0.3643	0.3665	0.3686	0.3708	0.3729	0.3749	0.3770	0.3790	0.3810	0.3830
1.2	0.3849	0.3869	0.3888	0.3907	0.3925	0.3944	0.3962	0.3980	0.3997	0.4015

To read a z-score, use the left ("z") column for the whole number and "tenths" part of the score, and the top row for the "hundredths" part. In the body of the table are areas corresponding to the shaded part of the above diagram. That is, for a given z-score, the table shows the area under the standard normal curve between the mean of 0 and that z-score. Since the normal curve is symmetric, only areas to the right of the mean are shown; you can work out, with a careful sketch, any area you need. For example, the area between the mean ($z = 0$) and a cut line at $z = 1.15$ is 0.3749. Reversing the procedure, the cut line which traps an area of 0.3597 to the right of the mean is approximately at $z = 1.08$, taking the nearest table reading. Do you have the idea? Follow closely all parts of Example 24.

■ EXAMPLE 24

Using the preceding table excerpt, and showing the necessary sketches, find:

(a) the area between the mean and $z = 1.25$.

(b) the area between the mean and $z = -1.25$.

(c) the area between $z = -1.25$ and $z = 1.10$.

(d) the area between $z = 0.80$ and $z = 0.90$.

(e) the area to the right of $z = 0.92$.

(f) the area to the right of $z = -0.92$.

(g) the area to the left of $z = 0.92$.

(h) the area to the left of $z = -0.92$.

(i) $P[-0.7 \leq Z \leq 1.28]$.

(j) z_1 so that $P[0 \leq Z \leq z_1] = 0.3212$. (*Caution*: Here, given a desired probability—area under the normal curve—you are asked to find the z-score which cuts off that area.)

(k) z_2 so that $P[Z \leq z_2] = 0.8365$.

SOLUTION

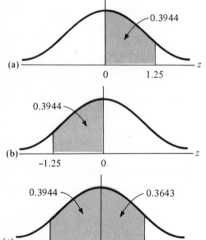

(a) This area, to the right of the mean, is 0.3944.

(b) By symmetry, this area left of the mean is also 0.3944. Note that every area (probability), whether left or right of the mean, is positive. *Probability is never negative.*

(c) $0.3944 + 0.3643 = 0.7587$

(d) $0.3159 - 0.2881 = 0.0278$

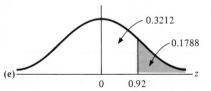

(e) $0.5 - 0.3212 = 0.1788$

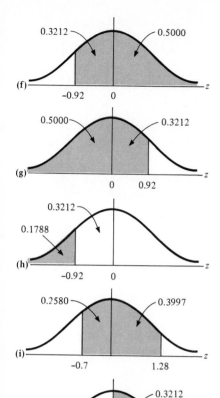

(f) $0.3212 + 0.5 = 0.8212$

(g) $0.5 + 0.3212 = 0.8212$

(h) $0.5 - 0.3212 = 0.1788$

(i) $0.2580 + 0.3997 = 0.6577$

(j) 0.92

(k) Since area exceeds 0.5, the cut line at z_2 traps an area of 0.3365 to the right of the mean; therefore $z_2 = 0.98$.

Study Example 24 carefully. It illustrates a variety of questions one can answer about a standard normal distribution, using the Standard Normal Distribution table. In Example 25, we show how to answer similar questions for any normally distributed population, still using the table.

■ EXAMPLE 25

Weights of eggs produced at Walker's Egg Farm are approximately normally distributed, with a mean of 5.5 ounces and a standard deviation of 0.2 ounce.

(a) What percentage of all the eggs weigh between 5.2 and 6 ounces?

(b) What is the probability that exactly two of the next 5 eggs will weigh between 5.2 and 6 ounces?

(c) What weight interval, centered at the mean, contains 50% of the eggs?

(d) On the average, how many eggs out of a day's production of 420 eggs will be "large" (more than 6 ounces)? (You will recognize this as a "binomial probability" question.)

(e) Find the minimum weight of an egg if it is to be at the 90th percentile; only 10% of all eggs would weigh at least this much.

SOLUTION

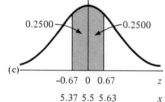

(a) $P[5.2 \le X \le 6] = P[-1.5 \le Z \le 2.5] = 0.4332 + 0.4938 = 0.9270$. About 93% of all eggs fall within the interval.

(b) A *binomial* experiment, once one gets "success" probability from part (a).

(b) By (a), "success" probability is 0.9270. The probability of two successes is $C(5,2) \cdot 0.9270^2 \cdot 0.0730^3 \approx 0.0003$.

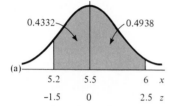

(c) Must trap an area of 0.25 on each side of the mean. This is done by standard scores of 0.67 to the right, and -0.67 to the left. In compact notation: $P[-z_1 \le Z \le z_1] = 0.50$ if $z_1 = 0.67$; and this occurs if x is between $5.5 - 0.67 \cdot 0.2 \approx 5.37$ ounces and $5.5 + 0.67 \cdot 2 \approx 5.63$ ounces.

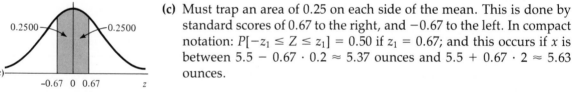

(d) $P[X \ge 5.95] = P[Z \ge 2.25] = 0.5 - 0.4878 = 0.0122$; thus a day's production of 420 eggs may be viewed as 420 trials of a binomial experiment with "success" probability 0.0122. The expected number is $\mu = n \cdot p = 420 \cdot 0.0122 \approx 5$ eggs.

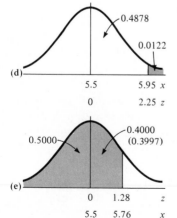

(e) The area to the left of the mean is 0.5, so the area between the mean and the 90th percentile must be 0.40. Checking the body of the table, we find that 0.3997 is the closest entry, at $z = 1.28$ standard deviations. The weight 1.28 standard deviations above the mean is $5.5 + 1.28 \cdot 0.2 \approx 5.76$ ounces. Only 10% of egg weights exceed this amount.

Persons enthusiastic over "normal distribution" methods tend thereafter to assume that every population is normally distributed. This is not so. While it is always valid to express raw ("x") scores as standard scores for comparison's sake, do not automatically assume that every distribution is "normal!"

EXERCISES 8.7

PRACTICING THE MOVES AND MANEUVERS

Exercises 189–193: Refer to the Standard Normal Distribution table (inside the back cover). For any normally distributed population, find the probability that a randomly chosen outcome will fall:

189. between the mean and 1.28 standard deviations above the mean.
190. more than 2.2 standard deviations below the mean.
191. between $z = -1.64$ and $z = -0.26$.
192. between $z = -0.47$ and $z = 1.55$.
193. at least 2.36 standard deviations above the mean.

Exercises 194–197: For any normally distributed population, what z-score(s) cut off:

194. the bottom 10% of the entire population?
195. the top 15% of the population?
196. the 30% of the population centered at the mean?
197. the top 70% of the population?

Exercises 198–202: For any normally distributed population,

198. on the average, how many individual outcomes out of 50,000 fall between 1.2 standard deviations below, and 2.1 standard deviations above, the mean?
199. on the average, how many out of 50,000 fall below $z = 2.73$?
200. what is the value of $P[-1.47 \le Z \le 2.53]$?
201. about what percent of the population is above $z = -0.65$?
202. about how many individual outcomes out of 400 lie between $z = 0.5$ and $z = 1.5$?

Exercises 203–207: A normally distributed population has mean 80 and variance 36.

203. What is the probability that a randomly chosen member of the population will fall between 75 and 82?
204. What interval of scores includes the middle half of the population?
205. Out of 1000 individual scores, about how many fall between 80 and 90?
206. What is the probability that a randomly chosen score will be less than 71?
207. What is the 90th percentile score (cutting off the bottom 90% of the population)?

APPLYING THE CONCEPTS

Exercises 208–211:   Annual incomes in Myopia (population 200,000) are normally distributed with mean 20 kilokopeks and standard deviation 4 kilokopeks.

208.   What percentage of the entire population earns in excess of 30 kilokopeks? (Most Myopic plumbers are in this group.)

209.   What is the probability that a randomly selected Myopian has an income between 14 and 30 kilokopeks?

210.   What income bracket, centered at the mean, contains the middle third of the entire population?

211.   What is the lower income limit for the best-paid 10% of Myopians?

Exercises 212–215:   The verbal portion of a nationally administered achievement test is scaled so that the mean score is 500 and the standard deviation is 100. Assuming the distribution of scores to be normal,

212.   What fraction of scores fall between 400 and 600?

213.   What is the probability that a randomly selected score is between 340 and 660?

214.   On the average, how many scores out of 6000 would be greater than 250?

215.   What score cuts off the bottom 20%?

Exercises 216–218:   Scientists studying links between environment and life span found an island culture in which the life span of males who survive childhood (reach age 15) are normally distributed with a mean of 88 years and a standard deviation of 5.5 years. In this culture,

216.   What is the probability that a 15-year-old male will survive to age 90?

217.   What is the probability that a 15-year-old male will die between 79 and 93?

218.   What percentage of 15-year-old males will live to see age 75?

219.   The top 5% (as determined by a standardized test) of high school senior math students will receive $2000 scholarships. If scores are normally distributed with mean 180 and variance 64, what cutoff score determines the winners?

220.   Bottles filled by machine at the local Fizzwater factory contain, on the average, 16 ounces; however, due to variations in the equipment, bottle contents are normally distributed with a variance of 0.4 ounce. Bottles containing 15 ounces or less are rejected as being underfilled. In a day's run of 20,000 bottles, about how many will be rejected?

221.   A transistor manufacturer averages 68.7 defective transistors per day, with a standard deviation of 2.2. Each defective costs her 7 cents in lost profits. What is the probability that she will lose at least $5.18 on a given day?

222.   In a normally distributed set of test scores with mean 72 and standard deviation 10, what percentage of the students scored 90 or higher?

*223.   A z-score of 1.5 is found to correspond to a measurement of 18; the standard deviation for this population is 4. What is the mean for this population?

*224.   A company manufactures an automobile part whose mean length is 5.0 inches. Any part whose length is within 0.4% of the mean length is considered acceptable. The standard deviation for 15,000 parts made on a given day is 0.01 inch. Approximately how many of that day's parts would not be acceptable?

225.   A track coach informs her elementary P.E. class that their grades will be determined by how well they do in the long jump. A student must outjump 80% of his or her classmates to get an A. If the mean jump is 3.2 meters with a standard deviation of 0.8 meter, what is an "A" jump?

*226. Life spans of electric razor motors are approximately normally distributed with mean 8 years and standard deviation 1.5 years. The manufacturer is willing to replace at most 5% of the motors that fail. What maximum whole number of years should he write into the "free replacement if your motor fails" guarantee?

Exercises 227–229: Tread-life tests on a new Notsohot tire design yield miles-to-wearout figures that are normally distributed, with a mean of 20,000 miles and a standard deviation of 2,500 miles. What is the probability that a new tire will last

227. more than 25,000 miles?
228. less than 17,200 miles?

229. between 18,000 and 22,000 miles?

*230. Gourmet Canners sells dehydrated gnat-knees in bags marked "contents: 4 ounces." The packaging machinery can be set to produce any desired mean weight, with a standard deviation of 0.08 ounce. If only 3% of the bags are to contain less than 4 ounces, what must the mean be? (This is a challenging problem. Be courageous; draw a picture!)

*231. A quality-control inspector on a glass bottle production line is instructed to shut the line down if, among eight bottles she picks at random on the line, three or more are underweight (below 42 grams) or overweight (above 46 grams). The line is producing bottles having normally distributed weights with mean 43 grams and standard deviation 0.4 gram. What is the probability that, on her next inspection, the inspector will shut the line down?

8.8 THE NORMAL APPROXIMATION TO THE BINOMIAL DISTRIBUTION (OPTIONAL)

Binomial distribution problems like "find the probability of three heads in six tosses of a fair coin" are easy. Small changes can make such a problem considerably more difficult. The modified problem "find the probability of 300 heads in the next 600 tosses" looks similar (all we did was add a few zeros!), but consider the computation:

$$p(300) = P[300 \text{ heads in } 600 \text{ trials}] = C(600,300)\left(\frac{1}{2}\right)^{300} \cdot \left(\frac{1}{2}\right)^{300}$$

While easy in concept, this problem is difficult in execution, because it requires computing 600! and 300!, problems that even computers cannot handle without skillful programming. Fortunately, we can use the normal distribution to help us. To see how, consider again the probability distribution for the binomial random variable $Y = $ # heads in $n = 6$ tosses of a fair coin. This distribution and its histogram are shown in Figure 8.16.

y	0	1	2	3	4	5	6
$p(y)$	0.016	0.094	0.234	0.312	0.234	0.094	0.016

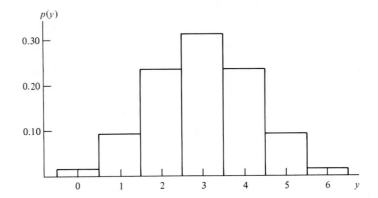

Figure 8.16
Table and histogram for
binomial distribution with
$n = 6$, $p = 0.5$

The resemblance of Figure 8.16 to a normal distribution is striking. Symmetry of this histogram is guaranteed by the "success" probability 0.5: the probability of two heads is the same as the probability of two tails (or four heads). The mean of this binomial distribution is $\mu = np = 3$; the standard deviation of the distribution is $\sigma = \sqrt{npq} \approx 1.225$.

Selecting a Suitable Normal Distribution

Which normal distribution comes closest to fitting the histogram of Figure 8.16? Intuitively, the normal distribution with the same mean and standard deviation as the given binomial distribution would seem a logical choice. In Figure 8.17, we overlay the binomial distribution with a normal distribution having mean 3 and standard deviation 1.225:

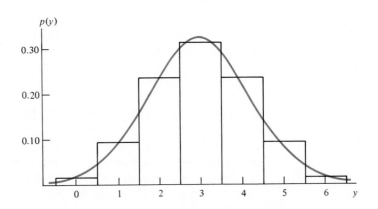

Figure 8.17
Binomial distribution with
normal curve overlay

Out of curiosity, let us find the area under the normal curve between $y = 2.5$ and $y = 3.5$. This area corresponds roughly to the area of the histogram bar centered at 3, which is the exact probability that $Y = 3$ (found in table of Figure 8.16 to be 0.312). To find the normal curve area between $y = 2.5$ and $y = 3.5$, we find corresponding z-scores, and use the Standard Normal Distribution table to find the area between these z-scores. The details are as follows:

For $y = 2.5$: $z = \dfrac{2.5 - 3}{1.225} \approx -0.41$

For $y = 4.5$: $z = \dfrac{3.5 - 3}{1.225} \approx 0.41$

The area under the z-score curve between -0.41 and 0.41 is $2(0.1591) = 0.3182$. Comparing this with the exact (to 3 decimal places) probability of 0.312, we see that the "error" (forget sign) is only 0.006. Compared to the true value, the *relative error* is only $0.006/0.312 \approx 0.019 = 1.9\%$.

Let's analyze what we just did. The binomial distribution assigns a definite, nonzero answer to $P[Y = 3]$. The normal distribution, however, does not deal kindly with $P[Y = 3]$, presenting us with a zero answer since there is no area under the curve at $y = 3$ (that is, between $y = 3$ and $y = 3$). To use the *continuous* normal distribution to approximate the *discrete* binomial, we trick the normal into thinking $y = 3$ has nonzero probability by representing $y = 3$ as *an interval of length one centered at 3*—the interval from 2.5 to 3.5. This is in no way "cheating!" If Y has a binomial distribution, then $P[Y = 3]$ is exactly the same as $P[2.5 \leq Y \leq 3.5]$ because the only possibility between 2.5 and 3.5 is $y = 3$. The answer obtained is "off" slightly because the area under the superimposed normal does not match the true probability—the area of the histogram bar at 3. Replacing the binomial value "3" by the interval from 2.5 to 3.5 is called the **continuity correction**.

In our original problem (find probability of three heads in six coin tosses), the exact binomial solution is a simple computation: $p(3) = C(6,3)(1/2)^3(1/2)^3 = 0.312$; there is no reason to settle for an approximate answer when the exact answer is easily obtained. Finding the exact answer in our "modified" problem (probability of 300 heads in 600 tosses) is a different story. If we come reasonably close by finding a normal curve area, the ease of the solution would justify getting an approximate answer.

How would we use the normal in our modified problem? With $n = 600$ trials and $p = 1/2$, the mean and standard deviation for the number of heads are $np = 300$ and $\sigma = \sqrt{[300 \cdot (1/2)]} \approx 12.25$, respectively. The correct (binomial) answer, difficult to compute, is $P[Y = 300] = C(600,300)(1/2)^{300} \cdot (1/2)^{300}$. Using the normal curve approximation, we would find the area under the normal curve from 299.5 (the bar for 300 begins there) to 300.5 (the bar for 300 ends there). The z-scores are:

$$\textbf{For 299.5:} \quad z = \frac{299.5 - 300}{12.25} \approx -0.04$$

$$\textbf{For 300.5:} \quad z = \frac{300.5 - 300}{12.25} \approx 0.04$$

The area under the z-score curve between −0.04 and 0.04 is 2(0.0160) = 0.0320, making roughly a 3% chance that we will see exactly 300 heads in 600 tosses of a fair coin. Thus, even though the mean number of heads in 600 tosses is 300, there is little chance of seeing exactly that number in a typical set of 600 tosses. In the next example, we continue this problem.

■ EXAMPLE 26

When a fair coin is tossed 600 times, find the probability of getting at least 300 heads but no more than 315 heads.

SOLUTION   The mean and standard deviation of the numbers of heads in 600 tosses are np = 300 and σ = 12.25, as found earlier. The exact binomial answer is a horrendous computation: $p(300) + p(301) + \cdots + p(315)$. The normal approximation needs only the area under the normal curve from 299.5 (where 300 begins) to 315.5 (where 315 ends). The z-score for 299.5 is (still) −0.04; the z-score for 315.5 is (315.5 − 300)/12.25 ≈ 1.27. The area between these two z-scores is 0.0160 + 0.3980 = 0.414. This says in many, many sets of 600 die tosses, we would observe between 300 and 315 heads about 41% of the time. Is this close to the exact answer we would get with the binomial? Let's do another example using both the normal approximation and the exact figure so we can compare.   ■

■ EXAMPLE 27

The fertility rate for pheasant eggs on a game preserve in South Dakota is 70%. What is the probability of finding between 10 and 15 (inclusive) fertile eggs in a basket of 20 eggs?

SOLUTION   The number of fertile eggs has a binomial distribution with n = 20 and p = 0.7. To find the exact answer to $P(10 \leq Y \leq 15)$, use Table I: $P(Y \leq 15)$ = 0.762 and $P(Y \leq 9)$ = 0.017, so that $P(10 \leq Y \leq 15)$ = 0.762 − 0.017 = 0.745.

To approximate this probability with the normal distribution, we first compute $\mu = np = 14$ and $\sigma = \sqrt{npq} = 2.05$. We then find the area under the normal curve (see Figure 8.18) having these values of μ and σ between 9.5 (where 10 begins) and 15.5 (where 15 ends). The z-scores for 9.5 and 15.5 are −2.20 and 0.73, respectively. Thus, the Figure 8.18 sketch parallels the mathematical argument.

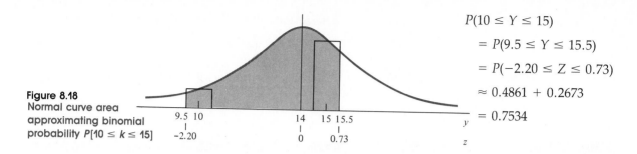

$$P(10 \leq Y \leq 15)$$
$$= P(9.5 \leq Y \leq 15.5)$$
$$= P(-2.20 \leq Z \leq 0.73)$$
$$\approx 0.4861 + 0.2673$$
$$= 0.7534$$

Figure 8.18
Normal curve area
approximating binomial
probability $P[10 \leq k \leq 15]$

How does this normal approximation compare to the binomial probability, 0.745, obtained earlier? The relative error (actual error, compared to true value), to three places, is only $(0.753 - 0.745)/0.745 \approx 0.011$, or about one percent. Not bad!   ■

Deciding When the Normal Can Be Used to Approximate the Binomial

Under what conditions can we expect to get good answers when we use the normal to approximate the binomial distribution? Recall that virtually all area under a normal curve (99.74%) lies between $\mu - 3\sigma$ and $\mu + 3\sigma$.

> **If, for a given binomial distribution, the boundaries $\mu - 3\sigma$ and $\mu + 3\sigma$ fall between 0 and n (where the binomial places 100% of its probability), the overlaid normal curve will have virtually all of its area between 0 and n, and should do a good job of "fitting" the binomial distribution.**

This criterion for using the normal distribution to approximate the binomial is used by many practitioners of statistics.[5]

APPROXIMATING A BINOMIAL DISTRIBUTION WITH A NORMAL

Calculate $\mu = np$, $\sigma = \sqrt{npq}$ and the interval from $\mu - 3\sigma$ to $\mu + 3\sigma$. If this interval lies entirely between 0 and n, then it is permissible to use the normal distribution to approximate binomial probabilities.

PRACTICE PROBLEM 10

For the given binomial distributions, use the "$\mu \pm 3\sigma$ within 0 to n" criterion to determine if the normal approximation is okay. **(a)** $n = 50$, $p = 0.3$; **(b)** $n = 50$, $p = 0.03$; **(c)** $n = 4$, $p = 0.4$; **(d)** $n = 200$, $p = 0.25$.

ANSWER(S)   **(a)** yes;   **(b)** no;   **(c)** no;   **(d)** yes.   □

[5] An alternative criterion, preferred by some, is that both np and nq should be at least 5. We prefer the stated criterion because it is easy to justify intuitively.

PRACTICE PROBLEM 11   See Example 27. More recent information suggests that the fertility rate for pheasant eggs is now 74%. What is the probability of finding at least 65 fertile eggs in a basket of 100?

ANSWER(S)   0.9846; the exact answer, via computer, is 0.9826. The relative error is only 0.002/0.9826 ≈ 0.002 = 0.2%.   □

EXERCISES 8.8

PRACTICING THE MOVES AND MANEUVERS

Exercises 232–235: Decide whether the normal distribution can be used to approximate the binomial distribution having the given values of n and p.

232. $n = 10, p = 0.5$ 233. $n = 20, p = 0.4$ 234. $n = 30, p = 0.2$ 235. $n = 40, p = 0.1$

Exercises 236–239: Use the normal distribution to approximate probabilities for a binomial distribution Y with $n = 20$ and $p = 0.4$. Then, find exact answers (Table I) and compare.

236. $P[Y = 9]$ 237. $P[Y \geq 12]$ 238. $P[4 \leq Y \leq 9]$ 239. $P[6 < Y \leq 11]$

APPLYING THE CONCEPTS

240. A fair coin is to be tossed 12 times. Find the probability of obtaining exactly 3 heads by using **(a)** the binomial and **(b)** the normal approximation.

241. A tossed thumbtack falls point up about 30% of the time. In 84 tosses, what is the approximate probability that it will fall point up at least 18, but no more than 25, times? (Use the normal approximation only.) (The binomial probability, obtained by computer, is 0.4827. How well did you do?)

242. Approximately 6% of the male population is color-blind. If a random sample of 250 male adults were tested, what is the approximate probability that at least 10 but no more than 20 of the subjects would be color-blind?

243. If 25% of statistics students study for a test, what is the approximate probability that less than one third of a random sample of 48 students will study for tomorrow's test?

*244. If 60% of the population actually favors a new anti-pollution law, what is the approximate probability that a majority (more than half) of a

random sample of 96 persons will nevertheless be opposed to the law?

245. A psychologist conducts an experiment to see if rats prefer squares or triangles. A rat accustomed to obtaining food pellets by pressing a button is offered two buttons, one marked with a square and the other with a triangle. If the rat really does not prefer either shape, what is the approximate probability that it will still choose the triangle 40 or more times in 60 trials?

*246. A coin is tossed 25 times. If 15 or more heads appear, a player receives $20. If 15 or more tails appear, he must pay $10. What is the mathematical expectation of the player?

247. The Society of Actuaries gives a 50-question multiple-choice exam, each question having 5 possible answer choices (one of which is correct). Suppose the society has determined that 30 or more correct answers yield a passing score. Is there much chance for a person to pass by randomly selecting an answer to each question? Explain with probability.

A Brief Summary of Important Ideas

A **random variable** is a numerical-valued quantity associated with the outcome of a random experiment. A random variable is said to be discrete if there are gaps between any pair of possible values. For example, the number of defective items in a sample, or the number of Republicans in a voter-sample are discrete random variables. All discrete random variables have probability distributions, which describe how the total probability of one unit is distributed among the various possible values.

A **continuous random variable** may take any value in some interval on the real-number line. Continuous random variables are described not by probability distributions but by probability density functions. A probability density function (pdf) is a nonnegative function $f(x)$ such that the total area between $f(x)$ and the x-axis is one. Areas under $f(x)$ supply probabilities about the random variable X. In particular, $P[a \leq X \leq b] =$ area under $f(x)$ between a and b.

In addition to being described by their probability distributions or density functions, random variables can also be described by certain **parameters.** The **mean** or **expected value** of a random variable X is the long-range average value of the random variable and is also the "balance point" for the distribution. The **standard deviation** is a parameter which indicates concentration of values about the mean: a distribution whose values are tightly packed near the mean will have smaller standard deviation than a distribution whose values are more widely dispersed. **Chebyshev's inequality** helps us to interpret the standard deviation by telling us that in any distribution at least 3/4 of the values are within two standard deviations either side of the mean, and at least 8/9 of the values are within three standard deviations of the mean.

A frequently occurring discrete random variable is the **binomial** random variable Y, which records the number of successes in n independent and identical trials of an experiment in which the result of any trial can be classified as either success or failure. The probability distribution for the binomial random variable is given by $p(y) = P[y$ successes in n trials$] = C(n, y)p^y(1 - p)^{n-y}$. The mean and standard deviation for the number of successes in n trials are given by np and $\sqrt{np(1 - p)}$, respectively. Binomial probabilities can be found either by direct calculation or by using Table I in the Appendix.

We studied two continuous probability density functions: the **uniform distribution** and the **normal distribution**. The uniform distribution is appropriate when every interval of the same size has the same probability. The symmetric, bell-shaped normal distribution, which occurs more frequently in nature, has the following properties: about 68% of the values are within one standard deviation of the mean, about 95% within two standard deviations of the mean, and virtually all values are within three standard deviations of the mean. Probabilities for the standard normal distribution having mean 0 and standard deviation 1 are given in table form inside the back cover of the text. Probabilities about any other normal distribution may be found by first converting the problem into an equivalent problem involving the standard normal distribution.

The continuous normal distribution can also be used to approximate the discrete binomial distribution if we represent the value y by the interval from $y - 1/2$ to $y + 1/2$. This approximation will be effective whenever the binomial distribution is moderately symmetric. Specifically, if the interval from $\mu - 3\sigma$ to $\mu + 3\sigma$ is contained entirely between 0 and n (the range of possible values in a binomial), then the normal approximation to the binomial will be effective.

REVIEW EXERCISES

PRACTICING THE MOVES AND MANEUVERS

Exercises 248–252:   Use the following finite population of x-values:

4, 3, 3, 5, 7, 2, 4, 3, 5, 9, 3, 6, 5, 3, 7, 3

248.   Express this population with a probability distribution.
249.   Express your probability distribution by using a histogram.
250.   Find the mean of this population.
251.   Find the expected value of X.
252.   Find the variance and standard deviation.

253.   A discrete random variable X has probability distribution given by:

x	$p(x)$
-2	$1/12$
1	$1/4$
3	?

(a) Find $p(3)$.
(b) Find $P[X > -2]$.
(c) Find $P[X \geq -2]$.
(d) Find $E[X]$.
(e) Find σ^2 and σ for X.

Exercises 254–263:   A collection of experimental data has mean 62 and variance 25. Convert each of the following data values to a z-score:

254. 68   255. 49   256. 74   257. 57.5   258. 60.2

Convert each of the following z-scores to a raw score:

259. 1.7   260. −2.45   261. 3.18   262. 5   263. −1.5

Exercises 264 and 265:   A set of raw values has mean 29 and standard deviation 4.

264. Knowing nothing more about the values, at least what percentage of the values fall between 21 and 37?

265. If the set of values is normally distributed, approximately what percentage of all values fall between 21 and 37?

Exercises 266–268: A normally distributed set of scores has mean 120 and standard deviation 10.

*266. What score cuts off the top 15% of the distribution?

267. What is the probability of a randomly chosen score being between 105 and 125?

268. What percentage of all scores are less than 100?

*269. For a certain normal distribution, $\sigma = 8$. About 20% of all scores are less than 83. What is the mean of the distribution?

APPLYING THE CONCEPTS

Exercises 270–273: Consider a multiple-choice test having 225 questions, each with one correct answer among 5 possibilities. If Mike Williams answers each question by guessing, find the approximate probability (use normal approximation) that he

270. will get more than 60 correct answers.

271. will get at least 40 correct answers.

272. will get at least 45 correct, but no more than 54 correct.

273. will get at most 50 correct answers.

*274. Delmo Dweeb's favorite game is called Chuck-a-Buck, and it can only be played in the country of Nerdelvania. Delmo bets one million Nerdelvanian Rubelstilskis (value: one American dollar) on any one number from one to six. Three dice are then rolled. If Delmo's number appears on one of the dice, he gets his dollar back, plus an American dollar. If his number appears on two of the dice, he gets his dollar back plus two American dollars. If his number appears on all three dice, he gets his dollar back plus three American dollars and a coupon good for one kiss from Trixie Flubug, the current Miss Nerdelvania. The coupon is valued (optimistically!) at $0.17. If Delmo's number does not appear at all, a violinist does, presenting Delmo with a dozen Nerdelvanian roses (dandelions) valued at $0.08. Further, he forfeits his dollar. In the long run, how much can Delmo expect to win or lose?

Exercises 275–278: Rainbow trout from a certain lake have lengths following a normal distribution with mean 8.5 inches and standard deviation 2.5 inches.

275. Find the probability that a randomly caught trout will be at least 8 inches long.

276. Find the probability that a randomly caught trout will be somewhere between 7 and 9 inches in length.

277. If a fisherman has 6 of these trout in his creel, how likely is it that at least 5 of them exceed 8 inches?

278. What is the minimum length a trout needs to be in order that only 20% of all trout will be smaller than this length?

Exercises 279–281 use the following information: An imported car has six spark plugs, two of which are fouled. Three plugs are selected at random and tested. Let random variable Y represent the number of bad plugs in the sample of three.

279. Find the probability distribution for Y.

280. Represent the probability distribution with a histogram.
281. Find the mean, variance, and standard deviation for the random variable Y.

Exercises 282–287: Consider Delmo's twin sister, Delamina, who is a professional mud wrestler. The probability that she wins any match is 0.8, regardless of who her opponent is. In the next nine matches, find the probability that she wins

282. at most seven.

283. at least six.

284. between five and eight, inclusive.

285. no more than 12.

286. 10 or more.

287. no less than five.

*288. A random variable X is normally distributed with a mean of 60 and a standard deviation of 5. If 100 values of X are selected at random, approximate the probability that at least 54 of them exceed 60.

Exercises 289–291: The president of Botulism Beer Company wants to compare the taste of his new premium beer El Coliform to that of its largest competitor. Four beer connoisseurs are each given three glasses of beer, two of which contain El Coliform, and the third contains the competing beer. The beers are all in the same type of container, and the beer-tasting experts don't know which is which. Each expert is asked to pick the brew he prefers most. Let us suppose that the two brands of beer are absolutely identical. Let the random variable Y represent the number of beer experts who pick El Coliform.

289. Find the probability distribution for Y.
290. What is the probability that at most two of the beer-tasting experts pick El Coliform? At least one?
291. Find μ_y, σ_y^2, and σ_y.

Exercises 292–296: Blood samples are taken from residents of a certain district in a large city. The probability of finding lead in such a sample is 0.3. If 10 residents of this district are given blood tests, find

292. the probability that at least four of them have lead in their blood.
293. the probability that at most seven of them have lead in their blood.
294. the probability that exactly four of them have lead in their blood.
295. the probability that no more than three of them have lead in their blood.
296. the mean and standard deviation for the number who have lead in their blood.

Introduction to Statistics

INTRODUCTION

Descriptive versus Inferential Statistics

Statistics is the science that deals with the collection, processing, summarizing, and interpretation of data. If our only objective is to summarize data, then we use **descriptive statistics**. If, however, we wish to make inferences (draw conclusions) about other data sets similar to ours, then we use **inferential statistics**. The following data, which represent gas mileages for ten new-model compact cars at 55 mph, illustrate these ideas:

$$28.5, \ 34.2, \ 29.6, \ 26.5, \ 33.4, \ 36.8, \ 27.9, \ 41.6, \ 38.5, \ 37.4$$

If we say "half of these cars got less than 34 mpg," or "60% of these cars exceeded 30 mpg," we are using descriptive statistics. If, however, we infer that "the average miles per gallon of all imported compacts is between 30.3 and 36.5 mpg," then we are employing inferential statistics in generalizing our results to a larger data set that statisticians call a **population**.

We have mentioned the term *population* previously. The dictionary defines a population as "all people inhabiting a specific area." We shall define it in a more general way.

POPULATION

> The set of all objects under investigation and about which information is desired is called a **population**.

In most instances, it will not be the objects themselves that are of interest, but some numerical characteristic of interest associated with the outcome. This should sound familiar! This is just another way of saying that a population consists of all possible values of a random variable. In our gas-mileage example, we view the population as being the mpg figures for all new-model compact imports. The 10 data values above represent a **sample** from this population. If a sample is not representative of the population, then any generalizations we make are liable to be in error.

Why should we make statistical inferences and run the risk of being incorrect? Why not just examine the entire population? If it were possible, both in terms of effort and cost, we should do just that. Unfortunately, a typical "real-world" population is so big that we cannot examine the entire population. In addition, some populations are conceptual, and we could not examine them even if we wanted to. For example, a population may consist of the bacterial counts of all possible 1-cubic-centimeter scoops of water from the Ohio River. This population is clearly conceptual; there is no way we could examine the entire population.

As another example where it would be impossible to examine the entire population, suppose we work for a large chain of sporting goods stores, and we have an opportunity to buy 20,000 shotgun shells at an extremely low price. Should we buy? If the shells are of good quality then we probably should. But why are we being offered such a good deal? Maybe the shells are old and contain several duds. We could remove all uncertainty by checking the entire population of 20,000 shells—if the shell fires, it's good; if not, it's a dud. Unfortunately, unless we can get a government contract, we would have little chance of selling our 20,000 "used" shotgun shells! *Destructive testing* is the name given to a testing procedure which ruins an item. Thus, for one reason or another, we cannot usually examine the entire population; we need to select a sample.

Sampling   There are many ways to sample, but the only method we shall consider is called *simple random sampling*.

SIMPLE RANDOM SAMPLING

> A **simple random sample** of size n is a set of n items chosen from the population in such a way that each possible sample of size n has the same probability.

■ EXAMPLE 1

A population consists of salaries for 14 members of a university department. Give a procedure for selecting a random sample of size four from this population.

SOLUTION

We need to be sure that all possible samples of size four have the same probability. Order is of no importance, so there are $C(14,4) = 1001$ possible samples of size four. To ensure a random sample, each set of four salaries would have to have probability 1/1001. Fortunately, it would not be necessary to identify all 1001 possibilities. We could guarantee randomness by using the following procedure: **(a)** number the 14 professors from 1 to 14 by any means you wish. **(b)** Write numbers from 1 through 14 on identical-sized pieces of paper, put them in a hat, mix them thoroughly, and draw four. It makes no difference whether you choose four all at once, or select them one after the other without replacing previously drawn slips. ∎

While not always the best way, simple random sampling yields a major benefit: rules of probability apply to such samples. This will be important in determining whether or not a sample could have come from a specified population.

In this brief introduction, we have discussed several important ideas: population, sample, simple random sampling, and the basic notions of descriptive and inferential statistics. In the next section, we begin our study of descriptive statistics.

9.1 DESCRIPTIVE STATISTICS I: GRAPHICAL METHODS

The objective of descriptive statistics is to describe and/or summarize data in such a way that the salient features are easily detected. Data can be of two types: *quantitative* or *qualitative*.

TYPES OF DATA

> **Quantitative data** are ordinary numerical data that result from counting or measuring items. **Qualitative data** record characteristics or attributes of population and sample items.

■ EXAMPLE 2

Consider the following data for running backs on an NFL team:

	Running Backs for NFL Team				
No.	Name	Height	Weight	Age	Exp.
37	Aroun, Horse	6'1''	215	27	5
42	Drawback, Deep	6'	200	25	2
7	Amway, John	5'1''	285	26	3
32	Fulldeck, Notta	5'11''	232	22	0

Using this table, identify the types of data given.

SOLUTION   A player's number, although numerical, is **qualitative**, since it identifies a player uniquely but measures nothing. Height, weight, and age are all **quantitative**, continuous data since each may assume any value in some interval of the real line. (Even though age is only reported as of the most recent birthday, it is still continuous.)

Experience is quantitative discrete data—it is discrete, since only full seasons are counted when reporting experience.   ■

Graphic Displays of Data   Our main goal in this section is the following: given a large mass of unorganized data, what can we do with graphic displays to present the important features of the data? We shall use the data in the following example to illustrate several techniques.

■ EXAMPLE 3   A grammar analyst chose a random sample of 52 paragraphs from the works of a popular romance novelist and recorded the number of words in each paragraph. The data are as follows:

63 73 85 42 69 67 39 76 68 90 73 69 57

65 71 49 83 78 69 70 82 58 71 74 85 49

58 67 70 72 65 68 92 78 52 57 60 88 73

77 68 55 58 92 65 73 57 46 78 93 51 67

Summarize these data.

SOLUTION   Our first step is to construct a **frequency distribution** by dividing the data into classes and counting the number in each class. In choosing classes, it helps to know the range of the data. The low is 39 and the high is 93, so our classes should cover this extent. We arbitrarily decide to use five classes in making our frequency distribution. Since the data cover a range of $93 - 39 = 54$, then each class should cover a span of about $54/5 = 10.8$. We shall round this to 11, and use the following classes:

36–47,   48–59,   60–71,   72–83,   84–95

There is nothing sacred about these classes—we could just as well have used the following "nicer" classes:

30–39,   40–49,   50–59,   60–69,   70–79,   80–89,   90–99

But this would require seven classes. There is no one "right way" for determining either the number or location of the classes, although you need enough classes to cover the data, and there should be no trouble deciding where to put a piece of data. In both choices above, there is no ambiguity as to where an observation belongs. If, however, classes were 35–45, 45–55, etc., then you would have a real problem deciding where to put a 45, for example. *Suggestion*: Try one set of classes; if it doesn't look good, then experiment. Many statisticians suggest using between five and 20 classes. Within this range, it clearly depends on how many data points you have. When practical, use classes having the same size, as in both examples above.

Once classes are decided upon, we determine how many values are in each class. We could search the entire data set to see how many fall into the first class, and then repeat this search for each class. This is a time-consuming and error-prone procedure. It is much simpler to go through the data, one-by-one, and put a mark in the appropriate "tally" column: (Remember, we are using the first set of classes given above.)

Class	Tally	Frequency	Relative Frequency
36–47	|||	3	$3/52 \approx 0.058$
48–59	◫◫		11	$11/52 \approx 0.212$
60–71	◫◫◫ |||	18	$18/52 \approx 0.346$
72–83	◫◫ |||	13	$13/52 \approx 0.250$
84–95	◫ ||	7	$7/52 \approx 0.135$

Things are beginning to take shape. This frequency distribution is clearly more informative than the "raw" data. The majority of the data are in the three middle classes, with relatively few in the extreme classes, although the right-hand "tail" is heavier (has more data) than the left-hand tail. The column headed "relative frequency" is the important information; if someone asked the grammar analyst whether the author used small paragraphs, he could answer "three paragraphs had 47 words or less." This information is correct, but helpful *only* if you know how many paragraphs there were. Three of five would indicate that the author was prone to short, choppy paragraphs, while three out of one hundred would suggest much longer paragraphs. Using relative frequency, the analyst could say "about 6% of the paragraphs had 47 words or less." This is preferable to saying "three paragraphs had 47 words or less." The above frequency distribution with tally marks is simply a working copy. In final form, you should omit the tally column, and report only the classes, frequencies, and relative frequencies.

We know that probabilities can be interpreted as relative frequencies. We can also view relative frequencies as estimates of probabilities. The probability of an event is a parameter, since it describes the population; in particular, it measures the proportion of the population having the properties specified by the event. If, for example, we estimate that 21% of the population[1] will score between 48 and 59 on this exam, then

[1] The population we envision here is conceptual, consisting of the scores on this exam of all possible students who could ever take this course.

we are making a statistical inference, and we run the risk of being incorrect.

Observe that the frequency distribution does for a sample what a probability distribution or density does for a population—it is a convenient summary. If we want a graphical representation of our frequency distribution, we can make a **relative frequency histogram** (see Figure 9.1) by constructing a rectangle over each class, making the height of each rectangle equal to the relative frequency of that class.

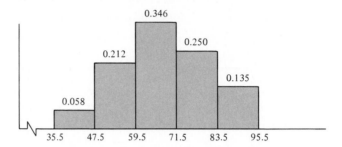

Figure 9.1
Relative frequency histogram for paragraph sizes

Two things bear comment: **(1)** The jagged line on the exam score axis indicates that the scale has been "cosmetically adjusted" so that bars of the histogram do not begin three feet to the right of the 0 mark! and **(2)** The bars over each class have been extended to cover gaps between the end of one class and the start of the next. Thus, instead of class one ending at 47 and class two beginning at 48 (leaving a gap from 47 to 48), class one is extended to 47.5, and class two is pulled back to begin at 47.5. This philosophy is followed throughout the histogram; the histogram looks better if bars are adjacent.

The shape of the histogram reflects well the features we noted in the frequency distribution, but these features are even easier to see in histogram form.

A modern technique of data analysis is a display known as a *stem-and-leaf diagram*. This is much like a histogram, but it has the added advantage that the actual data are used in "building the bars." To construct a **stem-and-leaf diagram**, we first divide each number into two parts: the first part is called a *stem* and the part following the stem is called a *leaf*. Since our data are all two-digit numbers, we shall let the stem be the first digit ("tens" digit), and the leaf be the second digit ("units" digit). A score of 47, for example, has stem "4" and leaf "7." In our data there are seven stems—namely, 3, 4, 5, 6, 7, 8, 9. We arrange the data into the diagram shown below in Figure 9.2.

This stem-and-leaf display looks like a sideways histogram; the benefit is that we see the shape and preserve the raw data as well. The stem-and-leaf display is a relatively recent technique, developed around 1970 by the famous mathematician-turned-statistician Professor John Tukey

Figure 9.2
Stem-and-leaf diagram of
paragraph sizes

Stem	Leaves
3	9
4	2 9 9 6
5	7 8 8 2 7 5 8
6	3 9 7 8 9 5 9 7 5 8 0 8 5 7
7	3 6 3 1 8 0 1 4 0 0 8 3 7 3 8
8	5 3 2 5 8
9	0 2 2 3

of Princeton University. Although quite simple, it has much to recommend it.   ■

■ EXAMPLE 4

Eligibility is a concern in collegiate sports. At Anemia Tech, academic standards are especially rigorous—a G.P.A. of 1.8 is required. With this stiff requirement, G.P.A.'s for Delmo and the other 39 members of the varsity sock-matching team are under constant scrutiny. The latest grades are out and listed below:

   2.26 1.97 2.16 2.43 1.85 2.14 2.28 2.36 1.94 2.25

   2.12 2.23 2.33 1.76 2.15 2.37 2.41 1.86 2.13 1.74

   2.34 2.24 1.92 1.83 2.03 2.04 2.35 1.98 2.01 2.00

   2.05 2.09 2.01 2.02 2.29 2.19 2.02 2.06 2.44 2.17

Display these data with a stem-and-leaf diagram.

SOLUTION

With data like these, we use the first two digits as the stem and let the leaf be the last digit. The display is shown below:

Stem	Leaves
1.7	6 4
1.8	5 6 3
1.9	7 4 2 8
2.0	3 4 1 0 5 9 1 2 2 6
2.1	6 4 2 5 3 9 7
2.2	6 8 5 3 4 9
2.3	6 3 7 4 5
2.4	3 1 4

From this display it is apparent that most of the team will be eligible for next quarter's revelries. Delmo, with a G.P.A. of 1.74, is relegated to being the nonplaying Captain!   ■

Comparing Samples from Different Populations

A stem-and-leaf diagram can also be used to compare samples from different populations, as discussed in the next example.

■ EXAMPLE 5

A large group of college students was asked the nature of their diet and food patterns. A random sample of 25 students was then taken from the group that said their diet was heavy in animal fat and dairy products. A second random sample of 25 was taken from the group that claimed to be largely vegetarian. The serum total cholesterol level was then measured for each of the two groups. Are the serum total cholesterol levels for these groups comparable, or do those with the vegetarian diet have lower levels?

Animal fat and dairy products	178 135 228 244 256 228 209
	203 244 258 190 211 167
	237 207 225 187 195 225
	214 216 215 218 149 205
Vegetarian diet	145 97 105 137 167 148 124
	123 128 114 120 128 137
	154 167 132 104 119 121
	141 115 127 119 113 108

A "two-way" stem-and-leaf display of cholesterol samples for the samples from each group is shown in Figure 9.3.

Animal Fat and Dairy Products	Stem	Vegetarian Diet
	9	7
	10	5 4 8
	11	9 4 5 9 3
	12	1 3 0 8 7 4 8
5	13	7 2 7
9	14	5 8 1
	15	4
7	16	7 7
8	17	
7	18	
0 5	19	
5 3 9 7	20	
8 5 6 4 1	21	
5 5 8 8	22	
7	23	
4 4	24	
8 6	25	
	26	

Figure 9.3
Two-way stem-and-leaf display

The stem-and-leaf display makes it apparent that the group with the diet high in animal fats and dairy products has far more cholesterol than the vegetarian group. Even so, this does not imply that the animal fats and dairy products in the diet are responsible. ■

EXERCISES 9.1

PRACTICING THE MOVES AND MANEUVERS

Exercises 1–5: Use the following data representing percentage yields for 40 money market mutual funds:

5.4 5.6 5.4 5.3 5.6 5.5 5.8 6.1 5.5 5.9 5.8 6.0 5.6 5.3 5.5 6.2 5.3 5.5 5.5 5.6

6.2 5.6 6.3 5.2 6.4 5.5 5.8 5.2 5.9 5.3 5.8 6.4 5.1 5.5 6.0 6.1 5.6 5.9 6.2 5.8

1. Construct a relative frequency distribution. Use five classes of equal width.
2. Construct a relative frequency distribution. Use six classes of equal width.
3. Construct a relative frequency histogram, using the classes of Exercise 1.
4. Construct a relative frequency histogram, using the classes of Exercise 2.
5. Construct a stem-and-leaf display.

Exercises 6–10: Use the following data representing ages of a random sample of 42 assistant professors at Anemia Tech:

67 71 59 77 71 86 69 34 73 81 67 68 71 65 69 70 72 81 77 76 68

71 73 68 62 63 60 61 68 58 58 63 71 57 78 81 73 67 62 78 64 66

6. Construct a relative frequency distribution. Use six classes of equal width.
7. Construct a relative frequency distribution. Use fives classes of equal width.
8. Construct a relative frequency histogram using the classes of Exercise 6.
9. Construct a relative frequency histogram using the classes of Exercise 7.
10. Construct a stem-and-leaf display.

Exercises 11–15: Use the following data, which represent heights in centimeters of a random sample of 34 10-year-old "Colorado" Blue Spruce trees at a tree farm:

175 189 167 178 184 166 176 177 159 170 184 166 160 149 190 177 168

169 163 154 158 170 176 159 174 170 165 160 162 178 168 182 177 177

11. Construct a relative frequency distribution. Use four classes of equal width.
12. Construct a relative frequency distribution. Use five classes of equal width.
13. Construct a relative frequency histogram using the classes of Exercise 11.
14. Construct a relative frequency histogram using the classes of Exercise 12.
15. Construct a stem-and-leaf display.

Exercises 16–18: Use the following data, which represent burning times prior to failure of sixty 75-watt light bulbs:

540 460 479 664 855 776 657 745 685 635 587 396 487 566 487 645

543 662 557 775 687 745 705 697 577 634 701 634 523 476 515 692

466 567 713 487 645 543 577 656 802 765 675 587 634 388 467 558

557 512 467 478 543 567 674 612 634 661 540 610

16. Construct a relative frequency distribution. Use six classes of equal width.

17. Construct a relative frequency histogram using the classes in Exercise 16.
18. Construct a stem-and-leaf display.

19. The following data represent annual rental rates ($/square foot) at two malls in different cities. Use a "two-way" stem-and-leaf display to compare these samples. Is it likely that these samples come from different populations?

Yakima, WA	Los Angeles, CA
6.45 6.78 5.75 6.35	4.45 5.35 4.86 5.50
6.75 6.00 7.15 5.95	4.00 4.25 3.95 4.12
7.60 6.85 7.55 6.75	4.85 4.35 3.85 4.15
7.45 6.45 6.50 7.20	3.90 4.20 4.56 4.40
7.85 6.50 6.85 7.25	5.35 4.95 4.65 4.35
6.50 6.45 7.45 7.24	4.35 4.85 5.15 4.95

Exercises 20–22: Use the data below, which represent wind velocity measurements at the summit of Mt. Rainier on May 15 for the last 28 years:

21 25 34 18 17 3 21 24 32 20 17 25 27 26 23 30 9 24 19 16 17 26 23 17 29 25 12 10

20. Construct a relative frequency distribution by using five classes of equal width.
21. Construct a relative frequency histogram using the classes of Exercise 19.
22. Construct a stem-and-leaf display.

9.2 DESCRIPTIVE STATISTICS II: MEASURES OF CENTRAL TENDENCY

In Chapter 8, we described and summarized populations of values of random variables. We have already seen that similar things can be done with samples. In particular, *a relative frequency distribution is the sample analogue of a probability distribution or a probability density function.* In describing populations, we went beyond the probability distribution to find even more concise summary measures provided by parameters such as the mean (or expected value) of the random variable. We now look for similar ways to describe samples.

STATISTIC

A **statistic** is a quantity calculated from a sample. A statistic has two main uses:

1. A statistic can be used to describe a sample.

2. A statistic can be used to make inferences about the corresponding population parameter.

In most samples there is a tendency for data to cluster about some central point. This phenomenon, known as "central tendency," suggests that the value of a centrally located statistic could describe the entire sample. Statistics whose function it is to describe the center of a sample are called **measures of central tendency**. Many statistics could be used for this purpose. A logical first choice is the *sample mean*.

SAMPLE MEAN

> If $x_1, \ldots, x_n$ represent the n items in a random sample of size n, then the **sample mean**, denoted by $\overline{X}$, is their sum divided by n:
>
> $$\overline{X} = \frac{\sum X_i}{n}$$

Note: We shall often drop the subscript i on $\sum X_i$ and write just $\sum X$. Similarly, we will write $\sum X_i^2$ as $\sum X^2$, it being understood that *all* X-values in the sample are to be used.

If, for example, you have scores of 76, 82, 69, and 91 on your finite math exams, then your mean score is

$$\overline{X} = \frac{76 + 82 + 69 + 91}{4} = \frac{318}{4} = 79.5$$

PRACTICE PROBLEM 1   In Example 3, find the mean paragraph length for this particular romance novelist.

ANSWER(S) $\overline{X} = 68.365$ ☐

In addition to the mean, many other statistics describe the center of a sample, including the *sample median, M*.

SAMPLE MEDIAN

> If the sample size n is an odd integer, then the **sample median**, denoted by M, is the middle number when the data are arranged in order. If the sample size n is even, there is no one middle number; the median is taken to be the average of the two middle-most numbers.

When the data are put in an **array** (the data set ordered from smallest to largest), the middle number is the observation located at position $(n + 1)/2$ in the array. This calculated position will be an integer when the sample size n is odd. When n is even, the value $(n + 1)/2$ will be halfway between two integers. This is why we average the two middle-most numbers when the sample size is even. Try the following example.

■ EXAMPLE 6

In the first paragraph of this chapter, we had ten measurements representing gas mileage at 55 miles per hour. These data are:

$$28.5, \ 34.2, \ 29.6, \ 26.5, \ 33.4, \ 36.8, \ 27.9, \ 41.6, \ 38.5, \ 37.4$$

Find the sample mean and median.

SOLUTION

To find the median, we first construct the array, getting

$$26.5, \ 27.9, \ 28.5, \ 29.6, \ 33.4, \ 34.2, \ 36.8, \ 37.4, \ 38.5, \ 41.6$$

Since the sample size n is 10, the halfway position is $(10 + 1)/2 = 5.5$. With no observation at position 5.5, we average the observations at positions 5 and 6 (these are the two middle numbers 33.4 and 34.2), obtaining a sample median of 33.8. Averaging the ten numbers, we find that the sample mean is:

$$\overline{X} = \frac{\Sigma \ X_i}{10} = \frac{334.4}{10} = 33.44$$

The mean and median being almost the same, as they are here, indicates **symmetry** in the data. (With symmetry, the distribution looks the same on the right side of the "middle" as it does on the left.) When the sample mean and median are not close in value, this suggests **skewness** (a lack of symmetry). ■

PRACTICE PROBLEM 2

Find the median for the data in Examples 3 and 4.

ANSWER(S)

For Example 3, $M = 69$; for Example 4, $M = 2.125$. □

In addition to the mean and median, there are other statistics that measure central tendency. The **sample mode** is the most frequent value in the sample. When the data have been summarized with a frequency distribution, the mode is the midpoint of the class having the greatest frequency. Sometimes, however, the mode does not exist. For the above gas mileage data, there is no mode, as no value appears more than once. A sample can also have many modes, none of which may be good descriptions. Only on rare occasions is a mode useful. For example, if a shoe store is given a special price in return for ordering only one size, then the modal size would be a good choice as it would fit the most people. (Not many people wear a mean shoe size of 9.413468!) We'll say no more about the mode.

Comparing the Mean and Median

There are many other ways of describing "central tendency," but in a first exposure to statistics, knowledge of the mean and median is sufficient. Since the median and the mean both describe "middle," it is reasonable to ask which is better. The next example helps to answer that question.

■ EXAMPLE 7

The faculty of the Sofa Burning and Steam Engine Repair Department at Anemia Tech is up in arms, claiming they are grossly underpaid. In response to requests for a salary increase, the administration suggests that the department ought to be content—after all, the average department salary is $25,000, which puts Anemia Tech's department right up there with the truly great ones like Harvard, Yale, Pomona, Stanford, and Eastern Bologna Tech. To these comments, the faculty scoffs, claiming the median salary is only $4500. Who is right?

SOLUTION

At a hearing with the provost, the department chair presents the departmental salaries, which are as follows:

$4500, $3720, $4800, $4960, $149,400, $3750, $3870

The chairman skillfully arrays the data, arriving at:

$3720, $3750, $3870, $4500, $4800, $4960, $149,400

With painstaking care, he points out that, since there is an odd number of faculty members (all the faculty members are odd!), the median is the middle value, or $4500. Having made his case, the chairperson smiles smugly, taking his seat next to a bronze statue of Beauregard Blatant, inventor of the self-propelled streetlight.

Does the chairperson's contention indicate that the administration is wrong? Let's check. The administration claim is that the "average salary" is $25,000. Summing the data and dividing by seven, we find that the sample mean $\overline{X}$ is $175,000/7 = $25,000.

Both the chairperson and the administration are correct! The large discrepancy between the mean and the median is due to the one extraordinarily large salary of $149,400. Further study reveals that this is the salary of Bewfus Pewterdinkle, the only legitimate son of Arf Pewterdinkle, president of Anemia Tech. Even though Bewfus is legitimate, his salary isn't; it has the effect of grossly distorting the picture. In computing the mean, the extreme value $149,400 has distributed itself over all the other pieces of data. The mean salary of $25,000 is correct, but it is not representative of the data—in fact, six-sevenths of the sample data have values less than one-fifth of the mean!   ■

You have just seen one disadvantage that a mean may have as a descriptive measure—*it is overly sensitive to extreme values* (either large or small). The median, on the other hand, is not susceptible to extremes, and is thus preferable to the mean as a descriptive statistic in the presence of extremes. Since the median ignores all but the middle of the data, it is not as good as the mean when there are no extremes. Rather than choosing between a mean and a median, however, it is recommended that you report both. A large discrepancy between them is valuable information and serves to illustrate skewness in the data.

For example, if the mean is less than the median, then the data must be skewed to the left, as shown in Figure 9.4. Similarly, if the mean is larger than the median, then the data exhibit right-hand skewness as shown in Figure 9.5.

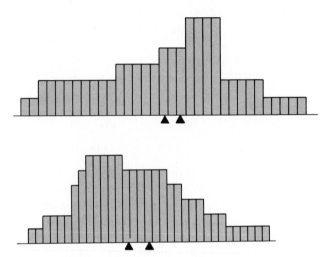

Figure 9.4
Left-hand skewness
(mean < median)

Figure 9.5
Right-hand skewness
(mean > median)

In general, we can state that the mean is always on the long-tailed side of the median.

Note: When you encounter extremes in data, it is a good idea to check them. An extreme value could be an **outlier**—a value that is suspect because it is either conspicuously large or small. Such an observation may have been recorded in error, or it could be from a different population. Such values should be investigated carefully; only when there is justification (recording error, for example) should such an observation be discarded.

A final note: The sample mean has drawbacks as a purely descriptive statistic, but for making statistical inferences, the sample mean is the single most important measure of central tendency. Although we will only scratch the surface of statistical inference, you should be aware of the importance of the sample mean in making statistical inferences.

EXERCISES 9.2

PRACTICING THE MOVES AND MANEUVERS

23. Find the sample mean and median for the following sample of size 10 representing yardage per game of a running back in the NFL:

    87 76 113 98 145 123 95 134 45 78

24. The data below are pulse rates for 12 finite math students after an exam.

    86 76 89 77 67 36 76 69 98 88 104 98

    Find the sample mean and median for these data.

25. The data from Exercises 1–5, representing money market yields, are reproduced below. Find the sample mean and median.

    5.4 5.6 5.4 5.3 5.6 5.5 5.8 6.1 5.5 5.9 5.8 6.0 5.6 5.3 5.5 6.2 5.3 5.5 5.5 5.6

    6.2 5.6 6.3 5.2 6.4 5.5 5.8 5.2 5.9 5.3 5.8 6.4 5.1 5.5 6.0 6.1 5.6 5.9 6.2 5.8

26. Shown below are the data from Exercises 6–10, representing ages of a sample of assistant professors at Anemia Tech. Find the sample mean and median.

    67 71 59 77 71 86 69 34 73 81 71 73 68 62 63 60 61 68 58 58 66

    67 68 71 65 69 70 72 81 77 76 68 63 71 57 78 81 73 67 62 78 64

27. Given below are the heights in centimeters of Colorado Blue Spruce trees from Exercises 11–14. Find the sample mean and median.

    175 189 167 178 184 166 176 177 169 163 154 158 170 176 159 174 177

    159 170 184 166 160 149 190 177 168 170 165 160 162 178 168 182 177

28. The burning times before failure of 75-watt light bulbs are reproduced below. Find the sample mean and median for these data.

    540 460 479 664 855 776 657 745 685 635 587 396 487 566 487

    543 662 557 775 687 745 705 697 577 634 701 634 523 476 515

    466 567 713 487 645 543 577 656 802 765 675 587 634 388 467

    557 512 467 478 543 567 674 612 634 661 540 610 645 692 558

29. Reproduced below are data from Exercise 19, representing rental rates. Find the sample mean and median for the Yakima, WA, data.

Yakima, WA	Los Angeles, CA
6.45 6.78 5.75 6.35	4.45 5.35 4.86 5.50
6.75 6.00 7.15 5.95	4.00 4.25 3.95 4.12
7.60 6.85 7.55 6.75	4.85 4.35 3.85 4.15
7.45 6.45 6.50 7.20	3.90 4.20 4.56 4.40
7.85 6.50 6.85 7.25	5.35 4.95 4.65 4.35
6.50 6.45 7.45 7.24	4.35 4.85 5.15 4.95

30. In Exercise 29, find the sample mean and median for the Los Angeles data.
31. Reproduced below are the data from Exercise 20, representing wind velocity measurements on the summit of Mt. Rainier. Find the sample mean and median.

    21 25 34 18 17 3 21 24 32 20 17 25 27 26

    29 25 12 10 23 30 9 24 19 16 17 26 23 17

9.3 DESCRIPTIVE STATISTICS III: MEASURES OF DISPERSION

In the previous section we discussed measures of central tendency. In particular, we looked at the sample mean and median as ways of describing the "center" of a sample. When describing populations in Chapter 8, we decided that the mean would be a good descriptive parameter if the distribution was concentrated tightly about the mean. We measured dispersion about the mean by using the parameters σ^2 and σ—the population variance and standard deviation. When describing samples, we should see if the sample mean provides a good description of the entire sample. The answer is just as it was with the population mean: If the data are tightly packed around $\overline{X}$, then $\overline{X}$ will be a good, single-number description of the entire sample. Sample analogues of σ^2 and σ are the statistics S^2 and S, the *sample variance* and *sample standard deviation*.

SAMPLE VARIANCE AND STANDARD DEVIATION

For a random sample of size n, the **sample variance**, S^2, is the sum of squared deviations about the sample mean, divided by $n - 1$:

$$S^2 = \frac{\sum (X_i - \overline{X})^2}{n - 1}$$

The **sample standard deviation**, S, is the positive square root of the sample variance.

Looking at the formula (we call this the "definition formula") for S^2, it can be seen that S^2 is almost the average of the squared deviations—if the $n - 1$ in the denominator were an n, then it would be. Why the $n - 1$ instead of n? In addition to describing sample variability, S^2 is often used to estimate the (usually) unknown population variance, σ^2. Dividing by $n - 1$, rather than n, produces an estimate that is closer, on the average, to σ^2.

Another measure of dispersion is the sample **range**, which is the positive difference between the largest and smallest sample values. The range is easy to compute, but it ignores all but the extreme values. In addition, if one of the extremes happens to be an outlier, then the range is not useful. A case in point is Arf Pewterdinkle's $149,400 salary in Example 7. With this salary included, the range is $149{,}400 - 3720 = 145{,}680$; when this observation is removed, the range is only $4960 - 3720 = 1240$. The range is typically not as useful as the standard deviation in describing dispersion, but as you will see in the next section, it sometimes affords a quick way of estimating the sample standard deviation.

■ EXAMPLE 8

The total number of runs scored by American League West teams on 10 consecutive nights of baseball is shown below.

$$23, \ 45, \ 54, \ 66, \ 47, \ 66, \ 87, \ 76, \ 31, \ 48$$

Find the sample variance and standard deviation.

SOLUTION

To use the formula for S^2, we need $\overline{X}$, which is 54.3. The sample variance is found by subtracting the mean from each observation, squaring, accumulating, and then dividing by $n - 1 = 9$:

$$S^2 = [(23 - 54.3)^2 + (45 - 54.3)^2 + (54 - 54.3)^2 + (66 - 54.3)^2$$
$$+ \ (47 - 54.3)^2 + (66 - 54.3)^2 + (87 - 54.3)^2 + (76 - 54.3)^2$$
$$+ \ (31 - 54.3)^2 + (48 - 54.3)^2]/9 \approx 390.667$$
$$S \approx \sqrt{390.67} \approx 19.766$$

■

Just as there was an easier way to compute the population variance σ^2, so also is there an easier way to compute S^2.

COMPUTING FORMULA FOR S^2

The sample variance S^2 may be computed by using the following formula:

$$S^2 = \frac{\sum X^2 - \dfrac{(\sum X)^2}{n}}{n - 1}$$

At first glance, this may not look like a better way, but this computing formula has several things going for it. In the "definition" formula, you have to subtract $\overline{X}$ from each value and then square the resulting deviation from the mean. This requires n subtractions, and, if you "round off" before squaring, you will compound the loss of accuracy made in rounding. The computing formula requires only one subtraction—making the computing task much simpler and also minimizing round-off errors. Note that to use the computing formula, you need only three quantities: n, ΣX^2, and ΣX. Let's try it on Example 8.

$$\Sigma X^2 = 23^2 + 45^2 + 54^2 + \cdots + 48^2 = 33001 \quad \Sigma X = 543$$

$$n = 10$$

Plugging these into the computing formula gives

$$S^2 = \frac{(33001) - \frac{(543)^2}{10}}{9} = \frac{33001 - 29484.9}{9} = 390.667$$

which is what we obtained by using the definition formula.

The Empirical Rule   Measures of dispersion give us an idea of spread of the data about the mean. Using Chebyshev's Theorem, which also applies to samples, we can describe where much of the data lie by using only the mean and standard deviation. Chebyshev's Rules, as mentioned previously, tend to be quite conservative—when we claim that at least 75% of a set of data is within two standard deviations of the mean, the actual percentage is apt to be much larger. Through observation of many data sets, statisticians have discovered that if a data set is "mound-shaped," then more useful descriptive statements can be made. Samples of data from a normal probability distribution are likely to exhibit such a mound shape. Other probability distributions besides the normal have this feature as well. When this is the case, you can use the following *Empirical Rule* to help describe your data.

THE EMPIRICAL RULE

If a set of data is *mound-shaped*, then you can say that:

1. Approximately 68% of the values in the data set are between $\overline{X} - S$ and $\overline{X} + S$, that is, within one standard deviation of the mean.

2. Approximately 95% of the values are between $\overline{X} - 2S$ and $\overline{X} + 2S$, that is, within two standard deviations of the mean.

3. Virtually all the data are between $\overline{X} - 3S$ and $\overline{X} + 3S$, that is, within three standard deviations of the mean. ("Virtually all" means that typically, in a set of 1000 observations, you might see two or three that are *not* within three standard deviations of the mean.)

Recalling what we know about the normal distribution, these statements should seem plausible. The Empirical Rule, however, applies not only to normal distributions but also to other mound-shaped distributions, even some that are moderately skewed.

■ EXAMPLE 9

The professor of the 11 A.M. section of Advanced Shoelace Repair at Anemia Tech is upset—his entire class comes from a building far across campus. Most students seem to take longer than the allotted 10 minutes between classes. Perplexed, the professor does a scientific study of times required by his class. He discovers that his data are mound-shaped with $\overline{X}$ = 12.5 minutes and S = 2.4 minutes. In addition, he notes that the median is 11.8 minutes. Use this information to describe the data.

SOLUTION   Using the Empirical Rule, we can say that:

1. About 68% of the students take between $12.5 - 2.4 = 10.1$ minutes and $12.5 + 2.4 = 14.9$ minutes to get to class.

2. About 95% of the students take between $12.5 - 4.8 = 7.7$ minutes and $12.5 + 4.8 = 17.3$ minutes to get to class.

3. Virtually all of the students take between $12.5 - 7.2 = 5.3$ minutes and $12.5 + 7.2 = 19.7$ minutes to get to class.

In addition, the median is somewhat smaller than the mean, indicating right-hand skewing, presumably due to a few students taking excessively long to make the journey. A rough sketch of the distribution for travel times is shown in Figure 9.6.

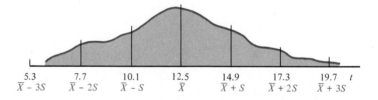

Figure 9.6
Between-class travel times

| 5.3 | 7.7 | 10.1 | 12.5 | 14.9 | 17.3 | 19.7 t |
| $\overline{X} - 3S$ | $\overline{X} - 2S$ | $\overline{X} - S$ | $\overline{X}$ | $\overline{X} + S$ | $\overline{X} + 2S$ | $\overline{X} + 3S$ |

A Quick Approximation for S   The Empirical Rule also provides a quick way to approximate a sample standard deviation. Since virtually all data are within three standard deviations of the mean, then the difference between the largest and smallest observations should span a range of about six standard deviations. This suggests approximating S with the following procedure: calculate the **range** (largest value minus the smallest), and divide by six. But this works well only for sample sizes of 200 or more. For sample sizes between 50 and 199, you get a better approximation by dividing the range by 5. For sample sizes of 16 through 49, you do better yet by dividing by 4. For sample sizes of 15 or less, you can do remarkably well in approximating S by dividing the range by the square root of sample size. In summary:

Sample Size n	Range Approximation for S
$n \geq 200$	$\dfrac{\text{Range}}{6}$
$50 \leq n \leq 199$	$\dfrac{\text{Range}}{5}$
$16 \leq n \leq 49$	$\dfrac{\text{Range}}{4}$
$n \leq 15$	$\dfrac{\text{Range}}{\sqrt{n}}$

Let's try this approximation on Example 8. We found that S was 19.766. Using our "range estimate," we get $(87 - 23)/\sqrt{10} \approx 20.238$. This approximation is off by about 2%. This range estimate or range approximation for S provides you with an extremely quick check on your calculations, and it also enables you to approximate S when a calculator is not handy.

EXERCISES 9.3

PRACTICING THE MOVES AND MANEUVERS

Exercises 32–34: Consider the following data, which represent systolic blood pressure measurements for a person's blood pressure on ten consecutive days. Find the:

85 70 74 69 72 76 87 73 84 75

32. sample mean and median.
33. sample variance and sample standard deviation.
34. sample range, and the range approximation for S.

Exercises 35–40: Use the data from Example 2, repeated below. Consider these data to be a random sample from the population of all NFL running backs.

No.	Name	Height	Weight	Age	Exp.
37	Aroun, Horse	6'1"	215	27	5
42	Drawback, Deep	6'	200	25	2
7	Amway, John	5'1"	285	26	3
32	Fulldeck, Notta	5'11"	232	22	0

35. Find the mean and median of the weights.
36. Find the variance and standard deviation of the weights.
37. Approximate the standard deviation of weights by using the range.
38. Find the mean and median of the ages.
39. Find the variance and standard deviation of the ages.
40. Approximate the standard deviations of ages by using the range.

Exercises 41–44: Use the data shown below, which represent annual rental rates ($/square foot) at malls in two cities. (Data are from Exercise 19.)

Yakima, WA	Los Angeles, CA
6.45 6.78 5.75 6.35	4.45 5.35 4.86 5.50
6.75 6.00 7.15 5.95	4.00 4.25 3.95 4.12
7.60 6.85 7.55 6.75	4.85 4.35 3.85 4.15
7.45 6.45 6.50 7.20	3.90 4.20 4.56 4.40
7.85 6.50 6.85 7.25	5.35 4.95 4.65 4.35
6.50 6.45 7.45 7.24	4.35 4.85 5.15 4.95

41. Find the sample variance and standard deviation for the Yakima, WA, data.
42. Find the range and range approximation for S for the Yakima, WA, data.
43. Find the sample variance and standard deviation for the Los Angeles data.
44. Find the range and range approximation for S for the Los Angeles data.

45. Find the variance, standard deviation, range, and range approximation for S using wind velocity measurements on Mt. Rainier, shown below:

    21 25 34 18 17 3 21 24 32 20 17 25 27 26

    25 12 10 23 30 9 24 19 16 17 26 23 17 29

Exercises 46–48: Use the Colorado Blue Spruce height data from Exercise 27, reproduced below.

    175 189 167 178 184 166 176 177 159 169 163 154 158 170 176 159 174

    170 184 166 160 149 190 177 168 165 160 162 178 168 182 177 177 170

46. Find the variance and standard deviation for this sample.
47. Find the range and range approximation for S.
48. Calculate the three intervals $\bar{X} \pm S$, $\bar{X} \pm 2S$, and $\bar{X} \pm 3S$. Determine what proportion of the data falls in these intervals and compare the results with those given by the Empirical Rule.

Exercises 49 and 50: Use the following data from Exercise 23, representing yardage per game measurements for an NFL running back.

    87 76 113 98 145 123 95 134 45 78

49. Find the sample variance and standard deviation.
50. Find the sample range, and the range approximation for S.

9.4 MEASURING RELATIVE STANDING: TUKEY'S FIVE-NUMBER SUMMARY AND BOX PLOTS

Measures of central tendency describe clustering, and measures of dispersion describe concentration of the data about middle values. Being able to compare observations within the same data set (population or sample) is also of interest. We have encountered one such measure of relative standing when we studied z-scores in Chapter 8. We saw that a z-score was a way of measuring performance relative to the mean, measured in terms of standard deviations. In Chapter 8, we discussed z-scores only for populations, but they are equally effective for samples. If x is a sample value, then the corresponding z-score is $(x - \overline{X})/S$.

PRACTICE PROBLEM 3

A random sample of weights for nine tight ends in the NFL was:

234, 229, 245, 255, 230, 225, 237, 240, 232

(a) Using the range estimate for S, find the z-score for the tight end weighing 240 pounds.

(b) Repeat part (a), but actually calculate S.

ANSWER(S) $\overline{X} = 236.33$; range estimate for S is $30/\sqrt{9} = 10$; $S = 9.25$. **(a)** 0.37; **(b)** 0.40.   □

Percentiles and Quartiles

Another measure of relative standing is the *percentile ranking* of a score. If your height on your 18th birthday placed you at the 95th percentile, that means 95% of all eighteen-year olds had heights less than or equal to yours; only 5% had heights greater than or equal to yours. Certain percentile measurements known as *quartiles* are quite helpful in summarizing a data set.

PERCENTILES AND QUARTILES

> The pth **percentile** in a data set is a value such that $p\%$ of the data fall at or below this value, while $(100 - p)\%$ of the data are at or above this value. The 25th, 50th, and 75th percentiles are called **quartiles** because they divide the data into four zones, each having 25% of the distribution. The 25th percentile is called the first or **lower quartile**, Q_1, while the 75th percentile is called the third or **upper quartile**, Q_3. The second quartile is the median.

Percentiles and quartiles are used primarily to describe large data sets. Quartiles are especially useful in that they combine information about location and dispersion. We shall calculate only quartiles; other percentiles can be calculated in a similar way. Figure 9.7 illustrates quartiles of a distribution. As you can see, quartiles are not necessarily equally

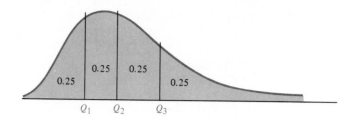

Figure 9.7
Quartiles of a distribution

spaced; they separate data into four nonoverlapping zones of equal probability (for a population) or relative frequency (for a sample).

Calculating Quartiles Here is a simple way to calcuiate quartiles,[2] similar to the way we calculated the median, a procedure we now review. The median is the obser-
vation at position $(n + 1)/2$ in the array. This position number is either a
whole number (when the sample size is odd) or halfway between two
consecutive whole numbers (when the sample size is even). The first
quartile, Q_1, is the observation at position $(n + 1)/4$. This is intuitively
reasonable, as it locates Q_1 halfway between the smallest observation
and the median. If the calculated value of $(n + 1)/4$ is an integer, then we
use the data value at that position as Q_1. If the calculated value is not an
integer, it will end in either .25, .50, or .75. This ending decimal tells us
how far we need to go between consecutive positions to locate Q_1. For
example, if there are $n = 9$ observations in our sample, then Q_1 is located
at position $(9 + 1)/4 = 2.5$. The first quartile is then halfway between the
second and third observations in the array. Similarly, Q_3 is at position
$3(n + 1)/4$.

In Practice Problem 3 (weights of NFL tight ends), the sample size
was 9. The array is 225, 229, 230, 232, 234, 237, 240, 245, and 255. The
second and third values are 229 and 230. Halfway between these two
(that is, position 2.5) is 229.5. Thus, $Q_1 = 229.5$.

PRACTICE PROBLEM 4 For the NFL tight end data, find Q_3, the third quartile.

ANSWER(S) $Q_3 = 242.5$.   ☐

Interquartile Range We add another measure of variability to our list. The **interquartile
range** (IQR) is the difference between the first and third quartiles, computed as IQR $= Q_3 - Q_1$ in order to produce a nonnegative number. The
interquartile range is the length of the gap spanned by the middle half of
the data. Unlike the range, the interquartile range is concerned only
with the middle of the data, and is not generally affected by extreme

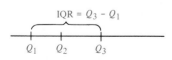

[2] Statisticians do not always agree on the proper way to compute quartiles in a small data set. The method we
describe is used by many statisticians, and is the method employed by MINITAB.

values. For this reason, the IQR is a good way of measuring variability. Because of their insensitivity to extremes, both the median and the interquartile range are said to be **robust**. The sample mean $\overline{X}$ and standard deviation S are *not* robust statistics as they are strongly influenced by the presence of extremes. The following example illustrates these notions.

EXAMPLE 10

Consider the following random sample: 24, 14, 19, 28, 25, 37, 29.

(a) Find the sample mean, the quartiles, IQR and S.

(b) Suppose the largest value "37" has been incorrectly recorded as 3.7. Redo part (a) with this change.

(c) Suppose "37" has been wrongly recorded as "377." Redo (a).

(d) Suppose "37" has been wrongly recorded as "3777." Redo (a).

SOLUTION

(a) Arraying the data gives: 14, 19, 24, 25, 28, 29, 37. The sample mean $\overline{X}$ is $176/7 \approx 25.14$. The median is at position $(7 + 1)/2 = 4$; hence, $M = 25$. Q_1 is the observation at position $(n + 1)/4$. Here, $(n + 1)/4 = 2$, indicating that Q_1 is the second observation in the array: $Q_1 = 19$. The upper quartile Q_3 is the observation at position $3(n + 1)/4 = 6$ in the array: $Q_3 = 29$. The interquartile range is IQR $= Q_3 - Q_1 = 29 - 19 = 10$. To calculate S, we shall use the computing formula, which requires ΣX and ΣX^2. The necessary values are $\Sigma X = 176$ and $\Sigma X^2 = 4752$. Substituting these into the computing formula for S^2 gives $S^2 \approx 54.476$; the standard deviation is then $\sqrt{54.476} \approx 7.38$.

(b) Replacing the correct value of "37" by "3.7" results in the following array: 3.7, 14, 19, 24, 25, 28, 29. The summary statistics now are as follows (verify these):

$$\overline{X} \approx 20.39; \quad M = 24; \quad Q_1 = 14; \quad Q_3 = 28; \quad \text{IQR} = 14; \quad S \approx 9.02$$

(c) Replacing "37" by "377" leads to the following array:

14, 19, 24, 25, 28, 29, 377

The summary statistics (verify these) become:

$$\overline{X} \approx 73.7; \quad M = 25; \quad Q_1 = 19.0; \quad Q_3 = 29; \quad \text{IQR} = 10; \quad S \approx 133.8$$

(d) Replacing "37" by "3777" (which could happen with a phenomenon known as "keyboard bounce") leads to the array: 14, 19, 24, 25, 28, 29, 3777. The summary statistics are:

$$\overline{X} \approx 559.4; \quad M = 25; \quad Q_1 = 19; \quad Q_3 = 29; \quad \text{IQR} = 10; \quad S \approx 1418.8$$

At this point, the following summary table is helpful:

Data Set	$\overline{X}$	M	S	IQR
14,19,24,25,28,29,37	25.14	25	7.38	10
14,19,24,25,28,29,3.7	20.39	24	9.02	14
14,19,24,25,28,29,377	73.71	25	133.8	10
14,19,24,25,28,29,3777	559.4	25	1418.8	10

It is easy to see the "robust" nature of both M and IQR, while the more well-known values of $\overline{X}$ and S are not at all robust.   ■

Tukey's Five-Number Summary

A brief, extremely convenient way of summarizing a data set is provided by stating the minimum, the maximum, and the three quartiles. These five values form **Tukey's Five-Number Summary**.

■ EXAMPLE 11

A random sample of speeds for 100 cars on a 65 mph maximum speed freeway section yields the following five-number summary:

$$\text{minimum} = 58, \quad Q_1 = 61, \quad M = 64, \quad Q_3 = 70, \quad \text{maximum} = 84$$

Henceforth, we write these five in the form (58,61,64,70,84). Interpret these data.

SOLUTION

All cars were traveling between 58 and 84 mph. "$M = 64$" indicates that there are as many cars going 64 mph or more as there are cars going 64 mph or less. The middle 50% of the drivers were going between 61 and 70; there were as many driving less than 61 as there were greater than 70. Furthermore, since the gap between Q_1 and M is only 3, while the gap between M and Q_3 is 6, there is an indication of right-hand (long tail to the right) skewness. In addition, the maximum is much farther above the median than the minimum is below the median, which further reinforces the right-hand skewness, indicating the mean speed is probably greater than median speed 64. A rough picture of a distribution suggested by these summary statistics is shown in Figure 9.8.   ■

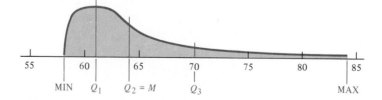

Figure 9.8
Distribution illustrating
Example 11

Box-and-Whisker Plots

A simple, but highly effective graphical version of the Five-Number summary is provided by a **box-and-whisker plot** (commonly shortened to "box plot"). In Figure 9.9, we present a simplified version of this plot[3] for Example 11. The "box" is drawn from Q_1 to Q_3, with the vertical line inside the box representing location of the median, which is the second quartile. The "whiskers" are the horizontal lines that emanate from the box, the left-hand whisker reaching down to the minimum value, and the right-hand whisker proceeding upward to the maximum value.

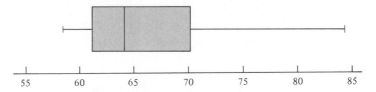

Figure 9.9
Box-and-whisker plot for
Example 11

All comments made earlier are confirmed by this plot. Lack of symmetry is evidenced by the median line being off center in the box. The length of the right whisker, relative to the left, is further substantiation of the right-hand skewness.

■ EXAMPLE 12

Weekly amounts, to the nearest dollar, spent on gasoline by a two-car family of commuters are recorded for 15 weeks, giving

47, 54, 49, 52, 53, 55, 48, 54, 57, 51, 52, 56, 49, 50, 52

Describe these data.

SOLUTION   First we calculate some typical "summary statistics:" $\overline{X}$, M, and S. The sample mean is $\overline{X} = 779/15 \approx \$51.93$. To calculate the median we first array the data, obtaining

47, 48, 49, 49, 50, 51, 52, 52, 52, 53, 54, 54, 55, 56, 57

The median M is the middle value, or the value at position $(n + 1)/2$ in the array. Here, the sample size $n = 15$, so the median is the 8th number in the array, which gives $M = 52$. The closeness of the mean to the median suggests symmetry in the data.

To find the sample standard deviation S, we use the computing formula, which requires calculation of $\sum X$ and $\sum X^2$, giving $\sum X = 779$ and $\sum X^2 = 40{,}579$. Substituting these values into the computing formula yields a sample variance of $S^2 \approx 8.781$. Taking the square root gives $S \approx 2.96$. The sample range is $57 - 47 = 10$.

Next, we compute the quartiles Q_1 and Q_3, and the interquartile range IQR. These values, along with the minimum, the median, and the

---

[3] A description of the more complete box-and-whisker plot can be found in many modern statistical inference texts such as *Statistics* by McClave and Dietrich, Dellen/Macmillan, 1988. Because of the disagreement among statisticians on how to calculate quartiles, some box plots use "hinges," which are essentially the same as our quartiles.

maximum value, allow us to produce a quick box-and-whisker plot of the data. (From now on, we say just "box plot.")

To find Q_1, we locate the observation at position $(n + 1)/4 = 4$. Checking our array reveals that the fourth value from the bottom is 49, so that $Q_1 = 49$. (*Note:* If $(n + 1)/4$ were 3.25, say, instead of an integer, then Q_1 would be one-fourth of the way between arrayed observations 3 and 4.) Since Q_1 was the fourth value from the bottom, Q_3 will be the fourth value down from the top, giving $Q_3 = 54$. Thus, the middle 50% of the data span the gap from 49 to 54, and IQR $= 54 - 49 = 5$. Tukey's five-number summary is given by (47,49,52,54,57). We now have the necessary ingredients to construct the quick box plot in Figure 9.10.

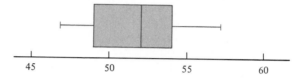

Figure 9.10
Box-plot of Example 12 data

The median line is slightly off center, but the left whisker is shorter than the right whisker, which says the bottom quartile is packed more densely than the upper quartile. The distance from the minimum value to the median is 5, the same as the distance from the median to the maximum, so the left-hand 50% of the data occupies the same space as the right-hand 50%, but the 25% of the data from the median to the third quartile are concentrated in a smaller range than the 25% of the data from the first quartile to the median. If our sample size were much larger, we might be tempted to read more into this; a sample size of only 15, however, does not justify any further analysis. ■

Using IQR to Check for Outliers

When should an extreme value be considered an outlier? This is indeed a difficult question, one that is faced daily by statisticians. Through analysis of many real-world data sets, the following rule, due once again to Tukey, and based on the interquartile range, IQR, is suggested.

DETECTING OUTLIERS IN A DATA SET

1. Calculate Q_1, Q_2, and IQR. Define a **step** as the number that is 1.5 times IQR.

2. Define the **upper fence** to be Q_3 + one step. Define the **lower fence** to be Q_1 − one step.

3. Any measurement *less than the lower fence* or *greater than the upper fence* should be considered an **outlier**.

■ EXAMPLE 13   Apply Tukey's test for outliers to the data sets in Example 10.

SOLUTION   **(a)** In the original data set containing "37," IQR = 10, so that the step is $1.5 \cdot 10 = 15$; values below $Q_1 - 15 = 4$ or above $Q_3 + 15 = 44$ are to be considered outliers. None of this data set falls below 4 or above 44. We conclude there are no outliers.

(b) In data set 2, the value 3.7 (37 with an improper decimal point) replaced 37. Here, IQR = 14, and the step is $14 \cdot 1.5 = 21$. "Fences" are at $Q_1 - 21 = 14 - 21 = -7$ and at $Q_3 + 21 = 49$. We have not successfully detected 3.7 as an outlier. (No method for detecting outliers is perfect!)

(c) Data set 3 replaces the correct value of 37 with 377. Here, IQR = 10, so that the step size is 15. The fences are at $Q_1 - 15 = 4$ and at $Q_3 + 15 = 44$. Since 377 is beyond 44, we have no trouble identifying 377 as an outlier.

(d) In data set 4, 37 has been entered improperly as 3777. The values of IQR, step size, and both fence values are as in **(c)**. The value of 3777 clearly exceeds the upper fence of 44, and is thus declared an outlier. ■

Having detected an outlier, the statistician's job is to determine why that value is an outlier. Was there an error in recording the data, or was there some unusual operating condition? Could the observation have come from a different population? The matter should be thoroughly investigated before simply discarding the "offending" observation.

EXERCISES 9.4

PRACTICING THE MOVES AND MANEUVERS

Exercises 51–55: Use cholesterol data for the animal fat, dairy product group in Example 5.

178, 135, 228, 244, 256, 228, 237, 207, 225, 187, 195, 225, 209
203, 244, 258, 190, 211, 167, 214, 216, 215, 218, 149, 205

51. Find the z-score for the girls whose cholesterol readings were 244.
52. Present Tukey's five-number summary for these data.
53. Interpret your results from Exercise 52.
54. Construct a quick box-plot of these data.
55. Test for outliers.

Exercises 56–59: Use the following data, which represent salaries, to the nearest thousand dollars, of full professors at a small, regional university.

34, 41, 39, 42, 38, 36, 41, 64, 32, 35, 37, 40, 42, 38

56. Present Tukey's five-number summary for these data, and interpret the results.
57. Find the z-score for the professor whose salary is $64,000.
58. Construct a quick box-plot of these data.
59. Test for outliers.

Exercises 60–63: Use the data below, which represent systolic blood pressure measurements of a person on ten consecutive days (from Exercises 32–34).

85 70 74 69 72 76 87 73 84 75

60. What is the z-score of a measurement equal to 73?
61. Present Tukey's five-number summary for these data, and interpret the results.
62. Construct a quick box-plot of these data.
63. Check for outliers.

Exercises 64–66: Use the data below (for Exercises 6–10) representing ages of assistant professors at Anemia Tech.

67 71 59 77 71 86 69 34 73 81 67 68 71 65 69 70 72 81 77 76 68
71 73 68 62 63 60 61 68 58 58 63 71 57 78 81 73 67 62 78 64 66

64. Find the z-score for those profs who are 77.
65. Give Tukey's five-number summary and interpret.
66. Construct a quick box-plot of these data.

67. Check for outliers.

Exercises 68–70: Use the Colorado Blue Spruce height data, which are shown below.

175 189 167 178 184 166 176 177 159 170 184 166 160 149 190 177 168
169 163 154 158 170 176 159 174 170 165 160 162 178 168 182 177 177

68. Give Tukey's five-number summary and interpret.
69. Construct a quick box-plot of these data.
70. Check for outliers.

9.5 SAMPLING DISTRIBUTIONS, POINT ESTIMATION, AND THE CENTRAL LIMIT THEOREM

The objective of statistical inference is to make inferences (draw conclusions about) populations of interest by using sample data. Populations are composed of numbers that represent values of some random variable. Special numbers called **parameters** provide a great deal of information about populations. Unless all values in a population are known

Statistical Inference

(extremely unlikely), the parameters that describe the population will also be unknown.

Two main areas of statistical inference are concerned with learning about the values of these unknown parameters that describe populations. The first is called *point and interval estimation*, and the second is *hypothesis testing*.

In **point and interval estimation**, we select a random sample of size n from the population and obtain certain statistics like $\overline{X}$ and S^2, which can be used to estimate corresponding population parameters μ and σ^2. A single number used to estimate an unknown parameter is called a **point estimator**. If we instead claim with a certain degree of confidence that an unknown parameter has a value in some interval of numbers, we are using an **interval estimator**.

The basic philosophy of **hypothesis testing** in statistical inference is this: a model which describes the population is proposed. For example, our model might be that data come from a normal distribution whose mean is 20. The model that specifies our distribution forms the null hypothesis. Data are then taken, and the statistician's job is to assess whether the data support the model. That is, do the data reflect what we would expect to see if the model were correct? If so, we have not proved that our model is correct, but at least we have no strong reason to doubt the model. On the other hand, if the data do not support the model, one of two possibilities has occurred: **(1)** the model really is appropriate, but we have observed what statisticians call a "rare event," data that are extremely improbable in our model, or **(2)** the model is incorrect. Since what we usually observe in the real world are the most probable happenings, choice **(2)** is the logical alternative. Thus, when data do not support our model, we should reject this model and consider an alternative model.

Sampling Distributions

We begin statistical inference by considering point and interval estimation. Both point and interval estimation require that we have a suitable statistic that can be used as a point estimator. After computing the value of such a statistic, we ask, "How well does that statistic work in estimating the unknown parameter?" To answer this question, we need to investigate and understand the concept of a *sampling distribution*. We shall introduce this vitally important concept in the following example.

■ EXAMPLE 14

A small population consists of the values: 4, 2, 6, 10, and 8, and the mean μ is seen to be $30/5 = 6$.

How would we estimate the mean if these population values were unknown? Our only recourse would be to sample the population, and use an appropriate statistic to estimate μ. We decide on a random sample of size $n = 2$, obtaining the values 6, 4. Using the sample mean $\overline{X}$ to estimate the population mean seems reasonable, and this gives $\overline{X} =$

10/2 = 5. Since (unknown to us) $\mu = 6$, our estimator $\overline{X}$ has done a reasonably good job—we are "off" by 1. ("Off by 1" indicates a difference of 1, without regard to sign. Thus, an $X = 7$ would also be "off by 1.") Instead of 6 and 4, suppose we had obtained the sample 8, 10. In this case, $\overline{X} = 9$, which is not nearly as good an estimate. (We are now "off" by 3.)

These two samples illustrate well the following principle: *different samples from the same population usually produce different values*. This sample-to-sample variability suggests that any statistic you calculate will take different values in different samples (just as $\overline{X}$ took values 5 and 9 in our two samples). In real-world applications, experimenters and statisticians would take only a single sample of size n. How are experimenters to know whether they have a "good" sample (such as the first, where $\overline{X} = 5$) or a "bad" sample (such as the second, where $\overline{X} = 9$)?

An analogy from sports is helpful in answering this question. A quarterback in the NFL is judged not by his performance in a single game but by his career performance. By the same token, the goodness of a statistic as an estimator of an unknown parameter is determined not by how well that statistic performs in a single sample, but by how well it works over the long haul. In other words, by how well that statistic works for every possible sample we could get from the population.

The statistical behavior of a statistic over all possible samples is described by its sampling distribution. The concept of sampling distribution is fundamental to all of statistical inference.

SAMPLING DISTRIBUTION OF A STATISTIC

> Consider any statistic W. Imagine the conceptual experiment of taking all possible random samples of a given size n from a population and calculating the value of W from each sample. This repeated sampling generates a new population of W-values. The **sampling distribution** for statistic W is the probability distribution that describes the values of the statistic W in this new population created by repeated random sampling.

The sampling distribution of a statistic enables us to find probabilities about that statistic. In particular, we can determine how likely we are to get a value of the statistic "close" to the parameter we are estimating. In our current example, where we use $\overline{X}$ to estimate μ, the sampling distribution of $W = \overline{X}$ will enable us to find a probability like $P[\mu - 1 \le \overline{X} \le \mu + 1]$. If this probability were 0.95, we would feel comfortable in using $\overline{X}$ to estimate μ; since 95% of all possible $\overline{X}$ values would be within one unit of μ, there would be only a 5% chance that a particular $\overline{X}$ would be "off" by more than 1.

The notion of a sampling distribution is purely conceptual. In real-world situations, a sampling distribution would be difficult (if not impossible) to construct; typical populations are simply too large to take "all possible samples." The reason for our interest in sampling distributions is this:

> **Knowing and understanding a statistic's behavior in all possible samples enables us to better judge its behavior in the one particular sample we would get.**

To help in illustrating the concept of a sampling distribution, we shall actually construct a sampling distribution for the statistic $\overline{X}$, using random samples of size 2 chosen from our population.

SOLUTION   First, note that our population could be summarized by the following discrete probability distribution:

x	2	4	6	8	10
$p(x)$	$\dfrac{1}{5}$	$\dfrac{1}{5}$	$\dfrac{1}{5}$	$\dfrac{1}{5}$	$\dfrac{1}{5}$

We have seen previously that the mean is $\mu = 6$. By using the computing formula, we find that the variance of the population is

$$\sigma^2 = \sum x^2 p(x) - \mu^2$$

$$= 2^2 \cdot \frac{1}{5} + 4^2 \cdot \frac{1}{5} + 6^2 \cdot \frac{1}{5} + 8^2 \cdot \frac{1}{5} + 10^2 \cdot \frac{1}{5} - 6^2 = 44 - 36 = 8$$

Constructing a Sampling Distribution   We now construct a sampling distribution for the statistic $W = \overline{X}$ by choosing all possible samples of size two and calculating $\overline{X}$ from each sample. Most real-world sampling would be done without replacement, not returning the first item to the population before choosing the second. For convenience, we examine the case of sampling with replacement. With minor modifications, sampling without replacement produces similar results. If a population is large, as most real-world populations are, there is little difference between the two procedures. Since there are five items in our population, there are $5 \cdot 5 = 25$ possible random samples of size two. These samples, and the corresponding values of $\overline{X}$, are shown below.

Possible Random Sample of Size Two	Sample Mean $\overline{X}$
2, 2	2
2, 4	3
2, 6	4
2, 8	5
2, 10	6
4, 2	3
4, 4	4
4, 6	5
4, 8	6
4, 10	7
6, 2	4
6, 4	5
6, 6	6
6, 8	7
6, 10	8
8, 2	5
8, 4	6
8, 6	7
8, 8	8
8, 10	9
10, 2	6
10, 4	7
10, 6	8
10, 8	9
10, 10	10

We form the sampling distribution of $\overline{X}$ by summarizing the above results:

$\overline{x}$	2	3	4	5	6	7	8	9	10
$p(\overline{x})$	$\dfrac{1}{25}$	$\dfrac{2}{25}$	$\dfrac{3}{25}$	$\dfrac{4}{25}$	$\dfrac{5}{25}$	$\dfrac{4}{25}$	$\dfrac{3}{25}$	$\dfrac{2}{25}$	$\dfrac{1}{25}$

Two parameters of interest in this $\overline{X}$ population are the mean and the variance. We calculate $E(\overline{X})$, the mean of $\overline{X}$, below:

$$E(\overline{X}) = \sum \overline{x} \cdot p(\overline{x})$$

$$= 2 \cdot \frac{1}{25} + 3 \cdot \frac{2}{25} + 4 \cdot \frac{3}{25} + 5 \cdot \frac{4}{25} + 6 \cdot \frac{5}{25}$$

$$+ 7 \cdot \frac{4}{25} + 8 \cdot \frac{3}{25} + 9 \cdot \frac{2}{25} + 10 \cdot \frac{1}{25} = 6$$

Observe that the mean of $\overline{X}$ is exactly the same as the mean of X. This is no accident. The mean of the sampling distribution of $\overline{X}$ will always match the mean of the original X population. Now let's check the variance of the sampling distribution of $\overline{X}$:

$$\sigma_{\overline{x}}^2 = \sum \overline{x}^2 \cdot p(\overline{x}) - \mu^2$$

$$= 2^2 \cdot \frac{1}{25} + 3^2 \cdot \frac{2}{25} + 4^2 \cdot \frac{3}{25} + 5^2 \cdot \frac{4}{25}$$

$$+ 6^2 \cdot \frac{5}{25} + 7^2 \cdot \frac{4}{25} + 8^2 \cdot \frac{3}{25} + 9^2 \cdot \frac{2}{25}$$

$$+ 10^2 \cdot \frac{1}{25} - 6^2 = 40 - 36 = 4$$

Did you expect that the variance of the $\overline{X}$ distribution would be the same as the variance of the original X distribution? Consider the process of computing a mean. Averaging tends to bring extremes toward the middle. This "squeezing to the middle" reduces variability. Hence, there should be less variability in the $\overline{X}$ distribution than in the X distribution. Here, the variance of $\overline{X}$ is exactly half the variance of X. This is no accident either.

> **In general, the variance of the sampling distribution of $\overline{X}$ will be the variance of the X distribution divided by the sample size n.**

Here, n is 2, so that $\sigma_{\overline{x}}^2$, the variance of $\overline{X}$, is $8/2 = 4$. We summarize the relation between the parameters of the distribution of X and the same parameters for the distribution of $\overline{X}$.

MEAN AND VARIANCE FOR SAMPLING DISTRIBUTION OF $\overline{X}$

Consider a population of x values whose mean is $E(X) = \mu$ and whose variance is σ^2. The mean and variance of the sampling distribution of $\overline{X}$, where each $\overline{X}$ is computed from a random sample of size n, taken with replacement, are given by:

Mean of $\overline{X}$: $E(\overline{X}) = E(X) = \mu$

Variance of $\overline{X}$: $\sigma_{\overline{x}}^2 = \dfrac{\sigma^2}{n}$

PRACTICE PROBLEM 5 You are to take a random sample of size 9 from a population whose mean is 20 and whose variance is 36. **(a)** Find the mean and variance of the sampling distribution of $\overline{X}$; **(b)** find the standard deviation of the sampling distribution of $\overline{X}$.

ANSWER(S) **(a)** $E(\overline{X}) = 20$, and $\sigma_{\bar{x}}^2 = 4$;   **(b)** $\sigma_{\bar{x}} = 2$.   ☐

The standard deviation of the sampling distribution of $\overline{X}$ is an important quantity, worthy of a special name.

STANDARD ERROR OF THE MEAN

> The standard deviation of the sampling distribution of $\overline{X}$, also known as the **standard error of the mean**, is of major importance in statistical inference.
>
> $$\sigma_{\bar{x}} = \frac{\sigma}{\sqrt{n}}$$

PRACTICE PROBLEM 6 A population of values has mean 115 and variance 36. For random samples of size 25, determine the mean of the sampling distribution of $\overline{X}$ and the standard error of the mean.

ANSWER(S) Mean = 115; standard error = 6/5 = 1.2.   ☐

The Central Limit Theorem While the mean and variance (or its square root, the standard error) of the sampling distribution of $\overline{X}$ are important quantities, they do not by themselves fully describe the sampling distribution. These parameters tell us the center of the distribution and the spread about that center, but they do not tell us anything about the *shape* of the distribution of $\overline{X}$. Recall that the original population in Example 14 consists of the five numbers 2, 4, 6, 8, and 10, each occurring with probability 1/5. This particular distribution is often known as a *discrete uniform distribution*, and its histogram (which we will not draw) is nothing more than a series of rectangles, all having the same height. What about the histogram for the sampling distribution of $\overline{X}$? We show this histogram in Figure 9.11.

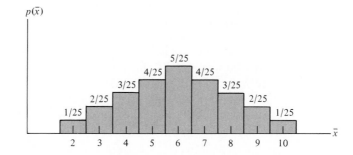

Figure 9.11
Histogram for sampling distribution of $\overline{X}$ for $n = 2$

While this histogram is for a discrete distribution, the shape of the sampling distribution of $\overline{X}$ really resembles rather remarkably (say that three times!) the normal distribution. This likeness is the subject of the famous **Central Limit Theorem**:

CENTRAL LIMIT THEOREM

> Consider any population of X values with mean μ and finite variance σ^2. The sampling distribution of $\overline{X}$, for random samples of size n taken without replacement, has approximately a normal distribution with mean μ and variance σ^2/n. The approximation to normality gets progressively better as n increases. In virtually all populations, this approximation will be excellent when $n \geq 30$. If the original population is even remotely symmetric, then the approximation to normality may be quite good for smaller values of n.

Note carefully what this says: regardless of the shape of the population you are sampling, the shape of the $\overline{X}$ distribution will be approximately normal—as long as the sample size is reasonably large. Many important results in statistical inference are based on the Central Limit Theorem. At the moment, all the Central Limit Theorem tells us is that we can use the normal distribution to approximate probabilities about a sample mean, regardless of the shape of the population.

Illustrating the Central Limit Theorem I

The top row of Figure 9.12 shows four different population distributions. Distribution 1 is a uniform distribution, and distribution 4 is normal. Distribution 2 has an unusual shape, putting most of its probability at the ends and very little at the middle—almost the opposite of a normal distribution.

Distribution 3 is a famous continuous distribution known as the exponential distribution. (We shall conduct a brief sampling experiment with this distribution very shortly.) Observe the diversity of shapes of these distributions.

In the second row of Figure 9.12, we give the sampling distribution for the statistic $\overline{X}$ computed for random samples of size $n = 2$. Even with this small sample size, the tendency to normality is beginning to show. Row 3 gives the sampling distribution of $\overline{X}$ for random samples of size $n = 5$. The resemblance to normality is much better than for $n = 2$, although skewness is still evident when sampling from the exponential distribution. Finally, in row 4, we show the sampling distribution of $\overline{X}$ for random samples of size $n = 30$. There is no doubt from this picture that the Central Limit Theorem is at work! When you are sampling from a normal distribution, the sampling distribution of $\overline{X}$ remains normal for

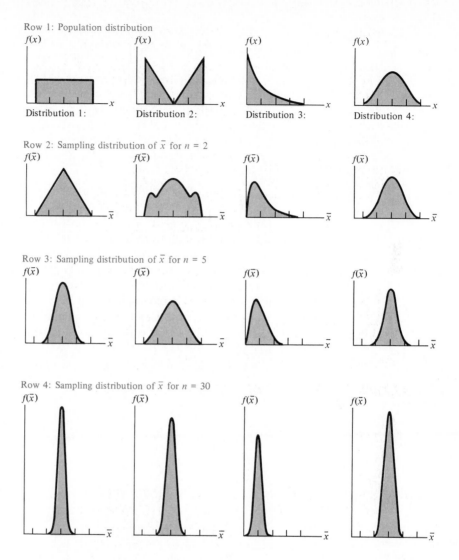

Figure 9.12
Sampling distributions of $\bar{X}$ for samples of sizes 2, 5, and 30 taken from four different populations

any sample size. This is clearly evident in the right-most column where only the variance changes as the sample size increases.

Illustrating the Central Limit Theorem II

To further illustrate the Central Limit Theorem, we return to a problem mentioned in Example 14. In that example we had a small population with values 4, 2, 6, 8, and 10. We found the mean μ to be 6. We said that knowing a probability like $P[\mu - 1 \leq \bar{X} \leq \mu + 1]$ would be immensely helpful; such information would tell us just how likely it is that our sample estimator $\bar{X}$ is "off target" by no more than one (that is, $\bar{X}$ is within one unit of the true, unknown value μ.) We now calculate this probability exactly by using the sampling distribution of $\bar{X}$ constructed at the end of Example 14. Then we compare this exact answer with the approximate answer from the normal distribution. Since $\mu = 6$, $P[\mu - 1 \leq \overline{X} \leq \mu + 1] = P[5 \leq \overline{X} \leq 7]$.

The exact answer is the area of Figure 9.11 bars at $\overline{X} = 5$, 6, and 7, which gives $P[5 \leq \overline{X} \leq 7] = 4/25 + 5/25 + 4/25 = 13/25 = 0.52$. Now, we shall use the normal distribution as an approximation to the sampling distribution of $\overline{X}$, and see how close we come to the exact answer of 0.52. To approximate $P[5 \leq \overline{X} \leq 7]$ with the normal distribution, we proceed as in Section 8.8, where we used the normal to approximate the binomial.

Imagine superimposing a normal curve over the histogram representing the probability distribution of $\overline{X}$. As we learned in Section 9.8, the best normal distribution for mirroring the shape of our histogram is the normal distribution having the same mean and variance as the exact $\overline{X}$ distribution has; namely, the normal distribution whose mean is 6, and whose variance is $8/2 = 4$, making the standard error 2. We want to find the area under the normal curve that corresponds to the exact answer, which is the area of bars 5, 6, and 7. Study Figure 9.13, where we have superimposed this approximating normal distribution onto our exact sampling distribution for $\overline{X}$. Since the histogram-bar for "5" begins at 4.5, and the bar for "7" extends to 7.5, we shall find the shaded area under the normal curve between 4.5 and 7.5. Clearly, this area is not exactly the same as the area of the three bars at 5, 6, and 7, but it appears to be "close."

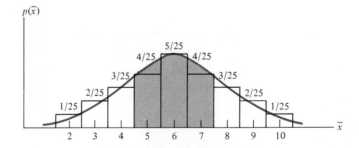

Figure 9.13
Normal curve approximating
$\overline{X}$ distribution

To find this normal curve area, we convert 4.5 and 7.5 to appropriate "z-scores," so that we can use the standard normal table. In doing this, it is important to recognize that we are finding a probability about $\overline{X}$, so we must use the standard deviation for $\overline{X}$ (the standard error of the mean). Here we go!

The z-score for 4.5 is $(4.5 - 6)/2 \approx -0.75$. The z-score for 7.5 is $(7.5 - 6)/2 \approx +0.75$. Thus, $P[5 \leq \overline{X} \leq 7] \approx$ area under normal curve between 4.5 and 7.5 $= P[-0.75 \leq Z \leq 0.75] = 2(0.2734) = 0.5468$.

The exact answer is $13/25 = 0.52$. We are "off" a bit, but we shouldn't feel that the Central Limit Theorem gives poor approximations. After all, it virtually guarantees good approximations only when the sample size $n \geq 30$. In our example, we have a sample size of only $n = 2$. The approximation is extraordinary when we consider the small sample size.

At this point, we make another comparison. Specifically, we compare $P[5 \leq \overline{X} \leq 7]$ with $P[5 \leq X \leq 7]$. In the original X distribution where the possible X values were 2, 4, 6, 8, and 10, the event "$5 \leq X \leq 7$" is true only when $X = 6$, and thus we get $P[5 \leq X \leq 7] = 1/5 = 0.20$. Note that the $\overline{X}$ distribution has much greater concentration between 5 and 7 than does the original X distribution. Stated simply, this says that someone using the mean of a random sample of size two has a better chance of being close to the unknown population mean μ than does someone who uses a single randomly chosen X.

Illustrating the Central Limit Theorem III

Example 14, in which we sampled from a discrete uniform distribution and discovered that the shape of the sampling distribution of $\overline{X}$ was remarkably normal, was intended to demonstrate the validity of the Central Limit Theorem. To further reinforce this notion, we provide the following MINITAB simulation, where we take 700 random samples of size 25 from a continuous random variable having an exponential distribution. This distribution, which is often used to describe time between the occurrence of certain kinds of events or the length of life of certain items not subject to aging, is also shown as "Distribution 3" in Figure 9.12.

Exponential Distribution

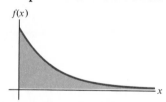

Note the severe skewness, or lack of symmetry, in this distribution. The MINITAB "macro" that we use to generate the 700 random samples of size 25 is given below:

MTB >Random 700 C1–C25;	Takes 25 samples of size 700
SUBC >Exponential 4.	from an exponential whose mean is 4
MTB >Rmeans C1–C25 C26	Finds the means by going across the rows, making 700 samples of size 25. These 700 $\overline{X}$ values are stored in column C26.

In column C26, there are 700 values of $\overline{X}$, each computed from a sample of size 25 taken from the exponential distribution pictured. A dot plot of these 700 sample means is shown in Figure 9.14. Each dot represents three sample means.

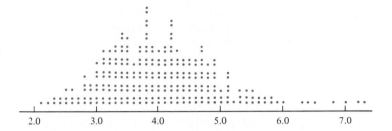

Figure 9.14
Dot plot of 700 $\bar{X}$ values for samples of size 25 from exponential distribution

The tendency towards a normal distribution is evident in the dot plot, even though we have only used samples of size 25—which, theoretically, is not quite enough to guarantee a good approximation to normality.

■ EXAMPLE 15

A "smooth" curve describing the distribution of a continuous random variable X (mean 110, variance 25) is shown in Figure 9.15. A random sample of size 100 is taken from this distribution.

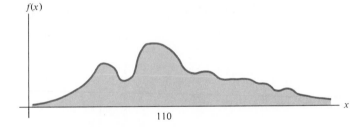

Figure 9.15
Population distribution for Example 15

(a) Find the probability that the mean of this random sample is between 109.5 and 111;

(b) Find the probability that X will have a value in the same range—i.e., between 109.5 and 111.

SOLUTION To work part **(a)**, note that since the sample size n is "large," use of the Central Limit Theorem is justified. The normal distribution that best approximates the distribution of $\bar{X}$ is the normal whose mean is 25, and whose variance is $\sigma^2/n = 25/100 = 1/4$. Since the variance of the sampling distribution of $\bar{X}$ is 1/4, the standard error of the mean is $\sqrt{1/4} = 1/2$. Thus, the z-score for 109.5 is given by $(109.5 - 110)/0.5 = -1$. Similarly, the z-score for 111 is $(111 - 110)/0.5 = 2$. Thus, $P[109.5 \leq \bar{X} \leq 111] = P[-1 \leq Z \leq 2] = 0.3413 + 0.4772 = 0.8185$. More than 4/5 of the random samples of size 100 would have means between 109.5 and 111.

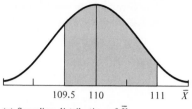

(a) Sampling distribution of $\bar{X}$

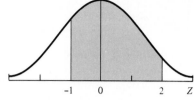

(b) Standard normal distribution

(b) To do this problem, we would need to find the area under the X curve between 109.5 and 111. If not impossible, finding this area would clearly be a nearly futile task. ∎

EXERCISES 9.5

PRACTICING THE MOVES AND MANEUVERS

Exercises 71–76: Consider a population with mean 40 and variance 16. Find the mean, variance, and standard error of $\bar{X}$ for random samples of size:

71. $n = 4$ 72. $n = 8$ 73. $n = 16$
74. $n = 32$ 75. $n = 64$ 76. $n = 128$

77. A population has mean 20 and variance 9. What are the mean and variance of $\bar{X}$ and the standard error of the mean for random samples of size 36?

78. The variance of a population is 25, and the standard error of the mean for a certain random sample is 1. What must the sample size n have been?

79. If the standard error of the mean is 3, based on a random sample of size n, what would the standard error of the mean be for samples of size $4n$?

Exercises 80–83: Use the information of Exercise 77 to find the probability that the sample mean (for a random sample of size 36) would have a value that is:

80. between 19 and 21.   81. greater than 20.   82. greater than 21.   83. less than 18.5.

84. Weights of people riding an elevator form a population with mean $\mu = 160$ pounds and variance $\sigma^2 = 400$. If a 4,600-pound load will crash the elevator, find the probability that a random sample of 30 people will crash.

Exercises 85–87: Records of the I.R.S. (Infernal Revenue Service) show that the average deduction for property taxes in a certain income class is $800, with standard deviation $450. If a sample of 225 returns is taken from this income class, find the probability that the sample mean is:

85. between $770 and $890.   86. between $740 and $860.   87. less than $710.

Exercises 88–90: The amount of cereal in a box is a random variable with mean 16 ounces, and variance 1 ounce. If a random sample of 64 of these boxes is selected from various grocery stores, find the probability that:

88. the sample mean of these boxes exceeds 16.2 ounces.
89. the sample mean of these boxes is between 15.7 and 16.5 ounces.
90. the sample mean is less than 15.5 ounces.

9.6 LARGE SAMPLE CONFIDENCE INTERVALS FOR THE POPULATION MEAN μ

The Central Limit Theorem makes it easy to find probabilities about $\overline{X}$ for large sample sizes, but an even more important use is in helping us to locate the value of an unknown population mean μ. To illustrate, suppose we take a random sample of size n, $n \geq 30$, and calculate typical sample statistics $\overline{X}$ and S^2. Since $n \geq 30$ the Central Limit Theorem applies, and the sampling distribution of $\overline{X}$ is approximately the normal distribution whose mean is μ and whose variance is σ^2/n. For any normal distribution, we know that about[4] 95% of the values are within two standard deviations of the mean. Let's mark these spots on the sampling distribution of $\overline{X}$ in Figure 9.16.

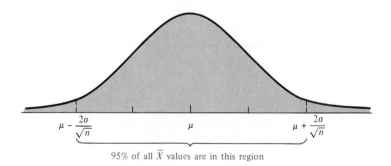

Figure 9.16
Sampling distribution of $\overline{X}$ for samples of size $n \geq 30$

95% of all $\overline{X}$ values are in this region

Alternatively, the probability is about 0.95 that the sample mean $\overline{X}$ will have a value between $\mu - 2\sigma/\sqrt{n}$ and $\mu + 2\sigma/\sqrt{n}$, where for the moment we suppose the population standard deviation σ is known.

Even though $\overline{X}$ is random, and will change values from sample to sample, 95% of all the possible $\overline{X}$ values will fall in the range from

[4] Using "2" standard deviations gives us 95.44% area. To get exactly 95% area in a normal distribution requires going 1.96 standard deviations on either side of the mean. Because of the Empirical Rule, we tend to think in terms of "2 standard deviations" (which gives 95.44%). We feel that the gain in simplicity offsets the small loss of accuracy. If this bothers you, use "1.96."

$\mu - 2\sigma/\sqrt{n}$ to $\mu + 2\sigma/\sqrt{n}$. Thus, whenever $\overline{X}$ is in this range (an event that occurs 95% of the time), the maximum amount by which we could be "off" (the difference, without regard to sign, between $\overline{X}$ and the true, unknown population mean μ) is $2\sigma/\sqrt{n}$.

This provides us with a good way of estimating μ. Imagine constructing a special "ruler-bar" whose length is $\sigma/\sqrt{n}$ (one standard error of $\overline{X}$). In Figure 9.17, we shall both add and subtract two of these ruler-bars to our $\overline{X}$, producing an interval which runs from $\overline{X} - 2\sigma/\sqrt{n}$ to $\overline{X} + 2\sigma/\sqrt{n}$.

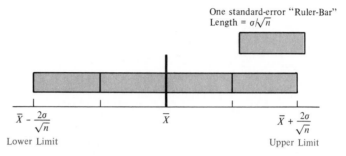

Figure 9.17
95% confidence interval
centered at $\overline{X}$

In 95% of all possible samples, the interval that we so construct will contain μ. For any one random sample of size n, we will not know whether the interval we have constructed contains μ. But the fact that 95% of all the possible intervals that could be formed do contain μ suggests that we can feel "95% confident" about our one interval. In fact, we shall say that *the interval from $\overline{X} - 2\sigma/\sqrt{n}$ to $\overline{X} + 2\sigma/\sqrt{n}$ is a 95% large-sample confidence interval for the unknown population mean μ.*

95% LARGE-SAMPLE CONFIDENCE INTERVAL FOR μ

> If $\overline{X}$ is the mean of a random sample of size $n \geq 30$ from any population having known variance σ^2, then the interval from $\overline{X} - 2\sigma/\sqrt{n}$ to $\overline{X} + 2\sigma/\sqrt{n}$ is a **95% large-sample confidence interval** for the unknown population mean μ.
>
> For any one interval (such as the one you compute), it is not known whether μ is in the interval or not, but in the long run, approximately 95% of all the intervals computed in this way would contain μ; about 5% would not.

■ EXAMPLE 16

A random sample of size 36 is taken from a population whose mean is unknown, but a study of similar populations for many years suggests that the population variance σ^2 is about 400. The sample mean $\overline{X} = 55.64$ for this sample. Use this information to set a 95% confidence interval on the unknown population mean μ.

SOLUTION   Marking off two standard error ruler-bars on each side of the sample mean will give us the 95% confidence interval for μ. Arithmetically, this is accomplished by adding and subtracting two standard errors to the sample mean of 55.64. The standard error of the mean, for random samples of size 36, is $\sigma/\sqrt{n} = 20/\sqrt{36} = 10/3 \approx 3.33$. This gives us a confidence interval that runs from $55.64 - 2(3.33)$ to $55.64 + 2(3.33)$, or from 48.98 to 62.30. We often present this 95% interval in the following form:

A 95% confidence interval for μ is $48.98 \leq \mu \leq 62.30$.

This is merely a claim on our part; we don't know whether μ is in this one interval or not. The procedure we have used, however, guarantees that, in the long run, 95% of all possible intervals like this one would contain μ. It is in this sense that we say the above interval is a "95% confidence interval."   ■

Other Confidence Levels   What if we want a level of confidence other than 95%? For 95%, we added and subtracted two standard error ruler-bars to $\overline{X}$. This worked because about 95% of a normal distribution falls within two such ruler-bars of the mean. For a different confidence level, we use a different number of ruler-bars. For 90% confidence, we use 1.645 ruler-bars. To verify this, check Figure 9.18.

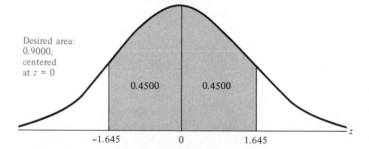

Figure 9.18
Determining number of ruler-bars for 90% confidence interval

Note that we need 45% area on each side of the mean. The standard normal table (inside back cover) reveals that 45% is halfway between the 0.4495 at $z = 1.64$ and 0.4505 at $z = 1.65$. Since 0.45 is halfway between 0.4495 and 0.4505, we go halfway between 1.64 and 1.65, arriving at 1.645.

90% LARGE-SAMPLE CONFIDENCE INTERVAL FOR μ

A **90% large-sample confidence interval** for the population mean μ is given by:

$$\overline{X} - \frac{1.645\sigma}{\sqrt{n}} \leq \mu \leq \overline{X} + \frac{1.645\sigma}{\sqrt{n}}$$

Other confidence levels are obtained similarly by using the standard normal table to find the appropriate number of standard-error ruler-bars to add and subtract to $\overline{X}$.

PRACTICE PROBLEM 7   Set a 90% confidence on the mean μ in Example 16.

ANSWER(S) $50.16 \leq \mu \leq 61.12$ is the 90% confidence interval.   □

PRACTICE PROBLEM 8   **(a)** Find the number of standard deviations needed to locate the central 98% of the area in a normal distribution; and **(b)** Use the results of part **(a)** to set a 98% confidence interval on the mean μ in Example 16.

ANSWER(S)   **(a)** 2.33 standard deviations; **(b)** $47.87 \leq \mu \leq 63.40$ □

It is interesting to compare the 90%, 95%, and 98% confidence intervals:

> 90% interval: $50.16 \leq \mu \leq 61.12$
>
> 95% interval: $48.98 \leq \mu \leq 62.30$
>
> 98% interval: $47.87 \leq \mu \leq 63.40$

The 90% interval is more informative in that it "pins μ down" better—everything else being equal, a small-width confidence interval is better. Everything else isn't equal, though. The 95% and 98% intervals, while wider, are more likely to be correct intervals. This trade off between level-of-confidence (which we want to be high) and the width of the interval (which we want to be small) is nicely paraphrased by saying, "The more confident we are, the less we have to be confident of!"

Confidence Intervals When σ Is Unknown   You might think that we would be in real trouble if we did not know σ. In Example 16, we had a long history of data which supplied a reasonable value for σ. What would you do if you had no idea about σ? The logical, commonsense approach would be to substitute the sample standard deviation S. This approach is not only logical, but it is also effective! When σ is unknown, as it almost always will be, large sample confidence intervals are obtained by using the appropriate number of ruler-bars of length $S/\sqrt{n}$ (rather than $\sigma/\sqrt{n}$). We summarize our results for large-sample confidence intervals when σ is unknown in the box on page 438.

PRACTICE PROBLEM 9   A random sample of 50 cars on I-25 between Ft. Collins and Denver, Colorado, showed an average speed of 71.4 miles an hour, and standard deviation 3.5 miles an hour. **(a)** Use this information to set a 90% confidence interval on the parameter μ; and **(b)** Describe the meaning of the parameter μ in this population.

ANSWER(S)   **(a)** $70.6 \le \mu \le 72.2$; **(b)** μ is the true, unknown average speed of all cars traveling this section of I-25.   ☐

LARGE-SAMPLE CONFIDENCE INTERVALS FOR μ: SUMMARY

To set a confidence interval on an unknown population mean μ, calculate $\overline{X}$ and S from a sample of size $n \ge 30$.

A 90% confidence interval is given by:

$$\overline{X} - \frac{1.645\,S}{\sqrt{n}} \le \mu \le \overline{X} + \frac{1.645\,S}{\sqrt{n}}$$

A 95% confidence interval is given by:

$$\overline{X} - \frac{2S}{\sqrt{n}} \le \mu \le \overline{X} + \frac{2S}{\sqrt{n}}$$

A 98% confidence interval is given by:

$$\overline{X} - \frac{2.33\,S}{\sqrt{n}} \le \mu \le \overline{X} + \frac{2.33\,S}{\sqrt{n}}$$

If the standard deviation σ should be known, then substitute it for S.

EXERCISES 9.6

PRACTICING THE MOVES AND MANEUVERS

Exercises 91–94:   Use the given statistics, obtained from a random sample of size 36, to set 90% and 95% confidence intervals on the unknown population mean μ.

91. $\overline{X} = 18.6$, $S = 4.5$ 92. $\overline{X} = 18.6$, $S = 6.2$ 93. $\overline{X} = 24.5$, $S = 1.1$ 94. $\overline{X} = 24.5$, $S = 4.2$

Exercises 95–98:   Use the given statistics, obtained from a random sample of size 72, to set 90% and 95% confidence intervals on the unknown population mean μ.

95. $\overline{X} = 18.6$, $S = 4.5$ 96. $\overline{X} = 18.6$, $S = 6.2$ 97. $\overline{X} = 24.5$, $S = 1.1$ 98. $\overline{X} = 24.5$, $S = 4.2$

Exercises 99–102:   Use the given statistics, obtained from a random sample of size 144, to set 90% and 95% confidence intervals on the unknown population mean μ.

99. $\overline{X} = 18.6$, $S = 4.5$ 100. $\overline{X} = 18.6$, $S = 6.2$ 101. $\overline{X} = 24.5$, $S = 1.1$ 102. $\overline{X} = 24.5$, $S = 4.2$

Exercises 103–107: Determine the appropriate number of standard-error ruler-bars neces-sary to give the prescribed level of confidence. (Do <u>not</u> read between entries in the normal table; use the closest value.)

103. 80%   104. 99%   105. 88%   106. 68.26%   107. 85%

APPLYING THE CONCEPTS

108. A random sample of 36 NFL defensive linemen showed an average weight of 288 pounds and a standard deviation of 9.5 pounds. Set a 95% confidence interval on the true, unknown aver-age weight of all NFL defensive linemen.

109. In Exercise 108, set a 90% confidence interval on μ.

110. In Exercise 108, set a 98% confidence interval on μ.

111. The average quantitative SAT score for a ran-dom sample of 40 freshmen from Anemia Tech was 280, and the standard deviation was 75. Set a 90% confidence interval on μ, the true, un-known mean quantitative SAT score of all en-tering freshmen at Anemia Tech.

112. In Exercise 111, set a 95% confidence interval on μ.

113. The verbal SAT measurements for the sample of Anemia Tech students in Exercise 111 had mean 340, and standard deviation 90. Establish a 95% confidence interval for the unknown mean μ.

114. In Exercise 113, describe what the unknown mean μ represents.

115. In Exercise 113, set a 90% confidence interval on μ.

116. Find a 90% confidence interval for the mean height, μ, of all Anemia Tech students, if a ran-dom sample of 49 students has mean 47 inches and the sample variance S^2 is 9.

117. In Exercise 116, set a 95% confidence interval on μ.

118. The wind velocity measurements on Mt. Rainier (from Exercises 20–22) are reproduced below. Set a 95% confidence interval on the true, unknown population mean velocity μ, and describe what μ represents.

21 25 34 18 17   3 21 24 32 20 17 25 27 26

30   9 24 19 16 17 26 23 17 29 25 12 10 23

119. In Exercise 118, set a 90% confidence interval on μ.

120. In Exercise 118, set a 68% confidence interval on μ.

Exercises 121–124: Consider the burning times prior to failure of 75-watt light bulbs. (Data shown below are taken from Exercises 16–19.)

540 460 479 664 855 776 657 745 543 662 557 775 687 745 705

697 466 567 713 487 645 543 577 656 557 512 467 478 543 567

674 612 685 635 587 396 487 566 487 645 577 634 701 634 523

476 515 692 802 765 675 587 634 388 467 558 634 661 540 610

121. Describe in words what the population mean μ represents.
122. Set a 95% confidence interval on μ.
123. Set a 90% confidence interval on μ.
124. Set a 68% confidence interval on μ.

9.7 CONFIDENCE INTERVALS ON *p*, THE BINOMIAL SUCCESS PROBABILITY (OPTIONAL)

Many real-world problems are concerned with estimating the unknown probability of success *p*, or equivalently, the proportion of the population that has a certain attribute, which we call "success." The Nielsen survey, for example, wants to estimate the proportion of TV viewers who watch a particular program on Thursday night at 10 P.M. The Gallup poll would like to estimate the proportion of voters who favor a particular candidate in an upcoming election. *Newsweek* magazine frequently conducts surveys with the intent of learning what proportion of the American public is in favor of a certain issue. For example, *Newsweek* might be interested in the proportion of adults over age 50 who are in favor of the death penalty for convicted drug dealers. A quality control inspector is faced daily with determining the proportion of defective items manufactured.

All these situations are similar in that the populations involved are composed of only two types of items—success and failure. Taking a random sample of size *n* from such a population can be viewed as performing *n* trials of a binomial experiment where *p* represents the probability of success (or, equivalently, the proportion of successes in the population). In our discussion that follows, it will be advantageous to replace the nonnumerical "success/failure" designation with a random variable *X* defined as follows: $X = 1$ if the selected item is a success and $X = 0$ if the item is a failure. Our random sample of size *n* is then composed of *n* numbers, each of which is either a "0" or a "1."

Estimating Success Probability *p*

Given such a sample of size *n*, how should we estimate *p*, the population proportion of successes? The logical way to estimate an unknown population proportion would be to use the sample proportion of successes. If 18 in a sample of 50 are in favor of a proposed rule, our best estimator for *p* (which we shall denote by $\hat{p}$, and read "*p*-hat") is $\hat{p} = 18/50 = 0.36$. Note this fact well: since a success is a "1" and a failure a "0," the value "18" is in fact the sum of the 50 sample values, 18 of which are "1" and 32 are "0." Thus, $\Sigma X_i = 18$, and $\overline{X} = 18/50 = 0.36$. In other words, the sample proportion, which is our best estimator of *p*, is a sample mean. Using the same reasoning, we see that the population proportion *p* is the same as the population mean μ. Why are these facts important? If the sample size *n* is "large," we know that the distribution of sample means is well described by the normal. In the last section, we learned that a 95%, large-sample confidence interval for a μ could be constructed by using the sample mean as a center point, and then adding and subtracting two standard deviations of the sample mean to this point estimate. Since *p* is in fact a μ and since $\hat{p}$ is a sample mean, we shall do exactly the same thing here in setting a confidence interval on *p*. We form the 95% confidence interval by adding and subtracting two standard errors of $\hat{p}$ to $\hat{p}$ itself. Our only problem is in determining the standard error of $\hat{p}$. Since $\hat{p}$ is a sample mean, we know its standard error is of the form

$\sigma/\sqrt{n}$, where σ is the population standard deviation. The population probability distribution has the following structure:

x	$p(x)$
0	$1 - p$
1	p

In order to determine $\sigma/\sqrt{n}$, we first need to find the population standard deviation σ. We shall use the computing formula for the population variance σ^2, and then take the square root. We begin by finding $E(X)$ and $E(X^2)$, both of which are needed to find σ^2:

$$\mu = E(X) = \sum x \cdot p(x) = 0 \cdot (1 - p) + 1 \cdot p = p$$

$$E(X^2) = \sum x^2 \cdot p(x) = 0^2 \cdot (1 - p) + 1^2 \cdot p = p$$

Plugging these into the computing formula for σ^2 gives $\sigma^2 = E(X^2) - \mu^2 = p - p^2 = p(1 - p)$, so the standard error of $\hat{p}$ is $\sigma/\sqrt{n} = \sqrt{p \cdot (1 - p)/n}$. Adding and subtracting two of these standard errors (ruler-bars) to $\hat{p}$ gives the following 95%, large-sample confidence interval for p:

$$\hat{p} - 2 \sqrt{\frac{p(1 - p)}{n}} \leq p \leq \hat{p} + 2 \sqrt{\frac{p(1 - p)}{n}}$$

This seems easy enough, but we have one small problem! Our intention is to estimate the unknown proportion p with a confidence interval. Our confidence interval formula involves p. *If we knew p, there wouldn't be any reason to set a confidence interval on it.* We encountered the same problem in the last section when σ was unknown, resolving the difficulty by simply substituting a good point estimate for the unknown parameter σ. We do the same here, substituting $\hat{p}$ for the unknown value of p. This gives the following, *approximate* 95% confidence interval:

LARGE-SAMPLE APPROXIMATE CONFIDENCE INTERVALS FOR p

If $\hat{p}$ is the sample proportion of successes computed from a large (see discussion below) sample, then a 95% **confidence interval for p** is given by the following:

$$\hat{p} - 2 \sqrt{\frac{\hat{p}(1 - \hat{p})}{n}} \leq p \leq \hat{p} + 2 \sqrt{\frac{\hat{p}(1 - \hat{p})}{n}}$$

For a 90% confidence interval, replace the "2" by 1.645; for 98% confidence, use 2.33.

When using the above confidence interval formulas, we are essentially using the normal distribution to approximate the binomial. Thus, we should be guided by the same considerations discussed in Section 8.8: "Use the normal approximation if the range from $np - 3\sqrt{npq}$ to $np + 3\sqrt{npq}$ is between 0 and n." In using this criterion, we make one small adjustment: since p is unknown, we use $\hat{p}$. Thus, the large sample confidence interval on p will be acceptable if the range from

$$np\hat{} - 3\sqrt{n\hat{p}(1 - \hat{p})} \quad \text{to} \quad n\hat{p} + 3\sqrt{n\hat{p}(1 - \hat{p})}$$

is contained inside the range from 0 to n. We shall spare the details, but this is precisely equivalent to the following check: Construct the confidence interval shown in the box above, but change the "2" to a "3," which gives you a 99.74% confidence interval. If this 99.74% interval falls inside 0 to 1 (the range of possible values for p), then it is appropriate to set the 95% confidence interval on p given in the box, or any other level confidence interval you wish.

■ EXAMPLE 17

In a random sample of 144 students from an all-male military academy, 95 indicated they would prefer capital punishment to life-imprisonment. Set a 95% large-sample confidence interval on p, the true unknown proportion of the entire military academy in favor of capital punishment.

SOLUTION

We check first to see if the large-sample confidence interval is appropriate. We calculate $95 \pm 3\sqrt{32.32} = 95 \pm 17.06$. This range is clearly inside 0 to 144, so the confidence interval calculation is permitted. The resulting 95% confidence interval turns out to be

$$0.66 - 2 \cdot (0.040) \leq p \leq 0.66 + 2 \cdot (0.040)$$

or

$$0.58 \leq p \leq 0.74$$

We are 95% confident that between 58% and 74% of the entire military academy is in favor of capital punishment.   ■

EXERCISES 9.7

PRACTICING THE MOVES AND MANEUVERS

Exercises 125–131: Set large-sample 95% confidence intervals on p by using the given values for Y = number of successes in n trials. Be sure to check whether the calculation is appropriate before proceeding.

125. $n = 60$, $Y = 34$
126. $n = 81$, $Y = 6$
127. $n = 100$, $Y = 60$
128. $n = 81$, $Y = 54$

129. $n = 40$, $Y = 4$
130. $n = 144$, $Y = 20$
131. $n = 25$, $Y = 12$

APPLYING THE CONCEPTS

132. An NFL quarterback completes 160 of 250 passes in his first season. Assuming this is a random sample from his career passing (it probably isn't), estimate his career completion percentage with a 95% confidence interval.

133. In Exercise 132, set a 90% confidence interval on p.

134. A poll of 400 residents of a large city shows 240 in favor of building a new park. Assuming this poll is a random sample, set a 95% confidence interval on the true proportion of all residents of this city who favor building the park.

135. In Exercise 134, set a 90% confidence interval on p.

136. A sample of 200 crayfish was taken from a large lake in order to assess the amounts of mercury. Forty-four of the crayfish exhibited unsafe levels of mercury. Use this information to set a 95% confidence interval on p, the true proportion of crayfish in this lake with unsafe levels of mercury.

137. In Exercise 136, set a 90% confidence interval on p.

138. A tree farm claims that 92% of their seedlings will live after being transplanted according to directions. An agronomist carefully transplants 300 such seedlings and observes that 252 survive.
    (a) Use the agronomist's results to set a 90% confidence interval on p, the true proportion of all trees from this farm that will survive after transplanting.
    (b) Based on your interval in part (a), do you think the claim made by the tree farm is correct?

139. In a recent study of students attending private colleges, it was found that 180 of 210 students polled wanted their own children to attend a private college. Being careful to interpret what p represents, use this information to set a 90% confidence interval on p.

140. A recent survey of emergency room admissions in Los Angeles showed that 78 of 210 admissions were the result of some form of violent crime. Use this information to set a 90% confidence interval on p. Be sure to define p carefully before setting the confidence interval.

141. An eminent baseball statistician has observed that in 420 cases when batters have a "zero ball, two strike" count, there have been only 84 hits. What is the binomial proportion p of interest in this problem?

142. Set a 95% confidence interval on p in Exercise 141.

143. A sociologist finds that, among 268 marriages where one of the partners is previously divorced, 175 of these marriages have lasted for at least five years. Explain what the binomial parameter p represents here.

144. Set a 98% confidence interval on p in Exercise 143.

9.8 A BRIEF INTRODUCTION TO HYPOTHESIS TESTING (OPTIONAL)

In Section 9.5 we discussed briefly the notion of hypothesis testing. We said that the basic idea in hypothesis testing is this: a model which describes the population of interest is suggested. This model is said to be the null hypothesis. We might propose that a new drug has at least a 90% chance of curing a particular disease. Thus, if p represents the probability of a cure with this new drug, we are hypothesizing that $p \geq 0.90$. This hypothesis is referred to as a **null hypothesis**; we denote this by "H_0: $p \geq 0.90$." If we doubt the validity of the null hypothesis H_0: $p \geq 0.90$, then the logical **alternative hypothesis**, denoted by H_a, is H_a: $p < 0.90$.

To test H_0, we take data, and see if these data support the model under H_0. (The phrase "under H_0" means "when H_0 is true.") That is, do our data reflect what we would expect to see if $p \geq 0.90$? The probability methods we have been studying will be useful in answering this question. If the data support our model under H_0, we will not have proved that H_0 is correct, but we will have no reason to doubt the model—we "fail to reject" H_0. On the other hand, if the data do not support the model described by H_0, then one of two possibilities has occurred: **(1)** the model under H_0 really is appropriate, but we have observed an "unusual sample," or **(2)** the null hypothesis is incorrect, and we should adopt the alternative.

If the cure rate p of this new drug is 90%, so that H_0 is true, then among many groups of 100 patients, we would see an average of 90 cures. Suppose that in our tests the new drug cures only 45 of 100 patients with this disease. A sample of size 100 with only 45 cures casts severe doubt on the null hypothesis. Faced with such a contrary result, we attempt to choose between the two following explanations: **(1)** the cure rate is ≥ 0.90, and we have observed an exceedingly unlikely sample, or **(2)** the alternative hypothesis is true and the actual cure rate is < 0.90.

We pose another situation, equivalent to deciding about the effectiveness of the new drug. A basketball player claims he can make at least 90% of his free throws. His coach puts him at the line, and the player makes only 45 of 100. Certainly we would be justified in rejecting the player's claim. It is possible that he would make at most 45 out of 100 even if his claim is true. Such an event is so rare, however, that faced with a choice between **(1)** his claim is true and we have seen a rare event or **(2)** his claim is false, we would opt easily for choice 2.

Type I Error

In testing hypotheses, we base our decision on sample data, which do not always reflect the true population structure. Hence, it is possible to make errors. If we conclude H_0 is false when it is in fact true, we have committed a **Type I error**. Thus, if the new drug really has a cure rate of 90% or more and we say that it does not, we have committed a Type I error. Similarly, if the basketball coach tells the basketball player that he cannot make at least 90% of his free throws when he in fact can, the coach has committed a Type I error.

Type II Error Suppose, however, that the new drug is not as effective as claimed, and the cure probability p is less than 0.90 so that H_0 is false. It is possible that our sample will mislead us into claiming that the new drug is effective—we will not reject H_0 when we should. This error of failing to reject a false null hypothesis is called a **Type II error**. If the basketball coach claims that his player is a 90% free-throw shooter, when in fact he can only make 60% (or any other number less than 90%), then he is making a Type II error.

ERRORS IN HYPOTHESIS TESTING

> When testing the null statistical hypothesis H_0 against the alternative hypothesis H_a, it is possible to make the wrong decision: *Rejecting a true null hypothesis is a Type I error; failing to reject a false null hypothesis is a Type II error.*

At the time you make the decision of whether or not to reject the null hypothesis, you will not know whether you are making an error. To know if you are making an error, you would need to know the correct value for the parameter you are testing—if you knew this value, there would be no reason to test this hypothesis! The best we can hope for, then, is to know the probability of making an error.

P-Values In many applications, the hypothesis testing procedure is designed to give a predefined, small probability of a Type I error, such as 0.05, or 0.01. In this text, however, we shall focus on a slightly different approach. We shall examine our data for conformance with the null hypothesis by seeking the answer to the following question:

> **If H_0 is true, how likely is it that we would see results as contradictory to H_0 as we did, or even more contradictory?**

The answer to this question is called **the descriptive level of significance**, or **p-value**. If this p-value is "small," we would be inclined to reject the null hypothesis in favor of H_a. In the real world, someone with ultimate responsibility for making the choice between H_0 and H_a would have to decide what "small" is. The job of a statistician is to present the appropriate information.

We shall now illustrate the procedure for calculating a p-value.

■ EXAMPLE 18

A male employer has been accused of sexual discrimination in hiring—the union claims he is hiring far too few female employees. The case goes to trial, and the employer's attorney is quite concerned—he feels that if the jury has too many women on it, there is little chance his client will be acquitted. Seven jury members are chosen on the first day, and the employer's attorney thinks they are "all right." The next day, however, the final five jurors will be chosen *at random* from a pool of 16. Since this jury pool consists of 11 men and only five women, the attorney breathes a sigh of relief—after all, the men outnumber the women by over two-to-one. Surely the jury will not be stacked against his client. The next day the trial begins. The employer's attorney is flabbergasted to find that the five jurors chosen "at random" are four women and one man. He asks for a recess and, after playing on the merry-go-round for half an hour, goes to the judge's chambers, where he protests the selection, claiming discrimination. Does he have a good case?

SOLUTION   The model to be examined here is: *Selection of the five jurors was random.* Do the observed data (four women, one man) support this hypothesis of random selection? On the surface, the answer would seem to be a resounding no; if the data are random, we would expect more men than women. Let us calculate the *p*-value, which is the answer to the following question:

> **If the selection were made at random, how likely is it that we would observe a selection as extreme as we did (four women, one man) or something even more extreme (the only result more extreme is five women and no men)?**

If this *p*-value is extremely small, then one of two things has happened: **(1)** there was a random selection, and we have been victimized by a rare event (a statistical Murphy's Law), or **(2)** there is evidence of non-randomness. Let's answer the above question by finding the required probability.

P[four or more women in a random sample of size five]

$$= P[\text{four women and one man}] + P[\text{five women and no men}]$$

$$P[\text{four women and one man}] = \frac{C(5,4) \cdot C(11,1)}{C(16,5)} = \frac{55}{4368}$$

$$P[\text{five women and no men}] = \frac{C(5,5) \cdot C(11,0)}{C(16,5)} = \frac{1}{4368}$$

Thus, the *p*-value, which is the probability of having observed a result as extreme as we did (four women and no men), or even more extreme (five women and no men), *if the selection process were really random*, is only $55/4368 + 1/4368 = 56/4368 \approx 0.0128$. What then should we conclude? We have two choices: **(1)** the selection process was random and we have observed an exceedingly rare event—an event that has probability less than 0.013; or **(2)** the selection process was not random (in which case there *may* have been bias in the selection of the last five jurors).

Since an event with probability 0.0128 happens roughly once in every 78 experiments, it is not what we anticipate seeing in our one experiment. We would thus conclude that the selection process was not random.

Could we be wrong in this conclusion? Yes, although we feel confident that we aren't—after all, if we are wrong, then we have observed a near miracle. It is important to note, however, that non-randomness is not conclusive evidence of foul play; there could simply be something awry in the selection process.

The preceding example illustrates the basic ideas of hypothesis testing. The following example gives another such example. Study the thinking again: we propose a model, take data, and see if these data support the model by examining how likely our observed data are under the model, that is, if the model is correct. If these data are extremely unlikely under our proposed model (that is, if the p-value is a small number such as 0.05), then either **(1)** the model is correct, but we have seen a rare event—an extraordinarily unlikely event that we would not expect to see if our hypothesis were true or **(2)** the model is incorrect. Reason **(1)** is somewhat like a "Murphy's Law" of statistics. If the model is incorrect, then we will have done the right thing by discarding this model and seeking a better explanation. If, however, we throw out the model when it is really correct, then we will have committed a Type I error.

■ EXAMPLE 19

A scientist claims to have developed an improved method of treating a certain disease. The current treatment cures 40% of the people within eight hours. If the new treatment is to be an improvement, there should be more than a 40% chance of cure within eight hours. To test the scientist's claim, government researchers try his remedy on 20 people. Within eight hours, 15 are cured. Is the new remedy more effective than the current?

SOLUTION

The model we propose is that the new treatment is equal (not better) in effectiveness to the current treatment. Stated as a null hypothesis, we write H_0: $p = 0.40$, where p represents the probability of a cure with the new treatment. A reasonable alternative hypothesis is H_a: $p > 0.40$. If the data cast severe doubt on H_0, then we have just cause for believing the alternative that the scientist has an improved method. Under H_0, we would expect $\mu = np = 20 \cdot (0.4) = 8$ cures. We observed 15, which is considerably more than eight and definitely indicative of an improved cure rate. Is 15 enough more than eight? Once again, we answer this by computing the p-value: "How likely is a result as extreme as we got (15), or something even more extreme (more than 15), if the new treatment is 40% effective?"

Since the cure or non-cure of any one person has no bearing on the others, the 20 people form 20 independent binomial trials where a success is a cure, and $p = 0.4$. Letting Y = number of cures in 20 trials, the descriptive level of significance (p-value) is

$P[15$ or more cures in 20 trials if cure probability is 0.4]

$$= P[Y \geq 15 \quad \text{when} \quad p = 0.4]$$

$$= C(20,15) \cdot (0.4)^{15} \cdot (0.6)^5 + \cdots + C(20,20) \cdot (0.4)^{20} \cdot (0.6)^0$$

Instead of doing all this arithmetic, we use Table I:

$$P[Y \geq 15 \quad \text{when} \quad p = 0.4] = 1 - P[Y \leq 14 \quad \text{when} \quad p = 0.4]$$

$$= 1 - 0.998 = 0.002$$

If the new remedy were exactly as effective as the current treatment ($p = 0.4$), it is exceedingly unlikely we would observe our result or a more extreme one. Thus, either the scientist's cure is no better (in which case we have observed an extremely rare event) or his treatment is in fact better. The rational choice would be to conclude that his treatment is better than the current method, but we leave the actual choice to the responsible decision maker. Our job ends with calculation of the p-value.

If the decision maker rejects the null hypothesis model that $p = 0.40$, he can feel confident that it is not the correct description of the population. On the other hand, if the data were such that he had failed to reject H_0, he would not have proved that the model given by H_0 is correct—he could have said only that there is not sufficient reason to doubt the validity of H_0. ∎

■ EXAMPLE 20

In quality control work, manufactured items are regularly checked to see if production is "under control." Consider a machine that makes precision parts designed to be 3 centimeters long. To determine if the process is in control, a quality control inspector examines a random sample of four items. If the process is in control, then experience has shown that the sample mean of these four should act like a value from a normal distribution whose mean is 3 centimeters, and whose standard deviation is 0.0002. We are particularly interested in being able to detect shifts in the production process that result in part-lengths greater than 3.0000. (Parts that are too small will still work, but if the average length is more than 3.0000, then too many of these precision parts will not work as advertised.) Thus, as our null hypothesis, we adopt H_0: $\mu = 3$, with the alternative H_a: $\mu > 3$. A random sample of 4 items produces the following data:

3.0007   3.0002   3.0009   3.0002

Is the process still in control (that is, is H_0 true) or is the mean part length now greater than 3.0000 (in which case H_a is true)?

SOLUTION   The sample mean for these data is 3.0005, which does not appear to be far from the nominal value of 3.0000. However, if the sample mean is really normally distributed around a population mean of 3.0000, then there is a 0.5 chance of having a value greater than 3.0000 and a 0.5 chance of having a value less than 3.0000. Here we have observed four consecutive values above 3.0000. If the values are independent, and the mean is really 3.0000, there is only a $(1/2)^4 = 1/16$ chance of this happening. Viewed in this light, things look more suspicious! This reasoning is very intuitive, and takes no account of the fact that the sample mean of these four should act like a randomly selected value from a normal distribution with a mean of 3.0000 and a standard deviation of 0.0002. Let's see how this information can be used. We observe that 3.0005 is extreme in the direction that indicates that the true population mean μ may have shifted above 3.0000. Once again we ask the by-now familiar question: How likely is it that we would observe a result as extreme as we did (a sample mean of 3.0005) or something even more extreme (an even larger sample mean) if the process is in control? To obtain the p-value, which is the answer to this question, we calculate

$$P[\overline{X} \geq 3.0005 \quad \text{when the process is in control}]$$

If the process is in control, a sample mean of 3.0005 has a z-score of $(3.0005 - 3.0000)/0.0002 = 2.5$. In other words, we have seen a sample mean that is 2.5 standard deviations above the population mean. Checking the standard normal tables reveals that the chances of getting a value at least this large if the process is in control is only 0.0062. With a p-value this small, either the process is in control, and we have observed another miracle, or else the process is out of control. Under these circumstances, the quality control inspector would shut production down and attempt to discover the reason for the increased mean.   ∎

The examples of this section are designed to give you only a brief introduction to the statistical flavor of hypothesis testing. In a statistics course, you would go into more depth, but the ideas are much the same.

EXERCISES 9.8

APPLYING THE CONCEPTS

145. Delmo claims to be able to toss heads at least 70% of the time with a fair coin. You ask him to demonstrate, and in 20 coin flips he produces 11 heads and 9 tails. What do you think of this claim? Answer by computing the p-value.

146. A video manufacturer claims his top-of-the-line VCR has at most a 5% defective rate. You are a technician at a video store, and you observe that three of the first 10 sets are defective when opened. What do you think of the manufactur-

er's claim? Answer by computing the appropriate p-value.

147. The drives (tee shots) of two professional golfers are recorded on nine par-four holes during an 18-hole round. The two play together, so conditions are the same, and both players use the same club and brand of ball. The data are:

Pro A	265 249 276 263 248 283 259 267 283
Pro B	248 245 265 256 256 276 251 257 278

Statisticians have special ways to handle such data; we do a quick analysis by noting that if the two golfers were "equally long," each should outdrive the other about half the time—determining long drive on a hole would be like flipping a coin. Here, professional A outdrove professional B in 8 of 9 holes. Does that guarantee A is the longer driver? If they have equal length drivers, what we have observed is like getting 8 heads in 9 tosses of a balanced coin. What is the probability of A outdriving B 8 or 9 times if A and B are equal in driving ability? Comment.

A Brief Summary of Important Ideas

A **statistic** is a quantity calculated from a sample. A statistic may be used to summarize sample information or to estimate an unknown population parameter. Describing and summarizing sample data is the realm of **descriptive statistics**, while **statistical inference** uses statistics to make inferences (draw conclusions) about populations. Graphical means of summarizing data are the **histogram**, the **stem-and-leaf display**, and the **box-and-whisker plot** or simply boxplot.

To present a numerical description of a data set, we use **measures of central tendency**, which characterize the "middle" of a data set, and **measures of dispersion**, which describe how closely the data are clustered about the middle. Typical measures of central tendency are the sample **mean**, sample **median**, and sample **mode**. The sample mean $\overline{X}$ uses all the data but may be overly influenced by extreme values. The sample median M, while not using all the data, is not affected by extreme values, and may afford a better picture of the data in the presence of extremes. Large discrepancies between the mean and the median are evidence of **skewness**, or lack of symmetry.

The sample variance S^2 and its square root, the standard deviation S, measure spread or dispersion in a data set. Chebyshev's inequality, which applies to samples as well as to probability distributions and populations, provides a way to interpret the size of a standard deviation. If we know that a data set is relatively symmetric or "mound-shaped," then the **Empirical Rule** asserts that about 68% of the sample values will be within one standard deviation of the mean, about 95% within two standard deviations of the mean, and virtually all the data will be within three standard deviations of the mean.

For larger data sets, **percentiles** and **quartiles** provide summary descriptions that contain information about both location and dispersion. The three statistics Q_1, Q_2, and Q_3 (the first, second, and third quartiles) divide a set of data into four zones containing (roughly) equal amounts of data. The interquartile range, IQR, is $Q_3 - Q_1$, and describes the range occupied by the middle 50% of the data. In addition, the IQR may be used to test for **outliers**, or values which are suspect because of being conspicuously large or small.

Tukey's **five-number summary**, which consists of the minimum value, the three quartiles, and the maximum value, provides a convenient but quick and useful summary of a data set. A box-plot is a graphical representation of Tukey's five-number summary.

Every statistic has a **sampling distribution,** which describes the statistical behavior (the distribution) of values of this statistic in repeated samples of the same size from a population. The sampling distribution of a statistic tells us how well that statistic will work as an estimator for an unknown population parameter. The **Central Limit Theorem** (CLT) asserts that the sampling distribution of the statistic $\overline{X}$ has approximately a normal distribution, regardless of the distribution we sample from, provided that we have a "reasonably large" sample size. (In most cases a sample size of $n = 30$ or larger will suffice.) The sampling distribution of $\overline{X}$ has the same mean μ as the original population, and the standard error or standard deviation of the sampling distribution of $\overline{X}$ is $\sigma/\sqrt{n}$, where σ is the standard deviation of the original population. With a large sample size, the CLT enables us to set confidence intervals on the mean of a distribution by following a simple procedure: add and subtract a certain number of standard errors of $\overline{X}$ to $\overline{X}$ itself. The number of standard errors we add and subtract is dictated by the level of confidence we wish to have in the resulting interval. In particular, an approximate 95% confidence interval on the population mean μ is given by

$$\overline{X} - \frac{2\sigma}{\sqrt{n}} \leq \mu \leq \overline{X} + \frac{2\sigma}{\sqrt{n}}$$

A **statistical hypothesis** is a model that describes a population. If the model specified by the hypothesis is reasonable, then data should support the hypothesis. If the data appear to support the hypothesis, we have no apparent cause for concern. If, however, the data seem contradictory to the model specified by the hypothesis, then we ask the following question: what is the probability of seeing a result as extreme as we saw, or a result even more extreme if the null hypothesis is true? The answer to this question is the *p*-**value** or the **descriptive level of significance**. If the *p*-value is small, then one of two possibilities holds: **(1)** the hypothesis we are testing is true and we have witnessed an extremely unlikely happening—a "rare event," or **(2)** the hypothesis is false. The logical alternative is **(2)**.

REVIEW EXERCISES

PRACTICING THE MOVES AND MANEUVERS

Exercises 148–152:   Use the following data, which represent the grade point averages of the varsity stamp-licking team at Anemia Tech.

3.45, 2.86, 2.76, 3.15, 2.94, 2.46, 2.88, 3.07, 2.99, 3.64, 2.76, 3.16, 3.02,

2.71, 3.00, 2.34, 3.37, 2.90, 3.11, 2.68, 2.44, 2.92, 2.83, 3.05, 3.21, 3.14,

2.78, 2.89, 2.64, 3.28

148. Display these data with a stem-and-leaf diagram.
149. Calculate the mean and median.
150. Calculate the range, variance, and standard deviation.
151. Calculate Q_1 and Q_3, and then present Tukey's five-number summary.
152. Draw a box plot.

Exercises 153–158:   Consider the following data, representing hay yields, in tons per acre, of 24 one-acre plots on an experimental farm.

4.5, 3.9, 4.4, 4.6, 4.2, 4.3, 4.0, 4.7, 4.5, 4.4, 3.1, 4.2

4.3, 4.6, 4.2, 4.0, 3.9, 4.2, 4.1, 4.0, 4.3, 4.4, 4.2, 4.3

153. Construct a stem-and-leaf display for these data.
154. Find the mean and median for these data.
155. Find the range, variance, and standard deviation of these data.
156. Calculate Q_1, Q_3, and present Tukey's five-number summary.
157. Construct a box plot of the data.
158. Test for outliers.

Exercises 159–164:   Use the following data, which represent number of completed passes in a random sample of 9 games chosen from a starting quarterback's career:

14, 21, 19, 17, 12, 24, 18, 4, 20

159. Find the mean and median number of completed passes.
160. Find the range, variance, and standard deviation for these data.
161. Approximate the standard deviation by using the range.
162. Present Tukey's five-number summary.
163. Draw a box plot for the data.
164. Check for outliers.

APPLYING THE CONCEPTS

Exercises 165 and 166:   Treat the varsity stamp lickers from Anemia Tech (Exercises 148–152) as if they were a random sample of size 30 from the population consisting of G.P.A.'s for all collegiate varsity stamp lickers in the United States.

165. Set a 95% confidence interval on the population mean μ.
166. Set a 90% confidence interval on the population mean μ.

Exercises 167–169: Use the data of Exercises 153–158.

167. Construct a frequency distribution having five classes.
168. Construct a histogram for your frequency distribution.

169. The 24 data values are less than the recommended 30 for application of the Central Limit Theorem. Ignore this fact, and set a 95% confidence interval on the population mean μ. Give an interpretation of what μ represents in this problem.

170. A poll of 250 residents in a large community revealed 180 that felt local taxes were too high. Treating this poll as a random sample, set a 90% confidence interval on p, the true unknown proportion of all people in this community who feel that local taxes are too high.

171. A random sample of 64 values is taken from a population having mean $\mu = 65$ and $\sigma = 6$. Nothing else is known about this population. Find the probability that the mean of this random sample exceeds 66.5.

172. In Exercise 171, find the probability that the mean of this random sample has a value less than 64.25.

173. A random sample of 40 quantitative GRE scores for students entering graduate school at Boondoggle A&M had mean 380, and standard deviation 84. Use this information to set a 95% confidence interval on μ, the true unknown average quantitative GRE score for all entering graduate students at Boondoggle A&M.

174. A salesman attempts to sell you a service contract on your new car that will provide for any repairs during the second year (your new car has a one-year warranty). To encourage your purchase, the salesman cites statistics showing that "60 percent of these cars need repairs dur-

ing the second year." You doubt his claim, and call 20 people taken from a list of registered owners. Only four of them needed repairs during the second year. You formulate the hypothesis H_0: $p = 0.60$ and the alternative H_a: $p < 0.60$.

(a) If H_0 is true, how many people would you have expected to need repairs in your sample?

(b) Find the p-value which describes just how likely it is that four or fewer people would need repairs if the car salesman's claim is correct.

175. An insurance company executive claims that the average starting salary for entry-level actuaries in the United States in a given year is \$34,000. You think that this is an inflated figure. To decide whether his claim is reasonable, you take a random sample of 40 starting salaries and find that the average is \$32,800. The standard deviation for this sample was \$2,400. Treat this sample standard deviation as if it were σ, and determine how likely it is that you would see a mean salary as low as you did or a mean salary even lower if the true mean is \$34,000. Note that your answer is in fact the p-value for testing H_0: $\mu = \$34,000$ against H_a: $\mu < \$34,000$.

10 Games and Decisions

We know a great deal about counting techniques and probabilities, and about probability distributions for random variables. We can, in standard language, describe populations and probability distributions, and can make predictive statements about future experiments.

Now we shall use our powerful new tools to analyze the economic consequences of alternatives, in order to make informed choices. The fundamental idea, from Chapter 8, is "expected value," which describes both a probability distribution and the "long-range average" of random numbers (here, the dollar payoffs to which we alluded) produced according to a fixed probability distribution. Knowing the expected payoff of a single option (like buying a risky stock) helps us to decide whether or not to choose that option. Knowing the expected payoffs of alternatives enables us to choose intelligently among them. This is the sort of question we pursue in Sections 10.1 (general "chance" situations), 10.2 (life insurance), and 10.3 (business decisions, risk assessment and a first approach to inventory control), culminating in Section 10.4 with "marginal analysis," a widely used tool for precise inventory control. The context up to this point is still evaluating choices whose outcomes occur according to fixed, known probabilities.

Finally, in Section 10.5 we meet the most interesting situation: decision making in competition with an intelligent, competitive opponent who sends "outcomes" to us in ways designed to minimize our gain at his or her expense. Sections 10.6 and 10.7 explore increasingly complex and difficult competitive environments. Let the games begin!

10.1 OUTCOMES AND VALUES; THE VALUE OF A GAME

A stranger beckons from a darkened doorway and proposes that you toss your own (hence fair, of course) coin, pay her one dollar for "heads" and collect $5 from her for "tails." Should you play? Since the odds in favor of a "head" are one to one, a fair bet is $1 to $1; since she will bet $5, not $1, against your $1, you have a tremendous advantage. Reasoning thus, you choose to play as long as she is willing and her money lasts.

Analyzing further: the "payoffs" $5 and − $1 will accrue to you with known, fixed probabilities (0.5 and 0.5, respectively). In 100 plays, you would win about 50 times, taking in about $250, and lose about 50 times, paying out about $50. Your net winnings in 100 plays would be about $200—an average gain of $2 per play. This analysis assumes that the relative frequencies of the outcomes (wins and losses) will closely approximate their probabilities. This entirely reasonable assumption illustrates the thinking behind "expected value." In Chapter 8 language, "the long range average value per play of this game is $2."

We now analyze a game with more than two possible outcomes:

EXAMPLE 1

In a brown paper bag you mix M&M candies (four green, six brown, one yellow, and nine red) and offer to let a friend select one M&M without looking. You will pay him $10 if it is yellow and $3 if it is green. He must pay you $2 if it is brown and $1 if it is red. Who has the advantage in this game—you or your opponent?

SOLUTION

In this two-player situation, you must take the point of view of one player and hold that viewpoint throughout the thinking process. You must know the possible outcomes, their related values and their probabilities. (See Figure 10.1.)

Figure 10.1
Outcomes/values/probabilities table for the M&M game

Outcomes	Green	Brown	Yellow	Red
Values	−3	2	−10	1
Probabilities	0.2	0.3	0.05	0.45

Things to notice about the table:

(a) "Outcomes" and "values" are recorded on separate lines.

(b) The "values" line, with its positive and negative entries, reflects a consistent point of view ("you," rather than "opponent"). This is extremely important!

(c) The probabilities of the various outcomes are also the probabilities of the values associated with those outcomes.

Thinking of the possible "values" as payoffs, we may find the expected payoff:

$$E = 0.2(-3) + 0.3(2) + 0.05(-10) + 0.45(1) = -0.05$$

Since the payoff table was constructed from *your* point of view, and the expected ("long-run average") payoff is negative five cents, you would lose about a nickel per play. This game is a money loser for you; your opponent has a small advantage. ∎

Value of a Game

Consider the structure of Example 1. By assigning numerical values (monetary payoffs) to the nonnumerical outcomes, we have introduced a "payoff" random variable X. Attaching probabilities to the payoffs ("values") produces the probability distribution of the random variable X. The expected value of this random variable (that is, the expected payoff), or the average value per play over a large number of plays, determines who has the advantage in the game, and how significant this advantage is. This single number, the expected net payoff of the game, is all we need to know in order to describe the game's worth to us.

GAME; VALUE OF A GAME

> A **game** is an experiment with monetary outcomes. The **value of a game** from one player's point of view is the expected net payoff to that person, taking into account the "cost to play." The terms "value" and "net value" mean the same thing.

PRACTICE PROBLEM 1

In each of the following, show outcomes, values, and probabilities in a table, and answer the question posed:

(a) Toss three coins. For 3 heads, collect $7 from your opponent. For 3 tails, collect $4. For "mixed" outcomes, pay your opponent $3. Point of view: opponent's. Who has the advantage? Explain.

(b) Your 14-pound textbook, *Better Living through Organic Economics*, is worth $50. There is one chance in 20 that your book will be lost or stolen during the quarter. What is the net value to you of buying, for $3, an insurance policy that will replace the lost or stolen book?

(c) Which would you rather do: toss one die, collect $5 per dot if the outcome is even and pay $5 per dot if the outcome is odd, or draw one card from a deck, collect $5 for an ace, $4 for a face card, and $2 otherwise?

ANSWER(S)

(a) Expected value: $0.875, positive from opponent's viewpoint. Opponent has advantage; you would lose about $0.875 per play.   (b) From your viewpoint: if you buy the policy and your book is not lost, you have "lost" $3; if your book is lost, you collect $47. Expected net value: −$0.50.   (c) Dice game value, $2.50; card game value, about $2.69. Card game is a bit better. ☐

Lessons from These Practice Problems

Practice Problem 1(b) highlights a new idea: in a game in which a fee (such as an insurance premium) is charged to enter the game, you may either find the expected gross payoff of the game, then subtract the entry price to determine the net value of the game, or you may reflect the entry price in each table entry in the "values" line and determine the net value of the game directly. The two possible tables for (b) are shown in Figure 10.2.

Figure 10.2
Gross and net payoff tables for insurance problem

Table for *GROSS* Value

Outcomes	Lost	Not Lost
Values	$50	$0
Probabilities	0.05	0.95

Table for *NET* Value

Outcomes	Lost	Not Lost
Values	$47	−$3
Probabilities	0.05	0.95

Gross value = $(50) \cdot 0.05 + 0 \cdot 0.95$

$\qquad$ = $2.50

Net value = gross value − cost

$\qquad$ = $2.50 − $3 = −$.50

Net value = $47 \cdot 0.05 + (−3) \cdot 0.95$

$\qquad$ = 2.35 − 2.85

$\qquad$ = −$.50

Both approaches yield the same net value. We may "build in" the entry fee (net value table), or subtract it from the expected gross payoff.

In Practice Problem 1(c) you chose between two games by comparing their (expected) values. This is a key idea; we will use it a great deal in this chapter.

Fair Games

One party or the other had an "advantage" in each of the above situations. In (a), your opponent had the advantage; in (b), it was the insurance company (since the value of the game from your point of view was negative); and in (c), you held the advantage in both games, and needed only to choose between them.

If one participant has a monetary advantage over the other, a game could hardly be called "fair." Many "plays" of the game would build up a significant gain for one player. The word "fair" should describe only a game in which neither player has an advantage. A **fair game** is one whose value is zero.

We have been using the word "game" as if we knew what we were talking about. Let's clarify our understanding:

A TWO-PARTY, ZERO-SUM GAME

> A two-party, zero-sum game involves two "players." Its outcomes occur according to fixed probabilities. Its "values" are specified from the point of view of one player. Each nonzero value represents a gain by one player, and an identical loss by the other. The total money held by the two players does not change. Only the distribution of money between the two players is affected by plays of the game. "Zero-sum" means "summing the two players' gains and losses yields zero."

A FAIR GAME

> A two-party, zero-sum game is said to be fair if the game value is zero.

Note that a fair game has value zero regardless of "point of view." This makes sense: a game cannot be fair for one party and not for the other.

EXERCISES 10.1

PRACTICING THE MOVES AND MANEUVERS

Exercises 1 and 2: Find the expected net payoff, using the given gross payoff table.

1.

Outcome	Red	Yellow	Blue	Green
Value	$2	−$5	$1	$3
Probabilities	0.1		0.4	0.3
	Cost per play: $1			

2.

Outcome	Ace	Face	Other
Value	$10	−$10	$3
Probabilities	$\frac{4}{52}$	$\frac{12}{52}$	
	Cost per play: $1		

3. Find the expected net payoff in Exercise 1 if the cost per play is $2.
4. Find the expected net payoff in Exercise 2 if the cost per play is $2.
5. What price to play would make the game of Exercise 1 perfectly fair?
6. What payoff for "other" would make the game of Exercise 2 fair?

APPLYING THE CONCEPTS

7. A lottery offers one first prize ($1,000), two second prizes ($500 each), and five third prizes ($100 each). Ten thousand $1 tickets will be sold. What is the value to you of this game if you buy one ticket?

8. In Game 1, you roll two fair dice, collect $5 if a "double" occurs, pay $2 if the two dice differ by three or more, and collect $1 otherwise. The cost per play of the game is $.50. What is the game value? What "cost" would make the game fair?

9. Game 2 uses a deck of cards. You draw two cards at random. If both are of one suit, collect $5; if both are the same denomination, collect $2. Collect nothing otherwise. The price to play is $.50. What is the game value? What price to play would make the game fair?

10. A letter to "occupant" at your address says "You may win $10,000! To enter, return the enclosed form, indicating whether or not you wish to subscribe to *Modern Skateboarding*." The same mailing has gone out to two million potential subscribers. Your "fee to play" this "game" is about 30 cents—the cost of an envelope and stamp. What is the value of the game?

11. Regardless of the value of games such as the one in Exercise 10, many people do choose to play. Why?

12. If in Exercise 10 the letter clearly says "you need not subscribe in order to qualify for the drawing," why do you think many people would say "yes" to the magazine subscription?

13. You are about to risk your professional video camera and recorder, valued at $10,000, in an attempt to produce a television program documenting your raft trip through the Grand Canyon. For $1200, Floyd's of Peoria, a world-famous insurance firm, will insure your equipment against being lost during the trip. You estimate your chances for a successful trip (no loss of equipment) at 80%. Is the insurance a good investment? What premium would be fair?

10.2 HUMAN MORTALITY AND THE INSURANCE "GAME"

Practice Problem 1(b) and Exercise 13 of Section 10.1 revealed some essential features of the insurance industry. In the present section we confine our attention to life insurance. To simplify, we ignore such items as the company's overhead expenses (buildings, people, advertising, etc.). We also set aside the company's very reason for existence: to generate profits for its stockholders. Such considerations, though within our capabilities, would require more time and space than is appropriate here.

Modern insurance companies tailor their plans to take into account differences of occupation, medical history, smoking habits, and the like. Each special group has its own risk characteristics. Some groups pay higher premiums because they constitute greater risks for the insurance company. For example, the unmarried under-25 male driver pays a much larger car insurance premium than does the older, married male. "Not fair," you say? If all male drivers were statistically lumped together and insured, the young unmarrieds would pay much less; but all others would pay a bit more. Ideally, each person should pay exactly what his or her (unknown) personal accident probability requires. Insurers do the next best thing: they group us with large numbers of persons who, for insurance purposes, are very much like us. As a group, we fall into patterns which yield appropriate premium structures.

A recent human mortality table is the 1980 Commissioners Standard Ordinary (CSO) Mortality Table. The preceding (1958) CSO table did not separate male and female mortality figures. Figures dating from 1980 may seem out of date to the layperson; but mortality patterns change very gradually, and the 1980 table does reflect the striking increases in longevity due to dietary, exercise, and medical advances of recent decades. Fascinating trends may be observed within each table, and between the 1958 and 1980 tables. For convenience in making comparisons, excerpts from both tables (with separate 1980 information for males and females) are shown side by side in Figure 10.3.

Take a few moments to study the Figure 10.3 table. For illustration purposes, the mortality of three initial populations of ten million people is traced, year by year, with the death rate for each year also shown. Follow the "Deaths per 1000" columns from Age 0 downward; you may be surprised at what you see!

Figure 10.3
Human mortality tables
(*Source:* National Association
of Insurance Commissioners.)

Excerpts from the Commissioners Standard Ordinary Mortality Tables								
1958 Data (Male W/Female)			1980 Data (Male Only)			1980 Data (Female Only)		
Age	Number Living	Deaths per 1000	Age	Number Living	Deaths per 1000	Age	Number Living	Deaths per 1000
0	10,000,000	7.08	0	10,000,000	4.18	0	10,000,000	2.89
1	9,929,200	1.76	1	9,958,200	1.07	1	9,971,100	0.87
2	9,911,725	1.52	2	9,947,545	0.99	2	9,962,425	0.81
3	9,896,659	1.46	3	9,937,697	0.98	3	9,954,355	0.79
4	9,882,210	1.40	4	9,927,958	0.95	4	9,946,491	0.77
5	9,868,375	1.35	5	9,918,526	0.90	5	9,938,832	0.76
6	9,855,053	1.30	6	9,909,599	0.86	6	9,931,278	0.73
7	9,842,241	1.26	7	9,901,077	0.80	7	9,924,028	0.72
8	9,829,840	1.23	8	9,893,156	0.76	8	9,916,883	0.70
9	9,817,749	1.21	9	9,885,637	0.74	9	9,909,941	0.69
10	9,805,870	1.21	10	9,878,322	0.73	10	9,903,103	0.68
11	9,794,005	1.23	11	9,871,111	0.77	11	9,896,369	0.69
12	9,781,958	1.26	12	9,863,510	0.85	12	9,889,541	0.72

Figure 10.3 *(continued)*

Excerpts from the Commissioners Standard Ordinary Mortality Tables								
1958 Data (Male W/Female)			1980 Data (Male Only)			1980 Data (Female Only)		
Age	Number Living	Deaths per 1000	Age	Number Living	Deaths per 1000	Age	Number Living	Deaths per 1000
13	9,769,633	1.32	13	9,855,126	0.99	13	9,882,421	0.75
14	9,756,737	1.39	14	9,845,369	1.15	14	9,875,009	0.80
15	9,743,175	1.46	15	9,834,047	1.33	15	9,867,109	0.85
16	9,728,950	1.54	16	9,820,968	1.51	16	9,858,722	0.90
17	9,713,967	1.62	17	9,806,138	1.67	17	9,849,849	0.95
18	9,698,230	1.69	18	9,789,762	1.78	18	9,840,492	0.98
19	9,681,840	1.74	19	9,772,336	1.86	19	9,830,848	1.02
20	9,664,994	1.79	20	9,754,159	1.90	20	9,820,821	1.05
21	9,647,694	1.83	21	9,735,626	1.91	21	9,810,509	1.07
22	9,630,039	1.86	22	9,717,031	1.89	22	9,800,012	1.09
23	9,612,127	1.89	23	9,698,666	1.86	23	9,789,330	1.11
24	9,593,960	1.91	24	9,680,626	1.82	24	9,778,464	1.14
25	9,575,636	1.93	25	9,663,007	1.77	25	9,767,317	1.16
26	9,557,155	1.96	26	9,645,903	1.73	26	9,755,987	1.19
27	9,538,423	1.99	27	9,629,216	1.71	27	9,744,377	1.22
28	9,519,442	2.03	28	9,612,750	1.70	28	9,732,489	1.26
29	9,500,118	2.08	29	9,596,408	1.71	29	9,720,226	1.30
30	9,480,358	2.13	30	9,579,998	1.73	30	9,707,590	1.35
31	9,460,165	2.19	31	9,563,425	1.78	31	9,694,485	1.40
32	9,439,447	2.25	32	9,546,402	1.83	32	9,680,913	1.45
33	9,418,208	2.32	33	9,528,932	1.91	33	9,666,876	1.50
34	9,396,358	2.40	34	9,510,732	2.00	34	9,652,376	1.58
35	9,373,807	2.51	35	9,491,711	2.11	35	9,637,125	1.65
36	9,350,279	2.64	36	9,471,683	2.24	36	9,621,224	1.76
37	9,325,594	2.80	37	9,450,466	2.40	37	9,604,291	1.89
38	9,299,482	3.01	38	9,427,785	2.58	38	9,586,139	2.04
39	9,271,491	3.25	39	9,403,461	2.79	39	9,566,583	2.22
40	9,241,359	3.53	40	9,377,225	3.02	40	9,545,345	2.42
50	8,762,306	8.32	50	8,966,618	6.71	50	9,219,130	4.96
60	7,698,698	20.34	60	8,084,266	16.08	60	8,603,801	9.47
70	5,592,012	49.79	70	6,274,160	39.51	70	7,448,816	22.11
80	2,626,372	109.98	80	3,274,541	98.84	80	5,056,025	65.99
90	468,174	228.14	90	645,788	221.77	90	1,496,826	190.75

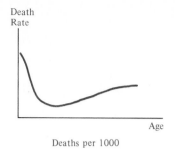

Death
Rate

Age

Deaths per 1000

Questions to consider when studying the mortality tables:

1. What was the death rate (deaths per thousand) for infants (age 0) in the 1958 table? For infant boys in the 1980 table? For infant girls in the 1980 table? For the 20 million infants (boys and girls together) of the 1980 table? (Be careful: adding the two death rates is not correct.)

2. At what ages were the death rates lowest for the three populations? Was there much change from 1958 to 1980?

3. If males and females are born in equal numbers, who will find it more difficult to find a mate of the opposite gender: a 60-year-old male, or a 60-year-old female? Back up your answer with figures.

4. What seems to have happened to death rates for persons 30 and over since the 1958 table was created? Why?

5. Which is the better life insurance risk from the insurance company's point of view: a 20-year-old male or a 35-year-old female?

6. At what age do females experience the same mortality rate as 16-year-old males? Why?

Mortality tables are closely linked to insurance premiums, as the following example demonstrates.

■ EXAMPLE 2

Using the Figure 10.3 table, obtain the probability that a 20-year-old male will survive to age 21. Then calculate the expected gross payoff to (the estate of) a 20-year-old of a $10,000, one-year term life insurance policy. Neglecting the insurance company's overhead costs and profit needs, what would be a perfectly fair premium for this one-year policy?

SOLUTION   Of 9,754,159 20-year-old males from the original pool of 10 million, 9,735,626 were still alive at age 21. (18,533 were not alive. . . .) Therefore a 20-year-old's one-year survival probability is 9,735,626/9,754,159 ≈ 0.9981. (His non-survival probability is about $1 - 0.9981 = 0.0019$. This could also be obtained as the result of 18,533/9,754,159.) (Incidentally, can you now interpret and use the "Deaths per 1000" column?) Figure 10.4 shows the gross payoff table.

Figure 10.4
Gross payoff table for a $10,000
life insurance policy on a
20-year-old male

Outcomes	Live	Die
Values	$0	$10,000
Probabilities	0.9981	0.0019

Expected payoff = $(0)0.9981 + (10,000)0.0019 = \$19.00$

A perfectly fair premium, neglecting costs, etc., exactly matches the expected payoff: $19.00. ∎

EXERCISES 10.2

Exercises 14–20: Use the 1980 Ordinary Mortality Table, Figure 10.3.

14. Among females less than 40 years of age, what single age group has the highest death rate? Why do you think this is so?

15. In the early years, the death rate declines, then climbs again. Why do you think it declines? Why does it begin to rise at the particular ages shown in the table?

16. Of the original 10 million males at the beginning of the table, how many are alive at age 20? What is the probability that a newborn male will live to age 20? What is the probability that a newborn male *will not* live to age 20?

17. Use the "Deaths per 1000" column to determine the probability that a 32-year-old female will not live to age 33. What is the probability that a 32-year-old female *will* live to age 33?

18. How many of the original 10 million females are alive at age 30? Use the "Deaths per 1000" column to calculate the number of 30-year-old females who will die that year, and calculate the number who will live to age 31. Your result should almost agree with the "Number living at age 31" table entry.

19. What is the probability that a 30-year-old female will live to age 31? What is the probability that such a person will die before age 31?

20. A 30-year-old male can buy a $10,000 term life insurance policy for one year for $50. Is this a fair price? If not, what price would be fair (neglecting, as usual, the insurance company's overhead and profit)?

10.3 CHOOSING A COURSE OF ACTION

How do we make choices? The considerations may be emotional or aesthetic ("Shall I wear my orange shirt or my pink shirt with my green plaid britches?" "What kind of picture would look nice over the mantel?" "What color shall I paint my dog?"); they may be quantifiable or economic ("Which diet will help me gain the most weight for football season?" "What car will give the lowest cost per mile over a five-year period?" "Shall I buy a stock or a mutual fund with profits from the sale of my hogs?"). We (your authors) would not touch the former kind of question with even a very long stick. If you want to dress that way, buy awful pictures, or have a pink poodle, that is your business!

However, when your alternatives involve numerical (especially dollars-and-cents) consequences, there are tools for identifying a choice or choices in order to optimize those consequences; then you may or may not choose such an optimal strategy, subject to other (for example legal, moral, aesthetic, or emotional) criteria. We begin with an example which embodies some such considerations.

EXAMPLE 3

Roger Chandler, in charge of cultural events for East Ennui, Oklahoma, during the summer tourist season, must choose between "Art on the Lawn" (an outdoor festival and auction of paintings) and an indoor rock concert by the Junkyard String Quartet.

Both events are very weather-sensitive. Rain would drown out the art festival, costing Roger $1000 spent on advertising. Fair weather would assure $5000 net profit from the art show. Fair weather would ruin the rock concert: rock fans would instead go water-skiing on the tepid waters of Brown Lagoon, the concert would be cancelled, and Roger would lose $1000 in advertising expenses and $3000 guaranteed to the band. Rainy weather, however, would drive people indoors, with a resulting $6000 net concert profit. What should Roger do?

SOLUTION

We shall examine Roger's options from four points of view: "The Optimist," "The Pessimist," "The Avoider of Regret," and "The Bayesian." Roger's actions and the weather interact to determine his payoff, according to Figure 10.5. Roger's possible choices, or actions, are shown at the left edge of the table. The possible weather conditions ("outcomes"), or states of nature, are shown at the top of the table. (Note: possible future conditions, whether of weather, the marketplace, gold prices or any other phenomena not under the decision maker's control, are commonly called "states of nature.") Payoffs are from Roger's viewpoint.

Figure 10.5
Payoff table for Roger's actions and "nature's" states

		States of Nature	
		Rain (R)	No Rain (Rᶜ)
Roger's Actions	Art Festival (F)	−$1000	$5000
	Rock Concert (C)	$6000	−$4000

The Optimist's Solution

For an optimist, the maximum possible payoff for each action "lights up."

The Optimist's Solution

	R	Rᶜ
(F)	−$1000	$5000
(C)	$6000	−$4000

The optimist targets the *maximum* among these *maximum row entries.* Adopting the optimist's view, Roger might say, "For the art festival, the best possible outcome would be 'no rain' and a $5000 profit. For the rock concert, the best is 'rain,' with a $6000 profit. Of these two good outcomes, the better is 'rock concert and rain.' Go for the maximum: schedule the rock concert, and hope!" Roger tries for the maximum among the maximum payoffs—he applies the **maximax criterion**.

The Pessimist's Solution   A pessimist sees the worst possible outcome resulting from any action.

The Pessimist's Solution

	R	R^c
(F)	−$1000	⟨$5000⟩
(C)	⟨$6000⟩	−$4000

If he is a pessimist, Roger will say "For the art festival, the weather could be rainy, producing a 'payoff' of −$1000. For the concert, sunny weather could yield −$4000. I would prefer the *maximum* of these *minimum payoffs:* −$1000, rather than −$4000." He hopes for the maximum among the minimum payoffs, and schedules the art show. This is the **maximin criterion**.

Avoidance of Regret   Roger may in fact not be free to consider both actions. If he could afford a $1000 loss, but would be ruined by a $4000 loss, he should stay away from the rock concert alternative! Even if his budget could afford a large loss, Roger might be terribly unhappy if the choice he makes turns out to be wrong. If so, perhaps he should prepare and examine a **regret table**— a table whose entries measure Roger's feelings if he guesses wrong. For example, if Roger elects the art festival and encounters rainy weather, he will not only lose $1000, but will think of the $6000 he would have made by choosing the rock concert instead. He will feel a "regret" of $7000, the distance from his actual payoff to his desired payoff under the same state of nature. If he schedules the concert and rain occurs, he did the right thing, and feels no regret whatsoever. In each column (corresponding to the revealed state of nature) of the table, Roger marks the "best" (greatest) entry, then in each cell of that column subtracts that cell's entry from the column's best entry. (The payoff table and regret table are shown in Figure 10.6.)

Figure 10.6
Regret table and original table

<table>
<tr><th colspan="3" style="text-align:center">Original Table</th></tr>
<tr><th></th><th>R</th><th>R^c</th></tr>
<tr><td>(F)</td><td>−$1000</td><td>$5000</td></tr>
<tr><td>(C)</td><td>$6000</td><td>−$4000</td></tr>
</table>

<table>
<tr><th colspan="3" style="text-align:center">Regret Table</th></tr>
<tr><th></th><th>R</th><th>R^c</th></tr>
<tr><td>(F)</td><td>$7000</td><td>$5000 − $5000   = $0</td></tr>
<tr><td>(C)</td><td>$ 0</td><td>$5000 − (−$4000) = $9000</td></tr>
</table>

To minimize his maximum possible regret (the **minimax regret crite-rion**), Roger should choose the art festival: a regret of $7000 is preferable to a regret of $9000.

All three decision methods (maximax, minimax, and minimax regret) view things in either-or terms: it will either rain or not rain; if it does rain, Roger will either lose $1000 or make $6000, etc. All three ignore the likelihood of rain. Clearly, if rain probability were zero, Roger should choose the art show. This idea (taking into account the probabilities of the various states of nature) reminds us of earlier choices we were invited to make—choices between two games of chance, based upon the games' (expected) values. In a sense, Roger is confronted with two games: he may play "Rock Concert" or he may play "Art Festival," with "nature" being the opponent.

The Bayesian Solution   Suppose, for example, that the rain probability is 70%. Adding a "probabilities" line to the payoff table in Figure 10.7, we compare the games' expected values.

Figure 10.7
Table for assessing expected payoffs of Roger's actions

Outcomes.	Rain	No Rain
Art Festival values.	−$1000	$5000
Rock Concert values	$6000	−$4000
Probabilities.	0.7	0.3

$$E[\text{Art Festival}] = (-1000) \cdot 0.7 + 5000 \cdot 0.3 = \$800$$

$$E[\text{Rock Concert}] = 6000 \cdot 0.7 + (-4000) \cdot 0.3 = \$3000$$

Because the table payoffs are from Roger's point of view, Roger selects the rock concert. This decision-making technique (choosing an action with the maximum expected payoff) is called a **Bayesian method**, and has the advantage of yielding the best possible results in the long run, if steadily used.

What should Roger do? There is no single answer. Much depends upon Roger's attitude: is he conservative, or inclined to gamble? If he makes many such decisions, Bayesian methods are attractive: though he may win or lose in a big way in any particular instance, Roger will do pretty well in the long run. ■

■ EXAMPLE 4

Using Bayesian methods, with rain probability 0.7, Roger clearly should schedule the rock concert. However, a greatly reduced chance of rain will swing Roger toward the art festival. He wishes to be poised to change plans at the last possible moment. What rain probability would justify a switch to the art festival?

SOLUTION

Roger needs to know what rain probability makes his two options equally attractive. Then lower rain probability favors the art show, and higher rain probability favors the concert. In Figure 10.8, we again consider the payoff table for Roger's situation, this time with "dummy" probabilities p and $1 - p$ in place of the "rain" and "no rain" probabilities:

Figure 10.8
Roger's payoff table, with outcome probabilities unspecified

Outcomes	Rain	No Rain
Art Festival values	−$1000	$5000
Rock Concert values	$6000	−$4000
Probabilities	p	$1 - p$

These probabilities sum to one, as usual. With these dummy probabilities in place, the expected values of the two choices are:

$$E[\text{Art Festival}] = (-1000) \cdot p + 5000 \cdot (1 - p)$$
$$= -1000p + 5000 - 5000p = 5000 - 6000p$$
$$E[\text{Rock Concert}] = 6000 \cdot p + (-4000) \cdot (1 - p)$$
$$= 6000p - 4000 + 4000p = 10{,}000p - 4000$$

For the two events to be equally attractive, these two expected values must be equal:

$$E[\text{Rock Concert}] = E[\text{Art Festival}]$$
$$10{,}000p - 4000 = 5000 - 6000p$$
$$16{,}000p - 4000 = 5000$$

$$16,000p \qquad = 9000$$

$$p \qquad = 9000/16,000 = 0.5625.$$

Remember our definition of p: it is the rain probability at which the events are equally attractive. Lower rain probability favors the art show; higher rain probability favors the rock concert. ∎

PRACTICE PROBLEM 2   Joe Zwieback will invest his $70,000 inheritance for one year. (At the end of that time, he will use all his money as down payment on a condominium on Maui.) The possibilities are: a bank CD (certificate of deposit) paying 5% simple interest for the year; an investment in a fast-food chain which will earn 20% in a strong economy, 3% in a steady economy, and will lose 15% if the economy weakens; and a stock which will rise 10% in a strong economy, show no growth in a steady economy, and fall 10% in a weak economy. Analysts claim the economy has a 40% chance of turning strong, and a 20% chance of weakening.

Show the given information in table form; then answer:

(a) What would a pessimist do? Why?

(b) What would an optimist do? Why?

(c) What would a Bayesian do, and what would be his expected payoff?

(d) What should Joe do to minimize his potential regret?

ANSWER(S)   **(a)** CD yields "best among the poor outcomes";   **(b)** fast-food, for "best among the good outcomes";   **(c)** fast-food, for $4340 expected value;   **(d)** a tie: CD or stock; be sure to construct regret table to see why.   □

Inventory Management   All businesses, large or small, involved in buying or selling goods or services, have a common problem: to know what inventory (in the case of goods) or staff and equipment (in the case of services) to have on hand in order to maximize profits. Example 5 gets at the inventory problem. The concerns and techniques are real; only names have been changed to protect the innocent!

■ EXAMPLE 5   The rutabaga problem: During last year's 50-day rutabaga season, Clyde Bucolic's vegetable market never ran out of rutabagas. Clyde's supplier, Bosco Anchovy, delivered a fresh supply each morning, and Clyde always discarded some at day's end. Pleased at never disappointing a customer, but annoyed at the excessive inventory and consequent waste, Clyde resolved to buy more wisely from Bosco next season.

Reviewing sales records for the past season, Clyde detected no pattern in the ups and downs of daily demands, but did learn that 14 rutabagas were sold on 6 different days, 15 were sold on 12 days, 16 on 7 days, 17 on 10 days, 18 on 12 days, and 19 on 3 days. He telephoned Bosco to verify that, again next year, Bosco will charge Clyde 50¢ per rutabaga for as many as Clyde wants. Local customers will pay Clyde 80¢ per rutabaga, but not a cent more. How many should Clyde stock?

SOLUTION   Clyde's goals must be clear. Does he wish never to disappoint a customer? Then, based upon sales records, he should stock 19 fresh rutabagas each morning. Does he wish never to discard a rutabaga? Then 14 is the preferred level. In truth, Clyde hopes to maximize his profits. He should stock at least 14: stocking only 13 would pass up a sure 30-cent profit on item number 14. He should not stock more than 19: each rutabaga beyond the 19th promises a 50-cent loss. The best inventory level is between 14 and 19, inclusive.

Clyde's problem of choosing among the possible inventory levels is much like Roger Chandler's Example 3 problem of choosing between the rock concert and art festival: each option (inventory level) has its own expected value, determined by the probabilities of the "states of nature" (in this case, demand levels) which might follow, and their corresponding payoffs. Clyde first uses the sales records in Figure 10.9 to determine probabilities of the possible demands.

Figure 10.9
Daily rutabaga demands, frequencies and probabilities

Demand	14	15	16	17	18	19
Frequencies	6	12	7	10	12	3
Probabilities	0.12	0.24	0.14	0.20	0.24	0.06

What would Clyde's expected profit be if he chose to stock 17 rutabagas? His day's profit depends upon that day's demand. Figure 10.10 shows the profits ("values") for all possible demands ("outcomes"), with their corresponding probabilities.

Figure 10.10
Profits for an inventory level of 17, at all demand levels

Demand Level	14	15	16	17	18	19
Net Profit ($)	2.7	3.5	4.3	5.1	5.1	5.1
Probability	0.12	0.24	0.14	0.20	0.24	0.06

On a day when demand is 15, for example, Clyde will buy 17 rutabagas (cash out: $8.50) and sell 15 (cash in: $12), for a net profit of $3.50. Do you see where each entry in the net profit line came from? Why are all entries from 17 through 19 alike?

By stocking 17 items, Clyde will experience a profit as low as $2.70 or as high as $5.10. His expected profit, treating "profit when 17 are stocked" as a random variable which takes on values 2.7, 3.5, 4.3, and 5.1, is:

$$E_{17} = 2.7(0.12) + 3.5(0.24) + 4.3(0.14) + 5.1(0.20 + 0.24 + 0.06)$$
$$\approx \$4.32$$

Is "stocking 17" Clyde's best choice? We can only find out by comparing his expected profit on stocking 17 with his expected profits for other inventory levels. All necessary information, including the expected value of each inventory level, is shown in Figure 10.11.

Figure 10.11
Expected profits for various inventory levels

Possible Actions (stock levels)	Possible Demands						Expected Profits
	14	15	16	17	18	19	
	Possible Profits ($)						
14	4.2	4.2	4.2	4.2	4.2	4.2	$4.20
15	3.7	4.5	4.5	4.5	4.5	4.5	$4.40
16	3.2	4.0	4.8	4.8	4.8	4.8	$4.42
17	2.7	3.5	4.3	5.1	5.1	5.1	$4.32
18	2.2	3.0	3.8*	4.6	5.4	5.4	$4.06
19	1.7	2.5	3.3	4.1	4.9	5.7	$3.60
Probabilities	0.12	0.24	0.14	0.20	0.24	0.06	

*Calculating Entry:

Buy 18: −$9.00
Sell 16: 12.80
Salvage 2:   0
Net: $3.80

Stock 18, Sell 16, with 40¢ Salvage:

Buy 18: −$9.00
Sell 16: 12.80
Salvage 2: .80
Net: $4.60

Each "possible profit" entry is the result of money paid out for inventory (stock level) and received in response to demand (column heading). The action "Stock 16" produces the greatest expected profit ($4.42). Does stocking 16 rutabagas actually produce a $4.42 profit? Never! The possible profits when stocking 16 are $3.20, $4.00, and $4.80. In the long run, however, an average daily profit of $4.42 results. The best inventory level, as long as the conditions (prices, demand patterns) which produced the above table persist, is to stock 16 rutabagas. ∎

PRACTICE PROBLEM 3

Clyde now sells leftover rutabagas for 40 cents each to Swenson the swineherd, who uses them to sweeten the swill for his favorite sow, Susie June. (This reduced price, 40 cents, is called the **salvage value** of each leftover rutabaga. Salvage value is the guaranteed value attached to each leftover item.) How many should Clyde buy per day under this new condition, in order to maximize his long-term profits? (*Hint:* The salvage value affects many entries in the body of the Figure 10.11 table. Rewrite the body of the table as necessary. Calculate the expected profit from stocking 16 items. Is this a maximum among expected profits? Compare with the expected profit from stocking 15, then 17; then do whatever is necessary to reach a conclusion.)

ANSWER(S) $E_{16} = \$4.61$; $E_{15} = \$4.45$ (a move in the wrong direction!); $E_{17} = \$4.71$ (an improvement over E_{16} so a change in the correct direction; but have we gone far enough in the direction of increasing inventory?); $E_{18} = \$4.73$; $E_{19} = \$4.65$. Conclusion: stocking 18 items yields the best long-term gain.   ☐

Review of Decision Methods   Given the same alternatives in the face of uncertain outcomes, different people may make different choices, depending upon their degree of optimism as well as their goals. "Going for the best among the good outcomes," the optimist's view, results in a *maximax* choice. "Seeking the best among the bad outcomes," the pessimist's stance, results in a *maximin* choice. "Minimizing maximum regret" is used to avoid self-recriminations over what turn out to be poor choices. Finally, a Bayesian approach, especially useful in a situation likely to be repeated many times, selects the action yielding the greatest expected profit among all possible actions.

What if two or more alternative actions have the same expected value? This results in a "don't care" condition: any of the actions may be chosen. If actions are to be used in sequence (as in a succession of rutabaga orders in Example 5), the "equally desirable" actions may be mixed in any order.

EXERCISES 10.3

PRACTICING THE MOVES AND MANEUVERS

Exercises 21–40: Utilize the following tables, all from the point of view of the "row player" with available actions A, B, C, etc. (Supply the missing probabilities.)

Table I

A values	70	40
B values	−20	90
Probabilities		0.6

Table II

C	−5	8
D	2	6
Probabilities	0.3	

Table III

E	25	0	−5
F	10	20	−10
Probabilities	0.5		0.2

21. What action would an optimist choose in Table I?
22. What action would a pessimist choose in Table I?
23. Construct the regret table for Table I, and name the minimax regret action.
24. What is the expected value of action A? of action B?
25. What is the Bayesian choice of action in Table I?
26. What is the maximin choice of action in Table II?
27. What is the maximax choice of action in Table II?
28. Construct the regret table for Table II, and choose the minimax regret action.
29. What is the expected value of action C? of action D?
30. What is the Bayesian choice of action in Table II?
31. What is the expected value of action E? of action F?
32. What is the Bayesian choice of action in Table III?
33. What is the pessimistic choice of action in Table III?
34. What is the maximin choice of action in Table III?
35. Give another name for the optimist's way of choosing an action in Table III.
36. Construct the regret table for Table III, and name the minimax regret action.
*37. What first-column probability in Table I makes actions A and B equally attractive from the Bayesian point of view?
*38. For any first-column probability less than your answer to Exercise 37, which action is better according to the Bayesian criterion?
*39. What first-column probability in Table II makes actions C and D equally desirable to a Bayesian?
*40. If the first-column probability in Table II is more than your answer to Exercise 39, which action would a Bayesian prefer?

APPLYING THE CONCEPTS

Exercises 41–44: Acme Heavy Equipment Rental reviewed its records to see how often a certain type of crane was needed on construction jobs in the area. On 26 days, 3 building contractors needed cranes; on 50 days, 4 contractors used cranes; 5 cranes were used on 76 days; and 6 were used on 48 days. Acme leases its cranes from an even bigger company for $800 per day and rents them out for $1200 per day. Prepare a payoff table for the Acme manager's possible actions, and answer:

41. How many cranes should the Acme manager have on hand daily if she is a pessimist?
42. How many if she is an optimist?
43. How many if she is interested in maximizing long-term profits?
44. What crane inventory level will minimize her maximum regret?

Exercises 45–49: Your ocean-going sailboat, *Gypsy*, is worth $100,000. You plan a one year, 'round-the-world voyage, and wish to insure your boat against total loss. A marine insurance company offers you such a policy for a premium of $3800. You estimate your chance of completing the voyage without losing your boat at 90%.

45. Neglecting insurance company expenses, who is favored by this price structure?
46. If your estimate of probability is correct, what is a fair price for the policy?
47. Prepare a regret table, showing both of your options (to insure, or not insure). Which option minimizes your potential regret?
48. What motive does Exercise 47 suggest for buying most kinds of insurance?

49. For the given pricing, what would be a "fair" loss probability (for you and the insurance company)?

50. Using the complete Figure 10.11 table from Example 5, construct the corresponding regret matrix. What inventory level, if any, clearly emerges as best if Clyde wishes to minimize his potential regret?

Exercises 51–55: Variations on the Rutabaga Problem (Example 5): For your convenience, the table of demands and probabilities is reproduced here. Clyde continues to buy rutabagas at $.50 and sell them (if he can) at $.80.

Daily rutabaga demands and probabilities

Demand:	14	15	16	17	18	19
Probabilities:	0.12	0.24	0.14	0.20	0.24	0.06

51. What is Clyde's best inventory level if Swenson agrees to pay him $.35 per leftover rutabaga? (Do as little work as possible! You need not complete the entire table; see Practice Problem 3.)
52. What is Clyde's best inventory if Swenson pays $.45 per leftover rutabaga?
53. In either Exercise 51 or Exercise 52, would Clyde be justified in stocking 20 or more rutabagas? Justify your answer.
54. What should Clyde's inventory be if Swenson signs a contract to pay him 70 cents for every leftover rutabaga at day's end? Why?
55. Susie June now requires an all-kumquat diet. Swenson no longer needs rutabagas. Clyde must pay a neighbor lad 30 cents each to haul away the leftovers in his red Porsche. What is Clyde's optimum inventory?

56. What is Clyde's best inventory if the neighbor boy upgrades to a Rolls Royce Corniche and charges $2 per leftover rutabaga?

10.4 MARGINAL ANALYSIS

In Example 5, we compared the expected values of inventory levels to determine the best inventory level for a given price structure. The method was tedious but effective.

We now solve the inventory problem in a new way. To maximize profit, we consider each single item of inventory, rather than simply the various total number of items we might stock. Of each, we ask "Does this item offer a positive expected profit?"

Suppose, for instance, that we are considering stocking a single item, which may or may not sell. Our only considerations become: what is the cost? the selling price? the salvage value, if any? the probability of selling? the expected profit?

■ EXAMPLE 6

A dealer in luxury cars is offered a 1972 Rolls Royce, tastefully custom-ized with purple paint, pink fur upholstery, and finned rear fenders, for $20,000. He hopes to sell the car for $30,000, and will not reduce the price. If the car does not sell within one year, he will sell it to his uncle for $14,000. What should be the car's selling probability, to justify the dealer's purchase?

SOLUTION

Letting x represent the unknown selling probability (and $1 - x$ the "not selling" probability), the net payoff table is shown in Figure 10.12.

Figure 10.12
Outcome/value/probability table for Rolls Royce investment

Outcomes	Sell	Not Sell
Values	$10000	−$6000
Probabilities	x	$1 - x$

The dealer's expected profit should be at least zero. (Naturally, the dealer hopes the expected profit is positive!) The expected profit associated with stocking this car is:

$$E(\text{profit}) = x \cdot (10000) + (1 - x) \cdot (-6000)$$

Thus, the dealer requires that:

$$x \cdot (10000) + (1 - x) \cdot (-6000) = 0$$

Solving,

$$10000x - 6000 + 6000x = 0$$
$$16000x - 6000 = 0$$
$$16000x = 6000$$
$$x = \frac{6000}{16000} = 0.375$$

For the dealer to even consider stocking the car, its selling probability should be 0.375 or more. No lower probability is acceptable.   ■

How does Example 6 relate to the general inventory problem? Each item of any kind that a merchant or a corporation puts into stock has its own cost, selling price, salvage value, and selling probability. Each item must offer a positive expected profit if it is to be considered worth stocking. Cost, selling price, and salvage value remain fixed from item to item; only selling probability varies. The decision to stock or not stock an item, then, should rest upon its selling probability. The selling probability of any item is determined by its "position" in the inventory. See Example 7.

■ EXAMPLE 7

Just before St. Patrick's Day, a clothing retailer stocks and sells woolen stocking caps of a bright green color not in demand at other times. She buys the caps from a supplier at $5 each, sells them before St. Patrick's Day at $10 each, and liquidates leftover caps after the holiday at $3 each. Sales records reveal a history of demands and their probabilities as shown in the table of Figure 10.13.

Figure 10.13
Green cap demands and probabilities

Demand	10	11	12	13	14	15
Probability	0.09	0.29	0.32	0.16	0.10	0.04

With the given price structure and demand probabilities, determine the expected contribution of each cap, numbers 1 through 16, to the store's profit, and tell whether or not to stock that item.

SOLUTION   **Analyzing cap #1:** Cap #1 sells when the St. Patrick's Day season demand is for 1 or more caps. The demand is always 10 or more; so cap #1 always sells (it has selling probability 1). In the following copy of Figure 10.13(a), we shade the demands which would cause Cap #1 to sell, and their probabilities.

Figure 10.13(a)
Cap demands, probabilities

Demand	10	11	12	13	14	15
Probability	0.09	0.29	0.32	0.16	0.10	0.04

Shaded: total "sell" probability of cap #1

We compute the expected profit of cap #1 by considering the two possible outcomes ("Sell" and "Not Sell") for that cap, the net values of those outcomes, and their probabilities:

Figure 10.14
Table for cap #1

Item #1	Outcomes	Sell	Not Sell
	Values	$5	−$2
	Probabilities	1	0

Expected profit of item #1: $1(5) + 0(-2) = \$5$.

Since the expected profit is positive, stock item #1.

Similarly, stock items #2 through #10. Each has selling probability 1 and offers expected profit $5. (Why does #10 have selling probability 1? Item 10 sells if the demand is 10 or more; the sum of the probabilities for demands 10 and more is 1.) What about item #11? Analyze! (See Figure 10.13(b).)

Figure 10.13(b)

Cap demands, probabilities

Demand	10	11	12	13	14	15
Probability	0.09	0.29	0.32	0.16	0.10	0.04

Shaded: total "sell" probabilities of Cap #11

Figure 10.15

Table for cap #11

Item #11	Outcomes	Sell	Not Sell
	Values	$5	−$2
	Probabilities	0.91	0.09

Expected Profit: $4.37

The selling probability for item #11 is the sum of the probabilities for demands 11 and greater. Also, the selling probability for #11 is less than that for #10, and the expected profit for #11 is less than that for #10.

What is the selling probability for item #12? #13? #14? #15? #16? What are their respective expected profits? What happens to selling probability and expected profit for later items in the sequence? To answer such questions, use the Figure 10.16 tables.

Figure 10.16(a)

Selling probabilities for caps 12 through 16

Demand	10	11	12	13	14	15
Probability	0.09	0.29	0.32	0.16	0.10	0.04

$$P[\#12 \text{ sells}] = 0.32 + 0.16 + 0.10 + 0.04 = 0.62$$
$$P[\#13 \text{ sells}] = \qquad\qquad 0.16 + 0.10 + 0.04 = 0.30$$
$$P[\#14 \text{ sells}] = \qquad\qquad\qquad\quad 0.10 + 0.04 = 0.14$$
$$P[\#15 \text{ sells}] = \qquad\qquad\qquad\qquad\qquad 0.04 = 0.10$$
$$P[\#16 \text{ sells}] = \qquad\qquad\qquad\qquad\qquad\qquad = 0.00$$

Figure 10.16(b)

Selling probabilities and expected profits for caps 1–16

Item	Sell Prob	Expected Profit	Stock?	Item	Sell Prob	Expected Profit	Stock?
#1	1	$5	yes	# 9	1	$5	yes
#2	1	$5	yes	#10	1	$5	yes
#3	1	$5	yes	#11	0.91	$4.37	yes
#4	1	$5	yes	#12	0.62	$2.34	yes
#5	1	$5	yes	#13	0.30	$0.10	yes
#6	1	$5	yes	#14	0.14	−$1.02	no
#7	1	$5	yes	#15	0.04	−$1.72	no
#8	1	$5	yes	#16	0.00	−$2.00	no

PRACTICE PROBLEM 4   In Figure 10.16(b), study the "Expected Profit" column for items #1 through #16.

(a) Which is the final item with a positive expected profit?

(b) How many items should be stocked for maximum profit?

(c) What is the total expected profit of items #1–#13?

(d) What is the expected profit, E_{13}, of stocking 13 items?

(e) Explain the connection between your answers to (c) and (d).

(f) Should items #14, #15, or beyond be stocked? Explain.

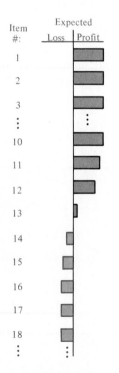

ANSWER(S)

(a) #13; (b) 13; (c) $56.81; (d) $56.81; (e) expected profit of 13 items is the sum of contributions of items 1–13. (f) #14 contributes a negative expected profit, and will reduce total expected profit. The same is true of #15 and greater. Do not stock them. ☐

Discussion question: We started with item #1 and proceeded until reaching an item of negative expected profit. How might you shorten the process of finding optimal inventory?

Discussion: Each item stocked contributes to the total expected profit. It is best to stock each item with a positive expected profit and reject each item with a negative expected profit. One could check the expected profit of some particular item—#12, for example—then skip to earlier or later items until the last one with positive expected value is detected.

Should one stock an item whose expected profit is zero? A quick, easy answer might be "Don't bother; it neither makes nor loses money in the long run." True; but our business colleagues tell us it is better to go ahead and stock such an item. Having it on hand when needed is a way to occasionally satisfy one more customer, building customer good will and perhaps in the long run even improving the demand for the product.

For a given price structure, the worth of any item as a member of the inventory depends solely upon that item's selling probability. Is there some way to scan the selling probabilities in the table of Figure 10.13 to decide which should be the final item stocked? To do so, we need to know the lowest selling probability at which we should be willing to stock an item.

■ EXAMPLE 8

Finding the Lowest Acceptable Selling Probability (LASP): For the St. Patrick's Day caps of Example 7 (cost, $5; sell, $10; salvage, $3), find the Lowest Acceptable Selling Probability (LASP) required of any particular cap which deserves to be stocked. Then, from the demands/probabilities table (Figure 10.13), determine the final cap to stock and hence the optimum inventory level.

SOLUTION   Let p denote the unknown "LASP," and set up a table:

Outcomes	Sell	Not Sell
Values	$5	−$2
Probabilities	p	$1 − p$

Cap #15
Selling Probability

Demand	Probability
10	0.09
11	0.29
12	0.32
13	0.16
14	0.10
15	0.04

The expected profit for an item with selling probability p is:

$$E = p(5) + (1 − p)(−2) = 5p − 2 + 2p = 7p − 2$$

The smallest expected profit which would justify stocking the item is $E = 0$.

If $E = 0$, then

$7p − 2 = 0$, and

$$p = \frac{2}{7} \approx 0.286$$

The lowest acceptable selling probability (LASP) is therefore 0.286. The merchant should stock any item whose selling probability is 0.286 or more, and not stock any item whose selling probability is less than 0.286.

Cap #14
Selling Probability

Demand	Probability
10	0.09
11	0.29
12	0.32
13	0.16
14	0.10
15	0.04

Item #15 sells only if demand is 15 or greater. The selling probability of #15 is thus 0.04: too small. Do not stock #15.

Item #14 has selling probability $0.10 + 0.04 = 0.14$ (too small).

Item #13 has selling probability $0.16 + 0.10 + 0.04 = 0.30$, larger than our LASP, and hence acceptable. As determined in Example 7, #13 is the final one the merchant should stock. ∎

**MARGINAL PROFIT;
MARGINAL ANALYSIS**

> The expected profit associated with any particular item is called that item's **marginal profit**. The process of determining the lowest acceptable selling probability (LASP), thereby obtaining the best inventory level, is called **marginal analysis**. Find the LASP, and stock all items—and only those items—whose selling probabilities are greater than or equal to the LASP.

PRACTICE PROBLEM 5   Find the Lowest Acceptable Selling Probability and the best inventory level for the caps of Example 8 under each of the following conditions:

(a) Cost, $5; selling price, $12; leftovers must be discarded (salvage value: $0).

(b) Cost, $12.00; selling price, $13.50; leftovers are sold, at $5 each, during the "After St. Paddy's Day Sale."

(c) Cost, $12.00; selling price, $13.00; leftovers cost the dealer an additional $5 each to have them taken by special messenger to the clothing recycle center.

ANSWER(S)   (a) LASP $\approx$ 0.417; stock 12. (b) LASP $=$ 0.824; stock 11. (c) LASP $=$ 0.944; stock 10. □

EXERCISES 10.4

Exercises 57–63: Using marginal analysis and the demand probability table below, find the most profitable inventory level under the given conditions:

Demand	14	15	16	17	18	19
Probability	0.24	0.06	0.29	0.17	0.09	0.15

57. cost, 10 cents; selling price, 50 cents; leftovers are discarded.

58. cost, 18 cents; selling price, 29 cents; salvage value, 10 cents.

59. cost, 30 cents; selling price, 60 cents; salvage value, 45 cents. (This may produce an unexpected LASP; how do you interpret it intuitively?)

60. Find the expected profit of item #16 using the Exercise 57 price structure.

61. Find the expected profit of stocking 16 items using the Exercise 57 price structure.

62. Find the expected profit of item #18 using the Exercise 58 price structure.

*63. Find the lowest price, in whole cents, at which one should be willing to stock #15 using the price structure in Exercise 58. (*Hint*: the unknown information in this case is the *selling price*. Represent it by a dummy letter, set up a table, and proceed as usual. You can do it!)

Exercises 64–66: Jack's Market sells strawberries, supplied to Jack at $7 per crate. By repackaging the contents of a crate into one-quart boxes, Jack sells each crate for $10. The weekly demand history is shown in the following table:

# of Crates	4	5	6	7	8	9	10
# of Weeks	6	3	2	5	4	2	3

If leftover berries are sold at week's end to a jelly manufacturer at $3 per crate, find:

64. the expected profit of stocking seven crates.
65. the expected profit of the 7th crate.
66. the best inventory level, using marginal analysis (a strawberry shortcut . . .).

Exercises 67–69: The jelly manufacturer of Exercises 64–66 has gone out of business; now Jack must pay $2 per crate to have leftover berries taken to the dump.

67. What is the expected profit of stocking eight crates?
68. What is the expected profit of the eighth crate?
69. What is the best inventory level?

*70. At the original $7 cost and $10 selling price, what is the lowest salvage value at which Jack should consider stocking the 9th crate?

*71. If the salvage value is zero and the cost remains $7, what is the lowest selling price at which Jack should stock the 6th crate?

*72. If Jack markets the berries at $12 per crate and the salvage value is zero, what is the most he should be willing to pay for crate #8?

*73. Answer question 72 if the salvage value is $5 per crate.

10.5 STRICTLY DETERMINED GAMES BETWEEN INTELLIGENT PLAYERS

Recall Roger Chandler's dilemma in Section 10.3: should he schedule the art festival or the rock concert, faced with the possibility (but not the certainty) of rain? In the language of Section 10.1, Roger was involved in a two-player, zero-sum game, with "nature" as Roger's opponent, and in which "nature" (the entire external world) transfers dollars to Roger or receives dollars from Roger, according to the Figure 10.17 table:

Figure 10.17
Payoff table for "Roger vs. nature" game

	Rain	No Rain
Art Festival	−$1000	$5000
Rock Concert	$6000	−$4000

Knowing the probability that his opponent, nature, would choose "Rain," Roger could make a more reasoned (Bayesian) selection, rather than just the maximax, maximin, or minimax regret choice, choosing his action to attain the greater expected value. In any case, Roger viewed nature as an "opponent" of either totally unpredictable tendencies or as one having already assigned probabilities (0.7 and 0.3 in Example 3) to "Rain" and "No Rain." Would Roger play differently if nature were an intelligent opponent, bent upon giving up as few dollars as possible to Roger? The answer may surprise you; read on!

■ EXAMPLE 9

As their train crawls eastward from Salt Lake City toward Denver, Roger and Carl play a simple game. Each marks the backs of two business cards with single digits: "1" on one card, "2" on the other. To play, each chooses one of his cards, concealing it from the other. The players simultaneously show their cards; the chosen pair determines a payoff according to the following matrix, written from Roger the row player's point of view. (Payoff matrices *always* reflect the point of view of the row player.) All payoffs are positive, representing both dollars transferred from Carl to Roger and Carl's willingness to pay for his entertainment. The payoff matrix, with "R1" indicating "Roger chose card #1 and Row 1," etc. is Figure 10.18.

Figure 10.18
Payoff matrix for game between Roger and Carl

	C1	C2
R1	5	2
R2	4	3

For example, if Roger plays card R1 and Carl plays C2, Carl will pay Roger $2. A game such as this, with payoffs chosen from a *payoff matrix* or *game matrix* by the players' choices of row and column, is called a **matrix game**.

Both players are strongly competitive. Roger wants to win as much money as possible, and Carl is determined to lose as little as possible. What should each do to attain his objective?

SOLUTION
Studying his rows R1 and R2, Roger reasons: "If I play R1, Carl will play C1 or C2. The minimum payoff I would then receive is $2, if Carl plays C2. If I play R2, the minimum I might receive is $3. To do as well as possible if Carl happens to play perfectly, I will play R2, knowing that I will then receive at least $3." Roger aims for the maximum among minimum row entries. He is using maximin thinking.

Carl analyzes: "If I play C1, my maximum possible loss to Roger is $5. If I play C2, my maximum possible loss is $3. To minimize my maximum possible loss, I will play C2." Carl aims for the minimum among the maximum column entries. He is using a minimax payoff criterion.

Each player then triumphantly plays his card numbered "2," and Carl pays Roger $3. Each player thereby attains his goal of doing as well as possible against perfect play by the other. ■

Saddle Point Analysis
A player's choice of "what to do" in a game is called a **strategy**. Most games are more complex than Example 9, requiring players to "mix up" their choices to keep each other guessing. The game in Example 9 was truly not very interesting: each player adopted a **pure strategy** (a fixed selection of one of his available actions) and stuck to it. For either player to do otherwise would open the door to a more advantageous play by the other. For example, if Carl played C1 and Roger played R2, Carl would surrender $4, rather than the $3 he would have lost by sticking to C2.

What, exactly, made it best for both players to adopt pure strategies? Reviewing, we see that both Roger and Carl target the $3 payoff as "doing as well as possible against my opponent's best play." Roger sees the $3 as the *larger of the two row minima*; Carl sees it as the *smaller of the two column maxima*. Such an entry in a payoff matrix is called a **saddle point**. A saddle point, then, is a payoff which is a minimum in its row and a maximum among all the row minima. In fact, there is a more easily stated way to detect a saddle point, if there is one:

SADDLE POINT

> The value v occurring in a payoff matrix is a **saddle point** of the matrix if v is both a minimum entry in its row and a maximum entry in its column.

■ EXAMPLE 10
In searching a game matrix for saddle points, row-player Roger is interested in doing as well as possible against column-player Carl's best play (that is, in finding the greatest value among the row minima: the maximin point of view). Carl, hoping to keep Roger's winnings low even if Roger plays well, looks for the smallest value among the column max-

ima (the minimax viewpoint). Search the Figure 10.19 game (payoff) matrix with these objectives in mind.

Figure 10.19
A 4 × 4 payoff matrix

$$\begin{bmatrix} 5 & 3 & 6 & 4 \\ 7 & 8 & 7 & 10 \\ 6 & 5 & 4 & 3 \\ 4 & 5 & 9 & 8 \end{bmatrix}$$

SOLUTION

□: Row minima
○: Column maxima

$$\begin{bmatrix} 5 & \boxed{3} & 6 & 4 \\ \boxed{\textcircled{7}} & \boxed{8} & \boxed{7} & \textcircled{10} \\ 6 & 5 & 4 & \boxed{3} \\ \boxed{4} & 5 & \textcircled{9} & 8 \end{bmatrix}$$

For convenience we "rectangle" the row minima. Similarly, we "circle" the column maxima. The minimum among the column maxima (Carl's target) and the maximum among the row minima (Roger's goal) agree, at the value "7" which is simultaneously a row minimum and a column maximum. (Though "7" occurs twice as a row minimum in R2, in only one instance is it also a column maximum.) Carl chooses C1, Roger chooses R2, and the game value is 7. ∎

If s is a saddle point, why does it offer both players their best strategies? A saddle point (minimum in its row and maximum in its column) is first of all a row minimum. Now think of any other row minimum t in the matrix. Either t is in the same column as s or t is not in the same column as s.

Remember that s is min in its row, max in its column, and t is a row minimum. If t is in the same column as s, then $s \geq t$ (since s is maximum in its column). (See top matrix at left.)

If t is not in the same column as s, then some entry u is in the column with s and also in the row with t. Since s is maximum in its column, $s \geq u$. Since t is minimum in its row, $u \geq t$. With both $s \geq u$ and $u \geq t$, we conclude $s \geq t$. Thus, in any possible case, $s \geq t$. The saddle point s is maximum among all the row minima, and is hence the row player's "best guaranteed payoff." Trace this logic for the saddle point "7" in Figure 10.19.

Likewise, by being a maximum in its column and a minimum in its row (notice that we have merely rearranged the description of "saddle point"), s is a column maximum (bad news for Carl if he plays s's column!), but is smallest among all column maxima, hence is the best Carl could do against perfect play by Roger. By targeting s, each plays the perfect defense against the other's perfect choice and does "as well as possible." The expected payoff (because it is the *only* payoff) is s.

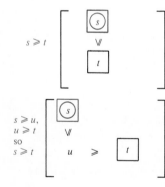

$s \geq t$

$s \geq u,$
$u \geq t$
so
$s \geq t$

OPTIMAL STRATEGY; GAME VALUE

For each competitor in a two-party, zero-sum game, that strategy which does "as well as possible" against the other player's best possible strategy is called the player's **optimal strategy**. When both players play their optimal strategies, the resulting expected value of the payoff is called the **game value**, denoted by v.

Why Is a Saddle Point Called a "Saddle Point?"

To illustrate, consider this game matrix:

$$\begin{bmatrix} x & 2 & x \\ 7 & 5 & 8 \\ x & 1 & x \end{bmatrix}$$

In this matrix, 5 is a saddle point, since 5 is minimum in its row and maximum in its column. The "x" entries do not matter, since they are not in 5's row or column.

Now imagine this matrix laid flat (see Figure 10.20), with a peg 2 units tall in row 1, column 2 (that is, on the location of the 2 in the game matrix), a peg of height 8 over the 8, etc.; ignore the x entries. Then stretch a "tent" over these five pegs and step back for a look:

Figure 10.20
Graphic interpretation of
"saddle point"

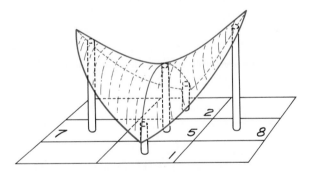

See how the fabric falls away on both sides of the "5" peg in the column direction and rises on both sides of the "5" peg in the row direction. The effect at the 5 peg is rather like a saddle!

PRACTICE PROBLEM 6

Still referring to the rows and columns of the payoff matrix as "R1, . . ." and "C1 . . .," respectively, identify the optimal strategies and game values for the following matrix games:

(a) $\begin{bmatrix} 7 & 8 \\ 9 & 10 \end{bmatrix}$ (b) $\begin{bmatrix} 1 & 5 & 10 \\ 3 & 4 & 4 \\ 2 & 1 & 2 \end{bmatrix}$ (c) $\begin{bmatrix} 10 & 2 \\ 3 & 1 \\ 9 & 9 \\ 6 & 4 \end{bmatrix}$ (d) $\begin{bmatrix} 7 & 5 & 8 \\ 9 & 2 & 1 \\ 6 & 5 & 7 \\ 1 & 4 & 10 \end{bmatrix}$

(a) R2,C1; 9. **(b)** R2,C1; 3. **(c)** R3,C2; 9. *Note:* though 9 appears twice, only the 9 in second column is minimal in its row, maximal in its column. **(d)** R1,C2; 5, or R3,C2; 5. Either 5 is min in its row, max in its column.   □

Strictly Determined Games

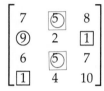

At this point, each of our heroes (Roger and Carl) has one tool for choosing a best strategy: find the saddle point of the game matrix, and play the option containing that saddle point. If the game matrix has more than one saddle point (and this is possible: see Practice Problem 6, part **(d)**), the players may play any options which include saddle points; the value of the game remains the saddle point value. (All saddle points in a matrix game have equal values; see Exercises 83–85 at the end of this section.) Indeed, if one player picks a saddle point option and the other does not, the second player fares worse than had he also played a saddle point. For example, if payoffs are in dollars, Roger's choice of R1 in the game **(d)** matrix (at left) guarantees him at least $5 (the saddle point value). If at the same time Carl plays C1 rather than his optimal (saddle point) pure strategy C2, Roger will gain $7 rather than $5. Carl's failure to play his optimal strategy costs him dearly!

For both players to fare "as well as possible" in the long run, or even in a single play, it is essential that neither deviate from playing the (pure) saddle point strategy. Even if Carl resolutely plays only his optimum strategy, C2, there is absolutely nothing Roger can do to increase his winnings beyond $5 per play. Furthermore, neither player need be secretive: each knows exactly what he should do and what the other should do. Perfect knowledge of Carl's intent is of no advantage to Roger. In this sense, saddle point strategies are said to be "spyproof."

STRICTLY DETERMINED GAME

A matrix game with one or more saddle points is said to be **strictly determined**. (So long as both players play optimally, the payoff is strictly determined: it is the saddle point value.)

By contrast, a game with no saddle points is a **nonstrictly determined matrix game**. For optimal play, both players must mix their selections of rows or columns according to fixed probabilities (more on this in Section 10.6), producing a variety of payoffs from the game matrix. The expected (value of the) payoff is the game value v.

EXERCISES 10.5

PRACTICING THE MOVES AND MANEUVERS

Exercises 74–82: For each strictly determined matrix game, determine optimal row and column strategies and the game value. If the game is not strictly determined, write "solution unknown." (This situation will be resolved in later sections.)

74. $\begin{bmatrix} 5 & 9 \\ 6 & 8 \end{bmatrix}$
75. $\begin{bmatrix} -5 & -7 \\ -6 & -8 \end{bmatrix}$
76. $\begin{bmatrix} 4 & 3 \\ 2 & 5 \end{bmatrix}$
77. $\begin{bmatrix} -2 & 0 \\ 4 & 5 \end{bmatrix}$
78. $\begin{bmatrix} 3 & 5 \\ 3 & -5 \end{bmatrix}$
79. $\begin{bmatrix} 7 & 3 \\ 4 & -7 \end{bmatrix}$

80. $\begin{bmatrix} -4 & 2 & 6 \\ 5 & 3 & 4 \\ 6 & -6 & 2 \end{bmatrix}$
81. $\begin{bmatrix} 9 & 1 & 12 & -3 \\ 7 & 0 & 5 & 4 \\ 9 & 11 & 8 & 10 \end{bmatrix}$
82. $\begin{bmatrix} 6 & -5 & 2 & -6 \\ 4 & 8 & -4 & -8 \\ -5 & 0 & 0 & -9 \end{bmatrix}$

APPLYING THE CONCEPTS

*83. Show that, in any matrix with two saddle points in the same row or in the same column, the saddle point values are identical. (*Hint*: Investigate a 2 × 2 matrix with entries **a**, **b**, **c**, **d**; describe relationships among the entries.)

*84. Show that, in any matrix with two saddle points which are neither in the same row nor the same column, there are at least two other saddle points, and that these four saddle points all have the same value. (See *Hint* in Exercise 83.)

*85. Show that all saddle points in any matrix have the same value.

86. Two fast-food restaurants, Andy's Drive-Thru and Bill's Take-Out, compete fiercely for a fixed number of weekday customers by offering week-long specials—chicken sandwiches or hamburgers. When both offer burgers, Andy's gets 40% of the business. When both offer chicken, Bill's gets 40%. When Andy's chicken competes with Bill's burger, Andy's claims 70%; and when Bill's chicken meets Andy's burger, Bill's gets 70% of the business. What is each firm's best strategy? What percentage of the business does each receive in the long run? (*Hint:* Construct a payoff table from Andy's point of view.)

87. Rowan and Collins, authors of two competing finite mathematics textbooks which dominate the market, are preparing revised editions. The publishers estimate that if neither includes a chapter on marketing ethics, Rowan will corner 65% of the market. If both include the chapter, the two will share the market equally. If only Collins includes the chapter, he will gather 70% of the market. If Rowan alone includes the chapter, she will own 60% of the market. What should each author do, and what is his or her expected market share?

10.6 MIXED STRATEGY 2 × 2 GAMES   Were life (or even matrix games) entirely concerned with finding and exploiting saddle point strategies, the world would be both simpler and less interesting. Fortunately, such is not the case!

Ruth (playing "rows") and Carol ("columns") create a 2 × 2 game matrix, taking turns filling in the entries. Each in her turn supplies an entry intended to increase her own, and block her opponent's, advantage. The result, with "saddle point analysis":

Figure 10.21
Game matrix for Ruth and Carol

$$
\begin{array}{c}
 & C1 \quad C2 \\
R1 & \left[\begin{array}{cc} \boxed{4} & ⑦ \\ ⑥ & \boxed{3} \end{array}\right] \\
R2 &
\end{array}
$$

□: Row minima
○: Column maxima

(a) What does saddle point analysis suggest?

(b) What would happen if, in a succession of plays of the game, each woman mixed her options, with Ruth playing R1 60% of the time and Carol playing C1 30% of the time, each using a random device, such as numbers drawn from a hat, to mix up her choices and confuse her opponent?

SOLUTION

(a) The maximin row entry is 4 and the minimax column entry is 6. There is no saddle point, hence no best single choice for either player. If, for example, Ruth and Carol play R1 and C1, respectively, the payoff is 4. (We avoid calling 4 the "game value," a title reserved for the expected payoff when both players play optimally. We are not certain that R1 and C1 are optimal plays.)

(b) Each woman privately draws a number from a hat before each play to make her choice. (Why "privately?" If Carol announced her intention to play C1, Ruth would counter with R2, thereby winning $6. Either player's choice would be affected by knowledge of the other player's intention.) The two "play" simultaneously, so that neither can alter her selection to counter the other's choice.

Since $P[R1] = 0.6$ and $P[C1] = 0.3$, with these choices being private and *independent*, it follows that $P[R1 \cap C1] = 0.6 \cdot 0.3 = 0.18$. That is, the payoff value 4 occurs with probability 0.18. The full table of payoffs and their probabilities is as follows:

Ruth	Carol	Probability	Payoff
R1	C1	$(0.6) \cdot (0.3) = 0.18$	4
R1	C2	$(0.6) \cdot (0.7) = 0.42$	7
R2	C1	$(0.4) \cdot (0.3) = 0.12$	6
R2	C2	$(0.4) \cdot (0.7) = 0.28$	3

With the given row and column probabilities, the expected (long-run average) payoff is therefore

$$E = 0.18(4) + 0.42(7) + 0.12(6) + 0.28(3)$$
$$= 0.72 \quad + 2.94 \quad + 0.72 \quad + 0.84 \quad = \$5.22$$ ∎

We earlier defined a player's "strategy" as the pattern of play adopted by that player. When the pattern of play consists of one action steadfastly repeated, the result is a pure strategy. Mixing the choices according to preselected probabilities is something new, deserving of a name:

MIXED STRATEGY

> A **mixed strategy** is an assignment of positive probabilities to two or more of a player's options. (By contrast, a pure strategy assigns probability 1 to a single option, and probability 0 to all others.)

We now introduce a very nice computational device hinted at in Example 11: writing Ruth the row player's row probabilities as the row vector

$$P = [.6 \quad .4]$$

and Carol the column player's column probabilities as the column vector

$$Q = \begin{bmatrix} .3 \\ .7 \end{bmatrix}$$

then the matrix product PAQ, where A is the game (payoff) matrix, is

$$PAQ = [.6 \quad .4] \cdot \begin{bmatrix} 4 & 7 \\ 6 & 3 \end{bmatrix} \cdot \begin{bmatrix} .3 \\ .7 \end{bmatrix} = [4.8 \quad 5.4] \cdot \begin{bmatrix} .3 \\ .7 \end{bmatrix} = 5.22$$

which is exactly the expected payoff we obtained in Example 11 for the mixed strategies case. Indeed, if we represent the Example 11 solution **(a)** pure strategies as vectors

$$P = [1 \quad 0] \quad \text{and} \quad Q = \begin{bmatrix} 1 \\ 0 \end{bmatrix}, \quad \text{then}$$

$$PAQ = [1 \quad 0] \cdot \begin{bmatrix} 4 & 7 \\ 6 & 3 \end{bmatrix} \cdot \begin{bmatrix} 1 \\ 0 \end{bmatrix} = [4 \quad 7] \cdot \begin{bmatrix} 1 \\ 0 \end{bmatrix} = 4$$

agreeing with the expected pure strategy payoff. In Example 11, which is "better": the $4 expected payoff resulting from the pure strategies R1 versus C1, or the $5.22 expected payoff resulting from the suggested mixed strategies? Clearly, the given pure strategies are better for Carol; Ruth would prefer the proposed mixed choices. We still do not know the game value, resulting from optimal play by both parties.

**EXPECTED PAYOFF (OF A
MATRIX GAME)**

> In a matrix game with payoff matrix A, if the row player's strategy (mixed or pure) is written as the row vector P, and the column player's strategy is written as the column vector Q, then the *expected payoff* is the matrix product PAQ.

What if one of the players opted for a pure strategy? For example, what if Ruth consistently played R1, hoping for a $7 payoff? Then Carol, detecting the pattern of Ruth's play, would repeatedly play C1, reducing Ruth's payoff to a steady $4. However, if Ruth noticed Carol playing C1 time after time, she (Ruth) could switch to R2 to grab a $6 payoff.

Both this discussion and Example 11 are persuasive evidence that it is sometimes better for one or both players to adopt a mixed strategy. There is, as we shall see, a way for both to optimally mix their strategies, each doing as well as possible against the other's "best play."

If saddle point analysis fails, how is one to select a strategy mix? Ruth, an analytical sort, gets right to the heart of the problem: "Since there is no saddle point, hence no best pure strategy, my goal is to maximize my expected winnings by mixing my choices of R1 and R2. What mix is best? If I assign probabilities p to R1 and $(1 - p)$ to R2, at least I can think about the consequences."

Let us follow Ruth's thinking. If Carol plays C1, Ruth, by her probability assignment, will collect $4 with probability p and $6 with probability $(1 - p)$. Her expected payoff if Carol plays C1 is $E = E(C1) = 4p + 6(1 - p)$. If Carol plays C2, Ruth's expected payoff is $E = E(C2) = 7p + 3(1 - p)$. Note that Ruth's two expected payoffs (corresponding to Carol's strategy options) are determined by her choice of p, the probability of R1, with its consequent assignment of probability $(1 - p)$ to R2.

What value of p "works best" (is optimal) for Ruth? A beautiful graphic interpretation, strikingly similar to the linear programming illustrations of Chapter 4, resolves the issue with astonishing swiftness and clarity.

Ruth's Logic:

$$[p \quad 1-p] \begin{bmatrix} ^{C1} 4 & ^{C2} 7 \\ 6 & 3 \end{bmatrix}$$

$E(C1) = 4p + 6(1 - p)$

$E(C2) = 7p + 3(1 - p)$

What p is best?

EXAMPLE 12

On a single coordinate system, graph the two expected payoffs (corresponding to Carol's options C1 and C2), which result from Ruth's assignment of probability p to her option R1. Use these graphs to select the value of p which gives Ruth the best possible expected payoff, no matter what Carol chooses.

SOLUTION   Since p is a probability, $0 \le p \le 1$. If Carol plays C1, Ruth's expected payoff is $E = 4p + 6(1 - p)$. As p sweeps through values from 0 to 1 this expected payoff E sweeps from $E = 6$ (when $p = 0$) to $E = 4$ (when $p = 1$). The expression $4p + 6(1 - p)$ is linear (see Chapter 0), so the graph of E is a line.

On the horizontal p-axis, as a sketching aid, pencil in vertical scales at $p = 0$ and at $p = 1$ upon which to plot these endpoint E values: $E = 6$ (at $p = 0$) and $E = 4$ (at $p = 1$). Line 1, connecting these two E values, shows all possible expected payoffs to Ruth if Carol plays C1. Likewise, line 2 [the graph of $E = 7p + 3(1 - p)$ as p runs from 0 to 1] shows the possible expected payoffs to Ruth if Carol plays C2.

Figure 10.22
Expected payoffs to Ruth of Carol's two columns, for Ruth's probability p of playing R1

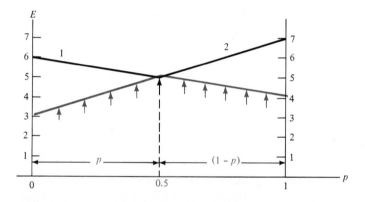

Ruth sets p to get as *high* a payoff as possible, against Carol's "best play."

Lines 1 and 2 cross at a certain value of p. To the left of this crossing value, line 2 is lower; to the right, line 1 is lower. If Ruth selects p to the left of the crossing point, her fate is influenced by Carol's choice. Carol can give Ruth a lower expected payoff by choosing C2. To the right of the crossover point, Carol can reduce Ruth's expected payoff by choosing C1.

To do as well as possible, no matter which column Carol chooses, Ruth should set p exactly at the crossover point. At this point,

$$E(C1) = E(C2)$$
$$4p + 6(1 - p) = 7p + 3(1 - p)$$
$$4p + 6 - 6p = 7p + 3 - 3p$$
$$-6p = -3$$
$$p = 0.5$$

Ruth should choose $p = 0.5$. Ruth's optimal strategy, in vector form, is $P = [.5 \quad .5]$. Ruth's expected payoff if Carol plays C1 is $E(C1) = 4(0.5) + 6(0.5) = \$5$; and, if Carol plays C2, is $E(C2) = \$5$. No matter which column Carol plays, Ruth's expected payoff is $5. Thus, the game value is $v = \$5$, and (so long as Ruth plays optimally) Carol may play any strategy, pure or mixed, without affecting the payoffs.

Geometrically, Ruth selects the value of p which occurs at the highest point of the region below lines 1 and 2. In linear programming terms
(Chapter 4), Ruth hopes to maximize the objective function E, within
constraints $E \le -2p + 6$, $E \le 4p + 3$, $0 \le p$ and $p \le 1$. By choosing $p =$
0.5, Ruth gives up the opportunity for a payoff greater than \$5 which
she might receive if Carol plays poorly; she also assures that she will not
receive a payment of less than \$5 if Carol plays well. For even a single-
play game, this is Ruth's optimal strategy.   ∎

Special Notation for   In Example 12, out of the many strategies available to Ruth, we found
Optimal Strategies   that the mixed strategy $P = [.5 \quad .5]$ is best. Though P is our "generic"
name for a row player strategy, an *optimal* row strategy will be called
"$P*$" (pronounced "P-star"). Similarly, an optimal column strategy will
be represented by the column vector $Q*$. The game value v is the expected payoff when both players play optimally. Thus,

$$P*AQ* = v$$

This prepares us for a key theorem, offered without proof:

THE FUNDAMENTAL THEOREM   Consider a game with payoff matrix A, optimal strategies $P*$
OF GAME THEORY   (row player's) and $Q*$ (column player's) and game value v.

If Q is any column player strategy, then $P*AQ \ge v$. (If Q is non-
optimal, the row player may do better than the game value v,
from the row player's point of view.)

If P is any row player strategy, then $PAQ* \le v$. (If P is non-
optimal, the column player may do better than the game value
v, from the column player's point of view.)

PRACTICE PROBLEM 7   For each of the following game matrices, determine the optimum strategy (pure or mixed) for Ralph, the row player:

(a) $\begin{bmatrix} 2 & 7 \\ 5 & 1 \end{bmatrix}$ (b) $\begin{bmatrix} 4 & 3 \\ 3 & 1 \end{bmatrix}$ (c) $\begin{bmatrix} 3 & 5 \\ 4 & 2 \end{bmatrix}$ (d) $\begin{bmatrix} 6 & 2 \\ 5 & 8 \end{bmatrix}$

ANSWER(S)   (a) No saddle point; optimal mixed strategy, $P* = [\frac{4}{9} \quad \frac{5}{9}]$. (b) Pure strategy: R1; in vector form, strategy is $P* = [1 \quad 0]$. (c) $P* = [.5 \quad .5]$;
(d) $P* = [\frac{3}{7} \quad \frac{4}{7}]$.   ☐

Mixed Strategies in   In any matrix game, one or more saddle points dictate the strategies of
Games with More Than   both players: each player chooses a row or column containing a saddle
One Saddle Point   point, every time. In a game with a single saddle point, this yields pure

strategies for both players. If there is more than one saddle point (all necessarily of equal value—see Exercises 83–85), optimal strategies may mix rows (columns) containing saddle points. The payoff is strictly determined; it is always the saddle point value.

In nonstrictly determined 2 × 2 games, the row player seeks a strategy mix producing a "highest possible" expected payoff in the region below the expected value lines of the columns.

The column player's strategy mix is similarly determined: assign probabilities q and $1 - q$ to columns C1 and C2, then plot the expected value lines $E(R1)$ and $E(R2)$ of the row player's two choices. The column player picks q to *minimize* the payoff to the row player, within the feasible region *above* the expected value lines of the rows and between $q = 0$ and $q = 1$.

■ EXAMPLE 13

Ross and Candy play rows and columns, respectively, of the following matrix. What is Candy's best strategy?

$$\begin{bmatrix} 8 & 5 \\ 3 & 7 \end{bmatrix}$$

SOLUTION

With no saddle point (verify), Candy assigns probabilities q and $1 - q$ to her two columns. Ross may play R1 or R2, with expected payoffs from Candy to Ross (since the payoffs are positive) given by $E(R1) = 8q + 5(1 - q)$ and $E(R2) = 3q + 7(1 - q)$. Candy sets q to keep the expected payoff to Ross as low as possible.

Figure 10.23
Candy the column player's graphs of possible payoffs to row player, if Candy plays C1 with probability q

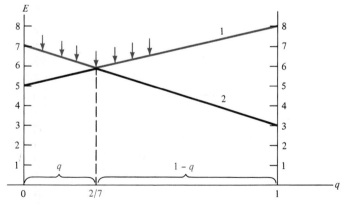

Candy sets q to produce as *low* an expected payoff as possible, against Ross's "best play."

The low point occurs where $8q + 5(1 - q) = 3q + 7(1 - q)$, at $q = 2/7$. Thus Candy's optimal strategy, in column vector form, is

$$Q^* = \begin{bmatrix} \frac{2}{7} \\ \frac{5}{7} \end{bmatrix}$$

This mix produces the same expected payoff no matter which row Ross plays. The game value is $E(R1) = E(R2) = \$41/7 \approx \$5.86$. ■

PRACTICE PROBLEM 8 Find Ross's best strategy in the game of Example 13.

ANSWER(S) $P^* = [4/7 \quad 3/7]$ ☐

Optimal Play by Either Player Determines Expected Payoff Let us examine Ross's and Candy's optimal strategies in matrix form. First, we multiply the game matrix on its left by Ross the row player's optimal strategy vector:

$$P^*A = [\tfrac{4}{7} \quad \tfrac{3}{7}] \cdot \begin{bmatrix} 8 & 5 \\ 3 & 7 \end{bmatrix} = [\tfrac{41}{7} \quad \tfrac{41}{7}]$$

The 41/7 resulting from [4/7 3/7] times column 1 shows that, with Ross's best strategy mix, the expected value if Candy plays C1 is 41/7. Likewise, the expected value of C2 is 41/7. If Ross plays his best strategy, it makes no difference what Candy does. The expected value in either case is the game value, 41/7.

Now multiply the game matrix on its right by Candy's optimal strategy vector Q^*:

$$AQ^* = \begin{bmatrix} 8 & 5 \\ 3 & 7 \end{bmatrix} \cdot \begin{bmatrix} \tfrac{2}{7} \\ \tfrac{5}{7} \end{bmatrix} = \begin{bmatrix} \tfrac{41}{7} \\ \tfrac{41}{7} \end{bmatrix}$$

If Candy plays her best strategy then, no matter which row Ross plays, the expected value is the game value, 41/7. What would happen if Ross played his best mixed strategy P^* but Candy decided to play the strategy $[.5\,.5]^T$? The expected outcome of this combination of actions is given by the product

$$[\tfrac{4}{7} \quad \tfrac{3}{7}] \cdot \begin{bmatrix} 8 & 5 \\ 3 & 7 \end{bmatrix} \cdot \begin{bmatrix} .5 \\ .5 \end{bmatrix} = [\tfrac{41}{7} \quad \tfrac{41}{7}] \cdot \begin{bmatrix} .5 \\ .5 \end{bmatrix} = \tfrac{41}{7}$$

This verifies that, even if Candy plays a non-optimal strategy, the expected payoff (resulting from Ross's optimal play) is the game value, $41/7 \approx 5.86$. Should Candy play carelessly, thinking she cannot affect the expected payoff? Certainly not; poor play by Ross could then make things worse for Candy. One cannot count on the opponent's perfect play to keep one out of trouble!

To illustrate, suppose Ross, lured by the largest payoff (8), decides to play Row 1 with probability 0.9, and that Candy, hoping to hit the smallest payoff, 3, assigns probability 0.7 to her column 1. The resulting expected value is:

$$[.9 \quad .1] \cdot \begin{bmatrix} 8 & 5 \\ 3 & 7 \end{bmatrix} \cdot \begin{bmatrix} .7 \\ .3 \end{bmatrix} = [7.5 \quad 5.2] \cdot \begin{bmatrix} .7 \\ .3 \end{bmatrix} = 6.81$$

With both players deviating from their optimal strategies, the expected value of the game shifts from 5.86, the game value (the result of optimal play), to 6.81. Ross does a bit better—and Candy a bit worse—than the game value.

We have considered game matrices with only positive entries, to set aside any concerns about mixed signs. The world (and intelligent opponents) seldom offer us "games" (that is, situations in which choices lead to payoffs) in which we cannot lose. However, everything we have developed applies equally well to matrix games with any mixture of positive and negative payoffs. For matrices with negative entries, the only adjustment in our graphic solution method (with vertical scales at $p = 0$ and $p = 1$, or at $q = 0$ and $q = 1$) is to label the vertical scales starting upward from the smallest value shown in the payoff matrix.

PRACTICE PROBLEM 9   For each matrix game, determine the optimal strategies for both players and the value of the game. (Recall that the value of the game is the expected payoff when both players play their optimal strategies.)

(a) $\begin{bmatrix} 4 & -6 \\ 5 & 3 \end{bmatrix}$ (b) $\begin{bmatrix} -8 & 10 \\ 5 & 2 \end{bmatrix}$ (c) $\begin{bmatrix} -4 & -5 \\ -7 & -8 \end{bmatrix}$ (d) $\begin{bmatrix} 1 & -2 \\ -3 & 4 \end{bmatrix}$

ANSWER(S)   (a) 3 is a saddle point. Row player: $P^* = [0 \quad 1]$; column strategy: $Q^* = [0 \quad 1]^T$. Game value: $v = 3$

(b) Optimal strategies: $P^* = [1/7 \quad 6/7]$, $Q^* = [8/21 \quad 13/21]^T$; $v = 22/7$

(c) $P^* = [1 \quad 0]$, $Q^* = [0 \quad 1]^T$; $v = -5$

(d) $P^* = [.7 \quad .3]$, $Q^* = [.6 \quad .4]^T$; $v = -.2$ □

SUMMARY OF 2 × 2 MATRIX GAME METHODS

1. Check the game matrix for a saddle point. A saddle point determines pure strategies for both players.

2. If there is no saddle point, find each player's optimal mixed strategy. If either player uses his or her best mixed strategy (or if both do), the expected payoff is the game value.

Algebraic Solution of Nonstrictly Determined 2 × 2 Games   Strongly motivated by the geometric solutions of Examples 12 and 13, we describe a purely algebraic solution method for nonstrictly determined 2 × 2 games:

Determining row player's optimal strategy:

1. Row player assigns probabilities p and $(1 - p)$ to R1 and R2, respectively.

2. With these assigned probabilities, row player obtains expressions for $E(C1)$ and $E(C2)$, the expected values of column player's two columns.

3. Row player solves the equation $E(C1) = E(C2)$ for p. Optimal strategy is $P^* = [p \quad 1 - p]$.

Determining column player's optimal strategy:

1. Column player assigns probabilities q and $(1 - q)$ to C1 and C2, respectively.

2. With these assigned probabilities, column player obtains expressions for $E(R1)$ and $E(R2)$, the expected values of row player's two rows.

3. Column player solves equation $E(R1) = E(R2)$ for q. Optimal strategy is $Q^* = [q \quad 1 - q]^T$.

■ EXAMPLE 14

Use algebraic techniques to find both players' optimal strategies and the game value for the following matrix game:

$$A = \begin{bmatrix} 5 & 2 \\ 4 & 6 \end{bmatrix}$$

SOLUTION   Row player: assign probabilities p and $(1 - p)$ to R1 and R2. Then,

$$E(C1) = 5p + 4(1 - p) \quad \text{and} \quad E(C2) = 2p + 6(1 - p)$$

Solving for p,

$$E(C1) = E(C2)$$

$$5p + 4(1 - p) = 2p + 6(1 - p)$$

$$5p + 4 - 4p = 2p + 6 - 6p$$

$$p = \frac{2}{5} = 0.4$$

Thus, row player's optimal strategy is $P^* = [.4 \quad .6]$. Column player: assign probabilities q and $(1 - q)$ to C1 and C2. Then,

$$E(R1) = 5q + 2(1 - q) \quad \text{and} \quad E(R2) = 4q + 6(1 - q)$$

Solving for q,

$$E(R1) = E(R2)$$

$$5q + 2(1 - q) = 4q + 6(1 - q)$$

$$5q + 2 - 2q = 4q + 6 - 6q$$

$$q = \frac{4}{5} = 0.8$$

Column player's optimal strategy is $Q^* = [.8 \quad .2]^T$. The game value is:

$$v = P^*AQ^* = [.4 \quad .6] \cdot \begin{bmatrix} 5 & 2 \\ 4 & 6 \end{bmatrix} \cdot \begin{bmatrix} .8 \\ .2 \end{bmatrix} = [4.4 \quad 4.4] \cdot \begin{bmatrix} .8 \\ .2 \end{bmatrix} = 4.4 \quad ■$$

PRACTICE PROBLEM 10 Use the (geometrically motivated) algebraic approach to find the optimal strategy mixes for row and column players for the following games, expressing your results in vector form. In each case, give the game value.

(a) $\begin{bmatrix} 5 & -2 \\ -4 & 3 \end{bmatrix}$ (b) $\begin{bmatrix} 12 & 3 \\ 4 & 5 \end{bmatrix}$ (c) $\begin{bmatrix} 8 & -6 \\ -12 & 4 \end{bmatrix}$ (d) $\begin{bmatrix} -4 & -5 \\ -8 & 7 \end{bmatrix}$

ANSWER(S) (a) $P^* = [.5 \quad .5]$; $Q^* = [5/14 \quad 9/14]^T$; $v = 0.5$.

(b) $P^* = [.1 \quad .9]$; $Q^* = [.2 \quad .8]^T$; $v = 4.8$.

(c) $P^* = [8/15 \quad 7/15]$; $Q^* = [1/3 \quad 2/3]^T$; $v = -4/3$.

(d) $P^* = [15/16 \quad 1/16]$; $Q^* = [3/4 \quad 1/4]^T$; $v = -17/4$. □

General Solution of Nonstrictly Determined 2 × 2 Games (Optional) Our geometric method, leaning heavily upon the visual representation of expected column (or row) values, is intuitively understandable and very reliable. Make it your own! Then, having mastered the geometric method, track the following development.

Consider the "general" 2 × 2 nonstrictly determined game matrix.

$$A = \begin{bmatrix} a & b \\ c & d \end{bmatrix}$$

As usual, row player assigns probabilities p and $(1 - p)$ to R1 and R2, then equates the resulting expected values $E(C1)$ and $E(C2)$. Elementary but careful algebra is now required.

$$E(C1) = ap + c(1 - p) \quad \text{and} \quad E(C2) = bp + d(1 - p)$$

Solving for p,

$$E(C1) = E(C2)$$
$$ap + c(1 - p) = bp + d(1 - p)$$
$$ap + c - cp = bp + d - dp$$
$$ap + dp - bp - cp = d - c$$
$$p(a + d - b - c) = d - c$$
$$p[(a + d) - (b + c)] = d - c$$
$$p = \frac{d - c}{(a + d) - (b + c)} = \frac{d - c}{D}$$
$$\text{where} \quad D = (a + d) - (b + c)$$

(It can be shown that, if A has no saddle point, D is not zero.) Then,

$$(1 - p) = 1 - \frac{d - c}{D} = \frac{D}{D} - \frac{d - c}{D}$$

$$(1 - p) = \frac{(a + d) - (b + c)}{D} - \frac{d - c}{D}$$

$$(1 - p) = \frac{a - b}{D}$$

So, $P^* = [p \quad (1 - p)]$, with p and $(1 - p)$ as above.

An entirely similar (exhausting, but elementary) development produces

$$q = \frac{d - b}{D} \quad \text{and} \quad (1 - q) = \frac{a - c}{D}, \quad \text{with} \quad Q^* = [q \quad (1 - q)]$$

The game value is then $v = P^*AQ^*$. We now summarize this algebraic treatment:

ALGEBRAIC SOLUTION OF NONSTRICTLY DETERMINED 2 × 2 MATRIX GAMES

If matrix game

$$A = \begin{bmatrix} a & b \\ c & d \end{bmatrix}$$

is nonstrictly determined, and we define $D = (a + d) - (b + c)$, then optimal strategies P^* and Q^* and game value v are as follows:

$$P^* = \begin{bmatrix} \dfrac{d - c}{D} & \dfrac{a - b}{D} \end{bmatrix} \quad Q^* = \begin{bmatrix} \dfrac{d - b}{D} & \dfrac{a - c}{D} \end{bmatrix}$$

and

$$v = P^*AQ^* = \frac{ad - bc}{D}$$

PRACTICE PROBLEM 11   Solve the following nonstrictly determined games:

(a) $\begin{bmatrix} 6 & 9 \\ 8 & 3 \end{bmatrix}$ (b) $\begin{bmatrix} 5 & -2 \\ -4 & 4 \end{bmatrix}$

ANSWER(S)   (a) $P^* = [.625 \quad .375]$; $Q^* = [.75 \quad .25]$; $v = 6.75$

(b) $P^* = [8/15 \quad 7/15]$; $Q^* = [6/15 \quad 9/15]$; $v = 12/15$ □

2 × m Games (m > 2)   A method very similar to the 2 × 2 (no saddle point) solution in Example 12 suffices. Assign probabilities p and $(1 - p)$ to R1 and R2, respectively. Graph the expected value lines of all columns. Find the p-value (always where two of the column expected value lines cross) yielding the highest possible value of E beneath the column expected value lines.

Incidentally, the two columns producing this maximum value of E are those to be used in the *column* player's optimal strategy, *to the exclusion of all others*. Use the two columns so discovered to then determine, in the manner of Example 12, the optimal (mixed) strategy for the column player.

■ EXAMPLE 15

(a) Find the row player's optimal strategy and the game value for the matrix game

$$\begin{bmatrix} 3 & 1 & 0 \\ -1 & 0 & 1 \end{bmatrix}$$

(b) Use your diagram for part (a) to determine exactly which columns should be included in the column player's strategies.

(c) What is the optimal strategy for the column player? (A "column player's view" diagram is required.)

SOLUTION To make graphing a bit more convenient, we slide the vertical axes at $p = 0$ and $p = 1$ upward so that lines of expected column value do not cross the horizontal axis. (We could instead adjust the matrix entries to be nonnegative, but for our purposes in this text the axis adjustment is sufficient.)

Assigning probabilities p and $1 - p$ to the two rows, we plot the expected value of column 1 as line (1), etc.

Figure 10.24
Graphic solution to 2 × 3 game from row player's point of view

Game Matrix
$$\begin{bmatrix} 3 & 1 & 0 \\ -1 & 0 & 1 \end{bmatrix}$$

Sketch for Row Player

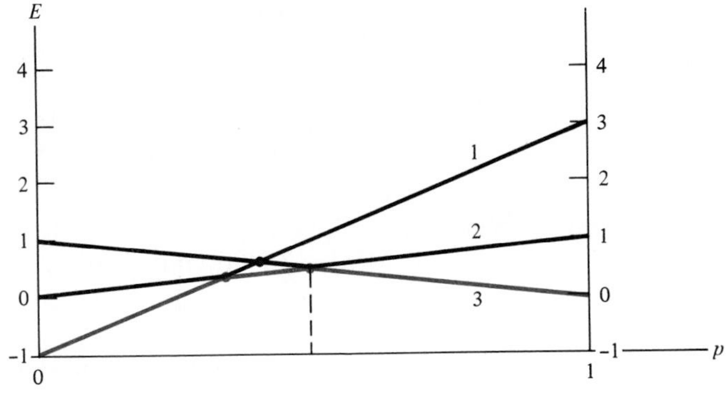

(a) Our very carefully drawn diagram shows that the maximum value of E, within constraints

$$0 \le p \le 1,$$
$$E \le 3p - 1(1 - p) = 4p - 1 \qquad \text{shown as line 1,}$$

$$E \le 1p + 0(1 - p) = p \qquad \text{line 2, and}$$
$$E \le 0p + 1(1 - p) = -p + 1 \qquad \text{line 3}$$

occurs where lines 2 and 3 cross, at $p = 0.5$. If the row player uses strategy $[.5 \quad .5]$ (plays optimally) and the column player plays either C2 or C3, the expected payoff is 0.5.

(b) If, however, the column player plays C1, and the row player uses strategy $[.5 \quad .5]$, the expected payoff is 0.6. The column player should stick to C2 and C3, columns which minimize the expected payoff when the row player (having two rows) plays optimally. C1 allows a slightly greater expected payoff. (See line 1, above $p = 0.5$, where line 1 reaches the value $E = 1$.)

(c) Ignore C1 because of reasoning in **(b)**. Find column player's optimal strategy by assigning probabilities q and $1 - q$ to C2 and C3, respectively, etc. Solution: $Q^* = [0 \quad .5 \quad .5]^T$. ∎

In a 2×2 game without a saddle point, if either player plays optimally, it does not matter what the other player does; the expected payoff is the game value. (However, each player should play optimally, just in case the other does not.) In Example 15, however, we saw that, in a $2 \times n$ matrix game ($n > 2$), if the row player plays optimally, the column player must play only those columns which minimize the expected value to the (optimally playing) row player. In Example 15, there were only two such columns. To determine an optimal strategy, the column player could ignore all other columns and use the diagram or algebraic approach to find the best probability mix for the two "good" columns. That is, once two "good" columns are identified, the problem becomes essentially a 2×2 problem. Determining column player's optimal strategy when there are more than two "good" columns is beyond our present methods.

A similar development shows that an $m \times 2$ game ($m > 2$) may reduce to a 2×2 game.

PRACTICE PROBLEM 12   Obtain optimal strategies for both players, and the game value, for each of the following matrix games:

$$\text{(a)} \begin{bmatrix} 5 & 1 & 3 & -1 \\ -1 & 2 & 1 & 4 \end{bmatrix} \quad \text{(b)} \begin{bmatrix} 1 & -2 \\ 2 & 0 \\ -2 & 2 \\ 3 & -1 \end{bmatrix}$$

ANSWER(S)   **(a)** $[3/7 \quad 4/7]$; $[1/7 \quad 6/7 \quad 0 \quad 0]^T$; 11/7.

(b) $[0 \quad 2/3 \quad 1/3 \quad 0]$; $[1/3 \quad 2/3]^T$; 2/3.   ☐

EXERCISES 10.6

PRACTICING THE MOVES AND MANEUVERS

Exercises 88–92: Determine optimal strategies for row and column players, and game values, for the following matrix games:

88. $\begin{bmatrix} 7 & -2 \\ 4 & 1 \end{bmatrix}$ 89. $\begin{bmatrix} -7 & -2 \\ 1 & 4 \end{bmatrix}$ 90. $\begin{bmatrix} -4 & 1 \\ 4 & -1 \end{bmatrix}$ 91. $\begin{bmatrix} 6 & -9 \\ -5 & 15 \end{bmatrix}$ 92. $\begin{bmatrix} 11 & 6 \\ 3 & 5 \end{bmatrix}$

Exercises 93–100: Find optimal strategies for both players, and the game values.

*93. $\begin{bmatrix} 6 & 9 & 5 & 1 \\ 4 & 8 & 0 & 5 \end{bmatrix}$ 94. $\begin{bmatrix} 3 & 5 \\ 4 & 2 \\ 2 & 0 \\ 7 & 7 \end{bmatrix}$ *95. $\begin{bmatrix} 6 & -2 & 3 & -3 & 5 \\ 4 & 5 & -4 & 2 & 0 \end{bmatrix}$ 96. $\begin{bmatrix} -2 & 1 \\ 1 & 0 \\ 3 & -1 \end{bmatrix}$

*97. $\begin{bmatrix} 2 & 4 & 5 \\ 4 & 4 & 3 \end{bmatrix}$ 98. $\begin{bmatrix} 5 & -3 & -2 & 2 \\ -2 & 5 & 0 & -2 \end{bmatrix}$ 99. $\begin{bmatrix} 6 & 3 & 2 & 5 \\ 0 & 5 & 8 & 5 \end{bmatrix}$ 100. $\begin{bmatrix} -3 & 1 \\ 2 & 0 \\ -2 & 4 \end{bmatrix}$

Exercises 101–104: For the matrix game

$$\begin{bmatrix} 2 & 1 \\ -3 & 4 \end{bmatrix}$$

101. Determine optimal strategies and the game value.
102. The players adopt strategies [.5 .5] and [.2 .8]^T. Find the expected payoff.
*103. If the column player continues to play [.2 .8]^T, what is the row player's best strategy, and

the expected payoff? (Examine sketch used in Exercise 101.)
*104. If the row player continues to play [.5 .5], what strategy should the column player adopt, and what is the expected payoff? (See Exercise 103.)

APPLYING THE CONCEPTS

105. Instead of waiting for Sandra at the bus stop near the library, Chuck decides to walk to meet her on her way from the computer center. One of Sandra's possible routes follows the Red Cedar River; the other passes the stadium. All of Chuck's prospects are pleasant. He mentally ascribes values of 5 points to intercepting Sandra, 3 points to taking the river walk, and 1 point to passing the stadium.

      Sandra is well aware of Chuck's pleasure-rating system. She is also well aware of his recent attentions to the attractive brunette at the periodicals desk, and is determined to deny Chuck as much pleasure as possible.

What strategies should the two employ, and what is the "pleasure value" of the game?
106. Colonel Black receives word that his lifelong adversary, General White, will soon attack one of Black's two warehouses. The warehouses contain supplies worth $30,000 and $50,000, respectively. Black has enough troops to ward off any attack on one of the locations, by leaving the other unprotected; and White will attack only one. Set up a 2 × 2 matrix for this "game," determine optimal strategies for both leaders, and find the value of the game.
*107. Automobile importers Eurocars and Nipponwerke compete in many market areas.

Eurocars imports Sports, Utility, and Sedan models; Nipponwerke brings in only Utility and Sedan models. In each market area, each importer can emphasize one of its vehicle categories, hoping to win customers away from the other importer. The relative effects of their campaigns, measured in share of the market captured by Nipponwerke, are shown in the following table. How should each importer mix its model emphases, and what will be the average market share captured by Nipponwerke?

		Eurocars Options		
		Sport	Util	Sed
Nipponwerke	Util	25	40	50
Options	Sed	50	30	20

10.7 SOLVING "LARGE" GAMES (OPTIONAL)

If both dimensions of a "no saddle point" matrix game are greater than two, we attempt first to reduce the game matrix by crossing out all rows and columns which no intelligent player would employ. We then attempt to solve the game displayed in the surviving rows and columns. If the reduced matrix has two rows, or two columns, methods from earlier sections will work.

■ EXAMPLE 16

In each matrix, at least one row or column should never be played. Identify it and cross it out. Then see if any other rows or columns can be eliminated from consideration.

(a) $\begin{bmatrix} -2 & 1 & 5 \\ 1 & -1 & 3 \end{bmatrix}$ (b) $\begin{bmatrix} 5 & -3 & 2 \\ 7 & 4 & 3 \\ -2 & 2 & 5 \end{bmatrix}$ (c) $\begin{bmatrix} -5 & -4 & 1 \\ 2 & 4 & 3 \\ 3 & 2 & -1 \end{bmatrix}$

SOLUTION

(a) $\begin{bmatrix} -2 & 1 & \not{5} \\ 1 & -1 & \not{3} \end{bmatrix}$

(a) From row player's point of view: the "1" in R2 is better than the "−2" in R1, so if the column player plays C1, then R2 is better for the row player. However, if the column player selects C2, then R1 is better for the row player. At this stage of things, then, the row player cannot completely rule out either R1 or R2.

From column player's point of view, C2 is better if row player plays R2, but C1 is better if row player plays R1. Neither C1 nor C2 can be ignored.

However, comparing C2 and C3, column player sees that C2 is better if row player plays R1 (because "1" is better than "5" from column player's point of view), and C2 is also better if row player plays R2. No matter what the row player does, column player does better with C2 than C3. Cross out C3, as in part **(a)** of the figure.

Removing one or more columns from consideration may expose the remainder of one row as being consistently better than the remainder of another. Compare R1 and R2 again. Still, neither is consistently better than the other. No further reduction of the game matrix is possible. There is no saddle point. The remaining 2×2 game can be solved by algebraic means as in Examples 12 and 13.

(b) $\begin{bmatrix} \cancel{5} \quad \cancel{3} \quad \cancel{2} \\ 7 \quad 4 \quad 3 \\ -2 \quad 2 \quad 5 \end{bmatrix}$

(b) R2 is better, entry by entry, than R1. Cross out R1, as in part **(b)** of the figure. No other rows or columns can be eliminated. Solve remaining matrix game by Section 10.8 method.

(c) $\begin{bmatrix} \cancel{-5} \quad \cancel{4} \quad \cancel{1} \\ 2 \quad 4 \quad 3 \\ 3 \quad 2 \quad -1 \end{bmatrix}$

(c) $\begin{bmatrix} \cancel{-5} \quad \cancel{4} \quad \cancel{1} \\ 2 \quad \cancel{4} \quad 3 \\ 3 \quad \cancel{2} \quad -1 \end{bmatrix}$

(c) R2 is better than R1. Cross out R1, as in part **(c)** of the figure. Now what remains of C3 is better than what remains of C2. Cross out C2, as in the *second* part **(c)** of the figure.

Further checking reveals no new possibilities for crossing out remainders of rows or columns.   ■

Dominance in Matrix Games

When one row (column) is "consistently better" than another row (column), we keep the *dominant* (better) row (column) and eliminate the *dominated* (poorer) row (column).

Once one player strikes out a dominated line, this reduction of the matrix may reveal one or more dominated lines for the other player. In reducing the matrix by elimination of dominated lines, both players should trace the process, alternating viewpoint between rows and columns until no further reduction is possible.

REDUCED MATRIX

> A game matrix with one or more dominated lines is said to be *reducible*. The matrix obtained from a game matrix by eliminating all dominated rows and columns is called the **reduced matrix** of the game.

Of course, once optimal strategies are determined using the reduced matrix, they must be expressed in terms of the rows and columns of the original matrix. For this reason, it is well to "tag" the original rows with R1, R2, . . ., C1, C2, . . . and retain unchanged the tags of rows and columns which escape reduction.

■ EXAMPLE 17

Obtain the reduced matrix, optimal strategies, and game value for the following matrix game:

$$
\begin{array}{c}
\begin{array}{cccc} \text{C1} & \text{C2} & \text{C3} & \text{C4} \end{array} \\
\begin{array}{c} \text{R1} \\ \text{R2} \\ \text{R3} \end{array}
\begin{bmatrix}
2 & -2 & 4 & 3 \\
0 & 2 & 4 & 1 \\
1 & -3 & 2 & -1
\end{bmatrix}
\end{array}
$$

(*Note:* Row and column tags are supplied for your convenience. You must ordinarily supply them.)

SOLUTION Reduction steps are shown, without comment. Verify each step. The processes of determining optimal strategies and game value are likewise not shown; you should verify them.

$$
\begin{array}{c}
\begin{array}{cccc} \text{C1} & \text{C2} & \text{C3} & \text{C4} \end{array} \\
\begin{array}{c} \text{R1} \\ \text{R2} \\ \text{R3} \end{array}
\begin{bmatrix}
2 & -2 & 1 & 3 \\
0 & 2 & 4 & 1 \\
1 & -3 & 2 & -1
\end{bmatrix}
\end{array}
\qquad
\begin{array}{c}
\begin{array}{cccc} \text{C1} & \text{C2} & \text{C3} & \text{C4} \end{array} \\
\begin{array}{c} \text{R1} \\ \text{R2} \\ \text{R3} \end{array}
\begin{bmatrix}
2 & -2 & 1 & 3 \\
0 & 2 & 4 & 1 \\
1 & -3 & 2 & -1
\end{bmatrix}
\end{array}
\qquad
\begin{array}{c}
\begin{array}{cccc} \text{C1} & \text{C2} & \text{C3} & \text{C4} \end{array} \\
\begin{array}{c} \text{R1} \\ \text{R2} \\ \text{R3} \end{array}
\begin{bmatrix}
2 & -2 & 1 & 3 \\
0 & 2 & 4 & 1 \\
1 & -3 & 2 & -1
\end{bmatrix}
\end{array}
\qquad
\begin{array}{c}
\begin{array}{cccc} \text{C1} & \text{C2} & \text{C3} & \text{C4} \end{array} \\
\begin{array}{c} \text{R1} \\ \text{R2} \\ \text{R3} \end{array}
\begin{bmatrix}
2 & -2 & 1 & 3 \\
0 & 2 & 4 & 1 \\
1 & -3 & 2 & -1
\end{bmatrix}
\end{array}
$$

Rows and columns eliminated should never be played; their probabilities of being played are all 0. The optimal mixes of the remaining rows and columns are obtained by the methods of Section 10.6. Finding the optimal strategy for the row player, we proceed as follows:

Let (surviving rows) R1 and R2 have temporary probabilities p and $1 - p$. Row player will choose p so that the surviving portions of C1 and C2 have equal expected values. (See matrix.) In algebraic terms,

$$E(C_1) = E(C_2)$$

$$p(2) + (1 - p)0 = p(-2) + (1 - p)2$$

$$2p = -4p + 2$$

$$6p = 2$$

$$p = \frac{1}{3}$$

Thus, the row player should play R1 with probability 1/3, R2 with probability 2/3, and R3 with probability 0. Row player's optimal strategy is $P^* = [1/3 \quad 2/3 \quad 0]$. Similarly, $Q^* = [2/3 \quad 1/3 \quad 0 \quad 0]^T$. Game value is $P^*AQ^* = 2/3$, where A is the game matrix. ∎

Simplex Method Solution for Larger Games (Optional)

What if the reduced, no saddle point matrix has more than two rows and more than two columns? The simplex method comes to the rescue!

■ EXAMPLE 18

Find the row player's optimal strategy, and the value of the game, for the matrix

$$\begin{bmatrix} 3 & -1 & 9 \\ 1 & 2 & -3 \\ -2 & 4 & 3 \end{bmatrix}$$

SOLUTION   The given matrix has no saddle point and is reduced (has no dominated rows or columns). Therefore, our present methods are insufficient. We assign to each row a probability, then maximize the row player's expected payoff E subject to limits imposed by the expected values of the various columns.

Instead of row probabilities p and $1 - p$ (which in the $2 \times n$ case led to a convenient graphic or algebraic solution), we assign probabilities p_1, p_2, and p_3 to the three rows, and then describe both the relationships among p_1, p_2, and p_3 and our row player's goal in algebraic language. To help in writing the appropriate statements, we show the probabilities next to the corresponding rows of the matrix:

$$\begin{matrix} p_1 \\ p_2 \\ p_3 \end{matrix} \begin{bmatrix} 3 & -1 & 9 \\ 1 & 2 & -3 \\ -2 & 4 & 3 \end{bmatrix}$$

Since the numbers p_1, p_2, p_3 are probabilities that entirely account for the row player's mixed strategy, we have the following constraints in terms of the numbers p_1, p_2, and p_3:

(i) $0 \le p_1$

(ii) $0 \le p_2$

(iii) $0 \le p_3$

and

(iv) $p_1 + p_2 + p_3 = 1$

Recall that, in the two-row case, we chose the probability p [and hence $(1 - p)$] to allow the maximum possible payoff E, which still remained below all of the lines of expected column value. In the present example, the limits imposed upon E by the expected column values become

(v) $E \le \ \ 3p_1 + 1p_2 - 2p_3$

(vi) $E \le -1p_1 + 2p_2 + 4p_3$

and

(vii) $E \le \ \ 9p_1 - 3p_2 + 3p_3$

Inequalities **(v–vii)**, the "probability" statements **(i–iv)**, and row player's wish to maximize E, taken together, become: "Bearing in mind that $p_1 + p_2 + p_3 = 1$, maximize E, subject to non-negativity constraints on p_1, p_2, and p_3 and the three constraints

$$\text{(v) } E \leq \quad 3p_1 + 1p_2 - 2p_3$$

$$\text{(vi) } E \leq -1p_1 + 2p_2 + 4p_3$$

and

$$\text{(vii) } E \leq \quad 9p_1 - 3p_2 + 3p_3$$

The coefficients in constraints **(v)** to **(vii)** are exactly the column entries from matrix A. This looks like a linear programming problem. To put the present formulation into more recognizable form requires several careful transitions. Please follow the steps carefully.

Step 1. If the payoff matrix A has any negative entries, add a suitable constant k to all entries in A to obtain a new matrix B with only positive entries. Then the (optimal) value F for matrix game B is just the (optimal) value E of matrix game A, increased by k: $F = E + k$. Further, the optimal row strategy for matrix B is the same as the optimal row strategy for matrix A.

$$A = \begin{matrix} p_1 \\ p_2 \\ p_3 \end{matrix}\begin{bmatrix} 3 & -1 & 9 \\ 1 & 2 & -3 \\ -2 & 4 & 3 \end{bmatrix} \quad \text{add "4" to all entries} \quad B = \begin{matrix} p_1 \\ p_2 \\ p_3 \end{matrix}\begin{bmatrix} 7 & 3 & 13 \\ 5 & 6 & 1 \\ 2 & 8 & 7 \end{bmatrix}$$

Now B has only positive entries, so F, the (optimal) value of game B, is positive. The problem has become: "Bearing in mind that $p_1 + p_2 + p_3 = 1$, maximize F, subject to non-negativity constraints on p_1, p_2, and p_3 and the three constraints

$$\text{(v) } F \leq \quad 7p_1 + 5p_2 + 2p_3$$

$$\text{(vi) } F \leq \quad 3p_1 + 6p_2 + 8p_3$$

and

$$\text{(vii) } F \leq 13p_1 + 1p_2 + 7p_3$$

(Coefficients in **(v–vii)** are column entries of B.)

Step 2. Since all entries in B are positive, so is the game value F. Divide all constraint inequalities by F (this does *not* change the direction of the "$\leq$"), and exchange sides of the inequalities (this *does* reverse the "$\leq$"):

$$\text{(v) } \quad 7(p_1/F) + 5(p_2/F) + 2(p_3/F) \geq 1$$

$$\text{(vi) } \quad 3(p_1/F) + 6(p_2/F) + 8(p_3/F) \geq 1$$

and

$$\text{(vii) } 13(p_1/F) + 1(p_2/F) + 7(p_3/F) \geq 1$$

Step 3. To heighten the resemblance to a familiar linear programming problem, replace p_1/F with x_1, p_2/F with x_2, and p_3/F with x_3:

(v) $7x_1 + 5x_2 + 2x_3 \geq 1$

(vi) $3x_1 + 6x_2 + 8x_3 \geq 1$

and

(vii) $13x_1 + 1x_2 + 7x_3 \geq 1$

Step 4. Note that

$$x_1 + x_2 + x_3 = \frac{p_1}{F} + \frac{p_2}{F} + \frac{p_3}{F}$$

$$= \frac{(p_1 + p_2 + p_3)}{F}$$

$$= \frac{1}{F}$$

Let $z = x_1 + x_2 + x_3 = \dfrac{1}{F}$

Final formulation: Since F is positive, "maximize F" means "minimize $1/F$" means "minimize $z = x_1 + x_2 + x_3$." The original problem has become "minimize $z = x_1 + x_2 + x_3$, subject to

(v) $7x_1 + 5x_2 + 2x_3 \geq 1$

(vi) $3x_1 + 6x_2 + 8x_3 \geq 1$

and

(vii) $13x_1 + 1x_2 + 7x_3 \geq 1$

This (final formulation) we recognize as a standard minimization problem. To finish, and retrace our steps to a solution of the original problem, do the following:

Step 5. Solve the final formulation by the Simplex Algorithm. (See Chapter 5.) This produces optimal strategy (x_1, x_2, x_3) and (final formulation) game value z. Solving by LINDO (see Chapter 5), a microcomputer software package, we obtain $x_1 \approx 0.057654$, $x_2 \approx 0.111332$, $x_3 \approx 0.019881$, and $z = 0.1888668$.

Step 6. Since $z = 1/F$, $F = 1/z$. Since $x_1 = p_1/F$, $p_1 = Fx_1$. (Similarly, $p_2 = Fx_2$, and $p_3 = Fx_3$.) Finally, recall that $E = F - 4$. (We added 4 to all matrix A entries to get matrix B.) Applying these relationships to the values in step 1, $p_1 \approx 0.305$, $p_2 \approx 0.590$, $p_3 \approx 0.105$, and $E \approx 1.295$.

Solution to original problem: Row player's optimal strategy is approximately [0.305 0.590 0.105]; game value is $E \approx 1.295$. The game value is the expected value if both players play optimally. Again using linear programming techniques, the column player's optimal strategy is $[.442 \quad .505 \quad .053]^T$. ∎

EXERCISES 10.7

PRACTICING THE MOVES AND MANEUVERS

Exercises 108–111: Cross out dominated rows and columns from each game matrix. Then solve the matrix game, giving optimal strategies P^* and Q^* and game value v.

108. $\begin{bmatrix} 6 & 4 & 10 & 0 \\ 11 & 3 & 5 & 8 \\ 5 & 2 & 6 & 1 \end{bmatrix}$
109. $\begin{bmatrix} 0 & 2 & 3 & 1 \\ -1 & 1 & 0 & 0 \\ 0 & -1 & 4 & 0 \end{bmatrix}$
110. $\begin{bmatrix} 4 & 4 & 5 \\ 1 & 3 & 2 \\ 7 & 3 & 6 \\ 2 & -2 & 3 \end{bmatrix}$
111. $\begin{bmatrix} 1 & 2 & 2 & -2 \\ 5 & -2 & 3 & 1 \\ 5 & 3 & -5 & -1 \\ 4 & 2 & 3 & 2 \end{bmatrix}$

Exercises 112 and 113: Deal with the following matrix:

$$A = \begin{bmatrix} 2 & -7 & 1 & 5 \\ 4 & 6 & -2 & -4 \\ 1 & 2 & 3 & 4 \end{bmatrix}$$

112. For matrix A, formulate (giving the constraints and objective function) the linear program to find the row player's optimal strategy and the game value. If you have access to a computer linear programming package, solve the game.
113. For matrix A, formulate the linear program to determine the column player's optimal strategy.

APPLYING THE CONCEPTS

*114. Does a reducible 2×2 game necessarily have a saddle point? Explain.
115. Show by example that a 3×3 game with a saddle point (say, in row 2, column 2) is not necessarily reducible.
*116. Is a 2×3 game with a saddle point necessarily reducible? Explain.

A Brief Summary of Important Ideas

The basic tool in this chapter was expected **net payoff** in a chance situation. Proceeding from early examples using expected (net) dollar payoff of a game, we defined a fair game as one with expected net payoff zero. We saw insurance as just a specialized "game" with all of the standard structure: outcomes determined by chance, net dollar values attached to those outcomes, and fixed probabilities for those outcomes.

We next moved into decision making: offered a choice of actions, we learned to analyze the consequences of those choices from an **optimist's** point of view, a **pessimist's** point of view, and from an **avoidance of regret** point of view. We then compared expected net payoffs of the various options, choosing one with the greatest expected net payoff (the **Bayesian** view).

We approached the **inventory problem** (choosing the best possible inventory level) from a Bayesian point of view, an entirely sufficient method: find the expected value of each possible inventory level, and choose accordingly. We then considered the expected values of individual items in the inventory, and solved the inventory problem by stocking only items with positive or zero expected values. As a short cut, we learned to find the **Lowest Acceptable Selling Probability (LASP)** in order to quickly detect the final item to be stocked.

The balance of the chapter dealt with **games** between intelligent players, each determined to do as well as possible by maximizing personal gain and minimizing payoffs to the opponent. All discussion assumed that both opponents played *optimally*—that is, as well as possible, without errors. A **strictly determined game** has one or more saddle points and always yields the same payoff. Both players play **pure strategies** (one option each). A **nonstrictly determined game** has no saddle point, and requires both players to use **mixed strategies**. To **solve a** game is to specify the strategies (pure or mixed) for both players, along with the game value (expected payoff). We completely solved all 2×2 games, and saw that $2 \times m$ games ($m > 2$) and $n \times 2$ games ($n > 2$) can be solved using 2×2 game methods.

Games of size $m \times n$, with $m > 2$ and $n > 2$, require special methods. Sometimes elimination of dominated rows and/or columns results in two surviving rows or columns, so that the game yields to $2 \times m$ or $n \times 2$ methods. If reduction to a game with 2 as one of its dimensions is not possible, we can still solve the game by linear programming methods.

REVIEW EXERCISES

APPLYING THE CONCEPTS

Exercises 117–122: Your stock in WIDCO, the world's foremost widget producer, is worth $10,000. You may trade the stock now to Bosco Anchovy for his mint-condition 1949 DeSoto, which will retain its $10,000 value indefinitely, or you may sell the stock after CALIPER, INC., announces whether it will use WIDCO widgets in its entire line of precision instruments next year. If CALIPER says "yes" to WIDCO widgets, your stock will increase in value by 20%. If CALIPER says "no," your stock will plunge by 30%. You estimate the probability that CALIPER will say "yes" to be 0.7.

117. What is the expected net value to you of trading for Bosco's DeSoto?
118. What is the expected net value to you of selling after CALIPER'S announcement?
119. What would an optimist do?
120. What would a pessimist do?
121. What should you do to minimize your maximum regret?
122. What would a Bayesian do?

Exercises 123–127: Weekly demands for roses (expressed in "number of dozens") are shown in the table below.

Demand	14	15	16	17	18	19
Probability	0.12	0.04	0.14	0.40	0.24	0.06

123. If Mario can buy roses (shelf life: one week) at $6 per dozen and sell them at $10.00, what is his optimum inventory and expected profit?

124. Fill in the following table, showing profits for each demand level if the exactly correct inventory is stocked.

Demand	14	15	16	17	18	19
"Correct Inventory" Profit						
Probability	0.12	0.04	0.14	0.40	0.24	0.06

125. What is Mario's expected profit if he stocks perfectly to match each day's demand?

127. Repeat Exercise 123 if Mario can buy roses for $7 per dozen, sell them fresh for $12 per dozen, and sell leftover roses at week's end for $4 per dozen.

126. Based upon your answers to Exercises 123 and 125, what is the maximum value to Mario of an exceedingly accurate daily forecast of the next day's demand? [This figure is called **the expected value of perfect information (EVPI)**.]

128. A painting by a young artist is offered to you for $400. If she develops a successful career, the painting will be worth $3000 ten years from now. If she does not achieve success, it will be worth $300, and you will have lost an estimated $350 in interest by which your $400 would have grown if invested in a certificate of deposit. You estimate her success probability to be 0.2. If this estimate is accurate, should you buy the painting or the CD?

129. Charlie Finch may buy a raffle ticket for $2. The prize is a $2700 motorcycle. Two thousand tickets will be sold. What is Charlie's expected value of buying a ticket?

130. What ticket price would make the game in Exercise 129 fair?

Exercises 131 and 132: In the racquetball match between Bjorn and Helga (Chapter 8), the first person to win two games wins the match. What is the expected number of games Bjorn and Helga will play to complete the tournament if

131. they are evenly matched?

132. Helga's probability of winning each game is 0.6?

133. A case of 12 cans of tuna contains 3 cans contaminated with dangerous bacteria. Five cans are to be opened and tested by an inspector who does not know of the contamination. If the tuna canning company is penalized $50 per "bad" can of tuna, what is the expected penalty?

Exercises 134 and 135: With time for at most five plays of a casino game before your chauffeur picks you up in the Rolls, you choose "coin toss." You must pay $3 to play each time; if you win, you get another dollar, and if you lose, you part with your $3. You start with $5, and will quit if you are ever $3 ahead, or you lack time or money to continue. What is your expected net gain if

*134. you start with $5, the coin is fair, and you win if the coin comes up "heads"?
*135. you start with $3, bet on "heads," and use your "lucky" coin ($P[H] = 0.7$)?

Exercises 136 and 137: Disregarding all costs and profit to the insurance company,

136. what is a perfectly fair price for a 25-year-old male to pay for a $5000 life insurance policy for one year?
137. how much insurance should $100 buy for a 20-year-old female for one year?

138. Your child is a skateboard competitor. Records show that, in skateboard contests, 13 young people out of 1000 suffer injuries, and the average cost of such an injury is $200. Would a single contest insurance policy costing $3 be a good investment? What premium would be perfectly fair?

Exercises 139–141: Barnacle Bill the Sailor operates a fish-and-chips concession at the region's carnivals, fairs, and rodeos. He buys fish in 10-pound bags. During a period in which he never ran out of fish, he sold 60 pounds of fish on 8 of the days, 70 pounds on 14 days, 80 pounds on 22 days, 90 pounds on 4 days, and 100 pounds on 2 days. Fish costs him $2 per pound (including cooking oil, other ingredients, and the cost of labor to prepare and sell the fish); he sells it at $5 per pound, and leftover fish at the end of the day has no salvage value.

139. What is the expected value of stocking seven bags?
140. What is the expected value of the seventh 10-pound bag?
141. What is his best daily inventory level and maximum expected profit?

Exercises 142–144: Refer to the sales data of Exercise 139, and find the Lowest Acceptable Selling Probability of a 10-pound bag of fish if

142. the cost per pound is $3, the selling price per pound is $5, and the salvage value of leftover fish is $1 per pound;

143. the cost per pound is $2, the selling price per pound is $6, and the salvage value is $1.50 per pound;

144. the cost is $3 per pound, the selling price is $5 per pound, and leftover fish costs an additional $.20 per pound for disposal.

145. Bjorn and Helga schedule a new racquetball tournament, with victory again going to the first person to win two games. Helga's probability of beating Bjorn is 0.6 each time they play. She will pay Bjorn $10 for each game he wins. Bjorn will pay Helga $8 each time he loses. What is Bjorn's expected gain in completing this tournament?

*146. Success encourages success: Helga's probability of winning her first game with Bjorn is 0.6;

but after each game, the winner's probability of winning the next game is increased by 0.20. What is Bjorn's expected gain in this new situation? (Use Exercise 145 dollar values.)

147. Which is more likely, according to the mortality table of Figure 10.3: that a one-year-old male will live to age 6, or that a 15-year-old male will live to age 20? Justify your answer.

Exercises 148 and 149: Max's Deli in Transylvania Station is famous for its aged liverwurst (easily recognized by the brown blotches on its skin), well known as the best wurst in town. Regular customers call Max's "the wurst shop in the station." Max buys wurst at $2.50 per pound at the start of each month, sells it at $4 per pound, and cuts the selling price in half on the last day of each month, liquidating all old stock. He has never run out. Monthly sales records for five years are:

Lbs Sold	60	65	70	75	80
# of Months	9	12	18	15	6

148. What is Max's best wurst inventory level?
149. What level is best if leftover wurst goes instead for $1 per pound?

Exercises 150 and 151: Jeremy Pinch buys the cheapest shotgun shells available. He recently got an exceptional buy on ammunition made in 1958: 20 cents per shell. There's only one problem: this ammunition contains 40% "duds" (shells that don't fire). With each shell which fires, Jeremy always bags one of his favorite wildfowl (elderly chickens), which he sells to Max's Deli for $5. (Biting down on an occasional lead shot convinces Max's customers they are eating exotic gamebirds!)

150. What is the expected net value to Jeremy of his next three shells?
*151. Solve Exercise 150 if, with each shell that fires, Jeremy has a 50% chance of bagging two chickens instead of just one.

Exercises 152 and 153: Computer retailers Roland Micronics and Cal's Computers simultaneously become interested in Creighton, a city with three major shopping centers: Alderbrook Mall, which attracts 30% of the city's business; Buckley Meadows, 45%; and City Center. Roland reasons as follows: "If my opponent and I open up in the same shopping center, I will get 55% of the city's computer business. If we open in separate centers, each of us will receive his center's proportion of computer business, and I will get 60% of the remaining center's business."

*152. If Roland is correct, where should each center open in order to be most successful? What is each dealer's expected market share?
*153. If instead the two dealers will equally share the city's business if both open in the same center, and each will get all of his center's business plus half of the unoccupied center's business if they open in separate centers, where should each open and what is the expected market share for each?

Exercises 154–157: Find the optimal row player strategy and game value.

154. $\begin{bmatrix} 2 & 1 & -2 & 5 \\ 4 & 3 & 1 & 5 \\ 1 & 4 & 6 & 4 \end{bmatrix}$ *155. $\begin{bmatrix} 6 & -5 & 5 \\ 8 & 4 & 1 \\ 3 & 2 & 4 \\ 2 & 1 & 7 \end{bmatrix}$ 156. $\begin{bmatrix} 6 & 2 \\ 1 & 4 \\ 3 & 3 \end{bmatrix}$ 157. $\begin{bmatrix} 3 & 4 & -2 & 5 \\ 5 & 2 & 6 & 1 \end{bmatrix}$

Exercises 158–159: Refer to matrix A:

$$A = \begin{bmatrix} -3 & 2 & 1 \\ 5 & -4 & 2 \\ 7 & 1 & -1 \\ -4 & 3 & 8 \end{bmatrix}$$

*158. For matrix A, formulate (giving constraints and objective function) the linear program to find row player's optimal strategy.

*159. Repeat Exercise 158 for the column player.

11 Finite Markov Chains

11.1 CONDITIONAL PROBABILITIES AND TRANSITION MATRICES

A substantial amount of what you have learned about matrices, probability, and expected value comes together in this chapter as we explore the fascinating world of finite Markov (pronounced "mark-off") chains. We introduce Markov chains by working a problem that is easy to solve with our current tree diagram methods.

■ EXAMPLE 1

A car insurance company issues policies only to well-screened drivers with good driving records. This company reclassifies its drivers each year as either normal risk (N) or low risk (L). Once this company insures a driver, it never refuses to insure that driver in later years, regardless of his or her driving record.

Having been in business a long time, the company has determined the following:

1. Eighty percent of drivers currently classified as low risk will also be classified as low risk next year.

2. Seventy percent of drivers currently classified as normal risk will also be classified as normal risk next year.

Find the following:

(a) What percentage of drivers currently classified as L will also be classified L two years from now?

(b) What percentage of drivers currently classified as N will be classified N two years from now?

SOLUTION

For part (a), we construct the tree in Figure 11.1. *Note:* Each node is labeled with the status of the driver. Since the driver's status at the start of this tree is L, the initial node is marked L instead of "Go."

Figure 11.1

	Probability	Path Label
0.8 L	0.64	a
0.2 N	0.16	b
0.3 L	0.06	c
0.7 N	0.14	d

(Tree diagram: L branches with 0.8 to L and 0.2 to N; 0.8 L subtree: 0.8→L (0.64, a), 0.2→N (0.16, b); 0.2 N subtree: 0.3→L (0.06, c), 0.7→N (0.14, d))

Part (a): Knowing that the driver is currently classified L, the event that he is also classified L in two years is the set of paths on the tree given by $\{a,c\}$. The probability of this event is $0.64 + 0.06 = 0.70$. This is a conditional probability since we are given the current classification:

$$P[\text{Low risk in two years|Low risk now}] = 0.70$$

Thus, 70% of those who are now classified L will be classified L two years from now.

Part (b): Consider the tree in Figure 11.2, which begins with current state N and progresses two years.

Figure 11.2

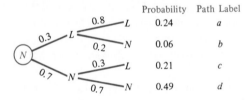

	Probability	Path Label
0.8 L	0.24	a
0.2 N	0.06	b
0.3 L	0.21	c
0.7 N	0.49	d

The event that a driver is classified L in two years when he is currently classified N, is the set of paths $\{a,c\}$, and thus

$$P[\text{Low risk in two years|Normal risk now}] = 0.24 + 0.21 = 0.45$$

This means that 45% of those who are currently in the normal-risk group will be in the low-risk group two years from now. ∎

PRACTICE PROBLEM 1   In Example 1, find the probability that a current L risk will be classified as N in two years.

ANSWER(S)   0.30 (Use tree paths **b** and **d** from Figure 11.1, or apply the Complement Rule.) ☐

PRACTICE PROBLEM 2   In Example 1, suppose a driver is currently classified N. Find the probability that he is also classified as N in two years.

ANSWER(S)   0.55 ☐

■ EXAMPLE 2   Using the conditions of Example 1, answer the following:

(a) What is the probability that a current N driver will be classified N three years from now?

(b) What is the probability that a current L driver will be classified L three years from now?

SOLUTION **Part (a):** Extending the tree of Figure 11.2 one more step, we arrive at the tree of Figure 11.3.

Figure 11.3

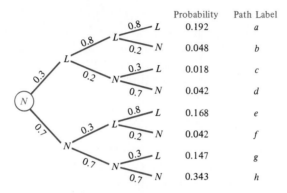

The conditional probability of being classified N in three years, given a current classification of N is the set of paths {**b,d,f,h**}, and the probability of this is

$$P[N \text{ in three years}|N \text{ now}] = 0.048 + 0.042 + 0.042 + 0.343$$
$$= 0.475$$

Part (b): We extend the tree of Figure 11.1 one more step, arriving at the tree of Figure 11.4.

Figure 11.4

	Probability	Path Label
0.8 L	0.512	a
0.2 N	0.128	b
0.3 L	0.048	c
0.7 N	0.112	d
0.8 L	0.048	e
0.2 N	0.012	f
0.3 L	0.042	g
0.7 N	0.098	h

The conditional probability of being classified L in three years, if now classified L, is the probability of event {**a,c,e,g**}:

$$P[L \text{ in three years}|L \text{ now}] = 0.512 + 0.048 + 0.048 + 0.042$$
$$= 0.65$$

PRACTICE PROBLEM 3   **(a)** In Example 2, find the probability of a driver being classified N three years from now if he or she is now an L. **(b)** Find the probability of a driver being classified as L three years from now if he is currently classified N.

ANSWER(S)   **(a)** 0.35;   **(b)** 0.525   □

The tree-diagram approach of Examples 1 and 2 is straightforward, but it has limitations. What if we were interested in a policyholder's classification 7 years from now? Drawing the tree diagram for seven years, while "do-able," is not everyone's favorite rainy-day activity!

We can, however, solve such problems with matrices. We shall use the framework of Examples 1 and 2 to illustrate the power of matrices in working with *Finite Markov*[1] *chains*.

Fundamental Notions of Markov Chains

Consider a repeatable random process where on any trial the outcome is one of a finite number n of possibilities, called **states**. In Example 1, the states are the two possible risk classifications for an insured driver: $s_1 =$ Low risk and $s_2 =$ Normal risk. The probability of a **move** (step or transition) from any state (classification) now to any "next" state (classification next year) is called a *transition probability*. In particular, we let p_{ij} represent the probability of going from state i on one step to state j on the next step. We assume that transition probabilities are *stationary*, which means that p_{ij} is the correct probability for a transition from state i to state j whether describing a move from trial 4 to trial 5, from trial 34 to trial 35, or from trial 419 to trial 420. (*Note:* Remaining in state i is considered a "move" from state i to itself.)

The Markov Property

We further assume that the probability of being in a given state on the next step depends only on the current state, and not on how the process got there. This assumption is called the **Markov property,** and the set of states, along with the transition probabilities p_{ij} having this Markov property, is called a **finite Markov chain.**

We will combine all transition probabilities into an $n \times n$ probability transition matrix P, whose i,j-th element is p_{ij}. In matrix P, rows represent current state possibilities, while columns represent state possibilities after the next move. We shall use descriptive state names (L or N) or formal state names (s_1 or s_2) or more casual names (like "state 1" and "state 2") interchangeably. Regardless of what we call the states, using the same ordering for both rows and columns is important. The probability transition matrix P of Example 1 is shown below.

[1] The name is in honor of the great Russian probabilist, Andrei Andreevich Markov, who died in 1922.

$$
\begin{array}{c}
\textbf{Next} \\
\textbf{State} \\
\begin{array}{cc} \textbf{\textit{L}} & \textbf{\textit{N}} \end{array}
\end{array}
$$

$$
\begin{array}{cc}
\textbf{Current} & \textit{L} \\
\textbf{State} & \textit{N}
\end{array}
\begin{bmatrix} .8 & .2 \\ .3 & .7 \end{bmatrix} = P
$$

The sum of the entries in each row is one since a driver has to be classified either as L or N after the next move (that is, after next year's classification), regardless of what state he or she is in now. A matrix like P, whose rows contain nonnegative entries that sum to one, is called a **stochastic matrix.** Each of its rows is called a **stochastic vector** or a **probability vector.**

In addition to using transition matrices, you can also use a transition diagram to convey the same information. Such a diagram is shown in Figure 11.5.

Figure 11.5
Transition diagram

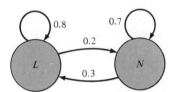

There are striking similarities between the transition diagram of Figure 11.5 and the digraphs of Section 3.2. Each state in Figure 11.5 is a vertex. Each possible transition from a current state to a next state is represented by an edge, labeled with the appropriate probability. For example, the probability that a driver, in state N now, will be in L next year, is 0.3. Note also that the directed edges leading from any state must have probabilities that total 1, indicating that a driver must be in either state L or N next year.

While helpful, transition diagrams do not lend themselves readily to computations like matrices do. To see how helpful working with transition matrices can be, form the product $P \cdot P = P^2$.

$$
P^2 = P \cdot P = \begin{bmatrix} .8 & .2 \\ .3 & .7 \end{bmatrix}\begin{bmatrix} .8 & .2 \\ .3 & .7 \end{bmatrix} = \begin{bmatrix} .70 & .30 \\ .45 & .55 \end{bmatrix}
$$

Entries in the first row of P^2 should look familiar—they are conditional probabilities for risk classifications two years from now for those currently classified as L. In Chapter 3, we saw that the square of a vertex matrix gave the number of two-step connections from one vertex to another. Thus, it should seem reasonable that probabilities of being in various states two days later are given by the square of P. Similarly, probabilities of moving to various states three days hence are given by entries in P^3:

$$\begin{array}{cc} & \begin{array}{cc} L & N \end{array} \\ P^3 = P^2 \cdot P = \begin{bmatrix} .70 & .30 \\ .45 & .55 \end{bmatrix}\begin{bmatrix} .80 & .20 \\ .30 & .70 \end{bmatrix} = \begin{array}{c} L \\ N \end{array}\begin{bmatrix} .65 & .35 \\ .525 & .475 \end{bmatrix} \end{array}$$

The main diagonal entries of P^3 were verified in Example 2. The other two entries were found in Practice Problem 3 and can be checked by using the tree diagrams of Figures 11.3 and 11.4.

In general, probabilities of going from any state to any next state in m moves or transitions are given by entries in matrix P^m. Important results are summarized below.

PROBABILITY TRANSITION MATRIX

> The probability of moving from current state i to next state j is called a **transition probability,** symbolized p_{ij}. Matrix P, whose i,j-th entry is p_{ij}, is the **probability transition matrix.** The i,j-th element of P^2 is the probability of moving to state j in two steps, given present state i. In general, the i,j-th element of P^m is the probability of being in state j in m moves, given present state i.

Consider the ith row of P^m. Since rows indicate "present state," all entries in the ith row represent probabilities of proceeding, in m moves, from state i to the state indicated by the column heading. Since the process must be in some state after m moves, the entries in this row will sum to one. This is true for every row of P^m, and thus P^m is itself a stochastic matrix.

POWERS OF A STOCHASTIC MATRIX

> If P is a stochastic matrix, then for any positive integer m, P^m is also a stochastic matrix.

■ EXAMPLE 3

In Examples 1 and 2, find the probability that

(a) A driver that is currently a low-risk driver will still be classified L five years from now.

(b) A driver that is currently classified N will be in the low-risk group five years from now.

(c) A driver that is currently in the low-risk group will still be in the low-risk group ten years from now.

(d) A driver that is currently in the normal-risk group will be in the low-risk group ten years from now.

SOLUTION   For parts **(a)** and **(b)**, we must calculate P^5; for parts **(c)** and **(d)**, we need P^{10}. Having already computed P^3 and P^2 in Examples 1 and 2, we compute P^5 by $P^3 \cdot P^2$. (Computations are rounded to four places.)

$$P^5 = \begin{bmatrix} .65 & .35 \\ .525 & .475 \end{bmatrix} \begin{bmatrix} .70 & .30 \\ .45 & .55 \end{bmatrix} \approx \begin{matrix} L \\ N \end{matrix} \begin{bmatrix} \overset{L}{.6125} & \overset{N}{.3875} \\ .5812 & .4188 \end{bmatrix}$$

Part (a): The L-to-L entry of P^5 indicates that a little over 61% of those that are in the low-risk group will be in the low-risk group in five years. (This does not mean they stayed there the whole time.)

   Part (b): The N-to-L entry of P^5 says that 58% of those currently in the normal risk group will be in the low-risk group after five years.

   For parts **(c)** and **(d)**, we calculated P^{10} by $P^5 \cdot P^5$:

$$P^{10} = \begin{bmatrix} .6125 & .3875 \\ .5812 & .4188 \end{bmatrix} \begin{bmatrix} .6125 & .3875 \\ .5812 & .4188 \end{bmatrix} = \begin{matrix} L \\ N \end{matrix} \begin{bmatrix} \overset{L}{.6004} & \overset{N}{.3996} \\ .5994 & .4006 \end{bmatrix}$$

Part (c): The L-to-L entry in P^{10}, 0.6004, indicates that about 60% of current low-risk drivers will be in the low-risk group ten years from now; the other 40% will be normal risks.

   Part (d): The N-to-L entry in P^{10}, 0.5994, indicates that about 60% of the current normal-risk drivers will have moved to the low-risk group in ten years.   ■

   In Example 3, the rows of P^{10} were almost identical. Since row position indicates the current state, this would suggest that the probabilities after 10 moves are essentially the same, regardless of the current state. Is this always to be expected? The answer is no, but for a certain kind of transition matrix, which we investigate shortly, rows of P^m will become more and more alike as the number of transitions m increases.

Brand Switching   Real-world applications of Markov chains abound. In many consumer-product categories, for example, there are several brands with similar quality and features. "Brand loyalty" among such products is not particularly strong, and consumers often switch between brands because of price, rebates, or even shopping convenience. In Example 4 we illustrate.

■ EXAMPLE 4   A study of blank videotape purchases reveals that among Brands T, M, and S, purchasing habits are as follows:

   1. If a customer has just purchased Brand T, there is a 50% chance he will choose Brand T again on his next purchase, but if he switches, he is just as likely to switch to Brand M as Brand S.

2. If a customer has just purchased Brand M, there is a 60% chance of him buying Brand M again on his next purchase. If he switches, he is three times as likely to switch to Brand T as Brand S.

3. If a customer has just purchased Brand S, there is a 70% chance he will stick with Brand S on his next purchase. If he switches, he will buy Brand M with twice the probability of Brand T.

(a) Find the probability transition matrix for this customer's videotape purchasing habits;

(b) Find the matrix that describes his buying habits two purchases from now;

(c) Find the probability that this customer will buy Brand S on the purchase after next if he now buys Brand M.

SOLUTION   This is a three-state Markov chain with states T, M, and S. From the given information, it is easy to construct the following transition matrix P:

$$
\begin{array}{c c}
 & \begin{array}{ccc} \text{T} & \text{M} & \text{S} \end{array} \\
P = \begin{array}{c} \text{T} \\ \text{M} \\ \text{S} \end{array} & \begin{bmatrix} .50 & .25 & .25 \\ .30 & .60 & .10 \\ .10 & .20 & .70 \end{bmatrix}
\end{array}
$$

The answer to part **(b)** is given by the matrix P^2:

$$
\begin{array}{c c}
 & \begin{array}{ccc} \text{T} & \text{M} & \text{S} \end{array} \\
P^2 = \begin{array}{c} \text{T} \\ \text{M} \\ \text{S} \end{array} & \begin{bmatrix} .350 & .325 & .325 \\ .340 & .455 & .205 \\ .180 & .285 & .535 \end{bmatrix}
\end{array}
$$

For part **(c)**, we pick the M to S element of P^2, which is 0.205.   ■

PRACTICE PROBLEM 4   In Example 4, find **(a)** the probability that a current Brand T purchaser will purchase Brand T again on the purchase after next; and **(b)** the probability that a current Brand M purchaser will not purchase Brand M the time after next.

ANSWER(S)   **(a)** 0.35;   **(b)** 0.545   ☐

PRACTICE PROBLEM 5   In Example 4, find the probability transition matrix that describes this consumer's videotape purchases on the third purchase after the current purchase.

ANSWER(S)

$$P^3 = \begin{matrix} & \text{T} & \text{M} & \text{S} \\ \begin{matrix}\text{T}\\\text{M}\\\text{S}\end{matrix} & \begin{bmatrix} .3050 & .3475 & .3475 \\ .3270 & .3990 & .2740 \\ .2290 & .3230 & .4480 \end{bmatrix} \end{matrix}$$

☐

PRACTICE PROBLEM 6   In Example 4, find **(a)** the probability that a current Brand T purchaser will again purchase Brand T three purchases from now; **(b)** the probability of a switch from Brand M now to Brand S three purchases from now.

ANSWER(S)   **(a)** 0.3050;   **(b)** 0.2740

☐

EXERCISES 11.1

PRACTICING THE MOVES AND MANEUVERS

Exercises 1–9:   Determine whether the given vector is a probability vector.

1. [.2 .5 .3]
2. [.6 .5 −.1]
3. [.6 .1 .1 0 .1]
4. [1 0 0 0]
5. [.8 .2 −.3 .3]
6. [.2 .7 .1]
7. [.1 0 .9]
8. [.4 .5 .2]
9. [.8 .3 −.1]

Exercises 10–13:   Determine if the given matrix is a probability transition matrix. If the matrix is not a transition matrix, explain why.

10. $P = \begin{bmatrix} .7 & .2 \\ .5 & .5 \end{bmatrix}$

11. $\begin{bmatrix} .5 & .2 & .1 \\ .3 & .4 & .3 \\ .5 & .5 & 0 \end{bmatrix}$

12. $\begin{bmatrix} .6 & .2 & .2 \\ .4 & .4 & .3 \\ .4 & .1 & .5 \end{bmatrix}$

13. $\begin{bmatrix} 1 & 0 \\ 1 & 0 \end{bmatrix}$

Exercises 14–16:   Fill in all missing edge probabilities, and find the transition matrix that goes with the indicated transition diagram.

14.
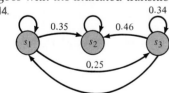

15.
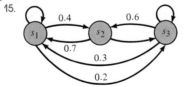

16.
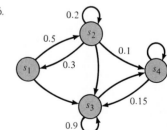

Exercises 17–20:   Construct transition diagrams for the given transition matrices.

17. $\begin{bmatrix} .9 & .1 \\ .5 & .5 \end{bmatrix}$

18. $\begin{bmatrix} .2 & .4 & .4 \\ .6 & .4 & 0 \\ .5 & .4 & .1 \end{bmatrix}$

19. $\begin{bmatrix} 1 & 0 & 0 \\ .4 & 0 & .6 \\ .4 & .3 & .3 \end{bmatrix}$

20. $\begin{bmatrix} 1 & 0 \\ 1 & 0 \end{bmatrix}$

Exercises 21–24: Find P^2 and P^3 and interpret first-row entries in each matrix.

21. $\begin{bmatrix} .8 & .2 \\ .5 & .5 \end{bmatrix}$

22. $\begin{bmatrix} .5 & .1 & .4 \\ .6 & .4 & 0 \\ .2 & 0 & .8 \end{bmatrix}$

23. $\begin{bmatrix} 1 & 0 & 0 \\ .4 & 0 & .6 \\ .3 & .5 & .2 \end{bmatrix}$

24. $\begin{bmatrix} 1 & 0 \\ 0 & 1 \end{bmatrix}$

APPLYING THE CONCEPTS

Exercises 25–32: Consider a customer who buys a new car every year, choosing from Honda, Mazda, and Nissan. If she buys a Honda, there is a 0.60 chance she will buy Honda the next time, and a 0.30 chance of buying a Mazda. If she buys a Mazda this time, there is a 0.70 chance of a Mazda being the next purchase, and a 0.20 chance of her switching to Honda. If she buys a Nissan this time, there is a 0.65 chance of her sticking with Nissan, and a 0.30 chance of switching to Mazda.

25. Find the transition matrix P for this three-state Markov chain.

Exercises 26–31: Find the probability that

26. she owns a Mazda in two years if she now has a Honda.
27. she will own a Honda in two years if she now has a Honda.
28. she will not own a Honda in two years if she drives a Honda now.
29. she will drive a Mazda in three years if she now drives a Mazda.
30. she will drive a Nissan in three years if she now drives a Honda.
31. she will not drive a Mazda in three years if she drives a Mazda now.
32. Find P^4 and P^5.

Exercises 33–36: Consider a consumer who purchases gasoline once a week, always purchasing either Brand A or B. If he purchased Brand A last week, he switches to Brand B with probability 0.7. If he purchased Brand B last week, he switches to Brand A with probability 0.9.

33. Find the probability transition matrix for this two-state Markov chain.
34. If the consumer purchased Brand A this week, how likely is it that he will purchase Brand B two weeks from now?
35. If the consumer is using Brand B this week, how likely is it that he will use Brand B three weeks from now?
36. If the consumer is using Brand A this week, how likely is it that he will be using Brand B in six weeks?

Exercises 37–39: Consider a young actuary who either takes her car to work or uses the bus. If she took her car on one day, she is just as likely to take the car as not on the following day. If she took the bus on her most recent trip, there is an 80% chance of her switching to her car on the next trip.

37. Find the probability transition matrix P for this two-state Markov chain.
38. If she took her car today, how likely is it that she will take her car three days from now?
39. If she rode the bus today, how likely is it that she will take her car the day after tomorrow?

Exercises 40–43: Fitness guru Joe Crider runs, lifts weights, or plays pickleball during lunch hour. If Joe ran today, there is no chance he will run tomorrow, and he is four times as likely to lift weights as to play pickleball. If he lifted weights today, there is no chance he will lift weights tomorrow, and he is nine times more likely to run than to play pickleball. If he played pickleball today, then there is an 0.8 chance he will also play pickleball tomorrow, and an equal chance of switching to either of the other two activities.

40. Find the transition matrix for this three-state Markov chain.
41. If Joe ran Monday, what is the probability that he will also run on Wednesday?
42. If he lifted weights Tuesday, how likely is it that he will run on Thursday?
43. If Joe played pickleball Monday, how likely is he to play pickleball Thursday?

Exercises 44–47: Use the following information: Educational districts now purchase computers on a regular basis. In one such large district, it has been observed that if an IBM or a compatible machine was purchased last time, then there is a 70% chance of the next purchase being the same, and a 30% chance of a switch to Macintosh. If Macintosh was the purchase last time, then there is an 80% chance of buying Macintosh again, and a 20% chance of switching to an IBM or an IBM-compatible machine.

44. Find the probability transition matrix for this two-state Markov chain.
45. If the district just purchased Macintosh, what is the probability that they will purchase Macintosh the time after next?
46. If the district just purchased an IBM or compatible, what is the probability that they will purchase Macintosh the time after next?
47. If the district just purchased Macintosh, how likely is it that the third purchase from now will also be Macintosh?

Exercises 48–51: Consider a teacher named Pam who has two hobbies: sewing and cross-stitching. If her current project is sewing, there is a 65% chance her next project will also be sewing. If her current project is cross-stitching, there is an 80% chance that her next project will also be a cross-stitch.

48. Display the transition matrix P for Pam's hobbies.
49. If Pam sewed her current project, how likely is she to sew the project after next?
50. If Pam is currently cross-stitching, how likely is it that she will be sewing two projects from now?
51. Find P^3 and interpret the entries.

Exercises 52–54: Consider a golfer with two putters who selects one at the start of each round and uses it throughout the round. If he used his "blade" putter this time, there is a 0.8 chance he will use his blade putter during the next round. If he just used his "blockhead" putter, there is a 40% chance he will use it next.

52. Present the transition matrix P for the golfer's choice of putters.
53. If the golfer is currently using the blade putter, how likely is it that he will be using the blade putter the third time after this round?
54. If the golfer is currently using his blockhead, find the probability that he will use the blade putter the time after next.

11.2 The *m*-step Probability Vector and Regular Transition Matrices

The transition matrix P and its powers give us *conditional* probabilities. Thus, for example, if for a certain Markov chain, we find that P^6 is

$$P^6 = \begin{array}{c} \\ A \\ B \\ C \end{array} \overset{\begin{array}{ccc} A & B & C \end{array}}{\begin{bmatrix} .6 & .3 & .1 \\ .2 & .5 & .3 \\ .8 & .1 & .1 \end{bmatrix}}$$

then we can say that of those that are currently in state B, 50% will be in state B after six moves. This information does not tell us what proportion of the "population" is in state B after six moves. Similarly, knowing that 80% (0.8 in the C-to-A position) of those in group C will be in group A six moves later, does not tell us what proportion of the distribution is in group C six moves later. To determine the actual distribution in each state, we need to know the proportions for each state when we begin observing the Markov chain. We illustrate this in Example 5.

■ EXAMPLE 5

In Example 1 we studied an insurance company that classified its policyholders as either low risk (L) or normal risk (N). Suppose that 10% of the policyholders are currently in the low-risk group and 90% are in the normal-risk group. We let this information be represented by an *initial probability vector* Π_0:

$$\begin{array}{cc} L & N \end{array}$$
$$\Pi_0 = [.10 \quad .90]$$

Find the distribution of policyholders

(a) in one year.

(b) after two years.

(c) after three years.

SOLUTION

We shall solve parts (a) and (b) with the aid of tree diagrams, and then use our results to illustrate a better approach with matrices. For part (a), the appropriate tree diagram is Figure 11.6.

Figure 11.6

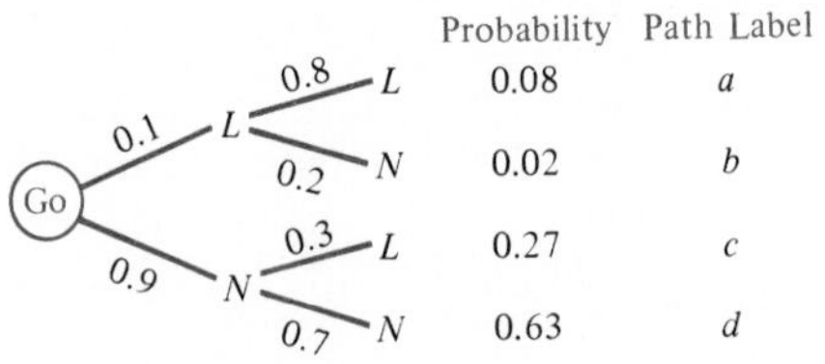

Part (a): The proportion of policyholders in the low-risk group next year is found by adding probabilities for paths **a** and **c**:

$$P[\text{being in group } L \text{ after one year}] = 0.08 + 0.27 = 0.35$$

The proportion of policyholders in the normal-risk group next year is found by adding probabilities for paths **b** and **d:**

$$P[\text{being in group } N \text{ in one year}] = 0.02 + 0.63 = 0.65$$

We could also have used the complement rule, obtaining

$$P[\text{being in group } N \text{ in one year}] = 1 - P[L \text{ in one year}]$$
$$= 1 - 0.35 = 0.65$$

This is easy enough, but there is an even easier way! Consider the matrix multiplication $\Pi_0 \cdot P$, where Π_0 is the initial probability vector:

$$\Pi_0 \cdot P = [.1 \quad .9]\begin{bmatrix} .8 & .2 \\ .3 & .7 \end{bmatrix} = [.35 \quad .65]$$

The vector $\Pi_0 \cdot P$ thus gives us the probabilities after one move or one step, and for that reason we call this vector Π_1 and name it the one-step probability vector: $\Pi_1 = \Pi_0 \cdot P = [.35 \quad .65]$.

Part (b): Continuing the notation introduced for Π_1, we let Π_2 denote the distribution of policyholders after two years, or the two-step probability vector. How do we arrive at Π_2? It seems reasonable that we would add one more set of branches to the tree of Figure 11.6, yielding the tree of Figure 11.7.

Figure 11.7

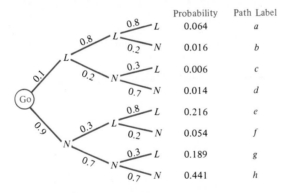

	Probability	Path Label
	0.064	*a*
	0.016	*b*
	0.006	*c*
	0.014	*d*
	0.216	*e*
	0.054	*f*
	0.189	*g*
	0.441	*h*

The first (left-most) element in Π_2 is the probability of being in the low-risk group after two years, found by summing probabilities for paths **a, c, e, g** from Figure 11.7:

$$P[\text{being in group } L \text{ after two years}] = 0.064 + 0.006 + 0.216 + 0.189$$
$$= 0.475$$

The second element in Π_2 is the probability of being in the normal-risk group after two years, found by summing probabilities for paths **b, d, f, h:**

$$P[\text{being in group } N \text{ after two years}] = 0.016 + 0.014 + 0.054 + 0.441$$
$$= 0.525$$

Or simply use the complement rule:

$P[N \text{ in 2 years}] = 1 - P[L \text{ in 2 years}] = 1 - 0.475 = 0.525$

Thus, $\Pi_2 = [.475 \quad .525]$. Now, observe how these calculations can be performed with matrices. Form the product $\Pi_0 \cdot P^2$:

$$\Pi_0 \cdot P^2 = [.1 \quad .9]\begin{bmatrix} .70 & .30 \\ .45 & .55 \end{bmatrix} = [.475 \quad .525]$$

which is Π_2 (that is, $\Pi_2 = \Pi_0 \cdot P^2$). After two years 47.5% of the policyholders will be in the low-risk group, and the remaining 52.5% will be in the normal-risk group. This concludes part **(b).**

Before proceeding to part **(c)**, let's take stock of what we have seen. The one-step probability vector is given by $\Pi_0 \cdot P^1$, while the two-step probability vector is given by $\Pi_0 \cdot P^2$. In general, we have the following result for the m-step probability vector.

CALCULATION OF THE m-STEP PROBABILITY VECTOR Π_m

> If probabilities for starting in various states are given by the initial probability vector Π_0, then unconditional probabilities of being in various states in m moves are given by the entries in the m-step probability vector Π_m:
>
> $$\Pi_m = \Pi_0 \cdot P^m$$

Part (c): To find the distribution of policyholders after 3 years, we need Π_3, which is $\Pi_0 \cdot P^3$. After having calculated Π_1 and Π_2, we shall demonstrate an even better way. Observe that

$$\Pi_2 = \Pi_0 \cdot P^2 = (\Pi_0 \cdot P) \cdot P = \Pi_1 \cdot P \qquad \text{remember, } \Pi_0 \cdot P = \Pi_1$$

Similarly,

$$\Pi_3 = \Pi_0 \cdot P^3 = (\Pi_0 \cdot P^2) \cdot P = \Pi_2 \cdot P \qquad \text{since } \Pi_0 \cdot P^2 = \Pi_2$$

Therefore,

$$\Pi_3 = \Pi_2 \cdot P = [.475 \quad .525]\begin{matrix} & L & N \\ & \begin{bmatrix} .80 & .20 \\ .30 & .70 \end{bmatrix} \end{matrix} = [.5375 \quad .4625].$$

After three years, 53.75% of the policyholders will be in the low-risk group and the remaining 46.25% will be in the normal-risk group.

Finding the value of Π_3 by multiplying the previous value, Π_2, times P is called a **recursive process**—each newly calculated term is used to generate the next term.

It is easy to see that this recursive process can be continued, yielding

$$\Pi_m = \Pi_0 \cdot P^m = (\Pi_0 \cdot P^{m-1}) \cdot P = \Pi_{m-1} \cdot P$$

Finding Π_m in this way does not require that we compute progressively higher powers of the transition matrix P. (*Note:* If you also want m-step conditional probabilities, you will need to calculate P^m. If you have already calculated several powers of P, then the recursive process we are describing may not be any easier than simply calculating $\Pi_m = \Pi_0 \cdot P^m$.) ■

Using the recursive process begun in Example 5, we extend the results a few more years:

$$\Pi_4 = \Pi_3 \cdot P = [.5375 \quad .4625] \begin{bmatrix} .80 & .20 \\ .30 & .70 \end{bmatrix} = [.56875 \quad .43125]$$

$$\Pi_5 = \Pi_4 \cdot P = [.56875 \quad .43125] \begin{bmatrix} .80 & .20 \\ .30 & .70 \end{bmatrix} = [.584375 \quad .415625]$$

Continuing these calculations and summarizing, we have:

$$\Pi_1 = [.35 \quad .65] \qquad\qquad \Pi_6 = [.592188 \quad .407812]$$

$$\Pi_2 = [.475 \quad .525] \qquad\qquad \Pi_7 = [.596094 \quad .403906]$$

$$\Pi_3 = [.5375 \quad .4625] \qquad\qquad \Pi_8 = [.598047 \quad .401953]$$

$$\Pi_4 = [.56875 \quad .43125] \qquad\qquad \Pi_9 = [.599023 \quad .400977]$$

$$\Pi_5 = [.584375 \quad .415625] \qquad \Pi_{10} = [.599512 \quad .400488]$$

There appears to be little change in values of Π_m after $m = 6$, and in fact it appears that Π_m is headed toward the vector $[.6 \quad .4]$ as m gets larger and larger. In Example 3 we found that

$$P^{10} = \begin{bmatrix} .6004 & .3996 \\ .5994 & .4006 \end{bmatrix}$$

It thus appears that both rows of P^m are also getting closer and closer to this same $[.6 \quad .4]$ vector as m gets larger. Since elements in P^m are conditional probabilities, this would say that the present state has very little influence on conditional probabilities after but a few transitions. At least for this example, probabilities after a few steps seem to be essentially independent of the starting state.

Influence of the Initial Vector Π_0   Is it coincidental that the rows of P^m seem to be converging to the same vector as Π_m, or could this have been due to our choice of Π_0? We now study the effect of changing Π_0 rather drastically, reversing the elements used previously. For our new initial probability vector, to be called Π_0' (say "pi-zero prime"), we choose $\Pi_0' = [.9 \quad .1]$. As before we compute successive Π-values by recursion:

$$\Pi_1' = \Pi_0' \cdot P = [.9 \quad .1]\begin{bmatrix} .80 & .20 \\ .30 & .70 \end{bmatrix} = [.75 \quad .25]$$

$$\Pi_2' = \Pi_1' \cdot P = [.75 \quad .25]\begin{bmatrix} .80 & .20 \\ .30 & .70 \end{bmatrix} = [.675 \quad .325]$$

$$\Pi_3' = \Pi_2' \cdot P = [.675 \quad .325]\begin{bmatrix} .80 & .20 \\ .30 & .70 \end{bmatrix} = [.6375 \quad .3625]$$

Continuing the recursion (we used MINITAB for our calculations) and then summarizing, we have:

$\Pi_4' = [.61875 \quad .38125]$ $\Pi_9' = [.600586 \quad .399414]$

$\Pi_5' = [.609375 \quad .390625]$ $\Pi_{10}' = [.600293 \quad .399707]$

$\Pi_6' = [.604688 \quad .395313]$ . . . .

$\Pi_7' = [.602344 \quad .397656]$ $\Pi_{19}' = [.60000 \quad .400000]$

$\Pi_8' = [.601172 \quad .398828]$ $\Pi_{20}' = [.60000 \quad .400000]$

Even with the change to Π_0', it once again appears as if Π_m' is converging to the probability vector [.6   .4], suggesting that the choice of initial probability vector does not make much difference after only a few transitions. Since $\Pi_{19}' = \Pi_{20}'$, does it then follow that Π_{21}' and all "later" values will also be the probability vector [.60000   .40000]? We answer these questions now.

Equilibrium Probability Vector

In the sequence of transitions $\Pi_1 = \Pi_0 \cdot P$, $\Pi_2 = \Pi_1 \cdot P$, $\Pi_3 = \Pi_2 \cdot P$, . . ., if we ever reach a point where a transition produces no change from one "generation" to the next (that is, $\Pi_{m+1} = \Pi_m$—this happened at Π_{19} and Π_{20} in our above calculations), we then reason as follows: Since $\mathbf{\Pi_{m+1} = \Pi_m}$, then, upon multiplying both sides on the right by matrix P, we arrive at

$$\Pi_{m+1} \cdot P = \Pi_m \cdot P, \quad \text{or} \quad \mathbf{\Pi_{m+2} = \Pi_{m+1}}$$

Multiply both sides of $\Pi_{m+2} = \Pi_{m+1}$ on the right by P, giving

$$\Pi_{m+2} \cdot P = \Pi_{m+1} \cdot P, \quad \text{or} \quad \mathbf{\Pi_{m+3} = \Pi_{m+2}}$$

We may continue in this fashion as long as we like, and then "string together" the boldfaced equations above, producing

$$\Pi_m = \Pi_{m+1} = \Pi_{m+2} = \Pi_{m+3} = \cdots$$

Thus, if we ever reach a point where there is no change from one transition to the next, all subsequent transition probabilities will remain unchanged. This is precisely what we shall mean by the phrase *long-run equilibrium*. Once there have been enough transitions to reach this point of equilibrium, multiplying any one of the succeeding Π vectors on the right by the transition matrix P will not change that vector, which we call the *equilibrium probability vector*.

We now drop the subscripts, and simply use Π to represent this equilibrium vector. Thus, $\Pi \cdot P = \Pi$ at equilibrium and for all transitions thereafter. In Example 5, the value of Π was the same for both choices of initial probability vectors. This suggests that the influence supplied by an initial probability vector diminishes rapidly.

At this point, we display conditional probabilities given by the elements of P^5 and P^{10}, along with the unconditional five- and ten-step probability vectors Π_5 and Π_{10}, calculated from both choices of initial probability vectors we have used:

$$P^5 = \begin{bmatrix} .6125 & .3875 \\ .5812 & .4188 \end{bmatrix} \qquad \begin{array}{l} \Pi_5 = [.584375 \quad .415625] \\[6pt] \Pi'_5 = [.609375 \quad .390625] \end{array}$$

$$P^{10} = \begin{bmatrix} .6004 & .3996 \\ .5994 & .4006 \end{bmatrix} \qquad \begin{array}{l} \Pi_{10} = [.599512 \quad .400488] \\[6pt] \Pi'_{10} = [.600293 \quad .399707] \end{array}$$

Even after only five transitions, there is little difference between the unconditional probabilities given by the Π-vectors and the conditional probabilities given by the rows of P^5. After ten transitions, things are even closer. Thus, at least for this problem, a long-run stability has occurred whereby both conditional probabilities and unconditional probabilities of being in the various states are essentially the same after only a few moves, regardless of the initial probability vector. Is this long-run stability guaranteed? Not always, but, for a certain kind of transition matrix, which we now investigate, the answer is "yes: long-run stability, independent of the initial probability vector, is assured."

Regular Transition Matrices and Long-Term Stability

The following definition is crucial in resolving long-term stability.

REGULAR TRANSITION MATRIX

> A probability transition matrix P is said to be **regular** if some power of P contains only positive entries. A Markov chain whose transition matrix is regular is said to be a **regular Markov chain.**

Checking for Regularity

To be regular, the transition matrix itself does not have to have all positive entries. It is only necessary that some power of P have all positive entries. Consider the following transition matrix:

$$P = \begin{bmatrix} .7 & .2 & .1 \\ .5 & .5 & 0 \\ 0 & .8 & .2 \end{bmatrix}$$

Although there are two zero entries in P, matrix P^2 has no zeros, and thus P is regular:

$$P^2 = \begin{bmatrix} .7 & .2 & .1 \\ .5 & .5 & 0 \\ 0 & .8 & .2 \end{bmatrix} \begin{bmatrix} .7 & .2 & .1 \\ .5 & .5 & 0 \\ 0 & .8 & .2 \end{bmatrix} = \begin{bmatrix} .59 & .32 & .09 \\ .60 & .35 & .05 \\ .40 & .56 & .04 \end{bmatrix}$$

If P^2 still had zeros, you would need to compute P^3, etc. until you found that all zeros were gone or you somehow decide that the zeros will not ever disappear. If you keep encountering zeros, how do you know whether to continue computing powers of P?

If P is an $n \times n$ transition matrix and you haven't gotten rid of all zeros by the time you reach the power of P given by $n^2 - 2n + 2$, then matrix P is not regular. With a 4×4 transition matrix, you would know whether P is regular after computing the $4^2 - 2 \cdot 4 + 2 = 10$th power of P. Regularity is often detectable much sooner.

PRACTICE PROBLEM 7   Determine whether the following transition matrices are regular.

$$\textbf{(a)} \; P = \begin{bmatrix} .5 & .5 & 0 \\ .8 & .1 & .1 \\ .1 & .8 & .1 \end{bmatrix} \quad \textbf{(b)} \; P = \begin{bmatrix} 1 & 0 & 0 \\ .6 & .4 & 0 \\ .7 & .2 & .1 \end{bmatrix} \quad \textbf{(c)} \; P = \begin{bmatrix} 0 & 1 \\ 1 & 0 \end{bmatrix}$$

ANSWER(S)   **(a)** yes;   **(b)** no;   **(c)** no   ☐

The Meaning of Regularity   Suppose P^r has all positive entries so that P is regular. Then, from any particular starting state, it is possible to get to every other state in r moves. The consequence of a matrix being regular is this:

> **If P is regular, then it is always possible, in a sufficiently large number of transitions, to get from any one state in the Markov chain to every other state.**

In forming successively higher powers of P, all rows of P^m (giving conditional probabilities after m steps) were progressing to the same probability vector, and unconditional m-step probabilities in Π_m were also tending toward that same probability vector. These results are due to the regularity of P. See the box at the top of the opposite page for a summary of results.

Different regular matrices can have the same equilibrium vector; saying the long-term vector is unique means that a given regular matrix cannot have more than one equilibrium vector.

Determining the Equilibrium Vector   If P is regular, one way of arriving at this long-run equilibrium vector Π is to calculate $\Pi_1, \Pi_2, \ldots$ until we reach a point where we can detect no change from one transition to the next. Equivalently, we can raise transition matrix P to successively higher powers until we observe a matrix

**IMPORTANT RESULTS FOR
REGULAR MARKOV CHAINS**

If a Markov chain is regular, then the following statements are all true (*m* being the number of transitions):

1. As *m* gets large, P^m approaches a matrix *W*, where every row of *W* is the same probability vector Π.

2. As *m* gets large, the unconditional probability vectors Π_m approach this same probability vector Π for any choice of initial probability vector Π_0.

3. The vector Π is said to be the **long-run probability vector** or the **equilibrium vector.**

4. The equilibrium vector Π is unique.

whose rows are identical. Both of these approaches work, but may require a significant amount of computation. We can, however, avoid all these calculations.

If Π (no subscript) is the equilibrium probability vector,[2] then we know $\Pi \cdot P = \Pi$. Using methods of Chapter 1, we solve this system for the unknown vector Π as illustrated in the following example.

■ EXAMPLE 6

We noted that the transition matrix *P* of Example 1 was regular as all entries in *P* itself are positive. Solve for the long-run probability vector Π.

SOLUTION

Let the vector Π consist of p_L and p_N. These are the unknown values we now determine. The matrix equation $\Pi P = \Pi$ is

$$[p_L \quad p_N]\begin{bmatrix} .8 & .2 \\ .3 & .7 \end{bmatrix} = [p_L \quad p_N]$$

Performing the left-hand side multiplication gives:

$$[.8p_L + .3p_N \quad .2p_L + .7p_N] = [p_L \quad p_N]$$

For these two matrices to be equal, corresponding elements must be the same. Equating both left-hand side elements to their corresponding right-hand side elements produces:

$$0.8p_L + 0.3p_N = p_L$$

$$0.2p_L + 0.7p_N = p_N$$

---

[2] The product $\Pi \cdot P$ is a mathematical operation performed on the vector Π by the matrix *P*. Since $\Pi \cdot P = \Pi$, this operation leaves Π unaltered: we input Π, multiply by *P* and we get Π as output. For this reason, the equilibrium vector is often called a **fixed point** vector. The equilibrium probability vector is the only probability vector that can be multiplied by a regular *P* and remain unchanged.

Moving all unknowns to the left-hand side gives us

$$-0.2p_L + 0.3p_N = 0$$

$$0.2p_L - 0.3p_N = 0$$

The augmented matrix of this system is given by

$$\begin{bmatrix} -.2 & .3 & | & 0 \\ .2 & -.3 & | & 0 \end{bmatrix}$$

To remove fractions and obtain "friendly" 1's, multiply both rows by "-5," giving

$$\begin{bmatrix} 1 & -1.5 & | & 0 \\ -1 & 1.5 & | & 0 \end{bmatrix}$$

Adding the first row to the second (replacing row 2 by row 2 + row 1) gives:

$$\begin{bmatrix} 1 & -1.5 & | & 0 \\ 0 & 0 & | & 0 \end{bmatrix}$$

The last row—all zeros—tells us that the solution is not unique—but yet boxed result 4 says the fixed point vector is unique. Check again—it says that every regular matrix has a unique fixed point *probability* vector. Thus, $p_L + p_N$ must be 1. We have not yet used this fact! This extra equation is exactly what it takes to guarantee a *unique* solution.

To incorporate this equation, replace the uninformative row of zeros by a row of 3 ones representing $p_L + p_N = 1$:

$$\begin{bmatrix} 1 & -1.5 & | & 0 \\ 1 & 1 & | & 1 \end{bmatrix}$$

Multiply the first row by -1 and add it to the second row, giving

$$\begin{bmatrix} 1 & -1.5 & | & 0 \\ 0 & 2.5 & | & 1 \end{bmatrix}$$

Now, multiply row 2 by (1/2.5) and use the resulting 1 to clear the remaining element in column 2, arriving at

$$\begin{bmatrix} 1 & 0 & | & .6 \\ 0 & 1 & | & .4 \end{bmatrix}$$

The unique fixed-point equilibrium vector is

$$\Pi = [p_L \quad p_N] = [.6 \quad .4]$$

a result anticipated from our numerical work; in the long run, we expect 60% of the policyholders to be in the low-risk group and the remaining 40% to be normal risks. ■

PRACTICE PROBLEM 8   Find the fixed-point equilibrium vector for the following regular transition matrices:

$$\text{(a)} \begin{bmatrix} .6 & .4 \\ .2 & .8 \end{bmatrix} \quad \text{(b)} \begin{bmatrix} .5 & .5 \\ .1 & .9 \end{bmatrix}$$

ANSWER(S)   **(a)** $\Pi = [1/3 \quad 2/3] \approx [.3333 \quad .6667]$
            (b) $\Pi = [1/6 \quad 5/6] \approx [.1667 \quad .8333]$ □

Expected Number of Moves to First Return   Continuing with our insurance company example, we introduce a row vector R whose elements are the reciprocals of the corresponding elements in Π. (The reciprocal of any nonzero number c is $1/c$.)

$$\begin{matrix} L & N & \quad & L & N \end{matrix}$$
$$R = [5/3 \quad 5/2] \approx [1.66667 \quad 2.5]$$

It can be shown that these elements represent the expected number of steps before a first return to the given state. For example, if a policy-holder is currently in the normal-risk group, then it will be 2.5 years on average before he is again in the normal-risk group. If he is currently in the low-risk group, it will be 1.66667 years on average before he is again in the low-risk group. The time it takes to get back to a state for the first time is called a **first return time.** We generalize this result.

EXPECTED NUMBER OF MOVES BEFORE FIRST RETURN

> If the equilibrium vector of a regular Markov chain having n states is given by $\Pi = [e_1, e_2, \ldots, e_n]$, then the ith element of the vector $R = [1/e_1, 1/e_2, \ldots, 1/e_n]$ gives the expected number of moves before returning to state i, given that the process is now in state i.

There are similar results for "first visits" to other states from a given starting state, rather than for "first returns." The interested reader is referred to the classic work, *Finite Markov Chains*, by Kemeny and Snell, D. Van Nostrand Company, 1960.

In Example 7, you can practice what you have just learned.

■ EXAMPLE 7

In Example 4, the following transition matrix described a consumer's videotape purchasing habits.

$$\begin{matrix} & \begin{matrix} T & M & S \end{matrix} \\ P = \begin{matrix} T \\ M \\ S \end{matrix} & \begin{bmatrix} .50 & .25 & .25 \\ .30 & .60 & .10 \\ .10 & .20 & .70 \end{bmatrix} \end{matrix}$$

(a) Show that this transition matrix is regular.

(b) Find Π_2 and Π_3 if $\Pi_0 = [.8 \quad .1 \quad .1]$.

(c) Find Π_2 and Π_3 if $\Pi_0 = [.1 \quad .1 \quad .8]$.

SOLUTION   **(a)** All entries in P itself are positive, so P is regular.

(b) We compute Π_1, and then Π_2 and Π_3 may be computed recursively:

$$\Pi_1 = \Pi_0 \cdot P = [.8 \quad .1 \quad .1] \cdot \begin{bmatrix} .50 & .25 & .25 \\ .30 & .60 & .10 \\ .10 & .20 & .70 \end{bmatrix} = [.44 \quad .28 \quad .28]$$

$$\Pi_2 = \Pi_1 \cdot P = [.332 \quad .334 \quad .334] \qquad \Pi_3 = [.2996 \quad .3502 \quad .3502]$$

(c) Proceed as in **(b)**, but use $\Pi_0 = [.1 \quad .1 \quad .8]$:

$$\Pi_1 = \Pi_0 \cdot P = [.1 \quad .1 \quad .8] \cdot \begin{bmatrix} .50 & .25 & .25 \\ .30 & .60 & .10 \\ .10 & .20 & .70 \end{bmatrix} = [.160 \quad .245 \quad .595]$$

$$\Pi_2 = \Pi_1 \cdot P = [.213 \quad .306 \quad .481] \qquad \Pi_3 = [.2464 \quad .33305 \quad .42055]$$

PRACTICE PROBLEM 9   **(a)** In Example 7, find the equilibrium probability vector.

(b) In Example 7, find the vector of first return times.

(c) If the consumer has just purchased Brand T of videotape, how long will it be on average before he purchases T again?

ANSWER(S)   **(a)** $\Pi = [4/14 \quad 5/14 \quad 5/14] \approx [.285714 \quad .357143 \quad .357143]$
(b) $[14/4 \quad 14/5 \quad 14/5] = [3.5 \quad 2.8 \quad 2.8]$
(c) 3.5 purchases

EXERCISES 11.2

PRACTICING THE MOVES AND MANEUVERS

Exercises 55–59: Use the given Π_0 to find Π_1, Π_2, and Π_3 for the transition matrix

$$P = \begin{bmatrix} .7 & .3 \\ .2 & .8 \end{bmatrix}$$

55. $\Pi_0 = [.9 \quad .1]$ 57. $\Pi_0 = [.5 \quad .5]$ 59. $\Pi_0 = [.1 \quad .9]$
56. $\Pi_0 = [.7 \quad .3]$ 58. $\Pi_0 = [.3 \quad .7]$

Exercises 60–64: Use the given Π_0 to find Π_1, Π_2, and Π_3 for the transition matrix

$$P = \begin{bmatrix} .2 & .8 \\ .3 & .7 \end{bmatrix}$$

60. $\Pi_0 = [.9 \quad .1]$ 62. $\Pi_0 = [.5 \quad .5]$ 64. $\Pi_0 = [.1 \quad .9]$
61. $\Pi_0 = [.7 \quad .3]$ 63. $\Pi_0 = [.3 \quad .7]$

Exercises 65–73: Use the given Π_0 to find Π_1, Π_2, and Π_3 for the transition matrix

$$P = \begin{bmatrix} .2 & .6 & .2 \\ .5 & .3 & .2 \\ .3 & .3 & .4 \end{bmatrix}$$

65. $\Pi_0 = [.8 \quad 0 \quad .2]$ 68. $\Pi_0 = [.5 \quad 0 \quad .5]$ 71. $\Pi_0 = [.2 \quad 0 \quad .8]$
66. $\Pi_0 = [.8 \quad .2 \quad 0]$ 69. $\Pi_0 = [.5 \quad .5 \quad 0]$ 72. $\Pi_0 = [.2 \quad .8 \quad 0]$
67. $\Pi_0 = [0 \quad .8 \quad .2]$ 70. $\Pi_0 = [0 \quad .5 \quad .5]$ 73. $\Pi_0 = [0 \quad .2 \quad .8]$

Exercises 74–81: Determine whether the given transition matrices are regular.

74. $\begin{bmatrix} .7 & .3 \\ .1 & .9 \end{bmatrix}$ 75. $\begin{bmatrix} .5 & .5 \\ 1 & 0 \end{bmatrix}$ 76. $\begin{bmatrix} .5 & .5 \\ 0 & 1 \end{bmatrix}$ 77. $\begin{bmatrix} 1 & 0 \\ 0 & 1 \end{bmatrix}$

78. $\begin{bmatrix} 0 & 1 \\ 1 & 0 \end{bmatrix}$ 79. $\begin{bmatrix} .7 & .2 & .1 \\ 0 & 0 & 1 \\ .1 & .1 & .8 \end{bmatrix}$ 80. $\begin{bmatrix} .4 & .4 & .2 \\ 0 & 1 & 0 \\ 1 & 0 & 0 \end{bmatrix}$ 81. $\begin{bmatrix} .2 & .7 & .1 \\ 1 & 0 & 0 \\ 1 & 0 & 0 \end{bmatrix}$

Exercises 82–89: Find P^4 for the given transition matrix P and interpret the entries. (*Note:* These transition matrices are the ones given in Exercises 55–62.)

82. $\begin{bmatrix} .7 & .3 \\ .1 & .9 \end{bmatrix}$ 83. $\begin{bmatrix} .5 & .5 \\ 1 & 0 \end{bmatrix}$ 84. $\begin{bmatrix} .5 & .5 \\ 0 & 1 \end{bmatrix}$ 85. $\begin{bmatrix} 1 & 0 \\ 0 & 1 \end{bmatrix}$

86. $\begin{bmatrix} 0 & 1 \\ 1 & 0 \end{bmatrix}$ 87. $\begin{bmatrix} .7 & .2 & .1 \\ 0 & 0 & 1 \\ .1 & .1 & .8 \end{bmatrix}$ 88. $\begin{bmatrix} .4 & .4 & .2 \\ 0 & 1 & 0 \\ 1 & 0 & 0 \end{bmatrix}$ 89. $\begin{bmatrix} .2 & .7 & .1 \\ 1 & 0 & 0 \\ 1 & 0 & 0 \end{bmatrix}$

Exercises 90–97: Find a fixed-point probability vector for the given transition matrix by solving $\Pi \cdot P = \Pi$. (*Note:* These matrices are the same transition matrices given in Exercises 74–81 and 82–89.) Also note that not all of these transition matrices are regular. This will help to answer the questions as to whether a nonregular transition matrix can have an equilibrium vector, and if so, whether it is unique.

90. $\begin{bmatrix} .7 & .3 \\ .1 & .9 \end{bmatrix}$ 91. $\begin{bmatrix} .5 & .5 \\ 1 & 0 \end{bmatrix}$ 92. $\begin{bmatrix} .5 & .5 \\ 0 & 1 \end{bmatrix}$ 93. $\begin{bmatrix} 1 & 0 \\ 0 & 1 \end{bmatrix}$

94. $\begin{bmatrix} 0 & 1 \\ 1 & 0 \end{bmatrix}$ 95. $\begin{bmatrix} .7 & .2 & .1 \\ 0 & 0 & 1 \\ .1 & .1 & .8 \end{bmatrix}$ 96. $\begin{bmatrix} .4 & .4 & .2 \\ 0 & 1 & 0 \\ 1 & 0 & 0 \end{bmatrix}$ 97. $\begin{bmatrix} .2 & .7 & .1 \\ 1 & 0 & 0 \\ 1 & 0 & 0 \end{bmatrix}$

98. Obtain P^4 for the matrix P of Exercise 90. Do the rows of P^4 seem to be tending toward the fixed-point vector you found in Exercise 90? Is P regular?

99. Obtain P^4 for the matrix P of Exercise 91. Do the rows of P^4 seem to be tending toward the fixed-point vector you found in Exercise 91? Is P regular?

100. Obtain P^4 for the matrix P of Exercise 92. Do the rows of P^4 seem to be tending toward the fixed-point vector you found in Exercise 92? Is P regular?
101. Obtain P^4 for the matrix P of Exercise 93. Do the rows of P^4 seem to be tending toward the fixed-point vector you found in Exercise 93? Is P regular?
102. Obtain P^4 for the matrix P of Exercise 94. Do the rows of P^4 seem to be tending toward the fixed-point vector you found in Exercise 94? Is P regular?
103. Obtain P^4 for the matrix P of Exercise 95. Do the rows of P^4 seem to be tending toward the fixed-point vector you found in Exercise 95? Is P regular?
104. Study your solutions to Exercises 92 and 94. What conclusions can be drawn?
105. Study your solutions to Exercises 93 and 94. What conclusions can be drawn?

APPLYING THE CONCEPTS

Exercises 106–110:   Consider a business which buys supplies each month from one of three stores, A, B, and C. In an effort to spread the business around, this business adopts the following policy: never buy at the same store twice in a row. If the business bought at store A the last time, then it is twice as likely to buy from B as C. If it bought at B, it is twice as likely to buy from C as from A. If it just bought from C, then it is twice as likely to buy from A as from B.

106. Find the transition matrix P for this Markov chain.
107. Show that this Markov chain is regular.
108. Find the equilibrium probability vector.
109. If this business just bought pens from store A, how long will it be on average before it again buys from store A?
110. Work Exercise 109 for stores B and C.

Exercises 111–114:   Consider a quarterback with the following passing traits: If he has completed his previous pass, there is a 50% chance of him completing the next pass, a 40% chance of an incompletion, and a 10% chance of an interception. If his last pass was incomplete, he has a 60% chance of completing the next pass, and a 40% chance of an incomplete pass. If he just threw an interception, he has an 80% chance of a completion, and a 20% chance of an incompletion.

111. Find the transition matrix for this three-state Markov chain.
112. Suppose we don't know the outcome of the quarterback's last pass attempt. This week's game is about to begin, and we hear the coach say that he looked "real sharp," in pregame drills. In fact, the coach goes on to say, "I think there is an 80% chance of him completing his first pass and only a 5% chance it will be intercepted." Using this information as an initial probability vector Π_0, determine Π_1, Π_2, and Π_3.
113. Determine this quarterback's long-run proportion of completions, incompletions, and interceptions.
114. If the quarterback has just thrown an interception, how long (how many passes) will it be on the average before he throws another interception?

Exercises 115–119:   Consider a traveler who regularly uses either Airline N or Airline A for his commutes, wanting to build mileage in both airlines' travel clubs. If he flew Airline A last time, there is a 40% chance he will fly Airline A on his next trip. If he flew Airline N on his most recent trip, there is a 30% chance he will use Airline N on his next trip. He flies only these two airlines.

115. Find the transition matrix for this two-state Markov chain.
116. We don't know what airline the salesman just flew, but we feel (this is a subjective probability) that there is a 95% chance he will take Airline A on his next trip. What are the probabilities for the two airlines on the trip after next? Two trips after the next?
117. In the long run, what portion of the time will he fly each airline?
118. If the salesman has just flown Airline N, how long will it be on average before he again flies Airline N?
119. If the salesman has just flown Airline A, how long on average will it be before he again flies Airline A?

Exercises 120–123: (Supermarket shopping in Southern California.) A consumer survey found that if people shopped at Alpha Beta one week, then 70% of them shopped at Alpha Beta the following week, 20% went to Albertson's, and 10% shopped elsewhere. Of those that shopped at Albertson's one week, 80% shopped at Albertson's the following week, 15% went to Alpha Beta, and the remaining 5% shopped elsewhere. Of those that did not shop at either Albertson's or Alpha Beta one week, it was found that 25% switched to Albertson's the following week, 20% switched to Alpha Beta, and the rest continued to shop elsewhere. In this survey it was also found that among current shoppers, 50% shop at Albertson's, 20% shop at Alpha Beta, and the remainder shop elsewhere. Using this information to provide an initial probability vector, and assuming these trends continue, answer the following.

120. Find the probability transition matrix for this three-state Markov chain.
121. What will the distribution of shoppers be one week after the survey?
122. What will the distribution of shoppers be two weeks after the survey?
*123. In the long run, what proportion of people will shop at each store?

Exercises 124–129: Consider an automobile insurance company. Each year this company classifies its insured drivers as either high risk (H), normal risk (N), or low risk (L). The company has found that among low-risk drivers one year, 90% are still classified as low risk the following year, and 10% move to the normal-risk group. Among normal-risk drivers, 70% are classified as normal risk the following year, and 10% move to the low-risk group. Among high-risk drivers one year, 80% of them are still classified as high-risk drivers the following year, and none move to the low-risk group.

124. Set up the transition matrix for this three-state Markov chain.
125. Determine whether the Markov chain is regular.
126. If we know that a driver is currently classified as low-risk, find the probability that she will still be a low-risk driver two years from now.
127. In the long run, what proportion of the drivers will be in each group?
128. If a driver is currently in the normal-risk group, how long will it be on the average before she is again in the normal-risk group?
129. If a driver is currently a high-risk driver, how long will it be on the average before she is again a high-risk driver?

Exercises 130–134: A nomadic Coloradan moves yearly. If he is currently in Eastern Colorado, there is a 60% chance he will move to Western Colorado the next year and a 40% chance of staying in Eastern Colorado. If he is currently residing in Western Colorado, there is a 30% chance of him living there the next year and a 70% chance of him moving to Eastern Colorado.

130. Find the transition matrix for this two-state Markov chain.
131. Show that this transition matrix is regular.
132. We don't know where the wandering Coloradan is living this year, but we feel (this is a subjective probability) that there is a 70% chance of him currently living in Western Colorado. What are the probabilities for living in the two regions in two years and in three years?
133. Find what proportion of the time he lives in each region in the long run.
134. If he now lives in Western Colorado, how many years will it be on the average before he next lives in Western Colorado?

Exercises 135–139: Consider a professor with three assistants who grade exams. She switches from student to student as follows: If student A grades the current exam, there is a 0.4 chance he will grade the next exam, and student B is twice as likely to grade the next exam as student C. If student B grades an exam, there is only a 20% chance she will grade the next exam, while students A and C are equally likely to draw the duty. If student C is grader, there is a 70% chance he will grade the next exam, while student A is twice as likely as student B to grade the next exam.

135. Find the probability transition matrix for this three-state Markov chain.
136. Is this transition matrix regular? Explain.
137. Determine conditional probabilities of being in the various states in two moves, given any possible state now.
*138. Find the long run distribution of exams graded by the three students.
139. If the professor has just used student A, how many exams will there be on average before that person uses student A again?

Exercises 140–144: use the following information: Income of parents can be classified as low, medium, or high. If parents' income is low, there is a 30% chance that their children's income will be low, a 50% chance of their income being medium, and a 20% chance of high income. If the parents' income is medium, there is a 20% chance of the children having a low income, a 60% chance of having medium income, and a 20% chance of high income. If the parents have high income, then there is a 10% chance of the children having low income, a 40% chance of them having medium income, and a 50% chance of them also having high income.

140. Set up the transition matrix for this three-state Markov chain.
141. Find the probability that grandchildren of low income parents have low income.
142. Find the probability that grandchildren of high income parents have low incomes.
143. Determine the long run distribution for incomes.
144. If the current generation is a high-income family, how many generations will there be on the average before this family is again a high-income family?

11.3 ABSORBING MARKOV CHAINS   In regular Markov chains, it is possible to get from any state to any other state after some number of transitions. Every regular transition matrix has a unique equilibrium probability vector that portrays the long-run characteristics of the Markov chain. Specifically, this vector tells us the proportion of time spent in each state.

Does a nonregular matrix have an equilibrium vector? If so, is it unique? In this section we shall answer these questions. Consider the following probability transition matrix:

$$P = \begin{bmatrix} 0 & 1 \\ 1 & 0 \end{bmatrix}$$

We calculate P^2 and P^3:

$$P^2 = \begin{bmatrix} 0 & 1 \\ 1 & 0 \end{bmatrix}\begin{bmatrix} 0 & 1 \\ 1 & 0 \end{bmatrix} = \begin{bmatrix} 1 & 0 \\ 0 & 1 \end{bmatrix}$$

$$P^3 = P^2 \cdot P = \begin{bmatrix} 1 & 0 \\ 0 & 1 \end{bmatrix}\begin{bmatrix} 0 & 1 \\ 1 & 0 \end{bmatrix} = \begin{bmatrix} 0 & 1 \\ 1 & 0 \end{bmatrix} = P$$

This cycling phenomenon continues. If the exponent of P is odd, then $P^n = P$, while if n is even, then $P^n = I_2$. Consequently, rows in higher powers of P will not "settle down" to the same row vector Π, and thus P is not regular. There is, however, a unique fixed-point probability vector satisfying $\Pi \cdot P = \Pi$. Intuition suggests that in the long run this process spends as much time in state 1 as in state 2. Indeed, it is easy to show that $\Pi = [.5 \quad .5]$ satisfies the equation $\Pi \cdot P = \Pi$, and is thus a fixed-point probability vector. Furthermore, $\Pi = [.5 \quad .5]$ is the only fixed-point probability vector. Thus, having a unique fixed-point probability vector is no guarantee that transition matrix P is regular, or that all rows in P "settle down" into the same long-run pattern.

EXAMPLE 8

Consider the transition matrix given below:

$$P = \begin{bmatrix} 1 & 0 \\ .5 & .5 \end{bmatrix}$$

Find P^2, P^3, P^4, P^5, and P^6 and discuss the long-term characteristics of this Markov chain.

SOLUTION

Whether the Markov chain is regular or absorbing, the entries in powers of P have the same meaning. Matrix multiplication gives:

$$P^2 = \begin{bmatrix} 1 & 0 \\ .75 & .25 \end{bmatrix} \quad P^3 = \begin{bmatrix} 1 & 0 \\ .875 & .125 \end{bmatrix} \quad P^4 = \begin{bmatrix} 1 & 0 \\ .9375 & .0625 \end{bmatrix}$$

$$P^5 = \begin{bmatrix} 1 & 0 \\ .96875 & .03125 \end{bmatrix} \quad P^6 = \begin{bmatrix} 1 & 0 \\ .984375 & .015625 \end{bmatrix}$$

Notice that the elements in the first row have not changed, nor will they ever—once you are in state 1, you stay there forever. For this reason, state 1 is said to be an absorbing state.

ABSORBING STATE AND ABSORBING MARKOV CHAIN

A state in a Markov chain is **absorbing** if once entered it is never left. State i is absorbing if $p_{ii} = 1$. An **absorbing Markov chain** must have at least one absorbing state, and it must be possible to get from every nonabsorbing state to some absorbing state.

Note: States that are not absorbing are said to be **transient.** Once the set of transient states is left, it is never again entered.

While elements in the first row of powers of P remain constant, elements in the second row are changing. What do these second-row elements tell us? The (2,1) element in P^4 is the probability of being in state 1 (absorbed!) in four moves, if the process is now in state 2. Similarly, the (2,2) element of P^4 is the probability of being in state 2 (not absorbed) after 4 moves if currently there. It appears that the (2,1) element in various powers of P is getting larger and larger (apparently approaching 1), while the (2,2) element is getting smaller and smaller (apparently approaching 0). Once the process reaches state 1, we know that it stays there forever. Will the process ever reach state 1? If currently in state 2, there is a 0.5 [(2,2) element in P] chance the process will still be there after the next move, a $0.5^2 = 0.25$ [(2,2) element of P^2] chance it will be there after 2 moves, and a $0.5^3 = .125$ [(2,2) element of P^3] chance of staying through 3 moves.

The pattern is apparent. The probability of remaining in state 2 (and thus avoiding state 1) for 10 consecutive moves is the same as the probability of throwing 10 consecutive heads with a fair coin—$0.5^{10} = 1/1024$. To prevent "capture" by state 1, the process has to remain in state 2 forever. The probability of remaining forever is the probability of throwing heads forever with the fair coin—zero. As a result, capture is certain; the process will eventually end up in state 1. This result generalizes: in any absorbing Markov chain, capture by an absorbing state is certain. ■

FUNDAMENTAL RESULT FOR AN ABSORBING MARKOV CHAIN

In any absorbing Markov chain, the probability of the process eventually ending in an absorbing state is one.

■ EXAMPLE 9

Determine whether the following transition matrix represents an absorbing Markov chain.

$$P = \begin{bmatrix} .7 & .3 & 0 \\ .1 & .9 & 0 \\ 0 & 0 & 1 \end{bmatrix}$$

SOLUTION   Checking for absorbing states, we find $p_{33} = 1$. Once the process reaches state 3, it remains there forever. But there is no way to get to state 3 unless the process begins there! When the process is in state 1, it remains there or moves to state 2. When in state 2, the process remains there or moves to state 1. Hence, this Markov chain is not absorbing. Neither is it regular. Other than noting the existence of transition matrices that are neither regular nor absorbing, we do no more with such matrices. ∎

PRACTICE PROBLEM 10   Which transition matrices represent absorbing Markov chains?

(a) $\begin{bmatrix} .8 & .2 \\ 1 & 0 \end{bmatrix}$ (b) $\begin{bmatrix} .4 & .4 & .2 \\ 0 & 1 & 0 \\ 1 & 0 & 0 \end{bmatrix}$ (c) $\begin{bmatrix} .6 & 0 & .3 \\ 0 & 1 & 0 \\ .5 & 0 & .5 \end{bmatrix}$

ANSWER(S)   Only **(b)** is absorbing.   □

■ EXAMPLE 10

Using the absorbing-chain matrix P of Example 8, find the unconditional probability vectors $\Pi_1, \ldots, \Pi_9$ for each of the following initial probability vectors:

    i. $\Pi_0 = [.5 \quad .5]$

    ii. $\Pi_0 = [.8 \quad .2]$

    iii. $\Pi_0 = [1 \quad 0]$

    iv. $\Pi_0 = [0 \quad 1]$

SOLUTION   Just as powers of P have the same meaning for both regular and absorbing chains, so also do unconditional m-step probability vectors. Thus $\Pi_1 = \Pi_0 \cdot P$, $\Pi_2 = \Pi_1 \cdot P$, $\Pi_3 = \Pi_2 \cdot P$, etc. Computing Π_1 through Π_9 for each of the above four choices of Π_0 gives:

$\Pi_0 = [.5 \quad .5]$	$\Pi_0 = [.8 \quad .2]$	$\Pi_0 = [1 \quad 0]$	$\Pi_0 = [0 \quad 1]$
$\Pi_1 = [.75 \quad .25]$	$\Pi_1 = [.9 \quad .1]$	$\Pi_1 = [1 \quad 0]$	$\Pi_1 = [.5 \quad .5]$
$\Pi_2 = [.875 \quad .125]$	$\Pi_2 = [.95 \quad .05]$	$\Pi_2 = [1 \quad 0]$	$\Pi_2 = [.75 \quad .25]$
$\Pi_3 = [.9375 \quad .0625]$	$\Pi_3 = [.975 \quad .025]$	$\Pi_3 = [1 \quad 0]$	$\Pi_3 = [.875 \quad .125]$
$\Pi_4 \approx [.9688 \quad .0312]$	$\Pi_4 = [.9875 \quad .0125]$	$\Pi_4 = [1 \quad 0]$	$\Pi_4 = [.9375 \quad .0625]$
$\Pi_5 \approx [.9844 \quad .0156]$	$\Pi_5 \approx [.9938 \quad .0062]$	$\Pi_5 = [1 \quad 0]$	$\Pi_5 \approx [.9688 \quad .0321]$
$\Pi_6 \approx [.9922 \quad .0078]$	$\Pi_6 \approx [.9969 \quad .0031]$	$\Pi_6 = [1 \quad 0]$	$\Pi_6 \approx [.9844 \quad .0156]$
$\Pi_7 \approx [.9961 \quad .0039]$	$\Pi_7 \approx [.9984 \quad .0016]$	$\Pi_7 = [1 \quad 0]$	$\Pi_7 \approx [.9922 \quad .0078]$
$\Pi_8 \approx [.9980 \quad .0020]$	$\Pi_8 \approx [.9992 \quad .0008]$	$\Pi_8 = [1 \quad 0]$	$\Pi_8 \approx [.9961 \quad .0039]$
$\Pi_9 \approx [.9990 \quad .0010]$	$\Pi_9 \approx [.9996 \quad .0004]$	$\Pi_9 = [1 \quad 0]$	$\Pi_9 \approx [.9980 \quad .0020]$

The long-term vector appears to be $[1 \quad 0]$, independent of the choice of Π_0. That $\Pi = [1 \quad 0]$ is a fixed-point vector is easy to verify; it is in fact the unique fixed-point probability vector. These are exactly the properties guaranteed by a regular matrix. Yet matrix P is clearly not regular. Why is this? Although this particular absorbing matrix P has a unique fixed-point vector which is independent of the initial probability vector, these properties do not hold for all absorbing chains. Even in this example there are failings relative to the regular case. In particular, only the second row of P^m tends to the equilibrium vector as m increases.   ■

The Gambler's Ruin   A classic example of an absorbing Markov chain is the "Gambler's Ruin," introduced in Example 11.

■ EXAMPLE 11   Jim and Rich play pool regularly, with Jim winning 60% of the games. They engage in the following contest: $1 goes to the winner of each pool game, and they continue playing until one of them is broke. When this occurs we say the contest is over. Note carefully the terminology: "game" refers to one game of pool; "contest" refers to a sequence of games leading to either Jim or Rich being broke. All contests begin with Jim having $2 and Rich $3. As states, take the amount of money Rich has. Find the transition matrix P and investigate this Markov chain.

SOLUTION   States are $0, $1, $2, $3, $4, and $5. The transition matrix P is:

**Rich's Fortune after
the Next Play of Game**

	$0	$1	$2	$3	$4	$5
$0	1	0	0	0	0	0
$1	.6	0	.4	0	0	0
$2	0	.6	0	.4	0	0
$3	0	0	.6	0	.4	0
$4	0	0	0	.6	0	.4
$5	0	0	0	0	0	1

Rich's Fortune Now (row labels) $= P$

States $0 and $5 are absorbing. Once Rich is broke ($0) or has all of Jim's money ($5), the contest ends. In studying absorbing chains, it is advantageous to rearrange the states so that the rows and columns associated with absorbing states are listed first. Be sure that the orderings of row and column labels are identical. Doing this produces the following variant of P:

Rich's Fortune after Next Play

	$0	$5	$1	$2	$3	$4
$0	1	0	0	0	0	0
$5	0	1	0	0	0	0
$1	.6	0	0	.4	0	0
$2	0	0	.6	0	.4	0
$3	0	0	0	.6	0	.4
$4	0	.4	0	0	.6	0

Rich's Fortune Now (row labels)

$$= \begin{array}{c} \text{Absorbing} \\ \text{Transient} \end{array} \left[\begin{array}{c|c} I_a & \emptyset \\ \hline R & Q \end{array} \right] = P$$

with column groupings labeled **Absorbing** and **Transient**.

This way of presenting the transition matrix is called the **canonical form** of the absorbing chain. Submatrix I_a (an a-by-a square matrix, where a is the number of absorbing states) concerns transitions from absorbing states to themselves. The upper-right submatrix, consisting entirely of zeros, abbreviated by a single large zero, indicates there is no exit from an absorbing state. Submatrix R concerns moves from transient to absorbing states. Finally, submatrix Q considers transitions among the transient states prior to absorption.

We know that eventually the contest will end; Rich will have either no money or $5. Some questions of interest:

1. How long (how many pool games) can we expect before the contest ends?

2. Will the contest end with Rich having no money (the Gambler's Ruin; having less than a 0.5 chance of winning, Rich is like a contestant in a casino) or $5?

Let's investigate some powers of P in an attempt to answer these questions as the contest progresses. We do this by multiplying the numbers, and also by taking powers of the canonical form. We first work with the canonical form, treating submatrix labels as if they were numbers in a 2×2 matrix, and computing P^2. We then generalize to P^m.

$$P^2 = \begin{bmatrix} I & \emptyset \\ R & Q \end{bmatrix} \begin{bmatrix} I & \emptyset \\ R & Q \end{bmatrix} = \begin{bmatrix} I & \emptyset \\ R + QR & Q^2 \end{bmatrix}$$

$$P^m = \begin{bmatrix} I & \emptyset \\ R + QR + \cdots + Q^{m-1}R & Q^m \end{bmatrix}$$

Submatrix I in the upper left-hand corner of P^2 emphasizes absorption: once we reach any absorbing state, we remain forever. The upper right-hand submatrix of zeros in P^2 indicates exit from an absorbing state is impossible. Now consider P^m. Since absorption is certain to occur, then Q^m must get closer to the null matrix as m gets large. Furthermore, the lower left-hand submatrix of P^m must look more and more like a stochastic matrix in its own right—its row sums should get closer to 1 as m gets large. Why? Each entry in this lower left-hand submatrix is the probability of being captured by a specific absorbing state in m (or fewer) moves if we are now in a particular transient state. Since eventual capture is certain, more and more of the probability in the Q^m section must "spill over" into this lower left-hand submatrix. We now illustrate these ideas numerically by computing several powers of P for the pool contest. (See page 546.) Consider the row labeled $1. If Rich has $1 now, there is a 0.60 chance of absorption in two plays—the same probability as absorption on one play. Can you determine why?

Rows of Q^2 are as yet nowhere near summing to zero. Thus, we proceed to P^4, P^8, and P^{16}:

Rich's Fortune after Two Plays

		$0	$5	$1	$2	$3	$4
	$0	1	0				
	$5	0	1		All zeros		
Fortune	$1	.60	0	.24	0	.16	0
Now	$2	.36	0	0	.48	0	.16
	$3	0	.16	.36	0	.48	0
	$4	0	.40	0	.36	0	.24

$= P^2$

Rich's Fortune after Four Plays

		$0	$5	$1	$2	$3	$4
	$0	1	0				
	$5	0	1		All zeros		
Fortune	$1	.744	.026	.115	0	.115	0
Now	$2	.533	.064	0	.288	0	.115
	$3	.216	.237	.259	0	.288	0
	$4	.130	.496	0	.259	0	.115

$\approx P^4$

Row sums in lower left-hand corner submatrix		Row sums in lower right-hand submatrix Q^4
$1:	.770	.230
$2:	.597	.403
$3:	.453	.547
$4:	.626	.374

These tell probabilities of contest ending within four plays when Rich's fortune is $1, $2, $3, $4.

These tell probabilities of not being absorbed in first four plays from given state.

Rich's Fortune after Eight Plays

		$0	$5	$1	$2	$3	$4
	$0	1	0				
	$5	0	1		All zeros		
Fortune	$1	.855	.056	.043	0	.046	0
Now	$2	.701	.140	0	.113	0	.046
	$3	.471	.312	.104	0	.113	0
	$4	.283	.570	0	.104	0	.043

$\approx P^8$

Row sums in lower left-hand corner submatrix		Row sums in lower right-hand submatrix Q^8
$1:	.911	.089
$2:	.841	.159
$3:	.783	.217
$4:	.853	.147

These tell probabilities of contest ending within eight plays.

These tell probabilities of *not* being absorbed in first eight plays from given state.

If Rich has \$3, there is about a 22% chance (0.217) of the contest lasting more than 8 plays; with \$1, there is only a 9% chance (0.089).

Rich's Fortune after 16 Plays

		\$0	\$5	\$1	\$2	\$3	\$4	
	\$0	1	0					
	\$5	0	1		All zeros			$\approx P^{16}$
Fortune	\$1	.913	.073	.007	0	.007	0	
Now	\$2	.793	.182	0	.018	0	.007	
	\$3	.614	.353	.016	0	.018	0	
	\$4	.368	.609	0	.016	0	.007	

Row sums in lower left-hand corner submatrix
\$1: .986
\$2: .975
\$3: .967
\$4: .977

.014
.025
.034
.023
Row sums in lower right-hand submatrix Q^{16}

These tell probabilities of contest ending within sixteen plays from given transient state.

These tell probabilities of not being absorbed in first sixteen plays from given state.

There is little chance of the contest lasting 16 plays because the sum of the entries in each row of Q^{16} is approaching zero.

If Rich has \$1, then it is highly likely (0.913) that absorption will be in state \$0—the Gambler's Ruin. Even if he now has \$3 (closer to \$5 than to \$0), there is about a 61% chance of him being ruined within 16 plays. Only when Rich has \$4 is there a better-than-even chance of breaking Jim by moving to state \$5.

Clearly, the probability of capture by a particular absorbing state depends on the current transient state occupied. This is in direct contrast to regular Markov chains, where the same long-run probability vector is obtained regardless of the choice of starting state. For regular Markov chains it is also true that the fixed-point, long-run vector is unique. No other probability vector satisfies the equation $\Pi \cdot P = P$. For our pool contest example, however, there are infinitely many fixed-point vectors Π that will satisfy the equation $\Pi \cdot P = \Pi$. Two of these are:

$$\Pi = [1 \quad 0 \quad 0 \quad 0 \quad 0 \quad 0] \quad \text{and} \quad \Pi = [0 \quad 1 \quad 0 \quad 0 \quad 0 \quad 0].$$

In fact, any 1×6 vector whose first two components are probabilities adding to 1 is a fixed-point vector. Thus, for absorbing chains having more than one absorbing state, fixed-point vectors do not provide the same nice "long-run distribution" interpretation as we found for regular Markov chains. ∎

Describing the Process: The Fundamental Matrix

Although there is little chance of the pool contest lasting more than 16 games, the number of games in the contest is a random variable. A question such as "How many pool games will there be, on the average, before the contest ends if Rich now has $4?" is worthy of exploration. To do so, we introduce random variables that keep track of the time spent in various transient states prior to absorption.

> **The random variable n_{ij} counts the number of times the process occupies transient state j, prior to absorption, given that the process is now in transient state i.**

Note: We shall now use a very natural notation for transient states: "state i" in the pool contest example will mean i; "state j" will mean j. (In other examples, "state 1" will refer to the first transient state, etc.) In the pool contest of Example 11, n_{34} is the number of times Rich has $4 before the contest ends, given that he now has $3. The random variable n_{22} is the number of times Rich has $2 prior to the contest ending, given that he now has $2.

To help describe this contest, we shall find the expected values of these n_{ij} variables. Answers to all questions about expected values of the n_{ij} can be found by computing the *fundamental matrix for an absorbing chain*.

FUNDAMENTAL MATRIX FOR AN ABSORBING MARKOV CHAIN

> Write the transition matrix for an absorbing Markov chain in canonical form as shown below:
>
> $$P = \left[\begin{array}{c|c} I & \emptyset \\ \hline R & Q \end{array}\right]$$
>
> Compute the matrix $N = (I - Q)^{-1}$. This matrix is known as the **fundamental matrix** for the absorbing Markov chain. The i,j-th entry in N is the expected value of n_{ij}, which tells us how many times, on average, the process occupies transient state j prior to absorption, given that the process is now in transient state i.

Notes:

1. The "I" used in forming $(I - Q)^{-1}$ must be of the same dimensions as Q, and is not necessarily the same "I" as appears in the canonical form of P.

2. Matrix N is called the "fundamental" matrix because virtually every important quantity used to describe absorbing Markov chains involves N.

■ EXAMPLE 12

Find the fundamental matrix for the pool contest in Example 11 and interpret the entries.

SOLUTION   We first reproduce the transition matrix for the pool contest in canonical form:

$$
\begin{array}{c c}
& \begin{array}{c c c c c c} \$0 & \$5 & \$1 & \$2 & \$3 & \$4 \end{array} \\
\begin{array}{c} \$0 \\ \$5 \\ \$1 \\ \$2 \\ \$3 \\ \$4 \end{array} &
\left[\begin{array}{c c | c c c c}
1 & 0 & 0 & 0 & 0 & 0 \\
0 & 1 & 0 & 0 & 0 & 0 \\ \hline
.6 & 0 & 0 & .4 & 0 & 0 \\
0 & 0 & .6 & 0 & .4 & 0 \\
0 & 0 & 0 & .6 & 0 & .4 \\
0 & .4 & 0 & 0 & .6 & 0
\end{array}\right]
\end{array}
$$

Identifying submatrix Q, and forming matrix $I - Q$ leads to:

$$
Q = \begin{bmatrix}
0 & .4 & 0 & 0 \\
.6 & 0 & .4 & 0 \\
0 & .6 & 0 & .4 \\
0 & 0 & .6 & 0
\end{bmatrix}
\qquad
I - Q = \begin{bmatrix}
1 & -.4 & 0 & 0 \\
-.6 & 1 & -.4 & 0 \\
0 & -.6 & 1 & -.4 \\
0 & 0 & -.6 & 1
\end{bmatrix}
$$

In Chapter 2 we learned that to invert a matrix, we can augment it with an identity matrix of the same order, and then reduce this augmented matrix $[I - Q | I]$ to the form $[I | B]$. The fundamental matrix $N = (I - Q)^{-1}$ will occupy the rows and columns designated as "B." The resulting matrix is

$$
N \approx
\begin{array}{c c}
& \begin{array}{c c c c} \$1 & \$2 & \$3 & \$4 \end{array} \\
\begin{array}{c} \$1 \\ \$2 \\ \$3 \\ \$4 \end{array} &
\begin{bmatrix}
1.540 & .900 & .474 & .190 \\
1.351 & 2.251 & 1.185 & .474 \\
1.066 & 1.777 & 2.251 & .900 \\
0.640 & 1.066 & 1.351 & 1.540
\end{bmatrix}
\end{array}
$$

Some Interpretations   In the $1 to $1 position, the 1.540 indicates that if Rich now has $1, then he will have $1 on the average 1.540 times prior to the contest ending. Having $1 now accounts for 1.000 of the 1.540, indicating that Rich will spend on the average only 0.54 additional steps (pool games) in the $1 state. The 0.540 indicates that over the course of many, many contests, the average number of times spent in state $1, after the original time, is 0.540. Diagonal entries of the N matrix must necessarily be greater than 1 because they detail the expected number of times in a given state, prior to absorption, given present occupancy of that state; current occupancy of that transient state contributes "1" to each diagonal entry in N.

If at any time Rich has $3, then on the average there will be 1.777 pool games that Rich begins with $2 before the contest ends. The smallest entry in N is 0.190 in the $1 to $4 position. If Rich currently has only $1, there is little chance he will see $4 before the contest ends.

Questions like the following are of interest: "If Rich now has $2, how many pool games will there be, on average, before the contest ends?" From a $2 start Rich will have $1 on the average for 1.351 games, $2 on the average for 2.251 games, $3 on the average 1.185 times, and $4 on average for 0.474 games prior to the contest ending. Summing these expected values in the second row gives us 5.261 pool games played, on average, with Rich having somewhere between $1 and $4, prior to the contest ending. To sum the rows of N, we multiply N on the right by a properly dimensioned column vector j of 1's:

$$
N \cdot j \approx
\begin{array}{c}
\\ \$1 \\ \$2 \\ \$3 \\ \$4
\end{array}
\begin{array}{cccc}
\$1 & \$2 & \$3 & \$4 \\
\left[\begin{array}{cccc}
1.540 & .900 & .474 & .190 \\
1.351 & 2.251 & 1.185 & .474 \\
1.066 & 1.777 & 2.251 & .900 \\
0.640 & 1.066 & 1.351 & 1.540
\end{array}\right]
\end{array}
\begin{bmatrix} 1 \\ 1 \\ 1 \\ 1 \end{bmatrix}
=
\begin{array}{c}
\$1 \\ \$2 \\ \$3 \\ \$4
\end{array}
\begin{bmatrix} 3.104 \\ 5.261 \\ 5.994 \\ 4.597 \end{bmatrix}
$$

More Interpretations   If Rich ever has $1, then, from that point on, there will be an average of 3.104 pool games before the contest ends.

Anytime Rich has $3, there are on average 5.994 pool games played from that point on prior to the contest ending. Note that if Rich has $4, there are on average almost 1.5 games more to the contest than if Rich has $1. Both states are only one game away from ending the contest, but Jim's superior ability makes it much harder for Rich to go from $4 to $5 than from $1 to $0.

To help us summarize and generalize our results to an absorbing chain with u transient states, we introduce random variables T_1, T_2, . . ., T_u defined as follows:

T_1 is the total time spent among all transient states prior to absorption, given the process is currently in transient state 1. (In our pool contest, T_1 would be the total number of pool games played from the time Rich has $1.)

T_2 is the total time spent among all transient states prior to absorption, given the process is currently in transient state 2. (In the pool contest, T_2 is the total number of pool games played from the time Rich has $2 until the contest ends.)

.
.
.

T_u is the total time spent among all transient states prior to absorption, given the process started in transient state u.

With these definitions, we now generalize:

EXPECTED NUMBER OF MOVES PRIOR TO ABSORPTION

In an absorbing Markov chain with u transient states $s_1, s_2, \ldots, s_u$, the expected values of $T_1, T_2, \ldots, T_u$ are precisely the entries in the $u \times 1$ vector $N \cdot j$. That is,

$$N \cdot j = \begin{bmatrix} E(T_1) \\ E(T_2) \\ \vdots \\ \vdots \\ E(T_u) \end{bmatrix}$$

In words, the *location* of an element in $N \cdot j$ indicates the *transient state* where the process currently resides; the *element* in this position gives the *expected total time remaining* (number of transitions) prior to absorption.

Which Absorbing State?

With only one absorbing state, there is little suspense as to where absorption occurs. With many absorbing states, however, it is reasonable to ask for the probability of capture by a specific absorbing state. In our pool contest, we have noted that the lower left-hand submatrix in higher powers of P^m describes the probability of going from some transient state to a given absorbing state in m moves (that is, of being absorbed within m moves). More information is given (without having to compute powers of P) by the matrix product $B = NR$, where N is the fundamental matrix, and R is the lower left-hand submatrix in the canonical form of P. For the pool contest, we compute $B = NR$:

$$B = NR$$

$$= \begin{array}{c} \\ \$1 \\ \$2 \\ \$3 \\ \$4 \end{array} \overset{\begin{array}{cccc} \$1 & \$2 & \$3 & \$4 \end{array}}{\begin{bmatrix} 1.540 & .900 & .474 & .190 \\ 1.351 & 2.251 & 1.185 & .474 \\ 1.066 & 1.777 & 2.251 & .900 \\ 0.640 & 1.066 & 1.351 & 1.540 \end{bmatrix}} \begin{bmatrix} .6 & 0 \\ 0 & 0 \\ 0 & 0 \\ 0 & .4 \end{bmatrix}$$

$$\approx \begin{array}{c} \\ \$1 \\ \$2 \\ \$3 \\ \$4 \end{array} \overset{\begin{array}{cc} \$0 & \$5 \end{array}}{\begin{bmatrix} .924 & .076 \\ .810 & .190 \\ .640 & .360 \\ .384 & .616 \end{bmatrix}}$$

Compare matrix B to the lower left-hand submatrix of P^{16}. After 16 games, there is strong agreement. If the fundamental matrix N has been computed, then it is much easier to get the exact answer $B = NR$ than to form higher powers of P.

CONDITIONAL CAPTURE PROBABILITIES

> Given that the process is in transient state i, the probability of being absorbed (captured by) absorbing state j is the i,j-th element of the matrix $B = NR$. Matrix B has as many rows as there are transient states and as many columns as there are absorbing states.

Interpreting B   The entry 0.810 indicates that whenever Rich has \$2, then probability of ruin (capture by state \$0) is 0.81. Even when Rich has \$3 (closer to \$5 than \$0), there is only a 0.36 chance of the contest ending with him at \$5. Only at state \$4 will Rich have a better than even chance of getting Jim's money.

Reaching One Transient State From Another Prior to Absorption   Suppose Rich now has \$1. Will he ever reach \$3 before the contest ends? We introduce a square matrix H with dimensions matching the number of transient states. The i,j-th element of H has the following meaning:

h_{ij} = **probability of ever reaching transient state j prior to absorption, given the process is now in transient state j**

The H matrix can be found conveniently by matrix multiplication.

PROBABILITY OF EVER REACHING A GIVEN TRANSIENT STATE

> Compute the matrix $H = (N - I)N_D^{-1}$, where N_D is a diagonal matrix whose diagonal elements are the diagonal elements of N and whose off-diagonal elements are all zero. The i,j-th element of matrix H represents the conditional probability of ever visiting transient state j given that the process is currently in transient state i.

■ **EXAMPLE 13**   Find the H matrix for the pool contest of Example 11, and interpret the entries.

SOLUTION   We list below the necessary matrices.

$$N - I \approx \begin{bmatrix} .540 & .900 & .474 & .190 \\ 1.351 & 1.251 & 1.185 & .474 \\ 1.066 & 1.777 & 1.251 & .900 \\ .640 & 1.066 & 1.351 & .540 \end{bmatrix}$$

$$N_D \approx \begin{bmatrix} 1.540 & 0 & 0 & 0 \\ 0 & 2.251 & 0 & 0 \\ 0 & 0 & 2.251 & 0 \\ 0 & 0 & 0 & 1.540 \end{bmatrix}$$

$$N_D^{-1} \approx \begin{bmatrix} .649 & 0 & 0 & 0 \\ 0 & .444 & 0 & 0 \\ 0 & 0 & .444 & 0 \\ 0 & 0 & 0 & .649 \end{bmatrix}$$

$$H \approx \begin{array}{c} \\ \$1 \\ \$2 \\ \$3 \\ \$4 \end{array} \begin{array}{cccc} \$1 & \$2 & \$3 & \$4 \\ \begin{bmatrix} .351 & .400 & .210 & .123 \\ .877 & .556 & .526 & .308 \\ .692 & .789 & .556 & .585 \\ .415 & .474 & .600 & .351 \end{bmatrix} \end{array}$$

Examine the elements in H. The \$1 to \$2 entry is 0.400, which is easily reasoned. The only way Rich will ever reach \$2 from \$1 is to win on the next step—otherwise, Rich has \$0 and the contest ends. Similar thinking applies to 0.600 in the \$4 to \$3 position. If Rich now has \$4, he will never reach \$3 unless he loses immediately (with probability 0.6); otherwise his fortune goes to \$5 and the contest ends.

Discussion   To understand just how helpful H is in averting troublesome computations, we describe the computing involved in arriving at the 0.351 in the \$1 to \$1 position of H. Getting from \$1 now to \$1 again, prior to absorption, can be accomplished in a variety of ways. We list just a few:

1. From \$1 to \$2 and back to \$1. Probability $= (0.4)(0.6) = 0.24$

2. From \$1 to \$2 to \$3 to \$2 to \$1. Probability $= (0.4)(0.4)(0.6)(0.6) = 0.0576$.

3. From \$1 to \$2 to \$3 to \$4 to \$3 to \$2 to \$1. Probability $= (0.4)(0.4)(0.4)(0.6)(0.6)(0.6) = 0.0138$.

4. From \$1 to \$2 to \$3 to \$2 to \$3 to \$2 to \$1. Probability $= (0.4)(0.4)(0.6)(0.4)(0.6)(0.6) = 0.0138$.

In addition to these four, there are infinitely many other ways to get from \$1 back to \$1 prior to capture. Summing the probabilities of all these ways would give 0.351.

The smallest entry in H is 0.123 in the position describing the likelihood of ever moving from \$1 to \$4. This agrees well with our intuition.

When certain entries of H have been calculated, others fall into place. For example, the probability of Rich ever going from state \$1 to state \$4 can be reasoned in this manner: to get from \$1 to \$4, Rich must first reach \$2. The probability of reaching \$2 from \$1 is 0.400. Having reached \$2, he would need eventually to reach \$3. The probability of ever reaching \$3 from \$2 is 0.526. Having reached state \$3, there is probability 0.585 of ever reaching state \$4. To reach \$4 from \$1 requires that all three of these independent operations be done in sequence. The probability of doing them all is the product of their separate probabilities, giving $(0.400)(0.526)(0.585) \approx 0.123$.

What about the original question we posed: If Rich now has $1, how likely is it that he will ever have $3? We see that there is only a 0.21 probability of ever getting from $1 to $3 prior to the contest ending in an absorbing state. ■

Simulation of the Gambler's Ruin

To help illustrate the results of the Gambler's Ruin of this section, we simulate several pool contests between Jim and Rich. Using MINITAB, we produce a random sequence of 0's and 1's—with "1" having probability 0.4, representing a win for Rich on any pool game, and "0" indicating a loss. MINITAB commands for generating these random numbers are shown below, along with simulated results of 100 pool games.

MTB > RANDOM 100 INTO C1;   These two lines take a random
SUBC > BERNOULLI .4.   sample of 100 by flipping a coin
MTB > PRINT C1   with $P[\text{head}] = 0.4$. This simu-
                             lates playing pool with "Head"
                             ("1") a win by Rich.

```
1 0 1 0 0 1 0 1 0 0 0 0 0 0 1 0 1 0 0 1
0 1 1 0 0 1 1 0 0 0 1 0 0 0 0 1 0 0 1 1
0 1 1 1 0 1 0 0 0 0 1 1 0 1 0 1 0 0 1 0
0 1 1 0 1 1 0 0 1 1 1 1 0 1 0 0 1 1 0 0
1 1 0 0 0 1 0 0 0 0 0 0 0 0 1 0 0 1 0 0
```

There are 60 0's and 40 1's, which agrees well[3] with what we would expect. We shall now suppose that Rich has $2, and trace his fortunes through several contests (Table 11.1), using the above outcomes. We are out of random numbers; the contest is suspended with Rich having $1 for bus fare home from the pool hall!

There are many possibilities here for comparing empirical results with theory. Checking matrix B, we find that the probability of being absorbed into $0 from a start in $2 is 0.810. Sorting through our simulation, we see 18 "complete contests" (absorptions); of these, 15 ended with Gambler's Ruin ($0). Since $15/18 \approx 0.833$, the empirical results agree well with theory. In Table 11.2, we summarize the results of our simulation.

---

[3] In a "typical" simulation like this, we would usually see somewhere between 35 and 45 1's and the balance 0's. Over many such simulations, there would be an average of 40 1's. Seeing exactly the expected number of 40 1's on our simulation tempted your authors not to use this simulation, but to exclude it for that reason would be as bad as "rigging the data"!

Table 11.1
The gambler's ruin

Out-come	Rich's Fortune After This Game	Result	Where Process Is Absorbed		Num-ber of Pool Games Played	Out-come	Rich's Fortune After This Game	Result	Where Process Is Absorbed		Num-ber of Pool Games Played
			$0	$5					$0	$5	
Start Contest 1						**Start again—Contest 7**					
1	$3	Continue				1	$3	Continue			
0	$2	Continue				1	$4	Continue			
1	$3	Continue				0	$3	Continue			
0	$2	Continue				1	$4	Continue			
0	$1	Continue				1	$5	**Contest Ends**		X	5
1	$2	Continue				**Start again—Contest 8**					
0	$1	Continue				1	$3	Continue			
1	$2	Continue				0	$2	Continue			
0	$1	Continue				1	$3	Continue			
0	$0	**Contest Ends**	X		10	0	$2	Continue			
Start again—Contest 2						0	$1	Continue			
0	$1	Continue				0	$0	**Contest Ends**	X		6
0	$0	**Contest Ends**	X		2	**Start again—Contest 9**					
Start again—Contest 3						0	$1	Continue			
0	$1	Continue				1	$2	Continue			
0	$0	**Contest Ends**	X		2	1	$3	Continue			
Start again—Contest 4						0	$2	Continue			
1	$3	Continue				1	$3	Continue			
0	$2	Continue				0	$2	Continue			
1	$3	Continue				1	$3	Continue			
0	$2	Continue				0	$2	Continue			
0	$1	Continue				0	$1	Continue			
1	$2	Continue				1	$2	Continue			
0	$1	Continue				0	$1	Continue			
1	$2	Continue				0	$0	**Contest Ends**	X		12
1	$3	Continue				**Start again—Contest 10**					
0	$2	Continue				1	$3	Continue			
0	$1	Continue				1	$4	Continue			
1	$2	Continue				0	$3	Continue			
1	$3	Continue				1	$4	Continue			
0	$2	Continue				1	$5	**Contest Ends**		X	5
0	$1	Continue				**Start again—Contest 11**					
0	$0	**Contest Ends**	X		16	0	$1	Continue			
Start again—Contest 5						0	$0	**Contest Ends**	X		2
1	$3	Continue				**Start again—Contest 12**					
0	$2	Continue				1	$3	Continue			
0	$1	Continue				1	$4	Continue			
0	$0	**Contest Ends**	X		4	1	$5	**Contest Ends**		X	3
Start again—Contest 6						**Start again—Contest 13**					
0	$1	Continue				1	$3	Continue			
1	$2	Continue				0	$2	Continue			
0	$1	Continue				1	$3	Continue			
0	$0	**Contest Ends**	X		4	0	$2	Continue			

Table 11.1
The gambler's ruin (*Continued*)

Outcome	Rich's Fortune After This Game	Result	Where Process Is Absorbed $0	$5	Number of Pool Games Played	Outcome	Rich's Fortune After This Game	Result	Where Process Is Absorbed $0	$5	Number of Pool Games Played
0	$1	Continue				Start again—Contest 15					
1	$2	Continue				0	$1	Continue			
1	$3	Continue				0	$0	Contest Ends	X		2
0	$2	Continue				Start again—Contest 16					
0	$1	Continue				0	$1	Continue			
1	$2	Continue				0	$0	Contest Ends			2
1	$3	Continue				Start again—Contest 17					
0	$2	Continue				0	$1	Continue			
0	$1	Continue				1	$2	Continue			
0	$0	Contest Ends	X		14	0	$1	Continue			
Start again—Contest 14						0	$0	Contest Ends	X		4
1	$3	Continue				Start again—Contest 18					
0	$2	Continue				1	$3	Continue			
0	$1	Continue				0	$2	Continue			
0	$0	Contest Ends	X		4	0	$1	Continue			

Below we reproduce the fundamental matrix N in order to make several nice comparisons with the empirical results in Table 11.2.

$$N \approx \begin{array}{c} \\ \$1 \\ \$2 \\ \$3 \\ \$4 \end{array} \begin{array}{cccc} \$1 & \$2 & \$3 & \$4 \\ \begin{bmatrix} 1.540 & .900 & .474 & .190 \\ 1.351 & 2.251 & 1.185 & .474 \\ 1.066 & 1.777 & 2.251 & .900 \\ 0.640 & 1.066 & 1.351 & 1.540 \end{bmatrix} \end{array}$$

Agreement between colored entries in the $2 row of N (representing expected number of pool games begun with each of the four transient states from a $2 start) and the sample average number of times given by [row 1] in Table 11.2 is good.

Similarly, the sum of the entries in [row 1] of Table 11.2 is 5.706; this says that the average number of pool games per contest in our simulation was 5.706. According to theory, the sum of the $2 row in N, which is 5.261, represents the expected number of plays per contest. Again, the agreement is notable.

Checking the *H* Matrix   Recall that each entry in the H matrix tells us the probability of at least one visit to a given transient state prior to absorption, given that the process is now the transient state indicated by that entry. Checking the

Table 11.2
Simulation of gambler's ruin

Contest #	Times Spent in Given Transient State Prior to Absorption					
	$1	$2[4]	$3	$4	Total Time	
1	3	5	2	0	10	
2	1	1	0	0	2	
3	1	1	0	0	2	
4	4	8	4	0	16	
5	1	2	1	0	4	
6	2	2	0	0	4	
7	0	1	2	2	5	
8	1	3	2	0	6	
9	3	6	3	0	12	
10	0	1	2	2	5	
11	1	1	0	0	2	
12	0	1	1	1	3	
13	3	7	4	0	14	
14	1	2	1	0	4	
15	1	1	0	0	2	
16	1	1	0	0	2	
17	2	2	0	0	4	
Totals:	25	45	22	5	97	
Avg. visits per contest (total ÷ 17 contests)	1.471	2.647	1.294	0.294	5.706	[Row 1]
Number of times this state was reached in the 17 contests[5] before absorption	14	9	10	3		[Row 2]
Proportion of contests in which transient state was visited before absorption	0.824	0.529	0.588	0.176		[Row 3]

[4] Don't forget that the process starts in state $2, so the entry here reflects 1, for the start, plus the number of returns.

[5] In state $2, this should be interpreted as "revisited" since the process is starting in state $2.

second row of H (all simulations began with Rich having $2), we find the following:

$$H \approx \begin{matrix} & \$1 & \$2 & \$3 & \$4 \\ \$2 & [.877 & .556 & .526 & .308] \end{matrix}$$

These "ever-visit probabilities" (or, ever-return probability in the case of state $2) should be compared with [row 3] of Table 11.2, which is reproduced below for easy comparison:

$$.824 \quad .529 \quad .588 \quad .176$$

Only in state $4 is there an appreciable difference; this difference in proportions would smooth out if the simulation were extended by taking larger sample sizes.

EXERCISES 11.3

PRACTICING THE MOVES AND MANEUVERS

Exercises 145–153: Classify the transition matrix as regular, absorbing, or neither.

145. $\begin{bmatrix} .74 & .26 \\ 1 & 0 \end{bmatrix}$ 146. $\begin{bmatrix} .69 & .31 \\ 0 & 1 \end{bmatrix}$ 147. $\begin{bmatrix} .95 & .05 \\ .08 & 92 \end{bmatrix}$ 148. $\begin{bmatrix} .4 & .6 \\ 1 & 0 \end{bmatrix}$

149. $\begin{bmatrix} 0 & 1 & 0 \\ 1 & 0 & 0 \\ 1 & 0 & 0 \end{bmatrix}$ 150. $\begin{bmatrix} 1 & 0 & 0 \\ .9 & 0 & .1 \\ .2 & .7 & .1 \end{bmatrix}$ 151. $\begin{bmatrix} .3 & .7 & 0 \\ 0 & 0 & 1 \\ 1 & 0 & 0 \end{bmatrix}$

152. $\begin{bmatrix} .2 & .2 & .2 & .4 \\ 1 & 0 & 0 & 0 \\ .5 & 0 & .5 & 0 \\ .2 & .6 & .2 & 0 \end{bmatrix}$ 153. $\begin{bmatrix} .3 & .3 & .1 & .3 \\ .4 & .2 & .4 & 0 \\ 1 & 0 & 0 & 0 \\ 0 & 0 & 0 & 1 \end{bmatrix}$

Exercises 154–159: Put the absorbing chains into canonical form.

154. $\begin{matrix} & 1 & 2 & 3 \\ 1 & [.8 & .1 & .1] \\ 2 & [0 & 1 & 0] \\ 3 & [.1 & .3 & .6] \end{matrix}$ 155. $\begin{matrix} & 1 & 2 \\ 1 & [.3 & .7] \\ 2 & [0 & 1] \end{matrix}$ 156. $\begin{matrix} & 1 & 2 & 3 \\ 1 & [.5 & .3 & .2] \\ 2 & [0 & 1 & 0] \\ 3 & [1 & 0 & 0] \end{matrix}$

157. $\begin{matrix} & 1 & 2 & 3 \\ 1 & [.4 & .3 & .3] \\ 2 & [.6 & 0 & .4] \\ 3 & [0 & 0 & 1] \end{matrix}$ 158. $\begin{matrix} & 1 & 2 \\ 1 & [1 & 0] \\ 2 & [.5 & .5] \end{matrix}$ 159. $\begin{matrix} & 1 & 2 & 3 \\ 1 & [.4 & .6 & 0] \\ 2 & [1 & 0 & 0] \\ 3 & [0 & 0 & 1] \end{matrix}$

Exercises 160–166: For each of the absorbing transition matrices (already in canonical form), determine the probability of being absorbed after four transitions from each of the transient states.

160. $\begin{bmatrix} 1 & 0 & 0 & 0 \\ 0 & 1 & 0 & 0 \\ .7 & .2 & .1 & 0 \\ .4 & .1 & .3 & .2 \end{bmatrix}$ 161. $\begin{bmatrix} 1 & 0 & 0 \\ .5 & .5 & 0 \\ .2 & .4 & .4 \end{bmatrix}$ 162. $\begin{bmatrix} 1 & 0 \\ .6 & .4 \end{bmatrix}$ 163. $\begin{bmatrix} 1 & 0 \\ .1 & .9 \end{bmatrix}$

164. $\begin{bmatrix} 1 & 0 & 0 & 0 \\ .4 & .1 & .1 & .4 \\ .8 & .1 & .1 & 0 \\ .4 & .5 & 0 & .1 \end{bmatrix}$ 165. $\begin{bmatrix} 1 & 0 & 0 & 0 \\ 0 & 1 & 0 & 0 \\ .2 & .8 & 0 & 0 \\ .2 & 0 & .7 & .1 \end{bmatrix}$ 166. $\begin{bmatrix} 1 & 0 & 0 \\ 0 & 1 & 0 \\ .2 & .6 & .2 \end{bmatrix}$

Exercises 167–173: Find the fundamental matrix N for the transition matrix from the exercise indicated. Be sure you understand its interpretation.

167. Exercise 160   169. Exercise 162   171. Exercise 164   173. Exercise 166
168. Exercise 161   170. Exercise 163   172. Exercise 165

Exercises 174–180: Find the B matrix for the transition matrix of the indicated exercise. Be sure you understand the interpretation of the entries in B.

174. Exercise 160   176. Exercise 162   178. Exercise 164   180. Exercise 166
175. Exercise 161   177. Exercise 163   179. Exercise 165

Exercises 181–187: Find the H matrix for the transition matrix of the indicated exercise. Be sure you understand the interpretation of the elements in H.

181. Exercise 160   183. Exercise 162   185. Exercise 164   187. Exercise 166
182. Exercise 161   184. Exercise 163   186. Exercise 165

APPLYING THE CONCEPTS

Exercises 188–194: Consider two avid golfers, Eric and Dave. Dave is better, having probability 0.7 of winning when they play a certain course that is well suited to Dave's game. Dave has $1 and Eric has $2, and they agree to play nine-hole matches for $1. They agree to the following contest: play continues until one player is broke.

188. Taking as states the amount of money Eric has, find the probability transition matrix P for this contest.
189. Put P in canonical form.
190. Find the probability that there will be at least four nine-hole matches before the contest ends.
191. How many times can Dave expect to have $1 prior to the game ending?
192. Find the expected duration of the contest (in nine-hole rounds).
193. Find the probability that the contest will end with Dave being broke.
194. If Dave now has $2, what is the probability that he will ever again have $2 before the contest ends?

Exercises 195–206: Refer to the following situation: A consumer buys a new car every year, always choosing from among Ford, Chevrolet, Plymouth, and Acura. If he buys a Ford this year, then 40% of the time he buys a Ford the following year; if he switches, however, then there is only a 10% chance of buying an Acura and a 20% chance of buying a Chevrolet. If he bought a Chevrolet this year, there is a 30% chance of him buying a Chevrolet next year, a 40% chance of him switching to Ford, a 25% chance of him switching to Plymouth and only a 5% chance of switching to Acura. If he bought a Plymouth this time, there is a 40% chance of him purchasing a Plymouth next time, and a

60% chance of him switching to Ford. Once a consumer buys an Acura, however, he never again buys any other make.

195. Find the transition matrix for this absorbing Markov chain.
196. Put the transition matrix into canonical form.
197. If he now owns a Ford, find the probability that he will drive a Chevrolet three model years from now.
198. If the customer now drives a Plymouth, how likely is it that he will drive an Acura the year after next?
199. Find the fundamental matrix N for this absorbing chain.
200. Find the expected number of Fords owned by a current Chevrolet driver prior to him owning an Acura.
201. If he now drives a Plymouth, find the expected number of Chevrolets he will drive before owning his first Acura.

202. If he is now driving a Ford, how many years will it be on the average until he owns his first Acura?
203. If he is now driving a Plymouth, how many years will it be on the average until he owns his first Acura?
204. If he now drives a Chevrolet, how many years will it be on the average before he owns his first Acura?
205. If he now drives a Ford, what are the chances of him driving another new Ford prior to owning his first Acura?
206. If he now drives a Chevrolet, what is the probability of him owning another new Chevrolet prior to owning his first Acura?

Exercises 207–217: A mouse lives in a pantry. After the humans who live in the house go to bed, the mouse goes foraging. There are two delights for the mouse: nacho chips and a large sack of dog food. In addition, there are two not-so-delightful rewards awaiting an unsuspecting mouse: an ordinary spring-loaded trap and poisoned bait, either of which will kill the mouse instantly. If the mouse had nacho chips one night, there is a 70% chance of her returning to nacho chips tomorrow, a 20% chance of her going to dog food, and a 10% chance of poison bait. If the mouse had dog food tonight, there is a 50% chance of her having dog food tomorrow, and a 30% chance of switching to nacho chips; if she does not have dog food or nacho chips, she is just as likely to visit the poison bait as the mouse trap.

207. Set up the transition matrix for this absorbing Markov chain.
208. Put the transition matrix in canonical form.
209. If the mouse is munching on nacho chips, what is the probability she will have dog food two nights from now?
210. Find the fundamental matrix for this absorbing chain.
211. If the mouse is currently nibbling on dog food, what is the probability that she will ever again have dog food prior to being trapped or poisoned?
212. If the mouse is currently eating nacho chips, how many days on the average will she eat nacho chips prior to being trapped or poisoned?

213. If the mouse is now eating dog food, on the average how many days will it be until she is either trapped or poisoned?
214. If the mouse is now eating nacho chips, how many days on the average will it be until she is either trapped or poisoned?
215. If the mouse is currently eating dog food, what is the probability she will ever have nacho chips prior to being trapped or poisoned?
216. If the mouse is now eating dog food, what is the probability that she will end up in the mouse trap?
217. If the mouse is now eating nacho chips, what is the probability that she will end up being poisoned?

A Brief Summary of Important Ideas

A **Markov chain** is a random process which progresses among a finite set of **states** in distinct steps called **moves** or **transitions**, never leaving the set of states.

From a given present state, several next states may be possible, with the actual selection occurring according to **transition probabilities** which depend only upon the present state and do not change as transitions continue to occur.

Probabilities governing movement from each present state to the possible next states are organized into a square matrix P, known as the **probability transition matrix**. Matrix P is said to be **stochastic**, since each of its rows sums to one. The Markov chain was started by supplying probabilities of being in various states at time zero. These initial probabilities, written in a 1-by-n row vector Π_0, were used to determine the probability vector Π_1, showing probabilities of being in the n states after one transition. We found that Π_1 was exactly $\Pi_0 \cdot P$. Keeping track of all possible next states and their probabilities with a single matrix multiplication was almost too good to be true! Further, we found that state-occupancy probabilities two transitions after the start are given by $\Pi_0 \cdot P^2 = (\Pi_0 \cdot P) \cdot P = \Pi_1 \cdot P$. In general, probabilities of being in the various states m transitions after the start are given by $\Pi_m = \Pi_0 \cdot P^m$, or by $\Pi_m = \Pi_{m-1} \cdot P$—again, a marvelous convenience.

We noticed a pattern for certain transition matrices: no matter what initial probability vector Π_0 we started with, the vectors Π_m looked more and more alike as m became larger. In fact, looking at rows of the matrix products P^m, we discovered that all rows evolved to look more and more like Π_m (and hence like each other) as m became large. We concluded (without "proof," but encouraged by our examples) that:

1. The "long-run" probability vector Π (being approached by the Π_m vectors as m gets large) is the same, regardless of initial probability vector. That is, the long-term vector Π is unique.

2. The rows of P^m look more and more like Π and like each other as m increases; and

3. the long run vector Π has the property that $\Pi \cdot P = \Pi$.

This nice long-term behavior always occurs when transition matrix P is **regular** (all entries in some power P^m of matrix P are positive).

We can tell if P is regular by examining powers of P up to $m = n^2 - 2n + 2$; if zero entries persist to this point, they will never go away, and P is not regular.

We studied one other major class of Markov chains: **absorbing Markov chains**. An absorbing Markov chain has two properties:

1. The process must have one or more **absorbing states**. Once entered, an absorbing state is never exited. Such a state is distin-

guished in the transition matrix P by an on-diagonal "1," in the row and column corresponding to the absorbing state. Every state which is *not* an absorbing state is called a **transient state**. (In contrast to an absorbing state, a transient (temporary) state permits exit to some other state.)

2. From each transient state it must be possible to get to one or more absorbing states.

In an absorbing Markov chain, capture by an absorbing state is certain. By grouping all absorbing states at the top of the matrix and all transient states at the bottom, we can write any absorbing Markov chain in the following **canonical form**:

$$
\begin{array}{cc}
& \begin{array}{cc} \textbf{Absorbing} & \textbf{Transient} \end{array} \\
\begin{array}{c} \textbf{Absorbing} \\ \textbf{Transient} \end{array} &
\left[\begin{array}{c|c} I & \emptyset \\ \hline R & Q \end{array} \right]
\end{array}
$$

The i,j-th element in the **fundamental matrix** $N = (I - Q)^{-1}$ is the expected number of times spent in a transient state j prior to absorption, given that the process is currently in transient state i. The row sums in matrix N describe how long the process spends in transient states on the average before absorption.

Table 11.3
Features of regular and absorbing Markov chains

	Regular Chains	Absorbing Chains
$\Pi_m = \Pi_0 \cdot P^m$	Shows probabilities of being in respective states, after m transitions from start Π_0.	
P^m	Rows all look more like Π_m as m grows; rows and Π_m all tend toward long-run Π.	Rows do not settle into like patterns as m grows.
Π (limiting vector)	Shows long-term tendency of process as m grows; is unique (same for all start vectors Π_0); shows relative frequencies of visits to states as process runs long.	If *one* absorbing state, then unique limiting vector Π; if more than one absorbing state, many possible long-term vectors Π; depends on starting vector Π_0.

The matrix $B = NR$ has elements which give probabilities of being captured by a particular absorbing state if the process is currently in a specific transient state.

The i,j-th element in matrix $H = (N - I)N_D^{-1}$ (N_D is a diagonal matrix whose diagonal elements are the diagonal elements of N and whose off-diagonal elements are all zero) represents the conditional probability of ever visiting transient state j given that the process is currently in transient state i.

Table 11.3 summarizes some essential features of both regular and absorbing Markov chains.

REVIEW EXERCISES

PRACTICING THE MOVES AND MANEUVERS

Exercises 218–223: Use the given Π_0 to find Π_1, Π_2, and Π_3 for transition matrix P:

$$P = \begin{bmatrix} .1 & .9 \\ .4 & .6 \end{bmatrix}$$

218. $\Pi_0 = [.4 \quad .6]$ 219. $\Pi_0 = [.05 \quad .95]$ 220. $\Pi_0 = [.8 \quad .2]$
221. $\Pi_0 = [.1 \quad .9]$ 222. $\Pi_0 = [.9 \quad .1]$ 223. $\Pi_0 = [.3 \quad .7]$
224. Using the matrix P of Exercises 218–223, find P^2, P^3, and P^4.

Exercises 225–232: Determine whether the given transition matrix is regular or absorbing. If it is absorbing, indicate which states are absorbing.

225. $\begin{bmatrix} .8 & .2 \\ .3 & .7 \end{bmatrix}$ 226. $\begin{bmatrix} .1 & .9 \\ 1 & 0 \end{bmatrix}$ 227. $\begin{bmatrix} .1 & .9 \\ 1 & 0 \end{bmatrix}$ 228. $\begin{bmatrix} 1 & 0 \\ .2 & .8 \end{bmatrix}$

229. $\begin{bmatrix} 0 & 1 \\ 1 & 0 \\ .8 & .2 \end{bmatrix}$ 230. $\begin{bmatrix} .4 & .2 & .4 \\ 0 & 1 & 0 \\ .1 & .2 & .7 \end{bmatrix}$ 231. $\begin{bmatrix} .4 & .4 & .2 \\ 0 & 1 & 0 \\ 0 & 1 & 0 \end{bmatrix}$ 232. $\begin{bmatrix} .5 & .4 & .1 \\ 1 & 0 & 0 \\ 0 & 0 & 1 \end{bmatrix}$

APPLYING THE CONCEPTS

Exercises 233–236: Professor Bill "Sailor" Eberly always uses one of two textbooks in his seminar on "RAM chip installation in your chain saw." If he used Harper's book this time, there is a 40% chance of switching to Lewis's book next time. If he used Lewis's book, there is a 60% chance of switching to Harper's next time.

233. Find the transition matrix for this two-state Markov chain.

234. If Professor Eberly uses Lewis's book this time, what is the probability that he will use Lewis's book the time after next?

235. In the long run, how often does Professor Eberly use each textbook?

236. If Professor Eberly is currently using Lewis's textbook, how long will it be on the average before he again uses Lewis's book?

Exercises 237–240: Consider an audio store with three salesmen, all of whom are full time and who vie each month for the "Top Salesman" award. If Henry was the top salesman last month, there is a 40% chance he will also be the top salesman next month, a 30% chance that Joe will be, and a 30% chance that Mike will be. If Joe was the top salesman this month, there is a 50% chance of him repeating the following month, a 40% chance of Henry dethroning him, and only a 10% chance of Mike being top. If Mike was the top salesman last month, there is a 60% chance of him repeating, while Joe and Henry are equally likely to assume the top position.

237. Write the transition matrix for this three-state Markov chain.

238. Joe is currently top salesman. How likely is he to repeat in two months?

*239. In the long run, how often does each salesman take home the top prize?

240. If Henry is currently the top salesman, how many months will it be on the average before he is again the top salesman?

Exercises 241–245: Consider the weather in East Fungicide, South Dakota, which can be any one of three conditions: windy and nice, windy and rainy, or windy and snowy. If it is windy and nice today, there is a 40% chance of the same tomorrow. If there is a change from windy and nice, half the time it is to windy and rainy, and half the time to windy and snowy. If it is windy and rainy today, it will never be windy and rainy tomorrow, and it is three times as likely to be windy and snowy as to be windy and nice. If it is windy and snowy today, there is an 80% chance of the same tomorrow, and a 10% chance of windy and nice.

241. Find the probability transition matrix for this three-state Markov chain.

242. If it is windy and nice today, determine the probabilities of the various states in three days.

243. If it is windy and snowy today, determine the probabilities of the various states in three days.

*244. Find the equilibrium vector describing the long-run weather in East Fungicide.

245. If it is currently windy and nice in East Fungicide, how many days will it be on the average before it is again nice and windy?

Exercises 246–249: Use the well-known fact that 80% of the sons and daughters of Pomona college alumnae (female form of alumni) go to Pomona, while 10% go to Harvard, 6% go to "other schools," and 4% do not go to college. Among sons and daughters of Harvard alumnae, 60% go to Harvard, 25% to Pomona, 10% to other schools, and 5% do not go to college. Among sons and daughters of "other school" alumnae, 60% go to colleges in this category, 15% go to Pomona, 10% go to Harvard, and 15% do not go to college. Among the sons and daughters of those who haven't gone to college, it is found that 30% do not go to college, 60% go to "other colleges," and 5% each go to Pomona and Harvard.

246. Give the transition matrix for this four-state Markov chain.

247. Consider the current group of college-age students. Suppose they are distributed as follows: 20% do not go to college, 70% go to the "other colleges," and 5% each to Pomona and Har-

vard. What will the mix be in the next year? The year after?

248. What is the probability that a grandchild of a Pomona alumna goes to Pomona?

*249. What is the long-run distribution in these four states?

Exercises 250–257: Refer to the following: Two duelists, A and B, fight a duel (what else do duelists do!!). Each fires at the other simultaneously, and the results of the shots are independent. The probability that A hits B is 0.2, while the probability of B hitting A is only 0.1. When a duelist is hit, he is considered "out of action." Our two contestants continue to fire until one (or both) contestants are out of action. As states, take the set of duelists that are still in action.

*250. Find the transition matrix for this four-state absorbing chain. (*Hint:* the possible states are $\Phi = \{\ \}, \{A\}, \{B\}, \text{ and } \{A,B\}$.)

251. Put the transition matrix in canonical form.

252. Find the probability that there are at least three duels before at least one of the contestants is out of action.

253. Find the fundamental matrix (with only one element) for this absorbing chain.

254. If the contestants are getting ready to duel for the first time, how long on average can they expect to fire at one another until at least one of the contestants is out of action?

255. If both contestants are still in action, find the probability that the duel ends with A being the ony survivor.

256. If both contestants are still in action, find the probability that the duel ends with B being the only survivor.

257. If both contestants are still in action, find the probability that the duel ends with both duelists out of action.

Exercises 258–263: We consider the notorious statistics professor, known affectionately as "D.B." D.B. has a favorite set of three questions, exactly one of which he asks on every oral examination. If he asked question 1 on the last exam, there is a 70% chance he will use that question again, a 20% chance he will switch to question 2, and a 10% chance of switching to question 3. If he used question 2 last time, there is no chance he will use question 2 next, and he is 4 times as likely to use question 1 as question 3. If he used question 3 last, there is a 40% chance he will use it again and a 20% chance of switching to question 2.

258. Find the probability transition matrix for this three-state Markov chain.

259. If he used question 1 this time, what is the probability that he will use question 1 two exams from now.

260. If he used question 3 this time, what is the probability that he will use question 2 two exams from now?

261. In the long run, how often will he use each question?

262. If D.B. has just used question 1, how many exams will there be on the average until he again uses question 1?

263. If D.B. has just used question 3, how many exams will there be on the average until he again uses question 3?

Exercises 264–268: An insurance company which classifies its automobile policyholders as being normal risk or high risk. This company has found that 80% of those in the normal-risk group one year stay in that group the following year. In the high-risk group, only 5% will move to the normal-risk group after one year.

264. Find the probability transition matrix for this two-state Markov chain.

265. Suppose that currently 85% of the policyholders are in the normal-risk group. What will the distribution of policyholders be next year?

266. If there are currently 25% of the policyholders in the high-risk group, determine the proportion in the high-risk group in three years.

267. Estimate the proportion of policyholders in each group after 28 years.

268. If a policyholder is now classified as a normal risk, how many years will it be on the average until she is again classified as a normal risk?

Exercises 269–280: Refer to the following situation: In assessing business, a small retailer analyzes: "If I have a small profit this month, there is a 50% chance of another small-profit month, a 40% chance of a large-profit month, and a 10% chance of going out of business next month. If I have a large profit this month, there is a 60% chance of having large profit next month, a 30% chance of small profit, a 6% chance of being bought out (desirable!), and a 4% chance of going out of business.''

269. Find the probability transition matrix for this four-state absorbing chain.
270. Put the transition matrix in canonical form.
271. If the retailer is currently having a high-profit month, what are the probabilities for being in each of the four states two months from now?
272. Find the fundamental matrix N for this chain.
273. If the retailer is currently having a small-profit month, how many months will there be on average before she is either bought out or goes out of business?
274. If the retailer is now having a small-profit month, how many more small-profit months can she expect before being bought out or going out of business?
275. If the retailer is now having a large-profit month, how many more large profit months can she expect prior to being bought out or going out of business?

276. If the retailer is currently having a large-profit month, how many months will it be on the average before she is either bought out or goes out of business?
277. If she is now having a small-profit month, find the probability she will ever have a large-profit month before being bought out or going out of business.
278. If she is now having a large-profit month, find the probability she will ever have a small-profit month prior to being bought out or going out of business.
279. If she is currently having a large-profit month, what is the probability that she will eventually be bought out?
280. If she is currently having a small-profit month, what is the probability that she will eventually go out of business?

Exercises 281–284: A mouse conducts experiments by placing a psychologist in a T-shaped maze. The psychologist has his choice of turning left and receiving a reward (a giant lollipop and a copy of B.F. Skinner's complete works) or turning right and being nudged with a cattle prod. After several trials with many different psychologists the mouse notes that a psychologist is just as likely to go left as right on the first trial. In resulting trials, however, the following pattern is noted: if the psychologist went left on the current trial, there is an 80% chance of him going left on the next trial, and if he went right on the current trial, there is a 30% chance of him going right on the next trial. A fresh psychologist has just been turned loose in the maze.

281. Find the transition matrix for this two-state Markov chain.
282. Find the probabilities for turning left and right on his second time through the maze.
283. Find the probability of the psychologist turning right on the third time through the maze.
284. In the long run, how often will a given psychologist turn left?

Exercises 285–289: Consider three video rental stores in a small town. In a year's time, store A is expected to maintain 70% of its customers while losing 20% to store B and the remainder to store C. Store B on the other hand maintains 90% of its customers, losing 5% each to the other stores. Store C maintains only 50% of its customers, losing 10% to A and 40% to B.

285. Find the probability transition matrix P for this three-state Markov chain.
286. If the distribution of customers at present is 50% to store A, 30% to store B, and 20% to store C, find the distribution of customers at the end of next year and at the end of two years.
287. If the present distribution of customers is 10% to store A, 20% to B, and 70% to C, find the distribution of customers one year and two years from now.
288. Find the long-run distribution of customers in each of the three stores.
289. If a customer now rents from store A, how many years will it be on the average before he returns to store A (having taken his business elsewhere in the meantime)?

12 *Money Matters*

In this chapter we discuss borrowing and investing money. After finishing this chapter, you will be able to solve problems like the following:

1. You have $1000 to put into a savings account for one year. Institution I offers you 5.25% compounded quarterly, while savings institution II offers you 5.5%, but compounded only once a year. Which is a better deal?

2. You buy an $80,000 house and you have $15,000 for a down payment. The interest rate is 10%. What will your monthly payment be with a 20-year loan? With a 30-year loan? How much interest will you pay with each loan?

3. Your six-year-old son wants to go to college. How much money will you have to invest monthly for the next 12 years in his college fund, earning 8% annual interest, in order to accumulate $40,000 after 12 years?

4. You and your spouse start a new-car fund by saving $200 at the end of each month at 6% interest. After four years, how much will you have accumulated? If you want to accumulate $14,000 after four years, what interest rate would each deposit have to earn?

5. One year ago, you borrowed $6000 from your bank at 10% interest for three years, and you also borrowed $10,000 from your bank at 11% for five years. In both cases, you were to repay the principal amount and the interest at the end of the loan with one payment. The bank will now let you combine the two loans into one loan due in three years at 10.5% interest. How much will you owe in three years?

6. You have just won $1,000,000 in the state lottery, payable at $50,000 per year for the next 20 years. What if the lottery commission were to offer you $400,000 cash *now* in lieu of the 20 annual payments? Should you accept their offer? After all, having the entire sum now should be worth something. Suppose you could earn 8% compounded annually by lending the $400,000 to a construction company. Is this a better deal than the 20-year payoff?

We begin by investigating the concept of interest.

12.1 SIMPLE AND COMPOUND INTEREST

When you were younger and needed money, you went to your parents with a simple request: "Lend me some money." What you really meant was, "give me some money." As you got older, you no doubt paid the money back, but you may have paid only the principal, or the exact amount of money borrowed. In the real world, money lenders are not as charitable as parents. When you use a bank's money, you must pay for the privilege. Stated simply, **interest** is rent paid for the use of money; it compensates the lender for the loss of use of the money while you have it.

Simple Interest

A common, easy-to-understand way of computing interest is known as **simple interest:** once the money is lent, the borrower pays a fixed percentage of the original amount borrowed for each time period during which he or she keeps the money. The regular time period may be a week, a month, a quarter (three months), a year, etc. The fixed percentage which the lender charges the borrower is called the **periodic rate.**

PRINCIPAL SIMPLE INTEREST AND ACCUMULATED VALUE

If an amount P, called the **principal,** is borrowed for t time periods at an interest rate of r per time period, then the simple interest is computed by

$$I = P \cdot r \cdot t$$

After the agreed-upon time number of time periods t, the interest I is paid to the lender along with the original principal P. The total returned to the investor is called the future value or **accumulated value,** denoted by the symbol A.

$$A = P + I = P + Prt = P(1 + rt)$$

In discussing loans and investments, it is important that the rate r and the time t be expressed using the same time units (for example, 1% per month for 7 months, or 10% a year for five years). The quantities "10%" and "0.10" are identical. In computing, we will express the interest rate r as a decimal, writing 10% as 0.10.

In our definition of simple interest, t need not be a whole number of time units. If, for example, interest is charged at a yearly rate and you borrow money for six months, then you may use the above formula with $t = 1/2$ year.

The simple interest formula $I = Prt$ involves four quantities, P, I, r, and t. Usually, P, r, and t will be given and the interest I will be calculated, but you may calculate any one of the four quantities from knowledge of the other three.

■ EXAMPLE 1

A student in need of tuition borrows $500 from a bank at 11% simple annual interest. If he borrows the money for 7 months, how much will he have to repay the bank?

SOLUTION

Since the interest rate is 11% per year, we express the seven-month time period t in terms of years, giving $t = 7/12$. Using the simple interest formula, we find

$$I = \$500(0.11)\,\frac{7}{12}$$
$$= \$32.08$$

After seven months the student will need to pay the $500 principal plus $32.08 interest for an accumulated value of $532.08.

Note: The way time is expressed varies from institution to institution. In our calculation, we expressed 7 months as 7/12 of a year, treating all months as being equal in length. With time defined in this way (12 equal-length months), calculation of interest is known as **ordinary simple interest.**

A more exact way of calculating time is to tally the exact number of days and then divide by 365 days. With time defined in this way—that is, t = exact # days/365—calculated interest is known as **exact simple interest.** While eminently fair, this method of calculation is not used by most lending institutions, which use the exact number of days, but assume a 360-day year. If, for example, there were 214 days in the seven months of Example 1, a bank's calculation would proceed like this:

$$I = \$500(0.11)\,\frac{214}{360}$$
$$= \$32.69$$

The bank's "creative" definition of a year as being 360 days (we call this the **"Banker's Rule"**) is definitely to the bank's advantage, because, were the bank to use 365 days, the exact simple interest would be only

$$I = \$500(0.11)\frac{214}{365}$$
$$= \$32.25$$

To any one borrower, that difference of 44 cents would not be alarming, but to a bank with thousands of borrowers, this calculation difference will produce thousands of dollars a year in additional interest. ■

■ EXAMPLE 2

If your father were to lend you $2000 at 8% ordinary simple interest and you were to later settle the debt with a $2200 payment, for how many years would you have held the money? (*Note:* Ordinary simple interest is always an annual rate.)

SOLUTION

Since the principal is $2000, you will be paying $200 interest. Using the basic relationship $I = P \cdot r \cdot t$, and filling in the three known quantities, we have $\$200 = \$2000(0.08) \cdot t$, or $\$200 = \$160 \cdot t$. Dividing both sides by 160 produces $t = 5/4$ year, or 15 months. ■

■ EXAMPLE 3

Your father lends you $1000 for the four-month period from March through June. What is the interest charge you will pay if the 8% interest rate (understood to be an annual rate) is

(a) ordinary simple interest?

(b) exact simple interest?

(c) "Banker's Rule" simple interest?

SOLUTION

For (a), the loan period is four months, and ordinary simple interest is calculated by $I = 1000 \cdot (0.08) \cdot 4/12 = \$26.67$.

For (b), we count the total number of days in the four months involved, arriving at 122. Substituting $t = 122/365$ into the simple interest formula, we obtain $I = 1000 \cdot (0.08) \cdot (122/365) = \$26.74$.

For part (c), the calculations proceed as in part (b), except that 360 replaces 365. This leads to $I = 1000 \cdot (0.08) \cdot (122/360) = \$27.11$. ■

PRACTICE PROBLEM 1

If you borrow $450 for 8 months, how much will you pay back if the ordinary simple interest rate is 10%?

ANSWER(S)

$480   □

PRACTICE PROBLEM 2

In Practice Problem 1, suppose the 10% is an exact simple interest rate and that you borrow the money from May 7th through July 15th. How much will your payoff be? (Count each elapsed day, starting with May 8th and ending with July 15th.)

ANSWER(S) $458.51   ☐

Compound Interest   If you lend someone $500 for two years at 10% simple interest, you will be paid $500 · (0.10) · 2 = $100 interest plus the original principal of $500 after two years. But consider this fact: after the first year, your accumulated value will be $A = P(1 + rt) = 500(1 + 0.10 \cdot 1) = 550$. During the second year, however, you will still earn only $50 interest, since simple interest is based not on the current value of your "account" ($550 after one year) but only on the original balance. The $50 of interest you earn the first year is not productive during the second year. For this reason, simple interest is not a good proposition for a lender if the time period is long. In the real world, it is rare to encounter simple interest on loans of more than one year. **Compound interest** is much fairer in that it assumes all your money is productive; specifically, any interest you have earned should not sit idle: it should also be earning interest. "Compound" means that earned interest automatically gets reinvested at the same terms as the original principal.

When interest is compounded, the time between interest computations is called the **interest conversion period,** and the named interest rate is assumed to be an annual rate, used proportionally for any number of compoundings per year. If a savings account pays 6% compounded semiannually, then 6/2 = 3% interest is calculated and added to your account (converted from interest to principal) each six months; the interest conversion period is six months. With quarterly compounding, 6/4 = 1.5% interest would be added to your account at the end of each quarter. With monthly compounding, 6/12 = 0.5% interest is figured on your account value after each month and converted to principal; the interest conversion period is monthly.

■ EXAMPLE 4 ─────────   If you put $1000 in a savings account earning 6% interest compounded semiannually, how much will you have after **(a)** six months; **(b)** one year; **(c)** two years?

SOLUTION   Earning 6% a year is equivalent to 6%/2 = 3% per each six-month compounding period. During the first six months you will earn 1000(0.03) = $30. The savings institution will not give you the $30, but will assume you want it credited to your account. After six months, then, you will have an accumulated account value of $1030. During the second six months, you will earn 1030(0.03) = $30.90. With compounding, you have earned an extra $0.90 interest in the second six-month period—3%

of the $30 interest earned the first six months. After one year, your account value will be $1000 + 30 + 30.90 = $1060.90. To determine the accumulated amount after two years, we construct Table 12.1:

Table 12.1

6-Month Period	Beginning Amount	Interest Earned	Accumulated Value at End of 6-Month Period
1	$1000	$30	$1000 + $30 = $1030
2	$1030	$30.90	$1030 + $30.90 = $1060.90
3	$1060.90	$31.83	$1060.90 + $31.83 = $1092.73
4	$1092.73	$32.78	$1092.73 + $32.78 = $1125.51

After two years (four compounding periods), the original $1000 will have grown to $1125.51. Not only will the amount grow during each six-month period, but it will grow at an increasing rate: from $30 growth during the first six-month period to $32.78 growth during the fourth six-month period. Contrast this with 6% simple interest: a steady $30 interest each six months, which would be paid to your account after each six-month period; the principal would remain $1000 during the entire investment period. ◼

Future Value or Accumulated Value

While Example 4 is instructive, we would not want to continue the calculations of Table 12.1 for very many years. We need a way to find the accumulated value[1] (for example, $1125.51 from Example 4) after any number of interest conversion periods without having to compute all intermediate amounts. We can arrive at just such a procedure by generalizing Example 4. We use P (instead of $1000) and an annual interest rate i (instead of 6%).[2] We also assume that there are m compounding periods per year, so that the interest in any one period is i/m. During the first period, for example, we will earn $P \cdot (i/m)$. We illustrate in Table 12.2.

Table 12.2

Period	Beginning Amount	Interest Earned	Accumulated Amount at End of Period	
1	P	$P \cdot (i/m)$	$P + P \cdot (i/m)$	$= P(1 + i/m)^1$
2	$P(1 + i/m)$	$P(1 + i/m) \cdot (i/m)$	$P(1 + i/m) + P(1 + i/m) \cdot (i/m)$	$= P(1 + i/m)^2$
3	$P(1 + i/m)^2$	$P(1 + i/m)^2 \cdot (i/m)$	$P(1 + i/m)^2 + P(1 + i/m)^2 \cdot (i/m)$	$= P(1 + i/m)^3$

[1] From now on we shall use the terms "future value" and "accumulated value" interchangeably, and will represent both quantities with the symbol "A."
[2] From now on, we shall use "i" rather than r to represent an interest rate. This conforms with usual procedure.

Amount P accumulates to $P(1 + i/m)^1$ after one compounding period, to $P(1 + i/m)^2$ after two compounding periods, and to $P(1 + i/m)^3$ after three periods. The pattern should now be clear. In general, we have the following relation for accumulated value with compound interest:

FUTURE VALUE WITH m COMPOUNDINGS ANNUALLY

> When amount P is invested for n periods at i percent per annum, with compounding m times a year, the amount P will grow to a **future value** or **accumulated value** of
>
> $$A = P \left(1 + \frac{i}{m}\right)^n$$

We stress that n is not the number of years, nor the number of periods per year but the total number of compounding periods in the time period involved. In a three-year period, with quarterly compounding, $n = 4 \cdot 3 = 12$; in ten years, with semiannual compounding, $n = 10 \cdot 2 = 20$.

PRACTICE PROBLEM 3   You borrow $740 for 2 years at 11% compounded quarterly. How much will you need to pay off your loan?

ANSWER(S) $919.36   □

EXAMPLE 5   You have just invested $100 at 9% interest compounded annually. Find the future value **(a)** in 2 years; **(b)** in 5 years.

SOLUTION   *Note:* The principal P = $100 which you now have is also known as the **present value;** it is the current worth of the money. For part **(a)** we want the future value of $100 in two years. The required amount is $100 \cdot (1 + 0.09)^2 \approx \$118.81$. We describe this result in two ways:

1. The future value or accumulated value of $100 at 9% in two years is $118.81.

2. The present value of $118.81 in two years at 9% is $100.

For part **(b)**, the future value of $100 in 5 years is $100 \cdot (1 + 0.09)^5 \approx \$153.86$. Having $100 now (present value) is like having $153.86 in five years (future value or accumulated value)—if you can invest the money now at 9% compounded annually.   ■

EXAMPLE 6   How much would you need to invest now at 9% compounded annually in order to accumulate $140 in two years?

SOLUTION We seek the present value of $140 two years from now at 9% interest. The required amount must be more than $100, because $100 will grow only to $118.81 (see Example 5). To find the exact amount, we first solve for P in the future value formula:

$$A = P\left(1 + \frac{i}{m}\right)^n$$

Divide both sides by $(1 + i/m)^n$, and switch the two sides:

$$P = \frac{A}{\left(1 + \dfrac{i}{m}\right)^n}$$

Substituting $A = \$140$, $i = 0.09$, $m = 1$ (annual compounding) and $n = 2$ (two compounding periods in two years), we obtain

$$P = \frac{140}{(1 + 0.09)^2} \approx \$117.84$$

We express this by saying "the present value of $140 in two years at 9% compounded annually is $117.84." ∎

We investigate present value more thoroughly in Section 12.3. For now, however, we concentrate on accumulated (future) value.

∎ EXAMPLE 7 You put $100 in C.D.'s (certificates of deposit) for Milksop's Mortuary Mortgages which pay 8% compounded annually. How much will your $100 grow to in **(a)** two years? **(b)** five years? **(c)** ten years?

SOLUTION For **(a)**, $A = 100(1 + 0.08)^2 = 100 \cdot 1.1664 = \$116.64$.
For **(b)**, $A = 100(1 + 0.08)^5 \approx 100 \cdot 1.469281 \approx \$146.93$.
For **(c)**, $A = 100(1 + 0.08)^{10} \approx 100 \cdot 2.158925 \approx \$215.89$.

The factor $(1 + i/m)^n = a^n$ is called the ***n*-period compound accumulation factor** because it is a growth factor describing what each $1 becomes after n compounding periods at annual rate i (rate is i/m per period). In **(a)**, for example, $1 grows to $1.1664 dollars in two years at 8% compounded annually; in **(b)**, $1 grows to $1.469281 after five years at 8% compounded annually. Until very recently, calculations like $(1 + i/m)^n$ use to require logarithms, special tables, or extraordinary patience. Today we routinely find such quantities by using a calculator's power key. This key, labeled x^y or y^x, is a real time-saver. If you have no such calculator, refer to Table II, Compound Accumulation Factors, in the Appendix. Table II gives values of $a^n = (1 + i/m)^n$ for a variety of interest rates and compounding periods. The compound accumulation factor a^n is of fundamental importance in financial mathematics. We use it extensively in this chapter. ∎

PRACTICE PROBLEM 4   Calculate (and verify from Table II) compound accumulation factors for the following investments: **(a)** three years at 12% compounded quarterly; **(b)** six years at 9% compounded monthly; **(c)** ten years at 10% compounded semiannually.

ANSWER(S)   **(a)** 1.42576;   **(b)** 1.71255;   **(c)** 2.65330   □

Examples 6 and 7 illustrated annual compounding. When interest is compounded more frequently, it is important to express the interest rate in terms of the compounding period. If interest is 12% annually and compounding occurs quarterly, then the periodic rate is 12%/4 = 3% per quarter; if compounding occurs monthly then the periodic interest rate is 12%/12 = 1% per month. The i/m term in the boxed formula for future value converts the annual interest rate to the interest rate per compounding period.

■ EXAMPLE 8

How much will a $1000 investment be worth in five years if interest is 12%, **(a)** compounded quarterly? **(b)** compounded monthly?

SOLUTION   **(a)** With quarterly compounding, 5 years contain 20 compounding periods. The accumulated value (future value) of $1000 after five years is

$$A = 1000 \left(1 + \frac{i}{m}\right)^n = 1000 \left(1 + \frac{0.12}{4}\right)^{20}$$
$$\approx 1000(1.806111) \approx \$1806.11$$

(b) With monthly compounding, the future value of $1000 in five years (60 compounding periods) is

$$A = 1000 \left(1 + \frac{i}{m}\right)^n = 1000 \left(1 + \frac{0.12}{12}\right)^{60}$$
$$\approx 1000(1.816697) \approx \$1816.70$$

In **(a)** the compound accumulation factor for $n = 20$ periods is $(1 + 0.03)^{20} = 1.806111$. Each dollar will grow to 1.806111 dollars after 20 quarters. In **(b)**, with monthly compounding, each dollar grows to 1.816697 dollars after five years.   ■

The effect of more frequent compounding is illustrated in Example 9.

■ EXAMPLE 9

Determine the value of $1000 when invested for five years at 8% with the following compoundings: **(a)** annual; **(b)** semiannual; **(c)** quarterly; **(d)** monthly; **(e)** daily.

SOLUTION   **(a)** $1000(1 + 0.08/1)^{5 \cdot 1} \approx 1000 \cdot 1.46933 = \$1469.33$ with annual compounding, since there are $5 \cdot 1 = 5$ compounding periods.

(b) $1000(1 + 0.08/2)^{10} = \$1480.24$ with semiannual compounding, since there are $5 \cdot 2 = 10$ semiannual periods in five years.

(c) $1000(1 + 0.08/4)^{20} = \$1485.95$ with quarterly compounding, since there are $5 \cdot 4 = 20$ quarterly periods in five years.

(d) $1000(1 + 0.08/12)^{60} = \$1489.85$ with monthly compounding, since there are $5 \cdot 12 = 60$ monthly periods in five years.

(e) $1000(1 + 0.08/360)^{1800} = \$1491.76$ with daily compounding, since there are $5 \cdot 360 = 1800$ days in five years. ■

PRACTICE PROBLEM 5 Rework Example 9, still at 8% but for a six-year period.

ANSWER(S) **(a)** $1586.87 **(b)** $1601.03 **(c)** $1608.44 **(d)** $1613.50 **(e)** $1615.99
□

In Practice Problem 5, you no doubt "started from scratch," computing $\$1000(1.08)^6 \approx 1586.87$ for part **(a)**. Correct; but you could have extended each Example 9 answer by one year's growth factor: **(a)** the six-year accumulated value is $\$1469.33 \cdot (1.08)^1 = \$1586.88$. (Don't be concerned if you are "off" by a few cents!) In **(b)** the accumulation is $\$1480.24(1 + 0.08/2)^2 \approx \$1601.03$.

From Example 9 and Practice Problem 5, we see that the more frequently interest is compounded, the more we gain. (A member of the famous Rothschild family is purported to have exclaimed that "compound interest is the eighth wonder of the world!")

Continuous Compounding Just how far can we carry this idea of more frequent compounding? In Example 9, what if compounding occurs hourly? A "Banker's Year" has $360 \cdot 24 = 8640$ hours. There are $5 \cdot 8640 = 43,200$ one-hour periods in five years. In five years of hourly compounding, $1000 would grow to $1000(1 + 0.08/8640)^{43,200} = \$1491.82$. More frequent compounding increases our fortune, but at an ever-dwindling rate. If compounding occurs instantaneously (continuous compounding), we state without justification that the compounded amount would grow to $1000e^{0.08 \cdot 5} = 1000e^{0.4}$ where the constant e, the base of natural logarithms, is approximately 2.71828. For emphasis:

FUTURE VALUE WITH CONTINUOUS COMPOUNDING

When amount P is invested for t years at i percent annual interest with continuous compounding, the amount P will grow to a **future value** or **accumulated value** of

$$A = Pe^{it}$$

To finish the continuous compounding computation begun above: if you have an "e^x" key on your calculator, simply enter 0.4 and depress this key. The result, 1.4918247, is the compound accumulation factor with continuous compounding; your $1000 will grow to $1491.8247 in five years. If you do not have an e^x key on your calculator, but do have an "ln x" or "ln" key and an "INV" key, enter the three keystrokes, "1," "INV," and "ln." This should produce 2.7182818 in your display. Use the y^x or x^y power key to finish calculations.

Comparing the continuous compound accumulation figure with the annual compound accumulation factor 1.46933 from **(a)**, we see that continuous compounding produces roughly 2 cents per dollar more than annual compounding over a five-year period. In Table 12.3, we summarize the results of compounding over different length periods.

Table 12.3

Growth of $1000 at 8% over 5 Years with Various Levels of Compounding	
Conversion Period	Future Value In 5 Years
1 year	$1469.33
6 Months	$1480.24
3 Months	$1485.95
1 Month	$1489.85
1 Day	$1491.76
1 Hour	$1491.82
Continuously	$1491.8247

Compounding more frequently than daily has little effect on future value. Continuous compounding is primarily a marketing ploy used by some lending institutions in the hope of luring funds from competitors that do not use continuous compounding.

Doubling Your Money

In Example 7, part **(c)**, a $100 investment accumulated to more than $215 after 10 years—you more than doubled your money. The next example shows the effect of various interest rates on the time it takes to double your money.

■ EXAMPLE 10

How long does it take to double your money at the following annual rates of interest, compounded annually:
(a) 0.01; **(b)** 0.03; **(c)** 0.05; **(d)** 0.07; **(e)** 0.10?

SOLUTION

We wish to find the number of years required for our original investment P to grow to $2P$. In terms of the "annual compounding" form of the future value formula

$$A = P\left(1 + \frac{i}{1}\right)^n$$

we want the n for which A becomes $2P$. Substituting $2P$ for A and simplifying, we obtain

$$2P = P(1 + i)^n$$

Dividing both sides by P, we get

$$2 = (1 + i)^n$$

The value of n that satisfies this equation will tell us how many years an investment must grow before doubling. We can solve this equation with logarithms, or we can look through Table II for a compound accumulation factor of 2, but it is instructive to use the power key on your calculator and simply explore.

(a) Try $n = 10$: $(1 + 0.01)^{10} = 1.105$; in ten years, each dollar will grow only to \$1.105, nowhere near the required \$2. Try $n = 20$: $1.01^{20} = 1.22$, still short of the required doubling. Be venturesome—try 1.01^{50}. This gives 1.645, which is still not enough. After 80 years, compounding produces $1.01^{80} = 2.217$—more than double. Thus, $n = 80$ years is too long. Continued experimentation shows that 69 years is not quite enough, but that 70 years will produce 2.0068. Take heart—there are few investments today that would produce as little as 5%, let alone only 1%.

(b) Solve $1.03^n = 2$. Trial and error reveals $1.03^{23} = 1.974$, while $1.03^{24} = 2.033$. At 3% compounded annually, it takes more than 23 years to double your money.

(c) At 5% compounded annually, your money will double at the value of n that satisfies $1.05^n = 2$. Power-key experimentation reveals that $1.05^{14} = 1.980$, while $1.05^{15} = 2.079$.

Parts (d) and (e): it takes slightly more than ten years for your money to double at 7% compounded annually, while at 10% it takes a little more than seven years. ■

The results of Example 10, and a few additional calculations, allow us to construct Table 12.4.

Table 12.4

Annual rate	1%	2%	3%	4%	5%	6%	7%	8%	9%	10%
Number of years (to nearest year) to double with annual compounding	70	35	23	18	14	12	10	9	8	7

A study of Table 12.4 yields the following simple rule for figuring approximately how long it takes money to double:

DOUBLING YOUR MONEY: THE RULE OF 72

Divide 72 by the annual interest rate. The answer indicates approximately how many years it takes for your money to double at that rate.

For example, at 7% compounded annually, it will take about $72/7 \approx 10$ years for your money to double; at 4%, it will take about $72/4 = 18$ years. The Rule of 72 works reasonably well regardless of how often interest is compounded, but the following simple adjustments work even better: with semiannual or quarterly compounding, replace 72 with 71; with daily compounding, use 70, and with continuous compounding, use 69.

PRACTICE PROBLEM 6   At 5% interest compounded daily, approximately how long would it take for your money to double?

ANSWER(S)   Approximately $70/5 = 14$ years ☐

PRACTICE PROBLEM 7   Determine how long (to the nearest year) it will take for your money to triple when compounded annually at **(a)** 10%; **(b)** 8%.

ANSWER(S)   **(a)** 12 years (exact calculation gives 11.53);   **(b)** 14 years (14.27) ☐

EXERCISES 12.1

PRACTICING THE MOVES AND MANEUVERS

Exercises 1–10: Find the ordinary simple interest charge on the following loans:

1. $2000 for four months at 8%
2. $4000 for six months at 9%
3. $1000 for seven months at 14%
4. $25,000 for 11 months at 7%
5. $10,000 for three months at 9%
6. $5850 for one year at 11%
7. $2430 for eight months at 8%
8. $647 for two months at 17%
9. $15,000 for five months at 6%
10. $1150 for 11 months at 7%

Exercises 11–20: Find the exact simple interest on the following loans:

11. $2750 for 211 days at 6%
12. $4400 for 45 days at 8%
13. $9400 for 63 days at 10%
14. $15,000 for 88 days at 9%

15. $1150 for 332 days at 11%
16. $9900 for 74 days at 8%
17. $12,250 for 96 days at 10%

18. $920 for 200 days at 9.5%
19. $74,000 for 88 days at 11%
20. $35,000 for 45 days at 9%

Exercises 21–25: Find the Banker's Rule simple interest on the following loans:

21. $9900 for 74 days at 8%
22. $35,000 for 45 days at 9%
23. $9200 for 200 days at 9.5%

24. $2000 for 89 days at 8%
25. $4500 for 245 days at 11%

Exercises 26–35: Calculate the compound accumulation factor a^n, and use it to find the accumulated value of the given investment under the compounding specified.

26. $4000 at 8% compounded annually for five years
27. $2500 at 6% compounded annually for four years
28. $4000 at 8% compounded semiannually for five years
29. $2500 at 6% compounded semiannually for four years
30. $10,000 at 4% compounded quarterly for six years
31. $12,000 at 10% compounded quarterly for nine years
32. $10,000 at 5% compounded quarterly for six years
33. $14,600 at 8% compounded daily for three years
34. $10,000 at 5% compounded daily for six years
35. $4000 at 20% compounded annually for half a year

APPLYING THE CONCEPTS

36. To get the lowest possible airfare for a trip, you must borrow $480 immediately. At 14% simple interest, how much will you have to repay in two weeks (14 days) if you use **(a)** ordinary simple interest (treat the 14 days as 2/52 of a year)? **(b)** exact simple interest? **(c)** Banker's Rule simple interest.
37. In Exercise 36, your banker objects to making such a small loan for only two weeks, and, in addition to the 14% simple interest, she imposes a $10 loan fee, which you pay after the 14 days. Assuming ordinary simple interest, and treating the $10 loan fee as interest, what is the actual interest rate?
38. You borrow $1200 for 90 days at 12% per annum. Using exact simple interest, determine how much you will need to repay your loan.
39. Your best friend borrows $50 for seven days, agreeing to repay you with $54. Viewing this seven-day period as 1/52 of a year, determine the ordinary simple interest rate that she is offering.
40. You borrow $100 today and agree to settle your loan with a $110 payment in 1/3 of a year. What ordinary simple interest rate will you be paying?

41. How much would you have to invest at 8% exact simple interest for 85 days in order that your investment mature to $400 after the 85 days?
42. Your local credit union offers 8% compounded monthly on deposits of $5000 or more. If you invest $7000 with them for 18 months, and then withdraw the entire accumulation, how much will you have?
43. If you invest $2500 for two years at 8% simple interest, how much will your investment be worth?
44. If you invest $2500 for two years at 8% compounded monthly, how much will your investment be worth? (Compare this answer with Exercise 43 to see the effect of monthly compounding.)
45. If you plan to invest for two years, which of the following is the preferred investment vehicle: **(a)** 8% compounded daily or **(b)** 8.25% compounded annually?
46. Suppose interest is compounded annually. By doing calculations similar to those in Practice Problem 7, determine a tripling rule similar to the "Rule of 72" devised for doubling your

money. (*Hint:* Use the results from Practice Problem 7 for 8% and 10%, and make new calculations for 1%, 2%, 5%, and 12%.)

47. $2000 will be invested for 125 days at 12% simple annual interest. Using the "Banker's Rule," determine
    (a) the interest that will be earned.
    (b) the worth of the investment after the 125 days.

48. You can buy a treasury bill from a bank for $9150. In one year (360 days), you can cash it in for $10,000.
    (a) If this investment is considered to be a simple interest investment, determine the Banker's Rule simple interest rate that you will earn.
    (b) If the bank were to charge you a $50 fee at the time of purchase, making your actual cost $9200, determine the Banker's Rule rate simple interest rate you will earn.

49. Using ordinary simple interest with a rate of 9.5% per annum, determine how long you would have to invest $300 in order to have it grow to $320.

50. If you invest $6000 for 4 years at 8.5% compounded daily, how much will your investment be worth
    (a) after the first year?
    (b) after the second year?
    (c) after the third year?
    (d) after the fourth year?

51. Suppose, on January 1, 1492, Columbus had invested one thin dime in Mayflower S&L, which, according to mythical historical records, paid and continues to pay a flat 4%, compounded monthly.
    (a) How much would Columbus's $0.10 be worth on the first day of the 21st century?
    (b) How much would the dime have grown to by January 1, 1812?
    (c) How much would the initial dime have grown to by January 1, 1992?

52. Rework Exercise 51 if Mayflower pays interest at 5% rate compounded monthly.

53. If Jim Whitmore borrowed $4500 from his father for graduate school at 9.6% ordinary simple interest, how much will he owe his father after 9 months?

54. You borrow $3500 from a bank at 10% simple interest for one year. You receive an inheritance 120 days after the loan begins and you wish to retire the loan immediately. Assuming there is no penalty for paying off the loan early, how much do you owe?

55. Suppose you can invest $1000 for two years at 10% ordinary simple interest, and then you reinvest the accumulated value for three more years at 9% ordinary simple interest. What will your accumulated value be after five years?

12.2 COMPARING INTEREST RATES: THE EFFECTIVE RATE OF INTEREST

As an investor, are you better off receiving 5% compounded daily or 5.25% compounded quarterly? The Truth-In-Lending Act passed by Congress in 1969 was designed to help consumers by requiring lenders to state a common reference rate which would be effective in comparing various stated rates with different compounding periods. The name given to this rate is the *effective rate,* sometimes known as the true annual interest rate or the *annual percentage rate* (APR).

EFFECTIVE RATE OF INTEREST

The **effective rate of interest,** or the **annual percentage rate (APR),** is the amount of interest earned during a one-year period as a proportion of the principal invested at the beginning of that year.

If an investment of $1000 pays 5% compounded annually, then the effective rate of interest is $50/$1000 = 0.05, or 5%. An effective rate of interest is nothing more than the annual interest rate where interest is paid once, at the year end (that is, annual compounding). Alternatively, the effective rate is the simple interest rate that would be needed to produce the same yearly return as the stated compounding procedure.

The beauty of effective rates is that they can be used to convert other-than-annual rates of compounding to an equivalent annual rate—the effective rate. For example, if $100 is invested at 5% compounded semiannually, you will have $100(1.025)^2 = \$105.06$ after one year. The effective rate of interest is then $5.06/$100 = 0.0506 or 5.06%. In other words, 5% compounded semiannually is equivalent to 5.06% compounded annually. Try your understanding of the effective rate of interest by working Example 11 and Practice Problem 8 that follows Example 11.

■ EXAMPLE 11

Delmo has a dreadful dilemma. Having just sold his prize possession (a Polaroid snapshot of the Chairman of Chrysler Corporation buying a new BMW) for $2000, he wants to invest the money. He has identified the following three alternatives:

1. A savings account paying 5.25% compounded quarterly.

2. A bank paying 5.4% compounded annually.

3. A certificate of deposit, which pays 5.3% compounded semiannually.

Which of the three will give him the best rate of interest if he invests his money for one year? How much will each produce?

SOLUTION

Since the rates and compounding periods are all different, we compare these investments by finding their effective rates.

1. With compounding quarterly, the four-period (one year) compound accumulation factor is $(1 + 0.0525/4)^4 \approx 1.053543$. Each dollar of principal will accumulate to $1.053543 in one year. Thus, in one year, $2000 will accumulate to

$$\$2000 \left(1 + \frac{0.0525}{4}\right)^4 = \$2000(1.053543) = \$2107.09$$

The interest earned during the year is $2107.09 − $2000 = $107.09. This makes the effective rate of interest $107.09/$2000 = 0.0535, or about 5.35%.

The figure "0.0535" should look familiar; it is the decimal part of the compound amount factor 1.053543 that was used just above in calculating $2107.09. (Note that we did not use all this accuracy when calculating the effective rate, as interest rates are usually stated to only two decimal places.) The occurrence of the compound accumulation factor is no accident; this provides us with a way to compute the effective rate in an alternative manner: we compute the compound accumulation factor and then subtract 1:

ALTERNATIVE CALCULATION OF EFFECTIVE RATE

If money is invested at annual rate i, compounded m times annually, then the effective rate of interest is given by

$$\text{APR} = \left(1 + \frac{i}{m}\right)^m - 1$$

Note: This calculation is appropriate for any compounding other than continuous compounding.

We shall use this alternative form in calculating the effective rate for Delmo's other two alternatives.

2. In this investment, Delmo gets 5.4% compounded annually, making the effective rate of interest $(1 + 0.054)^1 - 1 = 0.054$ or 5.4%. This reinforces a fact we noted earlier:

When compounding occurs annually, the effective rate of interest is just the stated annual rate.

Alternative 2, 5.4% compounded annually, is slightly better than alternative 1, 5.25% compounded quarterly. What about alternative 3?

3. With this investment, Delmo gets 5.3%, compounded semiannually. The effective rate is $(1 + 0.053/2)^2 - 1 = 0.0537$, or 5.37%.

Alternative 2 is still best, and alternative 1 is the worst.   ◼

PRACTICE PROBLEM 8   Find the effective rates for each of the following investments: **(a)** 6.2% compounded monthly; **(b)** 6.5% compounded annually; **(c)** 6.3% compounded quarterly; **(d)** 6.4% compounded semiannually; **(e)** 6.0% compounded daily.

ANSWER(S)   **(a)** 6.38%   **(b)** 6.5%   **(c)** 6.45%   **(d)** 6.502% [slightly higher than the answer to **(b)**]   **(e)** 6.18%   ☐

Nominal Rates of Interest   When interest is paid more than once a year, the phrase "nominal rate of interest" is often used. In this context nominal means "in name only." For example, 6.4% compounded semiannually is often called a nominal rate of 6.4% payable semiannually, and denoted by the symbol $i^{(2)} = 6.4\%$. The "2" in the superscript is *not* an exponent, but a tag indicating that compounding occurs twice yearly. From now on, we shall make extensive use of this notation.

Converting the nominal rate of $i^{(2)} = 6.4\%$ to an effective rate yields $(1 + 0.064/2)^2 - 1 = 0.065$, or 6.5%. Thus, the rate is 6.4% in name only; the effective (annual) rate is 6.50%.

Similarly, $i^{(4)} = 6.3\%$ means that the quarterly rate of interest is $0.063/4$ and compounding occurs quarterly. Thus, we could have phrased the answer to part **(a)** of Practice Problem 8 in the following way: "The effective rate for $i^{(12)} = 6.2$ is 6.38%."

Although nominal rates can be used for other periods, the semiannual, quarterly, and monthly rates $i^{(2)}$, $i^{(4)}$, and $i^{(12)}$ are the most frequent and typical applications of "nominal" rates.

From Example 10 and Practice Problem 8, we can see that when compounding occurs more frequently than annually, the effective rate always exceeds the corresponding nominal interest rate, and that as the number of compoundings per year increases, the gap between the two widens.

EXERCISES 12.2

PRACTICING THE MOVES AND MANEUVERS

Exercises 56–64: Find the effective rate for the stated nominal rate.

56. $i^{(4)} = 0.06$
57. $i^{(2)} = 0.08$
58. $i^{(12)} = 0.09$
59. $i^{(2)} = 0.12$
60. $i^{(4)} = 0.10$
61. $i^{(2)} = 0.10$
62. $i^{(4)} = 0.05$
63. $i^{(12)} = 0.06$
64. $i^{(12)} = 0.10$

APPLYING THE CONCEPTS

65. If you earn 8% compounded annually, what is the effective rate of interest?
66. If you earn 7% compounded quarterly, what is the effective rate of interest?
67. If you invest money at 6.4% compounded daily will you be making more than someone who gets 6.6% compounded semiannually? Justify your answer.
68. Would you rather have an investment earning 10% compounded annually or 9.8% compounded monthly? Justify your answer.

69. Which investment actually yields more: **(a)** 9% compounded quarterly; or **(b)** 8.5% compounded weekly? Justify your answer.
70. Compare and rank the following investments:
    (a) 8% compounded annually
    (b) 7.8% compounded semiannually
    (c) 7.5% compounded quarterly
    (d) 7.4% compounded monthly
    (e) 7.3% compounded daily
71. Compare and rank the following investments:
    (a) $i^{(4)} = 6.4\%$ **(b)** $i^{(6)} = 6\%$

(c) $i^{(12)} = 5.4\%$ **(d)** $i^{(2)} = 6.6\%$

72. How much interest would you earn on a $4000 investment for two years under each of the following schemes?
    (a) 10% compounded annually
    (b) 9% compounded monthly

(c) 9.5% compounded daily
(d) 9.25% compounded quarterly

73. Which is a better investment—5% compounded daily or 5.3% compounded quarterly? Justify your answer.

Simple Discount

Exercises 74–76: Refer to the concept of "simple discount," which has not been discussed in the text. In simple interest calculations, interest is added to the loan amount and paid back on the due date; you have full use of the face value of the loan for the entire loan period. In simple discount, the interest is deducted from the face amount of the loan at the beginning of the loan term, and the face amount is then paid back at the end of the term. For example, on a one-year 10% simple discount loan for $1000, you would receive $1000 minus 10% of $1000, or $900 (called the loan proceeds). You would pay $1000 back after the year. The effective rate can be used to convert this to a corresponding simple interest rate. On the $1000 loan you received $900 at the beginning of the year. You paid $100 in interest, which, as a proportion of the money you received at the beginning of the year, is $100/900 \approx .111$, or 11.1%. (This is equivalent to using $I = P \cdot r \cdot t$ with $I = 100$, $P = \$900$, and $t = 1$ year; and then solving for r.) Thus, the effective rate for a 10% simple discount loan is actually 11.1%.

74. A 7% simple discount loan for $25,000 is paid back in five months.
    (a) How much did the recipient receive at the beginning of the loan period?
    (b) What is the effective rate of this loan?
75. A 12% simple discount loan for $10,000 is repaid in eight months.
    (a) How much did the borrower receive at the beginning of the loan period?
    (b) What effective rate of interest did the borrower pay?
76. A 9% simple discount loan for $4500 is repaid in two months.
    (a) How much cash did the borrower receive?
    (b) What effective rate of interest did the borrower pay?

12.3 PRESENT VALUE OF AN INVESTMENT   The future value formula $A = P[1 + i^{(m)}/m]^n$ tells how much P dollars will grow to in n periods when the interest rate is $i^{(m)}$, that is, annual rate of i with m compoundings a year. We normally use this formula as written to determine what a present investment of P dollars will be worth at some future time (after n compoundings). Dividing both sides of the formula by the compound accumulation factor $a^n = [1 + i^{(m)}/m]^n$ yields

$$P = \frac{A}{\left[1 + \dfrac{i^{(m)}}{m}\right]^n} = \frac{A}{a^n}$$

P is the amount that must be invested now, at a nominal rate $i^{(m)}$, in order to accumulate \$$A$ after n periods. This amount is called the *present value* of A dollars in n periods when $i^{(m)}$ is the nominal rate.

PRESENT VALUE OF AN AMOUNT A

> The **present value** of amount A n periods in the future when interest is computed at a nominal rate $i^{(m)}$ is the amount P that would have to be invested now at a nominal rate of $i^{(m)}$ in order to produce an accumulated value of A after n periods:
>
> $$P = \frac{A}{\left[1 + \dfrac{i^{(m)}}{m}\right]^n} = \frac{A}{a^n}$$

The present value formula, though merely a restatement of the future value formula, is of extraordinary importance. Try Example 12.

■ EXAMPLE 12

You hope to send your six-year-old to college. How much must you invest now at nominal rate $i^{(4)} = 8\%$, in order to have \$40,000 in 12 years?

SOLUTION   With quarterly compounding, there are $n = 48$ periods in 12 years.

$$P = 40{,}000/a^{48} = 40{,}000/(1 + 0.08/4)^{48} = 40{,}000/2.58707 = 15{,}461.50$$

Thus, $P = \$15{,}461.50$ has to be invested now at $i^{(4)} = 8\%$ to accumulate \$40,000 in 12 years. The relationship of the compound accumulation factor to present value and accumulated value should be emphasized:

PRESENT VALUE, FUTURE VALUE, AND THE COMPOUND ACCUMULATION FACTOR

> To determine how much an amount P will be worth in the future, multiply P by the compound accumulation factor. Conversely, to determine what investment has to be made now to accumulate a certain amount A in the future, divide that future value A by the compound accumulation factor.
>
> The compound accumulation factor describes what \$1 will grow to under the prescribed investment terms; its reciprocal tells us how much must be invested now at the given terms to yield one dollar at the future time.

■ EXAMPLE 13

You have $12,000 to invest for eight years, with quarterly compounding. What nominal rate of interest will you need in order that your $12,000 grow to $21,000 after the eight years?

SOLUTION

Using the formula that connects present value ($12,000) to future value ($21,000), we solve for i in the expression

$$21{,}000 = 12{,}000 \cdot a^{32}$$

Although i does not appear explicitly, it is contained in the compound accumulation factor a^{32} with $(1 + i/4)^{32}$. Dividing both sides by 12,000 gives $1.75 = a^{32}$. We can now determine i by looking for the compound accumulation factor 1.75 in Table II or by using logarithms. Instead, we shall solve this equation by substituting trial values for i into $a^{32} = (1 + i/4)^{32}$ until we find an i that makes $a^{32} = 1.75$.

For $i = 0.08$, we get $(1 + 0.08/4)^{32} = 1.8845$, greater than 1.75, indicating that we don't need a return as high as 8%. Trying $i = 0.07$, we have $(1 + 0.07/4)^{32} = 1.7422$, which is ever so slightly under the goal of 1.75. Continued trial and error shows that the required nominal rate i is, to four decimal places, 0.0706, or 7.06%. ■

Rather than repeatedly solving such expressions by trial and error, we give you the following formula:

NOMINAL INTEREST RATE NECESSARY FOR AMOUNT P TO ACCUMULATE TO AMOUNT A IN n PERIODS

If an investment amount P is to grow to a future value of A in n periods when compounding occurs m times annually, then the required nominal interest rate $i^{(m)}$ is

$$i^{(m)} = m \cdot \left[\left(\frac{A}{P} \right)^{1/n} - 1 \right]$$

Try your skill with this formula in the following problem.

PRACTICE PROBLEM 9

Suppose you have $5000 cash, and you hope to accumulate $8000 in three years with semiannual compounding.

(a) With semiannual compounding, what nominal rate $i^{(2)}$ is necessary?

(b) What is the effective rate of your calculated $i^{(2)}$ in part (a)?

(c) Rework part (a) if you need only $7000 in three years.

(d) What is the effective rate of your calculated $i^{(2)}$ in part (c)?

ANSWER(S)   (a) 16.30%   (b) 16.96%   (c) 11.54%   (d) 11.87%   □

In the following example, we introduce a little more complexity by varying the interest rate during the course of time.

■ EXAMPLE 14

You have $1000 in cash from the sale of kumquat futures, and you are looking for a good investment. In the morning paper you see two competing advertisements that look appealing.

NOW GET BONUS INTEREST!!	NO GIMMICKS HERE!
Invest $1000 at Fleashoe S&L and get bonus interest! Earn 9% compounded quarterly for 5 years, and we give you 1% BONUS INTEREST the first two years.	Invest $1000 at Robbyew S&L for five years and get a gimmick-free 9.5% compounded monthly. See us today. No one can beat our deal!

Where should you put your money for the five years? At Robbyew S&L, the situation is straightforward, so we examine their offer first. The future value of $1000 in five years is $1000 \cdot a^{60} = 1000 \cdot (1 + 0.095/12)^{60} \approx$ $1,605.01.

The Fleashoe investment requires two calculations: First determine the value of $1000 after two years at 10%, and then invest that amount for three years at 9%. After two years, the $1000 will have grown to $1000(1 + 0.10/4)^8 \approx$ $1,218.40. This amount is then invested for three years at 9%, compounded quarterly, giving you $1,218.40(1 + 0.09/4)^{12}$ $\approx$ $1591.29. Robbyew's gimmick-free 9.5% betters Fleashoe's bonus interest offer. ■

PRACTICE PROBLEM 10

(a) In Example 14, suppose Fleashoe S&L changed from quarterly to monthly compounding, with everything else the same. How much would your $1000 grow to in five years? (b) Rework part (a) under daily compounding.

ANSWER(S)   (a) $1597.06   (b) $1599.90   ☐

Is Compound Interest Always Better than Simple Interest?

There is a strong temptation to answer with a resounding yes, but this would be incorrect! To illustrate, suppose you have put $1000 into a savings account which pays 6% compounded annually. You remove your money in six months. How much interest will you have earned? Because of annual compounding, a six-month period is only 1/2 period. The accumulated value will then be $1000(1.06)^{1/2} \approx$ $1029.56. You will have earned $29.56 compound interest. If you were earning simple interest, your accumulated value would be $1000 \cdot [1 + (0.06) \cdot (1/2)] =$

$1030. You will have earned $30 simple interest. When the investment period is less than the interest conversion period, compound interest pays less than simple interest!

For this reason, financial institutions will often give you the benefit of the doubt on fractional periods. For example, suppose you invest $1000 at 7% compounded annually for three years and three months. Many institutions will pay you compound interest for the three-year period and simple interest for the last three months. Under this scheme, you would earn $1000 \cdot (1.07)^3 \approx \$1225.04$ in the first three years. During the last three months you would earn an additional $1225.04 \cdot (0.07) \cdot (0.25) \approx \$21.44$ in simple interest. You would end up then with $1225.04 + \$21.44 = \$1246.48$. With compound interest paid for the full period, you would accumulate only $1000 \cdot (1.07)^{13/4} \approx \$1245.94$.

EXERCISES 12.3

PRACTICING THE MOVES AND MANEUVERS

Exercises 77–90: Find the present value of the indicated investment.

77. $5000 at 9% compounded annually in two years
78. $6500 at 7% compounded quarterly in three years
79. $10,000 at 8% compounded annually in four years
80. $3200 at 9% compounded monthly in two years
81. $5000 at 6% compounded quarterly in five years
82. $200 at 8% compounded daily in ten years
83. $1000 at 12% compounded hourly in four years
84. $100,000 at 10% compounded daily in 20 years
85. $1,000,000 at 8% compounded annually in 25 years
86. $1,000,000 at 9% compounded annually in 25 years
87. $1,000,000 at 12% compounded annually in 25 years
88. $1,000,000 at 9% compounded quarterly in 25 years
89. $1,000,000 at 9% compounded daily in 25 years
90. $1,000,000 at 20% compounded daily in 15 years

Exercises 91–97: Determine the nominal interest rate necessary for the given amount to accumulate to $10,000 in the stated number of compounding periods.

91. $5000 in three years with quarterly compounding
92. $3000 in six years with semiannual compounding
93. $2500 in eight years with monthly compounding
94. $7000 in one year with weekly compounding
95. $8000 in one year with annual compounding
96. $1000 in ten years with annual compounding
97. $200 in 20 years with semiannual compounding

APPLYING THE CONCEPTS

98. You and your wife will buy a new car four years from now at an estimated cost of $14,000. If you wish to pay for your new car by investing a lump sum today at 8% compounded quarterly, how much will you need to invest?

99. How much do you need to invest now in order to have $5000 in four years if your investment earns 10% compounded annually?

100. If you invest $7500 for 8 years at 6% compounded quarterly, how much interest will you earn?

101. What is the present value of $10,000 in 15 years if money earns 8% compounded semiannually?

102. The state of Washington issues education bonds which pay compound annual interest. If $417 invested now will return $1000 in 12 years, what is the nominal annual interest rate being paid?

103. If a $387 investment grows to $1000 when compounded annually for 14 years, what is the nominal interest rate?

104. How many years would it take for $500 to quadruple if your money earns 6% compounded annually?

105. Some of today's best mutual funds earn about 20% compounded annually. How much would you need to invest in such a fund if you wish to have $25,000 in 10 years?

106. If a mutual fund promises 15% compounded annually, how much would you need to invest now in order to have $50,000 in 25 years?

107. In order for $200 to grow to $5,000 in 10 years when compounding occurs annually, what must the nominal rate of interest be?

12.4 TIME DIAGRAMS AND EQUATIONS OF VALUE

We live in an inflationary society. With rare exceptions, an item that now costs $10 will cost more than $10 a year from now.

■ EXAMPLE 15

Suppose your uncle offers you as a graduation present the choice between taking $100 now or $120 when you graduate in two years. Which should you choose?

SOLUTION

A fundamental principle of interest theory says that

two or more amounts of money payable at different time periods cannot properly be compared unless these amounts are adjusted to the same point in time.

This common time is called the **comparison date.** Thus, in deciding between the two options offered by your uncle, you must value both options now, or after two years, or, as we shall see, at any other single time. A helpful device for making such valuations is a *time diagram* or time line.

A **time diagram** is a line on which time units are marked, and amounts are placed at appropriate times: amounts paid out will be written on top of the line and amounts received underneath the line. The comparison date will be indicated by a diamond (♦).

If, for example, you choose two years hence as a comparison date, then you need to determine how much $100 now will accumulate to in two years, and compare that to $120. In making this determination, you check various financial institutions and decide that your best investment is a two-year "CD" (Certificate of Deposit), which pays you 8% compounded annually. The future value or accumulated value of $100 in two years at 8% compounded annually is $100(1 + 0.08)^2 = \$116.64$. Clearly, you are better off waiting until graduation; you will come out $3.36 ahead by so doing. (*Note:* In this example, there were no "amounts paid out.")

"Amounts received," time-adjusted to the comparison date $t = 2$ years from now, are shown in the time diagram of Figure 12.1.

Figure 12.1
Time diagram with $t = 2$ years as the comparison date

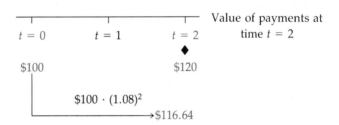

Could we have used "now" as our comparison date and achieved the same result? Let's check. By using "now" as our comparison date, $100 needs no time adjustment. You need, however, to adjust the $120 received in two years to its present value. Since you have decided that 8% compounded annually is a reasonable return, we look for the present value of $120 in two years if money earns 8% compounded annually. Substitute $A = 120$, $i = 0.08$, and $m = 2$ into the present value formula $P = A/(1 + i)^m$, and solve for P. This produces $P = 120/(1.08)^2 = \$102.88$. Since it would require $102.88 now to have $120 in two years, the option of waiting two years for $120 is better. A time diagram with "now" as a comparison date is shown in Figure 12.2.

Figure 12.2
Time diagram with "now" as the comparison date

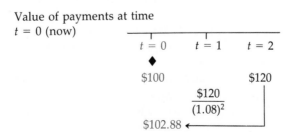

With "now" as a comparison date, the two alternatives differed by $102.88 − $100 = $2.88. With "two years later" as a comparison date, the difference was $120 − $116.64 = $3.36. Why the difference? There really isn't a difference; these amounts are equivalent when they are compared at the same date! The time diagram below illustrates this: the $2.88 difference "now" accumulates to $3.36 two years later.

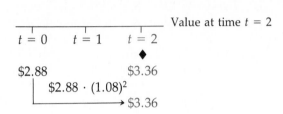

PRACTICE PROBLEM 11   In Example 15, suppose you could earn 9% compounded annually instead of 8%. Is it better to wait two years and get $120, or to take $100 now?

ANSWER(S)   Wait; in two years, $100 at 9% accumulates to $118.81.   ☐

PRACTICE PROBLEM 12   Approximately what interest rate, compounded annually, would make $100 now the equivalent of $120 in two years? Use your calculator and experiment, or refer to the discussion preceding Practice Problem 9.

ANSWER(S)   9.54%.   ☐

Equations of Value   With more complex problems, where there is a sequence of amounts received and/or paid out, we often write an equation that reflects the values of all amounts at a comparison date. Such an equation is called an **equation of value.** Present value and future value give us a way of writing such equations of value that adjust differing amounts to a common comparison date. We illustrate these ideas in the following example.

■ EXAMPLE 16   Just as you have decided to take the $120 at graduation in two years, your uncle offers you a third alternative. You can have $25 now, $50 in two years, and $50 one year later. What is the best alternative? (Money grows at 8% compounded annually.)

SOLUTION   We shall use two years from now as our comparison date. With this date, no time adjustment is necessary on the $120, because it is paid on this date. The sequence of three payments, however, needs careful handling. The equation of value here is quite simple. In words:

the value two years from now of the three payments equals the sum of the three separate payment values on that date.

The $25 now will accumulate to 25 · (1.08)² = $29.16 on the comparison date. The $50 payment in two years needs no time adjustment. The final payment of $50, made in three years, needs to be "brought back" one year to its present value on the comparison date; its value then is $P = 50/(1.08)^1 \approx \$46.30$. Table 12.5 and Figure 12.3 both illustrate these three separate payments.

Table 12.5

Payment	Date of Payment	Value Two Years from Now	
$25	Now	$25(1.08)^2 =$	$29.16
$50	In two years	$=$	$50
$50	In three years	$50/(1.08)^1 =$	$46.30

Total value of three payments in two years = $125.46

Adding the values of these three payments on the comparison date gives $29.16 + $50 + $46.30 = $125.46. This exceeds the one-time payment of $120 made on the comparison date, so the new, three-payment option is best. The time diagram adjusting each payment to the comparison date of two years from now is shown in Figure 12.3. ■

Figure 12.3
Time diagram for three-payment option

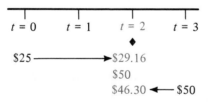

Let's spice things up a little! Try the following example.

■ EXAMPLE 17

In return for your payments to him of $300 after three years, and $700 after eight years, a man agrees to pay you $400 immediately, and make a final, "fair and reasonable" payment after four years. Find the amount of the final payment if money earns 7%, compounded semiannually.

SOLUTION

In Figure 12.4, we show the time diagram with your payments made above the line and amounts you receive below the line. The final payment to be given you in four years will be denoted by x. We first adopt an arbitrary comparison date of two years from now.

Figure 12.4
Time diagram for Example 17

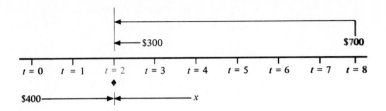

The equation of value is:

$$\begin{bmatrix} \textbf{Value at comparison date} \\ \textbf{(}t = 2\textbf{) of payments received} \end{bmatrix} = \begin{bmatrix} \textbf{Value at comparison date} \\ \textbf{of payments made} \end{bmatrix}$$

Payments Received	Value at Comparison Date	Payments Made	Value at Comparison Date
$400	$400 \cdot (1.035)^4$	$300	$300/(1.035)^2$
$x	$x/(1.035)^4$	$700	$700/(1.035)^{12}$

Substituting these numbers into the equation of value and solving for x yields the following succession of equations:

$$400 \cdot (1.035)^4 + \frac{x}{(1.035)^4} = \frac{300}{(1.035)^2} + \frac{700}{(1.035)^{12}}$$

$$459.01 \quad + \frac{x}{1.147523} = 280.05 + 463.25$$

which leads to

$$\frac{x}{1.147523} = 284.29$$

so that $x = \$326.23$. Thus, you should receive a payment of $326.23 in four years.   ∎

Using a Different Comparison Date   What if we had used a date other than "two years from now" as comparison date? In particular, suppose we use $t = 8$ years from now as comparison date. Would we obtain the same value of x? Let's check. Once again, we write an equation of value

$$\begin{bmatrix} \textbf{Value at } t = 8 \\ \textbf{of payments received} \end{bmatrix} = \begin{bmatrix} \textbf{Value at } t = 8 \\ \textbf{of payments made} \end{bmatrix}$$

The "new" time line, with comparison time $t = 8$ years from now, is shown in Figure 12.5.

Figure 12.5
Time diagram with $t = 8$ years from now as comparison date

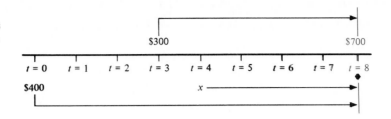

Payments Received	Value at Comparison Date	Payments Made	Value at Comparison Date
$400	$400 \cdot (1.035)^{16}$	$300	$300 \cdot (1.035)^{10}$
$x	$x \cdot (1.035)^{8}$	$700	700

Substituting the appropriate numbers into our equation of value leads to the following:

$t = 8$ years from now

$$400 \cdot (1.035)^{16} + x \cdot (1.035)^{8} = 300 \cdot (1.035)^{10} + 700$$

Before performing further arithmetic, compare this equation with the preceding equation of value at time $t = 2$, reproduced below:

$t = 2$ years from now

$$400 \cdot (1.035)^{4} + \frac{x}{(1.035)^{4}} = \frac{300}{(1.035)^{2}} + \frac{700}{(1.035)^{12}}$$

The equation of value for $t = 8$ can be obtained from that for $t = 2$ by simply multiplying all terms in the equation for $t = 2$ by $(1.035)^{12}$. Upon reflection, this should seem reasonable: time $t = 8$ years is $6 \cdot 2 = 12$ compounding periods later than $t = 2$. Hence, any amount P at time $t = 2$ will have grown to $P \cdot (1.035)^{12}$ at time $t = 8$.

When using compound interest,[3] it is always the case that

an equation of value at one time is simply a multiple of the equation of value at a different time.

This leads us to the conclusion that

when establishing an equation of value, the comparison date will not affect computations: the solution for x will be the same regardless of the comparison time used.

---

[3] When using simple interest, this result is not true. The value of x will change depending upon the comparison date used. This fact, along with our earlier comment that all funds should be productive, is a strong argument for considering only compound interest.

This fact does not mean that you should arbitrarily choose a comparison date. Be on the lookout for a comparison date that minimizes arithmetic involved.

We conclude this section by working Problem 5 proposed at the beginning of this chapter.

■ EXAMPLE 18

Exactly one year ago, you borrowed $6000 at 10% compounded annually for three years, and, in a separate transaction, borrowed an additional $10,000 for five years at 11% compounded annually. In both cases, you were to repay the principal and accumulated interest with a single payment after the loan period. You decide to combine the two loans into one, at 10.5% interest compounded annually, with a single payment due three years from now. How much will you owe in three years?

SOLUTION

First we adjust both loans to a comparison date of now—one year after they were begun. On the $6000 note, you owe the bank $6000 \cdot (1 + 0.10)^1$ = $6600. On the $10,000 note, you owe the bank $10,000 \cdot (1 + 0.11)^1$ = $11,100. The combined indebtedness now is $6600 + $11,100 = $17,700. The future value of $17,700 when you pay off the loan in three years, at 10.5% compounded annually, is found to be $17,700 \cdot (1.105)^3 \approx$ $23,881.42. ■

PRACTICE PROBLEM 13

In Example 18, you will have paid a total of $23,881.42 − $16,000 = $7381.42 in interest for the four-year period. Suppose you had borrowed all $16,000 in one transaction for four years, at a compound annual interest rate. What would the rate have to be in order that you pay the same amount of interest?

ANSWER(S)   10.53%.   □

EXERCISES 12.4

APPLYING THE CONCEPTS

108. If you value money at 10% compounded annually, would you rather have an immediate payment of $1000, or $500 now and $600 in two years?

109. Solve Exercise 108 if you value money at 8% compounded annually.

110. An investment company, in need of instant cash, offers investors the following deal: Give

the investment company $500 now, and they will return $150 a year for the next four years.
  (a) If you value money at 8% compounded annually, is this a wise investment?
  (b) Work part **(a)** if you value money at 7% compounded annually.
111. An insurance company offers you five annual payments of $250 beginning one year from now. To receive this money, you must give them $1000 now.
  (a) If you value money at 6% compounded annually, should you invest with the insurance company?
  (b) If you value money at 7% compounded annually, should you invest?
112. If you value money at 8% compounded quarterly, would you like the following scheme? You give a person $1000 now, and he gives you

$400 in six months, and then $250 six months later, and then $500 in an additional six months.
113. You see the following advertisement in the paper: "Give us $5,000 now, and we will return $1000 a year for the next seven years." Is this a good investment if you value money at 10% compounded annually?
114. You give your best friend $1000 in return for $200 after each of the next eight years. Have you struck a good bargain if you value money at 8% compounded annually?
115. A finance company promises to give you $2800 in two years if you give them $600 now and three payments of $600 made 6, 12, and 18 months from now. If you value money at 6% compounded semiannually, should you accept the offer?

12.5 ANNUITIES: FUTURE VALUES AND SINKING FUNDS

In previous sections we have solved problems like the following: "If you invest $1000 at 7% compounded annually, how much will you have in eight years?" This "future value" problem is a reasonable and useful calculation, but most people don't save money in exactly that fashion. They save a little bit at a time. Thus, problems like the following are more realistic: "If I put $200 in the bank every six months at 5% compounded semiannually, how much will I have after two years?" This is an example of an *annuity*. When most people hear the word *annuity*, they think of retirement, and in particular of receiving a fixed monthly amount for a certain period, which could be the rest of their lives. This is but one example of an annuity. The concept of annuity, however, is much more general:

ANNUITY

> An **annuity** is a sequence of equal[4] payments made (or received) at regular time intervals. The time from the beginning of the first payment period to the end of the last payment period is called the **term** of the annuity. We consider only **ordinary annuities**, where payments are made at the end of each period.

[4] An annuity does not have to consist of equal payments but in this book we shall restrict ourselves to equal payment annuities.

An annuity can represent not only payments made, but also payments received. As a consumer, you can be on either end of an annuity. Annuities where you pay are home mortgages, car loans, and even rent payments. These are not usually referred to as annuities, but they clearly satisfy our concept of "equal payments made at regular time periods."

Let's investigate a simple annuity in order to discover the mechanics involved.

■ EXAMPLE 19

(*Mentioned at the beginning of this section.*) If at the end of each six-month period you deposit $200 into an account earning $i^{(2)} = 8\%$, how much will you have accumulated after two years?

SOLUTION

The period for this annuity is six months. We seek the future value or accumulated value of the annuity: the worth of this sequence or "stream" of payments and the interest accumulated after the two-year term. We first construct a time diagram, with comparison date at $t = 24$ months, placing the payments after each six-month period.

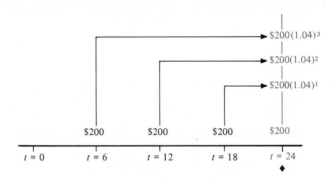

The last $200 has had no time to earn any interest: its worth at the comparison date is just $200. The equation of value is

"Accumulated value A of the annuity in two years = sum of the individual payment values two years from now."

On the comparison date of 24 months from now, we have

$$A = \text{Value in 2 years} = 200(1.04)^3 + 200(1.04)^2 + 200(1.04)^1 + 200$$
$$= \$200[(1.04)^3 + (1.04)^2 + (1.04)^1 + 1]$$
$$= \$200[1.124864 + 1.0816 + 1.04 + 1]$$
$$= \$200[4.246464]$$
$$= \$849.29 \qquad ■$$

Annuity Computation Pattern

The calculations needed in valuing the Example 19 annuity were nothing more than a sequence of future value problems designed to bring all contributions to the end of the term. Though not difficult, such calculations are tedious. We now know A, the accumulated value of the annuity, but by being clever, and observing a special pattern, we can avoid repeating such calculations. To see how, we start with the original "sum of payment values two years from now" equation:

$$A = 200(1.04)^3 + 200(1.04)^2 + 200(1.04)^1 + 200$$

Multiply both sides by 1.04, then subtract the original equation from the result:

Subtract bottom equation from top

$$1.04A = 200(1.04)^4 + 200(1.04)^3 + 200(1.04)^2 + 200(1.04)$$

$$\underline{A = \qquad\qquad\qquad 200(1.04)^3 + 200(1.04)^2 + 200(1.04)^1 + 200}$$

$$0.04A = 200(1.04)^4 \qquad\qquad\qquad\qquad\qquad\qquad\qquad\qquad - 200$$

Solving this last equation for A, the future value of the annuity, gives

$$A = 200 \cdot \left[\frac{(1.04)^4 - 1}{0.04} \right] = \text{PMT} \cdot \frac{a^4 - 1}{i_p}$$

The specific result of Example 19 is easy to generalize:

FUTURE VALUE OF AN ORDINARY ANNUITY

The future value A of an ordinary annuity consisting of n payments of PMT dollars, each earning interest at a nominal interest rate of $i^{(m)}$, is given by

$$A = \text{PMT} \cdot \left[\frac{a^n - 1}{i_p} \right]$$

where:

PMT is the payment made m times annually

$i_p = \dfrac{i^{(m)}}{m}$ is the interest rate per period

a^n is the n-period compound accumulation factor

In the expression above, PMT is not three separate symbols, but simply a convenient abbreviation of "payment." The multiplier of PMT (the term in brackets) is symbolized by $s_{\overline{n}|\,i_p}$, pronounced "s angle n at rate i_p." The value of $s_{\overline{n}|\,i_p}$ has the following meaning: it is the future value of a sequence of n payments of \$1, each earning interest at the nominal rate of $i^{(m)}$, on the date of the last payment. Table III in the Appendix gives values of $s_{\overline{n}|\,i_p}$ for various combinations of i_p (interest rate per period) and n.

EXAMPLE 20

(*From the beginning of this chapter.*) You and your spouse start a new car fund by depositing $200 at the end of each month at 6% interest, compounded monthly, for the next four years.

(a) After four years, how much will you have?

(b) What interest rate would each deposit have to earn, compounded monthly, in order that you have $14,000?

SOLUTION

(a) This is an ordinary annuity with PMT = $200, $n = 48$, $m = 12$ compoundings per year, and $i^{(12)} = 0.06$, so that $i_p = i^{(m)}/m$, the interest per monthly period, is $0.06/12 = 0.005$. The compound accumulation factor for 48 periods is $a^{48} = (1 + 0.005)^{48} = 1.2704892$. Substituting into the Future Value of an Ordinary Annuity formula gives

$$A = 200 \cdot \left[\frac{1.2704892 - 1}{0.005} \right] \approx \$10{,}819.57$$

Note: We can also work part **(a)** by using Table III, where we find that the bracketed term in the Future Value of an Annuity formula is $s_{\overline{48}|0.005} = 54.09783$, so that

$$A = 200 \cdot s_{\overline{48}|0.005} = 200 \cdot 54.09783 \approx \$10{,}819.57$$

For certain values of i_p (interest rate per period), s is not tabled, so from now on we shall use the Future Value of an Annuity formula in our calculations. Whenever possible, use Table III to check your calculations. Your answers may differ slightly due to rounding.

(b) Since 48 $200 payments at $i^{(12)} = 0.06$ do not produce anywhere near the desired $14,000, $i^{(12)}$ will have to be much more than 0.06. To determine exactly how much more, we substitute $A = 14{,}000$ and try to approximate $i^{(12)}$ with the calculator. First, try $i^{(12)} = 0.12$, giving

$$200 \cdot \left[\frac{1.61223 - 1}{0.01} \right] \approx 200 \cdot (61.223) \approx \$12{,}244.60$$

which is still not enough. Try $i^{(12)} = 0.15$, which makes the interest rate $0.15/12 = 0.0125$ per month. This gives

$$200 \cdot \left[\frac{1.81535 - 1}{0.0125} \right] \approx 200 \cdot (65.228) \approx \$13{,}045.60$$

which, once again, is shy of the desired $14,000. Try $i^{(12)} = 0.18$, which is $0.18/12 = 0.015$ per month. This gives

$$200 \cdot \left[\frac{2.04348 - 1}{0.015} \right] \approx 200 \cdot (69.565) \approx \$13{,}913.04$$

This is close enough for our purposes; to accumulate $14,000 after only four years with $200 per month deposits requires an interest rate of slightly more than $i^{(12)} = 18\%$. (Actual is 18.29%.)   ■

■ EXAMPLE 21

Suppose you need $14,000 in four years, but you cannot find an investment paying the necessary rate of $i^{(12)} = 0.18$. In fact, $i^{(12)} = 0.08$ is the best rate available. Clearly, you will need deposits exceeding $200 monthly. What monthly deposit will be required?

SOLUTION

Our "Future Value of an Ordinary Annuity" equation allows us to solve for the future value of the annuity when we know $i^{(m)}$, n, and PMT. Here, we know the desired future value A is $14,000, $i^{(12)} = 0.08$, and $n = 48$, but the monthly payment PMT is unknown. $i^{(12)} = 0.08$ means that the monthly rate is $i_p = 0.08/12 \approx 0.006667$. Calculating $a^{48} = (1.006667)^{48} = 1.37569$ and substituting into our future-value equation gives

$$14{,}000 = \text{PMT} \cdot \left[\frac{1.37569 - 1}{0.006667} \right]$$

or

$$14{,}000 \approx \text{PMT} \cdot 56.3503$$

Dividing both sides by 56.3503 yields PMT $\approx$ $248.45 as the required monthly deposit for four years.   ■

The calculations made in Examples 20 and 21 illustrate a sinking fund.

SINKING FUND

> A **sinking fund** is a specific amount of money to be accumulated at a given date by a sequence of regular payments. In other words, the sinking fund is generated by an annuity.

There is no need to give a special formula for a sinking fund; simply substitute the desired fund amount for A in the equation for the accumulated value of an annuity, and then solve for the payment PMT, just as we did in Example 21, or divide the desired future amount by the value of $s_{\overline{n}|i_p}$ from Table III.

PRACTICE PROBLEM 14

If you finance an annuity by making $500 payments semiannually, and this fund earns interest at $i^{(2)} = 0.09$, what is the accumulated value of this annuity in **(a)** three years? **(b)** five years? **(c)** ten years?

ANSWER(S)   **(a)** $3358.45   **(b)** $6144.10   **(c)** $15,685.71   □

PRACTICE PROBLEM 15   You need a $20,000 down payment in five years in order to buy a house. If you can earn interest at a rate of $i^{(4)} = 0.10$, what regular quarterly deposit is necessary?

ANSWER(S) $782.94   ☐

EXERCISES 12.5

PRACTICING THE MOVES AND MANEUVERS

Exercises 116–124: Find the future value of each of the following ordinary annuities.

116. $100 deposited at the end of each month for 24 months with interest figured at $i^{(12)} = 0.08$
117. $50 deposited at the end of each week for the next three years with interest figured weekly at $i^{(52)} = 0.08$
118. $200 deposited at the end of each quarter for the next ten years with interest figured at $i^{(4)} = 0.08$
119. $1000 at the end of each year for the next ten years if the account earns interest at 10% compounded annually
120. $250 at the end of each six-month period for the next ten years with money earning $i^{(2)} = 0.08$

121. $10 deposited into an account at the end of each day for the next five years with money earning $i^{(360)} = 0.08$
122. $5000 deposited at the end of each year for the next 12 years into an account earning 8% compound annual interest
123. $400 deposited at the end of each month for the next 20 years into an account earning interest at a rate of 11% compounded monthly
124. $1 deposited into an account at the end of each hour for the next three years, with money earning interest at 10% compounded hourly

APPLYING THE CONCEPTS

125. You establish a sinking fund by depositing $100 per quarter into an account earning 9% compounded quarterly. What is the value of this fund at the end of (a) three years? (b) five years? (c) ten years?
126. What should the annual deposit be into a fund earning 10% compounded annually in order that $4000 be accumulated at the end of five years?
127. In Exercise 126, suppose the fund earns only 8% interest compounded annually. What is the necessary annual deposit now?
128. A small company estimates that its laser printer will have to be replaced in five years. The estimated cost at that time is $2500.
    (a) A single deposit is to be made now into an

account earning 10% compounded quarterly, for the purpose of buying the new printer in five years. How much will the deposit have to be?
    (b) Suppose that instead of the one-time deposit of part (a), the firm decides to make deposits at the end of each of the next five years into an account earning 10% compounded annually. How much should the annual deposit be?
129. Barb and Doug are making monthly savings deposits toward the down payment on a home. Barb, a fledgling actuary, should be able to figure exactly how much is necessary in order that they accumulate $10,000 in three years. She is too busy, however, to do the calculations, and

they decide instead to put $250 a month into an account earning interest at a nominal rate of $i^{(12)} = 0.06$.

(a) Will they have enough at the end of three years? Justify your answer.

(b) What should their monthly deposits be to reach their $10,000 goal?

Exercises 131 and 132: Should be assigned as a unit.

131. To young adults the idea of tax deferring funds for retirement does not usually seem that important. Suppose Lori puts $2000 a year into an Individual Retirement Account (IRA) with a mutual fund that has a long history of earning 15% compounded annually. Beginning on December 31st of the year in which she turns 22, Lori does this for ten consecutive years, making total deposits of $20,000. She then makes no more deposits, but her money remains with this mutual fund which continues to earn 15% compounded annually. How much will Lori have accumulated when she retires on December 31st of the year in which she turns 60?

132. Krista, who works with Lori, does not begin saving for retirement until she is 30. Beginning on December 31st of the year in which she turns 30, she makes annual deposits of $2000 into the same mutual fund as Lori. Unlike Lori, she does not stop at the end of ten years, but continues through December 31st of the year in which she reaches 60, investing $31 \cdot \$2000 = \$62,000$. Assuming that this mutual fund continues to earn 15% compounded annually, determine how much Krista will have accumulated on December 31st of the year in which she reaches 60.

133. At the end of each quarter, Bill Bryan puts $500 into his IRA, which earns 8% compounded quarterly. If Bill does this each quarter for 25 years, how much will he have at the end of the 25 years?

134. Delmo's cousin Butane is saving his allowance for a trip to Disneyland. At the end of each month, he puts $8 into a credit union account that earns 6% compounded monthly. How much will he have at the end of four years?

130. Lisa, a 23-year-old Pacific Rim consultant, wishes to retire at age 50. To support herself at that time, she needs to accumulate $400,000. If her retirement plan accumulates at a rate of $i^{(2)} = 8\%$, how much should her regular semiannual deposit be in order to achieve her goal?

135. Rich "Wombat the Windsurfer" Minifie saves $100 at the end of each month in order to buy wind-surfing equipment. If his investment earns 9% compounded monthly, how much will he have accumulated at the end of **(a)** three years? **(b)** four years? **(c)** five years?

136. Bill Small needs $3,000 in four years to buy a home gym. At the end of each month he plans to make monthly deposits into a fund earning 6% compounded monthly. How much should be set aside each month?

137. Alyssa and John are saving for a mountain cabin. If they save $200 at the end of each month for the next ten years, how much will they have if their investment earns

(a) 8% compounded monthly?

(b) 9% compounded monthly?

(c) 10% compounded monthly?

(d) 11% compounded monthly?

138. Which of the following two investments will produce the most in five years?

(a) $200 at the end of each month for three years in a fund earning 8% compounded monthly. (No contributions will be made in the fourth and fifth years, but money invested in the first three years will continue to earn interest during the last two years.)

(b) $150 at the end of each month for the entire five years in a fund earning 8% compounded monthly.

12.6 MORE ON ANNUITIES: AMORTIZATIONS

Amortization

One way to repay a loan is with a single payment (a "lump sum" or "balloon" payment) at the end of the loan period. The borrower can use a sinking fund annuity to accumulate the necessary amount at the end of the loan term. A second way is to allocate a fixed amount to principal each payment and also include interest earned since the preceding payment. A $5000 loan, for example, could be repaid by paying $1000 a month on principal, plus the interest on the unpaid balance since the preceding payment. If the interest rate was 12%, then the first month's payment would be $1000 plus one month's (simple) interest on the beginning balance of $5000. This makes the first payment $1000 + $5000(0.12)(1/12) = $1000 + $5000(0.01) = $1050. The second month's payment would be $1000 + $4000(0.01) = $1040. Payments would continue in this manner as shown in Table 12.6.

Table 12.6

Payment #	Paid on Principal	Paid on Interest	Total Payment	Balance after Payment
1	$1000	$50	$1050	$4000
2	$1000	$40	$1040	$3000
3	$1000	$30	$1030	$2000
4	$1000	$20	$1020	$1000
5	$1000	$10	$1010	$0

This is a perfectly acceptable means of discharging a loan, but a more popular method is **amortization**, where the borrower repays the lender by making equal regular payments that include both principal and interest. The loan payments thus form an annuity. Common examples of such amortizations are house and car payments. There is a major difference, however, between a sinking fund annuity and an amortization annuity: in the sinking fund, you need, and are accumulating, a fund for the future. On the other hand, when you buy a car or a house, your debt is incurred at the time of the loan—the debt is a present value. The operative difference between a sinking fund annuity and an amortization annuity can be expressed by a single word: *time*. Having a certain amount now is worth considerably more than having that same amount 30 years from now. In Section 12.5, we developed a procedure for determining the appropriate annuity payment when we needed a certain amount in the future. What happens if we need the money now, but will pay the loan off over time? We illustrate in Example 22.

■ EXAMPLE 22

You borrow $80,000 to buy a house. You want to pay this loan off by making regular monthly payments at 12% compounded monthly for 30 years. How much will your monthly payment be?

SOLUTION   If you didn't need the $80,000 until the end of the 30 years, you would use the "Future Value of an Annuity" relation from Section 12.6, setting the future value equal to 80,000 and determining the monthly payment necessary to produce $80,000 in 30 years. The problem is that you will get the $80,000 now. Even so, you can still use "future value" thinking by time-adjusting the present value of $80,000 to its accumulated (future) value in 30 years at $i^{(12)} = 0.12$. See Figure 12.6.

Figure 12.6
Time-adjusting $80,000 to 30 years in the future

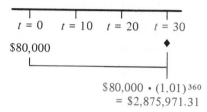

$$\$80,000 \cdot (1.01)^{360}$$
$$= \$2,875,971.31$$

Thus, the future value of $80,000 in 30 years at $i^{(12)} = 0.12$ is $2,875,971.31. This is the amount the lender would have in 30 years if he invested the $80,000 at $i^{(12)} = 0.12$. In lending the $80,000 to you, he should expect no less. Thus, the proper loan payment is the constant amount paid monthly into an annuity in order to accumulate $2,875,971.31 after 30 years. We determine the necessary payment by substituting this amount into our future value of an annuity formula and solving for PMT.

The arithmetic is as follows:

$$2,875,971.31 = \text{PMT} \cdot \frac{a^n - 1}{i_p} \qquad \text{formula for future value of annuity}$$

$$2,875,971.31 = \text{PMT} \cdot \frac{(1.01)^{360} - 1}{0.01} \qquad \text{substitute } n = 360 \text{ and } i_p = 0.01$$

$$2,875,971.31 = \text{PMT} \cdot 3494.9641$$

Dividing both sides by 3494.9641 gives PMT = $822.89.   ◼

Study Example 22 carefully, until you understand that the following three investment options are equivalent:

1. Having $80,000 cash now and being able to invest it at $i^{(12)} = 0.12$.

2. Having a lump sum payment of $2,875,971.31 in 30 years.

3. Having someone pay you $822.89 at the end of each month for the next 30 years and investing each payment immediately at 12% compounded monthly.

We express these ideas in yet another way: put $80,000 now into an account earning $i^{(12)} = 0.12$. Ignore this account for 30 years (360 months), and it will grow to $\$80,000 \cdot a^{360} = (1 + 0.12/12)^{360} = 80,000 \cdot$

35.94964 = \$2,875,971.31. Alternatively, \$80,000 invested at $i^{(12)} = 0.12$ would allow you to take regular monthly withdrawals of \$822.89 for 360 months before exhausting your account.

Note that the accumulated value in 30 years, \$2,875,971.31, is simply the present value of \$80,000 times the 30-year compound accumulation factor: $\$80,000 \cdot (1 + 0.01)^{360} = \$80,000 \cdot 35.94964$.

In solving Example 22, we employed the following equation of value:

$$\left[\begin{array}{c} \textbf{future value of } P \textbf{ at the end} \\ \textbf{of } n \textbf{ interest periods} \end{array} \right] = \left[\begin{array}{c} \textbf{accumulated value of } n \\ \textbf{payments of size PMT} \end{array} \right]$$

From the lender's point of view, we express this as:

$$\left[\begin{array}{c} \textbf{what the lender would} \\ \textbf{get by investing lump} \\ \textbf{sum } P \textbf{ now for } n \textbf{ interest} \\ \textbf{periods at nominal } i^{(m)} \end{array} \right] = \left[\begin{array}{c} \textbf{the future value of your string} \\ \textbf{of } n \textbf{ regular payments of size PMT} \\ \textbf{to the lender if he can invest each} \\ \textbf{payment at a nominal rate of } i^{(m)} \end{array} \right]$$

Expressing this relationship with symbols gives us:

FUNDAMENTAL ANNUITY RELATIONSHIP BETWEEN PRESENT VALUE *P*, ACCUMULATED VALUE *A*, AND PAYMENT SIZE PMT

$$A = a^n \cdot P = \text{PMT} \cdot \frac{a^n - 1}{i_p}$$

This relationship is identical to the "Future Value of an Annuity" form given in Section 12.5, but with one important addition: by inserting $A = a^n \cdot P$, we are emphasizing the connection between the present value P, the future value A, and the compound accumulation factor for the n periods of the annuity. Henceforth:

to answer any question regarding an annuity, whether it be to determine the present value *P*, the accumulated (future) value *A*, or the required payment, PMT, our first step is to write this fundamental relation. We then solve for the desired quantity.

To be sure you understand the "Relationship," try Practice Problems 16 and 17.

PRACTICE PROBLEM 16   Consider a stream of 36 monthly payments of \$50 earning $i^{(12)} = 0.06$. Find **(a)** the present value of this annuity, and **(b)** the future value.

ANSWER(S)   **(a)** \$1643.55;   **(b)** \$1966.81   ☐

Practice Problem 16 shows that the following three investment alternatives are equivalent:

1. Having $1643.55 now and being able to invest it for 36 months at $i^{(12)} = 0.06$.

2. Having $1966.81 paid to you 36 months from now.

3. Having a $50 per month "allowance" for the next 36 months if you can invest your allowance at $i^{(12)} = 0.06$.

PRACTICE PROBLEM 17   Consider a stream of 48 semiannual payments of $200 earning interest at a nominal rate of $i^{(2)} = 0.10$. Determine **(a)** the present value of this annuity, and **(b)** the future value.

ANSWER(S)   **(a)** $3,615.43;   **(b)** $37,605.08   □

Part **(a)** of Practice Problem 17 tells you that if you could put $3,615.43 into an account which pays 10% compounded semiannually, you could draw $200 at the end of each six-month period for 24 years. The account would then be exhausted. Or, you could leave the account alone for 24 years, and it will grow to $37,605.08.

Determining the Amortization Payment

After writing the Fundamental Annuity Relationship, we can solve for PMT, the payment necessary to amortize a loan of A with an n-payment annuity. We illustrate in Example 23.

■ EXAMPLE 23

You borrow $14,000 to buy a car and will pay this loan off by making 36 payments with interest at $i^{(12)} = 0.14$.

(a) What will your monthly payment be?
(b) How much will you pay in interest charges?

SOLUTION   **(a)** Substitute into the fundamental annuity relationship: $P = 14,000$, $i_p = 0.14/12 \approx 0.011667$, $a^n = (1.011667)^{36} \approx 1.51827$, giving

$$1.51827 \cdot 14,000 = \text{PMT} \cdot \frac{1.51827 - 1}{0.011667}$$

or

$$21,255.78 = \text{PMT} \cdot 44.42187$$

yielding the required payment:

$$\text{PMT} = \$478.50$$

(b) 36 payments of $478.49 total $17,226.00; the principal being repaid is $14,000. The difference of $3226.00 is interest.   ■

PRACTICE PROBLEM 18   **(a)** How much will your monthly payment be on a 60-month loan of $4000 if the nominal interest rate is $i^{(12)} = 0.12$?

(b) As in **(a)**, but the loan is only for 48 months.

ANSWER(S)   **(a)** $88.98;   **(b)** $105.33   □

■ EXAMPLE 24

After five years of scrimping, saving, and self-denial, you and your spouse have saved the $10,000 down payment needed for your first home. The balance, after the down payment, is $90,000. In talking with four savings and loan (S&L) institutions, you are offered the following propositions:

(a) Miserly S&L offers to write a 25-year amortization with monthly payments at 11%.
(b) Frugal S&L agrees to a 20-year loan at 10.5%.
(c) Parsimonious S&L agrees to a 30-year loan at 11%.
(d) Tight-Fisted S&L agrees to a 30-year loan at 10.5%.

Determine the monthly payment required for each plan.

SOLUTION

For all four loans, we use the Fundamental Annuity Relationship with the appropriate values of i_p, n, a^n, and P. We illustrate calculations for loan **(a)**; the rest are left to you. First we calculate $i_p = 0.11/12 \approx 0.0091667$ and $a^n = (1 + 0.11/12)^{300} \approx 15.44789$, giving

$$90,000 \cdot 15.44789 = \text{PMT} \cdot \frac{15.44789 - 1}{0.0091667}$$

or

$$1,390,310.1 = \text{PMT} \cdot 1576.1277$$

Dividing both sides by 1576.1277 gives PMT = $882.10. Continuing these calculations for **(b)**, **(c)**, and **(d)**, we have:

(a) At Miserly S&L, the monthly payments would be $882.10.
(b) At Frugal S&L, the monthly payments would be $898.54.
(c) At Parsimonious S&L, the monthly payments would be $857.09.
(d) At Tight-Fisted S&L, the monthly payments would be $823.27.

The monthly payments are not vastly different: only about $75 separates the low and high payments. However, there are some startling comparisons to be made, once we organize key information in Figure 12.7.

Consider loan **(a)** versus loan **(c)**. The interest rate and amount borrowed are the same; only the terms are different—25 years for **(a)** and 30 for **(c)**. If you and your spouse can afford the 25-year payments of $882.10—$25.01 more a month than the 30-year loan—you will pay 300 payments of $882.10, totaling $264,630, of which $264,630 − $90,000, or $174,630, is interest. Choosing the 30-year loan with its smaller pay-

Figure 12.7
Comparisons of $90,000 loan programs at four competing S&L's

	Lending Institution	Rate ($i^{(12)}$)	Term (yrs)	Monthly Payment	Total Interest
(a)	Miserly S&L	11 %	25	$882.10	$174,630
(b)	Frugal S&L	10.5%	20	$898.54	$125,649
(c)	Parsim. S&L	11 %	30	$857.09	$218,552
(d)	Tgt-Fst S&L	10.5%	30	$823.27	$206,377

ments ($857.09), you will pay $308,552.40 over the 30 years. Paying the loan off five years sooner will save about $43,922 in interest charges!

Now consider loan **(c)** versus loan **(d)**. The only difference is in the interest rates—loan **(d)** is 0.5% less. That one-half of a percent means $33.82 a month, which amounts to $12,175.20 over the 30-year term of the loan!

Compare loan **(b)** to loan **(d)**. Both are at 10.5%, but loan **(d)** has payments which are $75.27 less; the tradeoff is that you and your spouse must make these smaller payments for ten years longer. That 10-year extension with its slightly smaller payments will cost you almost $81,000 in interest charges! Reducing the monthly payment by extending the loan period an extra ten years is costly.   ■

PRACTICE PROBLEM 19   In Example 24, consider loans **(c)** and **(d).** Both are for 30 years. Suppose you get the lower rate of 10.5%, making your monthly payments only $823.27, but that you have budgeted $857.09, thinking you would get an 11% rate. If you were to invest the difference of $857.09 − $823.27, or $33.82, at the end of each month in a mutual fund that earns 15% compounded monthly, how much would your investment be worth in 30 years?

ANSWER(S) $234,145.32!!   □

■ **EXAMPLE 25**   Your spouse's great uncle Pious leaves you a large inheritance and you decide to pay off your house loan of Example 24, now exactly ten years old. How much would you owe under each of the four borrowing schemes?

SOLUTION   The problem is determining the unpaid loan balance after ten years' payments.

On loan **(a),** you would have 15 years of payments remaining at 11%. Your remaining obligation would be the present value of the remaining $12 \cdot 15 = 180$ payments.

To determine the present value of these payments, we use the Fundamental Relation for Annuities with PMT = \$882.10, i_p = 0.0091667, a^n = $(1.0091667)^{180}$ ≈ 5.16799, and n = 180. Substituting these gives

$$5.16799 \cdot P = 882.10 \cdot \frac{5.16799 - 1}{0.0091667}$$

or

$$5.16799\,P = 401{,}080$$

which yields

$$P = \$77{,}608.59$$

(*Note:* Your calculations may differ by a few cents.)

This result should seem somewhat distressing; after 120 payments of \$882.10—a total of \$105,852—you and your spouse would have reduced your mortgage by only \$90,000 − \$77,608.59, or \$12,391.41. Only \$12,391.41 out of \$105,852 would have gone toward the original balance. While distressing, this is also correct and very typical. During the first few years of any "long-term" loan, most of the monthly payment goes for interest; during the latter part, most goes toward principal. This is the tradeoff for the privilege of having the constant monthly payment provided by amortization.

For **(b),** we determine the present value of a monthly annuity of \$898.54 continuing for 10 years. Calculating as in part **(a),** we obtain the present value \$66,590.58; this is the "payoff" amount. Under this loan, you and your spouse would have made 120 payments of \$898.54—a total of \$107,824.80—and of this amount, \$90,000 − \$66,590.58, or \$23,409.42, would have gone toward the \$90,000 loan principal. This is much better than with loan **(a).**

For **(c),** we find the present value of the remaining 20 years of monthly payments of \$857.09. Making the appropriate calculations, we arrive at a payoff figure of \$83,036.20. During the first 10 years of this loan, you and your spouse would have paid \$102,850.80, and only \$90,000 − \$83,036.20, or \$6963.80, would have gone toward reduction of the original \$90,000 debt!

Finally, for loan **(d),** which was also originally for 30 years, we determine the present value of the remaining 20 years of \$823.27 monthly payments. Making the necessary calculations, we arrive at a payoff figure of \$82,460.60. In ten years, you and your spouse would have paid \$98,792.40, and only \$90,000 − \$82,460.60, or \$7539.40, would have gone toward principal.

The moral is this: if you will be able to pay off your loan early, go for the shortest term possible. Most of the first few years' payments will still be interest, but you will be reducing principal considerably more than with a longer term loan. ∎

PRACTICE PROBLEM 20   You take out a $9000 car loan with 60 monthly payments at 9%.

(a) What is your monthly payment?
(b) You want to pay off the balance after making 12 payments. How much cash will you need?
(c) If you pay the loan off after 12 payments, how much interest will you have paid?
(d) Suppose you pay the balance after having made 24 payments. How much cash will you need?
(e) In part (d), how much interest will you have paid?

ANSWER(S)   (a) $186.83;   (b) $7507.72;   (c) $749.68;   (d) $5875.21;
(e) $1359.13   ☐

■ EXAMPLE 26   Mike Kinzer bought a new house 12 years ago by taking out a 30-year $100,000 mortgage at 12%. Interest rates have gone down sharply, and Mike is considering "refinancing" his home by paying off the old mortgage and taking out a new one at the current interest rate of only 10%. His lending institution will be glad to do this—at a price. His original mortgage contains a "prepayment penalty" of 2%, which means that he has to pay an up-front fee equal to 2% of the remaining balance when he refinances. Discuss the costs and possible savings that Mike will incur by paying this penalty and rewriting the loan for 18 years.

SOLUTION   To determine Mike's prepayment penalty, we need first to determine the balance on his original loan. As he has made 12 years' worth of payments, his balance is the present value of the remaining 18 years of payments. To find this, we need to know Mike's current monthly payment. We first calculate $i_p = 0.12/12 = 0.01$, and $a^n = (1.01)^{360} \approx 35.94964$. Using the Fundamental Annuity Relation, we write:

$$35.949641 \cdot 100,000 = \text{PMT} \cdot \frac{35.949641 - 1}{0.01}$$

or

$$3,594,964.1 = 3494.6641 \cdot \text{PMT}$$

Dividing both sides by 3494.6641 produces PMT = $1028.61 as the current monthly payment.

Knowing that Mike's monthly payment is $1028.61 enables us to calculate the present value (his remaining balance) after 12 years of payments. Substitute the known quantities PMT = $1028.61, $n = 18 \cdot 12 = 216$, and $a^{216} = (1.01)^{216} \approx 8.5786063$ into the Fundamental Annuity Relation and get:

$$8.5786063 \cdot P = 1028.61 \cdot \frac{7.5786063}{0.01}$$

or

$$8.5786063 \cdot P = 779543.02$$

Dividing both sides by 8.5786063 gives $P = \$90{,}870.59$ as the present value of Mike's remaining obligation. The prepayment penalty is two percent of this amount, which is $1817.41. This is small enough to where the lending institution will let Mike add this to the remaining balance of $90,870.59 and finance the total of $92,688. Using an 18-year term, we find that the required monthly payment on the principal amount of $92,688 at the new rate of 10% is only $926.74. Even with the penalty, Mike will come out far ahead! His payments under the new mortgage, with the prepayment penalty included, are $1028.61 − $926.74, or $101.87, a month less. Over the 18-year term, Mike will save $18 \cdot 12 \cdot$ $101.87, or $22,003.92, by refinancing! (If Mike could invest this monthly savings of $101.87 at 8% compounded monthly, it would accumulate to $48,906 in 18 years.) ∎

PRACTICE PROBLEM 21   In Example 26, suppose Mike's prepayment penalty is 4%, and that the refinancing rate is 11%. Further, assume that the prepayment penalty can be added to the balance and the entire amount refinanced for 18 years. **(a)** Should Mike still refinance? **(b)** If so, how much will he save over the 18-year term?

ANSWER(S)   **(a)** yes; monthly payment will be $1006.53;   **(b)** $4769.28   ☐

EXERCISES 12.6

PRACTICING THE MOVES AND MANEUVERS

Exercises 139–147: Determine the monthly payment required for each amortization.

139. $10,000 for 20 years at 9%
140. $45,000 for 25 years at 10%
141. $10,000 for 20 years at 10%
142. $45,000 for 25 years at 12%
143. $80,000 for 30 years at 11.5%

144. $65,000 for 15 years at 8%
145. $80,000 for 20 years at 11.5%
146. $80,000 for 20 years at 10%
147. $12,000 for 4 years at 11%

Exercises 148–153: Find
(a) the present value of the given stream of payments.
(b) the future value.

148. A stream of 72 quarterly payments of $300 earning $i^{(4)} = 0.10$
149. A stream of 120 monthly payments of $150 earning $i^{(12)} = 0.12$
150. A stream of 20 annual payments of $2000 earning $i = 0.11$
151. A stream of 100 quarterly payments of $1000 earning $i^{(4)} = 0.12$
152. A stream of 20 semiannual payments of $4000 earning $i^{(2)} = 0.08$
153. A stream of 84 monthly payments of $250 earning $i^{(12)} = 0.11$

APPLYING THE CONCEPTS

154. Denise Stewart borrows $8000 to buy a horse. She plans to amortize the loan in five years with quarterly payments; the interest rate she is charged is 12% compounded quarterly. How much will her quarterly payment be?
155. In Exercise 154, suppose Denise talks the seller into 10% compounded quarterly.
    (a) How much will her quarterly amortization payment be?
    (b) How much will she save in interest over the 5-year period by paying 10% instead of 12%?
156. Shawn Leonard borrows $4500 to buy a fishing boat. If the interest rate is 10% compounded monthly, how much will his monthly payment be if he borrows the money for (a) two years? (b) three years? (c) four years?
157. When you purchase your new chocolate-covered noodle strainer, you cannot afford the cash price of $86.50. With no down payment and an interest rate of 9% compounded quarterly, what will your payments be on a two-year loan?
158. Mike Williams borrows $400 for three years in order to purchase some statistics books. If he makes regular monthly payments at 8% compounded monthly, what will his monthly payment be?
159. Gary Griesmeyer has a 20-year, $60,000 mortgage on which he makes monthly payments at 10% interest.
    (a) What is Gary's monthly payment?
    (b) Suppose Gary wants to terminate the loan after five years. How much will he have to pay? (Assume there is no penalty for paying off the loan.)
160. In Example 26, suppose that the prepayment penalty for Mike is 5% of the balance at the time of refinancing. If the refinancing rate is 11%, and the term is 18 years, should Mike refinance?
161. Jay Powers takes out a 25-year house mortgage for $70,000 at 11%.
    (a) What is his monthly payment?
    (b) How much interest will he pay in the first year?
    (c) If the loan runs its course, how much will he have paid in interest?
    (d) What is the balance of the mortgage after five years?
    (e) What is the balance of his mortgage after ten years?
    (f) If, at the end of ten years, Jay refinances at 9% for 15 years, without penalty, what will his new monthly payment be?
162. Michelle Manthe has just purchased a $15,000 car by paying $3000 down and financing the balance at 11.5% for four years.
    (a) What is her monthly payment?
    (b) How much is the first-year interest?
    (c) How much total interest will she pay during the four years?
    (d) How much interest would Michelle save by having an 11% loan?
163. A lending institution offers you a 9% rate (less than the "going rate") for your $50,000, 20-year mortgage, but there is a catch—you must pay "points." Specifically, one point is one percent of the amount financed. To get the 9% rate, you need to pay 4 points. Is this a good deal if the alternative is a 10% rate with no points? *Note:* You must borrow the amount needed for points and add this amount to $50,000.

A Brief Summary of Important Ideas

If an amount P, known as the principal, is borrowed for t time periods at a **simple interest** rate r per time period, the interest is computed by

$$I = P \cdot r \cdot t$$

and the total returned to the lender is called the **accumulated value,** denoted by the symbol A:

$$A = P + I = P + Prt = P(1 + rt)$$

When simple interest is used, only the original principal earns interest. If interest earned can also be reinvested at the same terms as the original principal, then the investor earns **compound interest.** If amount P is invested for n periods at i percent annual interest, with compounding m times a year, the amount P will grow to a **future value** or **accumulated value** of

$$A = P(1 + i/m)^n$$
$$= P \cdot a^n$$

where $a^n = (1 + i/m)^n$ is the **compound accumulation factor** which describes how much \$1 will grow to after n periods at annual interest rate i with m compoundings per year.

The **present value** of a specific future amount A is the amount of money P that would need to be invested now in order to accumulate A at the future time. The present value and future value are related via the compound accumulation factor a^n:

$$P = \frac{A}{a^n}$$

We use the phrase **nominal rate of interest** is $i^{(m)}$ to express the fact that the annual rate of interest is i with m compoundings per year. Because of the many different choices for m, it is important to have a reference rate to which all such nominal interest rates can be compared. This reference rate is called the **effective rate,** or the annual percentage rate APR, and it is found from the nominal rate by

$$APR = \left(1 + \frac{i}{m}\right)^m - 1$$

An **annuity** is a sequence of equal payments made (or received) at regular time intervals. The time from the beginning of the first payment period to the end of the last payment period is called the **term** of the annuity. In an ordinary annuity (the only kind we consider) payments are made at the end of each period. The **Fundamental Annuity Relationship** is

$$A = a^n \cdot P = \text{PMT} \cdot \frac{a^n - 1}{i_p}$$

where A is the future value or accumulated value, P is the present value of the annuity, a^n is the compound accumulation factor and there are n equal payments of size PMT, with each payment earning i_p per period. By rearranging this relation, it is possible to solve for any of the elements in terms of the remaining elements. In particular, to **amortize** a loan (pay it off in equal payments), substitute the loan amount P, the compound accumulation factor a^n, the interest rate per period, i_p, and solve for the required payment PMT.

REVIEW EXERCISES

PRACTICING THE MOVES AND MANEUVERS

Exercises 164–170: Find the ordinary simple interest charge.

164. $12,450 for nine months at 8%
165. $8600 for seven months at 9%
166. $3400 for five months at 12%
167. $878 for 11 months at 18%
168. $1450 for three months at 2%
169. $29,500 for four months at 10%
170. $1,500,000 for nine months at 8.5%

Exercises 171–180: Find the accumulated value (future value) of the given investment under the compounding specified.

171. $6000 at 9% compounded semiannually for four years
172. $9000 at 6% compounded weekly for two years
173. $25,000 at 7% compounded annually for ten years
174. $500 at 15% compounded daily for 25 years
175. $1000 at 3% compounded quarterly for 50 years
176. $900 at 6% compounded quarterly for 20 years
177. $1200 at 10% compounded semiannually for 15 years
178. $2000 at 7.5% compounded weekly for 10 years
179. $100,000 at 9.25% compounded monthly for 20 years
180. $75,000 at 10.5% compounded weekly for 18 years

Exercises 181–185: Find the effective rate for the given nominal rate.
181. $i^{(2)} = 0.095$
182. $i^{(12)} = 0.075$
183. $i^{(6)} = 0.10$
184. $i^{(4)} = 0.11$
185. $i^{(12)} = 0.15$

Exercises 186–194: Find the present value for the indicated investment.

186. $10,000 in five years at $i^{(4)} = 0.11$
187. $20,000 in six years at $i^{(2)} = 0.08$
188. $1000 in 20 years at $i = 0.12$
189. $1,000,000 in 14 years at $i^{(12)} = 0.075$
190. $1,000,000 in 30 years at $i^{(4)} = 0.11$

191. $1,000,000 in 20 years at $i^{(4)} = 0.12$
192. $1500 in two years at $i^{(2)} = 0.09$
193. $11,700 in four years at $i^{(12)} = 0.085$
194. $145,000 in ten years at $i^{(4)} = 0.10$

Exercises 195–200: Determine the nominal interest rate necessary for the given amount to accumulate to $25,000 in the stated number of compounding periods.

195. $12,000 in four years with semiannual compounding
196. $18,000 in two years with monthly compounding
197. $4000 in five years with monthly compounding
198. $6000 in ten years with quarterly compounding
199. $21,000 in three years with weekly compounding
200. $1000 in 20 years with annual compounding

Exercises 201–208: Find the future value for the following ordinary annuities.

201. $200 at the end of each month for the next five years with interest at $i^{(12)} = 0.06$
202. $50 at the end of each week for the next 10 years with interest at $i^{(52)} = 0.08$
203. $5000 at the end of each six-month period for 12 years with interest $i^{(2)} = 0.075$
204. $5 at the end of each day for the next 10 years with interest at $i^{(365)} = 0.064$
205. $2500 at the end of each year for 14 years at 9% compounded annually
206. $100 at the end of each month for the next 15 years with interest at $i^{(12)} = 0.08$
207. $150 at the end of each week for the next four years with interest at $i^{(52)} = 0.05$
208. $275 at the end of each two-week period for seven years with interest at $i^{(26)} = 0.08$

Exercises 209–213: Determine the monthly payment required for each amortization.

209. $65,000 for 25 years at 9%
210. $24,000 for five years at 10%
211. $108,000 for 30 years at 9.5%

212. $82,500 for 30 years at 8%
213. $12,600 for five years at 11%

Exercises 214–218: Determine the annual payment required for each amortization.

214. $125,000 for ten years at 9%
215. $10,000 for four years at 8%
216. $29,500 for six years at 9.5%

217. $250,000 for 25 years at 8.75%
218. $2400 for three years at 10%

APPLYING THE CONCEPTS

219. An article in the October 9, 1989, *USA Today* stated the following:
     (a) The average cost for a year of college (tuition, fees, room and board) in a private school was $5,249 in 1980–81, while the average cost for one year in 1988–89 was $10,800. Determine the compound annual rate of increase over this eight-year period.
     (b) The same data for public colleges gave figures of $2420 for 1980–81 and $4290 for 1988–89. Determine the compound annual rate of increase over this eight-year period.

220. You borrow $800 at 9% ordinary simple interest for eight months. How much will you need to pay off the loan at the end of the loan period?

221. You invest $4000 in a money market mutual fund that is currently paying 8.5% compounded monthly. If this fund continues to pay at this rate, how much will you have accumulated in three years?

222. You borrow $840 from a bank at 7% simple interest. Using the Banker's Rule, determine how much you will have to repay the bank in 88 days.

223. Which of the two following accumulated values would you rather have:
    (a) $1000 deposited for three years in a fund earning 6% with compounding annually, or
    (b) $1000 deposited for four years at 4% with monthly compounding?

224. Jim Rogacki invests $2500 under the following terms. If he leaves his money for two years, he will earn $i^{(4)} = 0.09$. He may then reinvest the accumulated value for the next three years at $i^{(12)} = 0.09$. If, however, he takes his money out before the full 2 years, he gets only $i^{(4)} = 0.06$ for the time he has had his money invested. If he takes his money out between three and five years, he gets $i^{(4)} = 0.09$ for the full time of investment.
    (a) What will Jim accumulate if he leaves his investment for the full five years?
    (b) How much will Jim have accumulated if he withdraws his investment at the end of the first two years?
    (c) How much will Jim accumulate if he withdraws his investment at the end of four years?
    (d) How much will Jim accumulate if he withdraws his money after three and a half years?

225. What is the minimum number of quarters necessary for an investment to quadruple in value if $i^{(4)} = 0.12$?

Exercises 226 and 227 should be assigned together.

226. If $1000 is invested at 10% compounded quarterly for two years, 11% quarterly for one year, and 12% quarterly for three years, find the accumulated value at the end of the six-year period.

227. What nominal rate $i^{(4)}$, effective for the entire six years, would be necessary in order that the accumulated value match the value given by the three-rate scheme of Exercise 226?

228. Find the effective rate of interest for each of the following:
    (a) 6% compounded quarterly
    (b) 5.8% compounded daily

229. Rank the following investments according to effective interest:
    (a) 5% compounded daily
    (b) 5.1% compounded quarterly
    (c) 5.2% compounded semiannually
    (d) 5.3% compounded annually

230. Jim Moon borrows $74,000 for 25 years at 10% in order to buy a house.
    (a) What will his monthly payment be?
    (b) How much interest will Jim pay during the first two years?
    (c) If Jim wants to pay the loan off after four years, how much cash will it take?
    (d) By paying a 5% prepayment penalty, Jim can refinance the loan at the end of seven years. If the new rate is 9.8%, and the prepayment penalty can be added to the balance and refinanced for 18 years, how will Jim's new monthly payment compare with the old?

231. You desire to have $5100 four years from now. You have located an investment which will pay 8% compounded quarterly for the first two years and then 9% compounded monthly for the next two years. How much do you need to invest now?

232. Lorijo Claunch wants a swimming pool for her new house. She figures that she will be able to afford one in seven years, at which time she estimates the cost will be $18,000. If her monthly investments will earn 7% compounded monthly, how much does she need to invest at the end of each month in order to achieve her goal?

233. In Exercise 232, suppose Lorijo were to make an immediate "lump-sum" investment at 7% compounded monthly, and no monthly investments. How much should this lump sum be?

234. (*Number 6 from the beginning of this chapter*) You have won $1,000,000 in the state lottery. This is

paid in 20 annual payments made at the end of each of the next 20 years.

(a) If you can invest this $50,000 at 8% compounded annually, how much will your accumulation be at the end of the 20-year period?

(b) Would you prefer an immediate lump-sum payment of $400,000 instead of the 20-year payout? Suppose you can invest the $400,000 at 8% compounded annually.

APPENDIX
Tables

Table I
Binomial probability distributions

Tabled values, rounded to three decimal places, represent the probability of observing k or fewer successes in n trials. The value "0+" means the actual value was greater than 0 but not large enough to deserve a rounded value of .001. Similarly, the value "1−" means the actual probability was greater than .9995.

k	.05	.10	.20	.30	.40	.50	.60	.70	.80	.90	k
				Probability of Success p							
$n = 5$ trials											
0	.774	.590	.328	.168	.078	.031	.010	.002	0+	0+	0
1	.977	.919	.737	.528	.337	.188	.087	.031	.007	0+	1
2	.999	.991	.942	.837	.683	.500	.317	.163	.058	.009	2
3	1−	1−	.993	.969	.913	.812	.663	.472	.263	.081	3
4	1−	1−	1−	.998	.990	.969	.922	.832	.672	.410	4
$n = 6$ trials											
0	.735	.531	.262	.118	.047	.016	.004	.001	0+	0+	0
1	.967	.886	.655	.420	.233	.109	.041	.011	.002	0+	1
2	.998	.984	.901	.744	.544	.344	.179	.070	.017	.001	2
3	1−	.999	.983	.930	.821	.656	.456	.256	.099	.016	3
4	1−	1−	.998	.989	.959	.891	.767	.580	.345	.114	4
5	1−	1−	1−	.999	.996	.984	.953	.882	.738	.469	5
$n = 7$ trials											
0	.698	.478	.210	.082	.028	.008	.002	0+	0+	0+	0
1	.956	.850	.577	.329	.159	.063	.019	.004	0+	0+	1
2	.996	.974	.852	.647	.420	.227	.096	.029	.005	0+	2
3	1−	.997	.967	.874	.710	.500	.290	.126	.033	.003	3
4	1−	1−	.995	.971	.904	.773	.580	.353	.148	.026	4
5	1−	1−	1−	.996	.981	.937	.841	.671	.423	.150	5
6	1−	1−	1−	1−	.998	.992	.972	.918	.790	.522	6

				Probability of Success p							
k	.05	.10	.20	.30	.40	.50	.60	.70	.80	.90	k
$n = 8$ trials											
0	.663	.430	.168	.058	.017	.004	.001	0+	0+	0+	0
1	.943	.813	.503	.255	.106	.035	.009	.001	0+	0+	1
2	.994	.962	.797	.552	.315	.145	.050	.011	.001	0+	2
3	1−	.995	.944	.806	.594	.363	.174	.058	.010	0+	3
4	1−	1−	.990	.942	.826	.637	.406	.194	.056	.005	4
5	1−	1−	.999	.989	.950	.855	.685	.448	.203	.038	5
6	1−	1−	1−	.999	.991	.965	.894	.745	.497	.187	6
7	1−	1−	1−	1−	.999	.996	.983	.942	.832	.570	7
$n = 9$ trials											
0	.630	.387	.134	.040	.010	.002	0+	0+	0+	0+	0
1	.929	.775	.436	.196	.071	.020	.004	0+	0+	0+	1
2	.992	.947	.738	.463	.232	.090	.025	.004	0+	0+	2
3	.999	.992	.914	.730	.483	.254	.099	.025	.003	0+	3
4	1−	.999	.980	.901	.733	.500	.267	.099	.020	.001	4
5	1−	1−	.997	.975	.901	.746	.517	.270	.086	.008	5
6	1−	1−	1−	.996	.975	.910	.768	.537	.262	.053	6
7	1−	1−	1−	1−	.996	.980	.929	.804	.564	.225	7
8	1−	1−	1−	1−	1−	.998	.990	.960	.866	.613	8
$n = 10$ trials											
0	.599	.349	.107	.028	.006	.001	0+	0+	0+	0+	0
1	.914	.736	.376	.149	.046	.011	.002	0+	0+	0+	1
2	.988	.930	.678	.383	.167	.055	.012	.002	0+	0+	2
3	.999	.987	.879	.650	.382	.172	.055	.011	.001	0+	3
4	1−	.998	.967	.850	.633	.377	.166	.047	.006	0+	4
5	1−	1−	.994	.953	.834	.623	.367	.150	.033	.002	5
6	1−	1−	.999	.989	.945	.828	.618	.350	.121	.013	6
7	1−	1−	1−	.998	.988	.945	.833	.617	.322	.070	7
8	1−	1−	1−	1−	.998	.989	.954	.851	.624	.264	8
9	1−	1−	1−	1−	1−	.999	.994	.972	.893	.651	9
$n = 15$ trials											
0	.463	.206	.035	.005	0+	0+	0+	0+	0+	0+	0
1	.829	.549	.167	.035	.005	0+	0+	0+	0+	0+	1
2	.964	.816	.398	.127	.027	.004	0+	0+	0+	0+	2
3	.995	.944	.648	.297	.091	.018	.002	0+	0+	0+	3
4	.999	.987	.836	.515	.217	.059	.009	.001	0+	0+	4
5	1−	.998	.939	.722	.403	.151	.034	.004	0+	0+	5
6	1−	1−	.982	.869	.610	.304	.095	.015	.001	0+	6
7	1−	1−	.996	.950	.787	.500	.213	.050	.004	0+	7

				Probability of Success p							
k	.05	.10	.20	.30	.40	.50	.60	.70	.80	.90	k
8	1−	1−	.999	.985	.905	.696	.390	.131	.018	0+	8
9	1−	1−	1−	.996	.966	.849	.597	.278	.061	.002	9
10	1−	1−	1−	.999	.991	.941	.783	.485	.164	.013	10
11	1−	1−	1−	1−	.998	.982	.909	.703	.352	.056	11
12	1−	1−	1−	1−	1−	.996	.973	.873	.602	.184	12
13	1−	1−	1−	1−	1−	1−	.995	.965	.833	.451	13
14	1−	1−	1−	1−	1−	1−	1−	.995	.965	.794	14

$n = 20$ trials

0	.358	.122	.012	.001	0+	0+	0+	0+	0+	0+	0
1	.736	.392	.069	.008	.001	0+	0+	0+	0+	0+	1
2	.925	.677	.206	.035	.004	0+	0+	0+	0+	0+	2
3	.984	.867	.411	.107	.016	.001	0+	0+	0+	0+	3
4	.997	.957	.630	.238	.051	.006	0+	0+	0+	0+	4
5	1−	.989	.804	.416	.126	.021	.002	0+	0+	0+	5
6	1−	.998	.913	.608	.250	.058	.006	0+	0+	0+	6
7	1−	1−	.968	.772	.416	.132	.021	.001	0+	0+	7
8	1−	1−	.990	.887	.596	.252	.057	.005	0+	0+	8
9	1−	1−	.997	.952	.755	.412	.128	.017	.001	0+	9
10	1−	1−	.999	.983	.872	.588	.245	.048	.003	0+	10
11	1−	1−	1−	.995	.943	.748	.404	.113	.010	0+	11
12	1−	1−	1−	.999	.979	.868	.584	.228	.032	0+	12
13	1−	1−	1−	1−	.994	.942	.750	.392	.087	.002	13
14	1−	1−	1−	1−	.998	.979	.874	.584	.196	.011	14
15	1−	1−	1−	1−	1−	.994	.949	.762	.370	.043	15
16	1−	1−	1−	1−	1−	.999	.984	.893	.589	.133	16
17	1−	1−	1−	1−	1−	1−	.996	.965	.794	.323	17
18	1−	1−	1−	1−	1−	1−	.999	.992	.931	.608	18
19	1−	1−	1−	1−	1−	1−	1−	.999	.988	.878	19

Table II
Compound accumulation factors (*See Section 12.2*)
$a^n = (1 + i/m)^n$ = value of \$1 invested for n periods at nominal annual rate $i^{(m)}$

n = No. Periods	Interest Rate per Period: $i^{(m)}/m$							
	0.2500%	0.5000%	0.6667%	0.7500%	0.8750%	1.000%	1.2500%	1.5000%
1	1.00250	1.00500	1.00667	1.00750	1.00875	1.01000	1.01250	1.01500
2	1.00501	1.01002	1.01338	1.01506	1.01758	1.02010	1.02516	1.03022
3	1.00752	1.01508	1.02013	1.02267	1.02648	1.03030	1.03797	1.04568
4	1.01004	1.02015	1.02693	1.03034	1.03546	1.04060	1.05095	1.06136
5	1.01256	1.02525	1.03378	1.03807	1.04452	1.05101	1.06408	1.07728

Table II *(continued)*

n = No. Periods	Interest Rate per Period: $i^{(m)}/m$							
	0.2500%	0.5000%	0.6667%	0.7500%	0.8750%	1.000%	1.2500%	1.5000%
6	1.01509	1.03038	1.04067	1.04585	1.05366	1.06152	1.07738	1.09344
7	1.01763	1.03553	1.04761	1.05370	1.06288	1.07214	1.09085	1.10984
8	1.02018	1.04071	1.05459	1.06160	1.07218	1.08286	1.10449	1.12649
9	1.02273	1.04591	1.06163	1.06956	1.08156	1.09369	1.11829	1.14339
10	1.02528	1.05114	1.06870	1.07758	1.09103	1.10462	1.13227	1.16054
11	1.02785	1.05640	1.07583	1.08566	1.10057	1.11567	1.14642	1.17795
12	1.03042	1.06168	1.08300	1.09381	1.11020	1.12683	1.16075	1.19562
13	1.03299	1.06699	1.09022	1.10201	1.11992	1.13809	1.17526	1.21355
14	1.03557	1.07232	1.09749	1.11028	1.12972	1.14947	1.18995	1.23176
15	1.03816	1.07768	1.10480	1.11860	1.13960	1.16097	1.20483	1.25023
16	1.04076	1.08307	1.11217	1.12699	1.14957	1.17258	1.21989	1.26899
17	1.04336	1.08849	1.11958	1.13544	1.15963	1.18430	1.23514	1.28802
18	1.04597	1.09393	1.12705	1.14396	1.16978	1.19615	1.25058	1.30734
19	1.04858	1.09940	1.13456	1.15254	1.18001	1.20811	1.26621	1.32695
20	1.05121	1.10490	1.14213	1.16118	1.19034	1.22019	1.28204	1.34686
21	1.05383	1.11042	1.14974	1.16989	1.20076	1.23239	1.29806	1.36706
22	1.05647	1.11597	1.15740	1.17867	1.21126	1.24472	1.31429	1.38756
23	1.05911	1.12155	1.16512	1.18751	1.22186	1.25716	1.33072	1.40838
24	1.06176	1.12716	1.17289	1.19641	1.23255	1.26973	1.34735	1.42950
25	1.06441	1.13280	1.18071	1.20539	1.24334	1.28243	1.36419	1.45095
26	1.06707	1.13846	1.18858	1.21443	1.25422	1.29526	1.38125	1.47271
27	1.06974	1.14415	1.19650	1.22354	1.26519	1.30821	1.39851	1.49480
28	1.07241	1.14987	1.20448	1.23271	1.27626	1.32129	1.41599	1.51722
29	1.07510	1.15562	1.21251	1.24196	1.28743	1.33450	1.43369	1.53998
30	1.07778	1.16140	1.22059	1.25127	1.29869	1.34785	1.45161	1.56308
31	1.08048	1.16721	1.22873	1.26066	1.31006	1.36133	1.46976	1.58653
32	1.08318	1.17304	1.23692	1.27011	1.32152	1.37494	1.48813	1.61032
33	1.08589	1.17891	1.24517	1.27964	1.33308	1.38869	1.50673	1.63448
34	1.08860	1.18480	1.25347	1.28923	1.34475	1.40258	1.52557	1.65900
35	1.09132	1.19073	1.26182	1.29890	1.35651	1.41660	1.54464	1.68388
36	1.09405	1.19668	1.27024	1.30865	1.36838	1.43077	1.56394	1.70914
37	1.09679	1.20266	1.27871	1.31846	1.38036	1.44508	1.58349	1.73478
38	1.09953	1.20868	1.28723	1.32835	1.39243	1.45953	1.60329	1.76080
39	1.10228	1.21472	1.29581	1.33831	1.40462	1.47412	1.62333	1.78721
40	1.10503	1.22079	1.30445	1.34835	1.41691	1.48886	1.64362	1.81402
41	1.10780	1.22690	1.31315	1.35846	1.42931	1.50375	1.66416	1.84123
42	1.11057	1.23303	1.32190	1.36865	1.44181	1.51879	1.68497	1.86885
43	1.11334	1.23920	1.33071	1.37891	1.45443	1.53398	1.70603	1.89688
44	1.11612	1.24539	1.33959	1.38926	1.46716	1.54932	1.72735	1.92533
45	1.11892	1.25162	1.34852	1.39968	1.47999	1.56481	1.74895	1.95421
46	1.12171	1.25788	1.35751	1.41017	1.49294	1.58046	1.77081	1.98353
47	1.12452	1.26417	1.36656	1.42075	1.50601	1.59626	1.79294	2.01328
48	1.12733	1.27049	1.37567	1.43141	1.51918	1.61223	1.81535	2.04348
60	1.16162	1.34885	1.48985	1.56568	1.68660	1.81670	2.10718	2.44322
72	1.19695	1.43204	1.61350	1.71255	1.87247	2.04710	2.44592	2.92116
84	1.23335	1.52037	1.74742	1.87320	2.07883	2.30672	2.83911	3.49259
96	1.27087	1.61414	1.89246	2.04892	2.30792	2.59927	3.29551	4.17580
108	1.30952	1.71370	2.04953	2.24112	2.56226	2.92893	3.82528	4.99267
120	1.34935	1.81940	2.21964	2.45136	2.84463	3.30039	4.44021	5.96932
180	1.56743	2.45409	3.30692	3.83804	4.79776	5.99580	9.35633	14.58437
240	1.82075	3.31020	4.92680	6.00915	8.09192	10.89255	19.71549	35.63282
300	2.11502	4.46497	7.34018	9.40841	13.64785	19.78847	41.54412	87.05880
360	2.45684	6.02258	10.93573	14.73058	23.01851	35.94964	87.54100	212.70378

Table II (*continued*)

n = No. Periods	Interest Rate per Period: $i^{(m)}/m$							
	1.750%	2.000%	2.250%	2.500%	2.750%	3.000%	4.000%	5.000%
1	1.0175	1.0200	1.0225	1.0250	1.0275	1.0300	1.0400	1.0500
2	1.0353	1.0404	1.0455	1.0506	1.0558	1.0609	1.0816	1.1025
3	1.0534	1.0612	1.0690	1.0769	1.0848	1.0927	1.1249	1.1576
4	1.0719	1.0824	1.0931	1.1038	1.1146	1.1255	1.1699	1.2155
5	1.0906	1.1041	1.1177	1.1314	1.1453	1.1593	1.2167	1.2763
6	1.1097	1.1262	1.1428	1.1597	1.1768	1.1941	1.2653	1.3401
7	1.1291	1.1487	1.1685	1.1887	1.2091	1.2299	1.3159	1.4071
8	1.1489	1.1717	1.1948	1.2184	1.2424	1.2668	1.3686	1.4775
9	1.1690	1.1951	1.2217	1.2489	1.2765	1.3048	1.4233	1.5513
10	1.1894	1.2190	1.2492	1.2801	1.3117	1.3439	1.4802	1.6289
11	1.2103	1.2434	1.2773	1.3121	1.3477	1.3842	1.5395	1.7103
12	1.2314	1.2682	1.3060	1.3449	1.3848	1.4258	1.6010	1.7959
13	1.2530	1.2936	1.3354	1.3785	1.4229	1.4685	1.6651	1.8856
14	1.2749	1.3195	1.3655	1.4130	1.4620	1.5126	1.7317	1.9799
15	1.2972	1.3459	1.3962	1.4483	1.5022	1.5580	1.8009	2.0789
16	1.3199	1.3728	1.4276	1.4845	1.5435	1.6047	1.8730	2.1829
17	1.3430	1.4002	1.4597	1.5216	1.5860	1.6528	1.9479	2.2920
18	1.3665	1.4282	1.4926	1.5597	1.6296	1.7024	2.0258	2.4066
19	1.3904	1.4568	1.5262	1.5987	1.6744	1.7535	2.1068	2.5270
20	1.4148	1.4859	1.5605	1.6386	1.7204	1.8061	2.1911	2.6533
21	1.4395	1.5157	1.5956	1.6796	1.7677	1.8603	2.2788	2.7860
22	1.4647	1.5460	1.6315	1.7216	1.8164	1.9161	2.3699	2.9253
23	1.4904	1.5769	1.6682	1.7646	1.8663	1.9736	2.4647	3.0715
24	1.5164	1.6084	1.7058	1.8087	1.9176	2.0328	2.5633	3.2251
25	1.5430	1.6406	1.7441	1.8539	1.9704	2.0938	2.6658	3.3864
26	1.5700	1.6734	1.7834	1.9003	2.0245	2.1566	2.7725	3.5557
27	1.5975	1.7069	1.8235	1.9478	2.0802	2.2213	2.8834	3.7335
28	1.6254	1.7410	1.8645	1.9965	2.1374	2.2879	2.9987	3.9201
29	1.6539	1.7758	1.9065	2.0464	2.1962	2.3566	3.1187	4.1161
30	1.6828	1.8114	1.9494	2.0976	2.2566	2.4273	3.2434	4.3219
31	1.7122	1.8476	1.9933	2.1500	2.3187	2.5001	3.3731	4.5380
32	1.7422	1.8845	2.0381	2.2038	2.3824	2.5751	3.5081	4.7649
33	1.7727	1.9222	2.0840	2.2589	2.4479	2.6523	3.6484	5.0032
34	1.8037	1.9607	2.1308	2.3153	2.5153	2.7319	3.7943	5.2533
35	1.8353	1.9999	2.1788	2.3732	2.5844	2.8139	3.9461	5.5160
36	1.8674	2.0399	2.2278	2.4325	2.6555	2.8983	4.1039	5.7918
37	1.9001	2.0807	2.2779	2.4933	2.7285	2.9852	4.2681	6.0814
38	1.9333	2.1223	2.3292	2.5557	2.8036	3.0748	4.4388	6.3855
39	1.9672	2.1647	2.3816	2.6196	2.8807	3.1670	4.6164	6.7048
40	2.0016	2.2080	2.4352	2.6851	2.9599	3.2620	4.8010	7.0400
41	2.0366	2.2522	2.4900	2.7522	3.0413	3.3599	4.9931	7.3920
42	2.0723	2.2972	2.5460	2.8210	3.1249	3.4607	5.1928	7.7616
43	2.1085	2.3432	2.6033	2.8915	3.2108	3.5645	5.4005	8.1497
44	2.1454	2.3901	2.6619	2.9638	3.2991	3.6715	5.6165	8.5572
45	2.1830	2.4379	2.7218	3.0379	3.3899	3.7816	5.8412	8.9850
46	2.2212	2.4866	2.7830	3.1139	3.4831	3.8950	6.0748	9.4343
47	2.2600	2.5363	2.8456	3.1917	3.5789	4.0119	6.3178	9.9060
48	2.2996	2.5871	2.9096	3.2715	3.6773	4.1323	6.5705	10.4013
60	2.8318	3.2810	3.8001	4.3998	5.0923	5.8916	10.5196	18.6792
72	3.4872	4.1611	4.9632	5.9172	7.0517	8.4000	16.8423	33.5451
84	4.2943	5.2773	6.4821	7.9580	9.7650	11.9764	26.9650	60.2422
96	5.2882	6.6929	8.4660	10.7026	13.5225	17.0755	43.1718	108.1864
108	6.5120	8.4883	11.0570	14.3939	18.7257	24.3456	69.1195	194.2872
120	8.0192	10.7652	14.4410	19.3581	25.9310	34.7110	110.6626	348.9120
180	22.7089	35.3208	54.8778	85.1718	132.0473	204.5034	1164.1289	6517.3918
240	64.3073	115.8887	208.5432	374.7380	672.4180	1204.8526	12246.2024	121739.5737
300	182.1065	380.2345	792.4922	1648.7683	3424.1215	7098.5135	128825.4860	2273996.1286
360	515.6921	1247.5611	3011.5772	7254.2337	17436.4873	41821.6241	1355196.1137	42476396.4087

Table II (*continued*)

n = No. Periods	Interest Rate per Period: $i^{(m)}/m$					
	6.000%	7.000%	8.000%	9.000%	10.000%	12.000%
1	1.060	1.070	1.080	1.090	1.10	1.12
2	1.124	1.145	1.166	1.188	1.21	1.25
3	1.191	1.225	1.260	1.295	1.33	1.40
4	1.262	1.311	1.360	1.412	1.46	1.57
5	1.338	1.403	1.469	1.539	1.61	1.76
6	1.419	1.501	1.587	1.677	1.77	1.97
7	1.504	1.606	1.714	1.828	1.95	2.21
8	1.594	1.718	1.851	1.993	2.14	2.48
9	1.689	1.838	1.999	2.172	2.36	2.77
10	1.791	1.967	2.159	2.367	2.59	3.11
11	1.898	2.105	2.332	2.580	2.85	3.48
12	2.012	2.252	2.518	2.813	3.14	3.90
13	2.133	2.410	2.720	3.066	3.45	4.36
14	2.261	2.579	2.937	3.342	3.80	4.89
15	2.397	2.759	3.172	3.642	4.18	5.47
16	2.540	2.952	3.426	3.970	4.59	6.13
17	2.693	3.159	3.700	4.328	5.05	6.87
18	2.854	3.380	3.996	4.717	5.56	7.69
19	3.026	3.617	4.316	5.142	6.12	8.61
20	3.207	3.870	4.661	5.604	6.73	9.65
21	3.400	4.141	5.034	6.109	7.40	10.80
22	3.604	4.430	5.437	6.659	8.14	12.10
23	3.820	4.741	5.871	7.258	8.95	13.55
24	4.049	5.072	6.341	7.911	9.85	15.18
25	4.292	5.427	6.848	8.623	10.83	17.00
26	4.549	5.807	7.396	9.399	11.92	19.04
27	4.822	6.214	7.988	10.245	13.11	21.32
28	5.112	6.649	8.627	11.167	14.42	23.88
29	5.418	7.114	9.317	12.172	15.86	26.75
30	5.743	7.612	10.063	13.268	17.45	29.96
31	6.088	8.145	10.868	14.462	19.19	33.56
32	6.453	8.715	11.737	15.763	21.11	37.58
33	6.841	9.325	12.676	17.182	23.23	42.09
34	7.251	9.978	13.690	18.728	25.55	47.14
35	7.686	10.677	14.785	20.414	28.10	52.80
36	8.147	11.424	15.968	22.251	30.91	59.14
37	8.636	12.224	17.246	24.254	34.00	66.23
38	9.154	13.079	18.625	26.437	37.40	74.18
39	9.704	13.995	20.115	28.816	41.14	83.08
40	10.286	14.974	21.725	31.409	45.26	93.05
41	10.903	16.023	23.462	34.236	49.79	104.22
42	11.557	17.144	25.339	37.318	54.76	116.72
43	12.250	18.344	27.367	40.676	60.24	130.73
44	12.985	19.628	29.556	44.337	66.26	146.42
45	13.765	21.002	31.920	48.327	72.89	163.99
46	14.590	22.473	34.474	52.677	80.18	183.67
47	15.466	24.046	37.232	57.418	88.20	205.71
48	16.394	25.729	40.211	62.585	97.02	230.39
60	32.988	57.946	101.257	176.031	304.48	897.60
72	66.378	130.506	254.983	495.117	955.59	3497.02
84	133.565	293.926	642.089	1392.598	2999.06	13624.29
96	268.759	661.977	1616.890	3916.912	9412.34	53079.91
108	540.796	1490.898	4071.605	11016.960	29539.97	206798.05
120	1088.188	3357.788	10252.993	30987.016	92709.07	805680.26
180	35896.801	194571.839	1038187.959	5454684.416	28228209.27	723176126.27
240	1184152.575	11274742.824	105123864.279	960195145.041	8594971441.07	649120673317.10
300	39062459.052	653331060.145	10644533818.252	169024391915.498	2617010996188.46	582648725835082.30
360	1288580323.180	37858200475.409	1077834238542.631	29753582081680.650	796831798817387.10	5229837096120442000.00

Table III

$s_{\overline{n}|i_p}$ = Future value of n \$1 payments immediately after the last payment. Each payment earns interest at nominal annual rate of $i^{(m)}$. See Section 12.6.

n = No. Periods	Interest Rate per Period: $i^{(m)}/m$							
	0.2500%	0.5000%	0.6667%	0.7500%	0.8750%	1.0000%	1.2500%	1.5000%
1	1.00000	1.00000	1.00000	1.00000	1.00000	1.00000	1.00000	1.00000
2	2.00250	2.00500	2.00667	2.00750	2.00875	2.01000	2.01250	2.01500
3	3.00751	3.01502	3.02004	3.02256	3.02633	3.03010	3.03766	3.04522
4	4.01503	4.03010	4.04018	4.04523	4.05281	4.06040	4.07563	4.09090
5	5.02506	5.05025	5.06711	5.07556	5.08827	5.10101	5.12657	5.15227
6	6.03763	6.07550	6.10089	6.11363	6.13279	6.15202	6.19065	6.22955
7	7.05272	7.10588	7.14157	7.15948	7.18645	7.21354	7.26804	7.32299
8	8.07035	8.14141	8.18918	8.21318	8.24933	8.28567	8.35889	8.43284
9	9.09053	9.18212	9.24377	9.27478	9.32152	9.36853	9.46337	9.55933
10	10.11325	10.22803	10.30540	10.34434	10.40308	10.46221	10.58167	10.70272
11	11.13854	11.27917	11.37410	11.42192	11.49411	11.56683	11.71394	11.86326
12	12.16638	12.33556	12.44993	12.50759	12.59468	12.68250	12.86036	13.04121
13	13.19680	13.39724	13.53293	13.60139	13.70488	13.80933	14.02112	14.23683
14	14.22979	14.46423	14.62315	14.70340	14.82480	14.94742	15.19638	15.45038
15	15.26537	15.53655	15.72063	15.81368	15.95452	16.09690	16.38633	16.68214
16	16.30353	16.61423	16.82544	16.93228	17.09412	17.25786	17.59116	17.93237
17	17.34429	17.69730	17.93761	18.05927	18.24369	18.43044	18.81105	19.20136
18	18.38765	18.78579	19.05719	19.19472	19.40333	19.61475	20.04619	20.48938
19	19.43362	19.87972	20.18424	20.33868	20.57311	20.81090	21.29677	21.79672
20	20.48220	20.97912	21.31880	21.49122	21.75312	22.01900	22.56298	23.12367
21	21.53341	22.08401	22.46093	22.65240	22.94346	23.23919	23.84502	24.47052
22	22.58724	23.19443	23.61066	23.82230	24.14421	24.47159	25.14308	25.83758
23	23.64371	24.31040	24.76807	25.00096	25.35548	25.71630	26.45737	27.22514
24	24.70282	25.43196	25.93319	26.18847	26.57734	26.97346	27.78808	28.63352
25	25.76457	26.55912	27.10608	27.38488	27.80989	28.24320	29.13544	30.06302
26	26.82899	27.69191	28.28678	28.59027	29.05323	29.52563	30.49963	31.51397
27	27.89606	28.83037	29.47536	29.80470	30.30744	30.82089	31.88087	32.98668
28	28.96580	29.97452	30.67187	31.02823	31.57263	32.12910	33.27938	34.48148
29	30.03821	31.12439	31.87634	32.26094	32.84889	33.45039	34.69538	35.99870
30	31.11331	32.28002	33.08885	33.50290	34.13632	34.78489	36.12907	37.53868
31	32.19109	33.44142	34.30945	34.75417	35.43501	36.13274	37.58068	39.10176
32	33.27157	34.60862	35.53818	36.01483	36.74507	37.49407	39.05044	40.68829
33	34.35475	35.78167	36.77510	37.28494	38.06659	38.86901	40.53857	42.29861
34	35.44064	36.96058	38.02026	38.56458	39.39967	40.25770	42.04530	43.93309
35	36.52924	38.14538	39.27373	39.85381	40.74442	41.66028	43.57087	45.59209
36	37.62056	39.33610	40.53556	41.15272	42.10093	43.07688	45.11551	47.27597
37	38.71461	40.53279	41.80579	42.46136	43.46931	44.50765	46.67945	48.98511
38	39.81140	41.73545	43.08450	43.77982	44.84967	45.95272	48.26294	50.71989
39	40.91093	42.94413	44.37173	45.10817	46.24211	47.41225	49.86623	52.48068
40	42.01320	44.15885	45.66754	46.44648	47.64672	48.88637	51.48956	54.26789
41	43.11824	45.37964	46.97199	47.79483	49.06363	50.37524	53.13318	56.08191
42	44.22603	46.60654	48.28514	49.15329	50.49294	51.87899	54.79734	57.92314
43	45.33660	47.83957	49.60704	50.52194	51.93475	53.39778	56.48231	59.79199
44	46.44994	49.07877	50.93775	51.90086	53.38918	54.93176	58.18834	61.68887
45	47.56606	50.32416	52.27734	53.29011	54.85634	56.48107	59.91569	63.61420
46	48.68498	51.57578	53.62585	54.68979	56.33633	58.04589	61.66464	65.56841
47	49.80669	52.83366	54.98336	56.09996	57.82927	59.62634	63.43545	67.55194
48	50.93121	54.09783	56.34992	57.52071	59.33528	61.22261	65.22839	69.56522
60	64.64671	69.77003	73.47686	75.42414	78.46891	81.66967	88.57451	96.21465
72	78.77939	86.40886	92.02533	95.00703	99.71114	104.70993	115.67362	128.07720
84	93.34192	104.07393	112.11331	116.42693	123.29433	130.67227	147.12904	166.17264
96	108.34739	122.82854	133.86858	139.85616	149.47647	159.92729	183.64106	211.72023
108	123.80926	142.73990	157.42954	165.48322	178.54397	192.89258	226.02255	266.17777
120	139.74142	163.87935	182.94604	193.51428	210.81481	230.03869	275.21706	331.28819
180	226.97269	290.81871	346.03822	378.40577	434.02981	499.58020	668.50676	905.62451
240	328.30200	462.04090	589.02042	667.88687	810.50488	989.25537	1497.23948	2308.85437
300	446.00782	692.99396	951.02639	1121.12194	1445.46885	1878.84663	3243.52962	5737.25331
360	582.73688	1004.51504	1490.35945	1830.74348	2516.40099	3494.96413	6923.27961	14113.58539

Table III   (continued)

n = No. Periods	Interest Rate per Period: $i^{(m)}/m$							
	1.750%	2.000%	2.250%	2.500%	2.750%	3.000%	4.000%	5.000%
1	1.0000	1.0000	1.0000	1.000	1.000	1.000	1.000	1.000
2	2.0175	2.0200	2.0225	2.025	2.028	2.030	2.040	2.050
3	3.0528	3.0604	3.0680	3.076	3.083	3.091	3.122	3.153
4	4.1062	4.1216	4.1370	4.153	4.168	4.184	4.246	4.310
5	5.1781	5.2040	5.2301	5.256	5.283	5.309	5.416	5.526
6	6.2687	6.3081	6.3478	6.388	6.428	6.468	6.633	6.802
7	7.3784	7.4343	7.4906	7.547	7.605	7.662	7.898	8.142
8	8.5075	8.5830	8.6592	8.736	8.814	8.892	9.214	9.549
9	9.6564	9.7546	9.8540	9.955	10.056	10.159	10.583	11.027
10	10.8254	10.9497	11.0757	11.203	11.333	11.464	12.006	12.578
11	12.0148	12.1687	12.3249	12.483	12.644	12.808	13.486	14.207
12	13.2251	13.4121	13.6022	13.796	13.992	14.192	15.026	15.917
13	14.4565	14.6803	14.9083	15.140	15.377	15.618	16.627	17.713
14	15.7095	15.9739	16.2437	16.519	16.800	17.086	18.292	19.599
15	16.9844	17.2934	17.6092	17.932	18.262	18.599	20.024	21.579
16	18.2817	18.6393	19.0054	19.380	19.764	20.157	21.825	23.657
17	19.6016	20.0121	20.4330	20.865	21.307	21.762	23.698	25.840
18	20.9446	21.4123	21.8928	22.386	22.893	23.414	25.645	28.132
19	22.3112	22.8406	23.3853	23.946	24.523	25.117	27.671	30.539
20	23.7016	24.2974	24.9115	25.545	26.197	26.870	29.778	33.066
21	25.1164	25.7833	26.4720	27.183	27.918	28.676	31.969	35.719
22	26.5559	27.2990	28.0676	28.863	29.686	30.537	34.248	38.505
23	28.0207	28.8450	29.6992	30.584	31.502	32.453	36.618	41.430
24	29.5110	30.4219	31.3674	32.349	33.368	34.426	39.083	44.502
25	31.0275	32.0303	33.0732	34.158	35.286	36.459	41.646	47.727
26	32.5704	33.6709	34.8173	36.012	37.256	38.553	44.312	51.113
27	34.1404	35.3443	36.6007	37.912	39.281	40.710	47.084	54.669
28	35.7379	37.0512	38.4242	39.860	41.361	42.931	49.968	58.403
29	37.3633	38.7922	40.2888	41.856	43.498	45.219	52.966	62.323
30	39.0172	40.5681	42.1953	43.903	45.695	47.575	56.085	66.439
31	40.7000	42.3794	44.1447	46.000	47.951	50.003	59.328	70.761
32	42.4122	44.2270	46.1379	48.150	50.270	52.503	62.701	75.299
33	44.1544	46.1116	48.1760	50.354	52.652	55.078	66.210	80.064
34	45.9271	48.0338	50.2600	52.613	55.100	57.730	69.858	85.067
35	47.7308	49.9945	52.3908	54.928	57.615	60.462	73.652	90.320
36	49.5661	51.9944	54.5696	57.301	60.200	63.276	77.598	95.836
37	51.4335	54.0343	56.7974	59.734	62.855	66.174	81.702	101.628
38	53.3336	56.1149	59.0754	62.227	65.584	69.159	85.970	107.710
39	55.2670	58.2372	61.4046	64.783	68.387	72.234	90.409	114.095
40	57.2341	60.4020	63.7862	67.403	71.268	75.401	95.026	120.800
41	59.2357	62.6100	66.2214	70.088	74.228	78.663	99.827	127.840
42	61.2724	64.8622	68.7113	72.840	77.269	82.023	104.820	135.232
43	63.3446	67.1595	71.2574	75.661	80.394	85.484	110.012	142.993
44	65.4532	69.5027	73.8606	78.552	83.605	89.048	115.413	151.143
45	67.5986	71.8927	76.5225	81.516	86.904	92.720	121.029	159.700
46	69.7816	74.3306	79.2443	84.554	90.294	96.501	126.871	168.685
47	72.0027	76.8172	82.0273	87.668	93.777	100.397	132.945	178.119
48	74.2628	79.3535	84.8729	90.860	97.356	104.408	139.263	188.025
60	104.6752	114.0515	124.4504	135.992	148.809	163.053	237.991	353.584
72	142.1263	158.0570	176.1407	196.689	220.061	246.667	396.057	650.903
84	188.2450	213.8666	243.6508	278.321	318.729	365.881	649.125	1184.845
96	245.0374	284.6467	331.8223	388.106	455.362	535.850	1054.296	2143.728
108	314.9738	374.4129	446.9788	535.755	644.570	778.186	1702.988	3865.745
120	401.0962	488.2582	597.3789	734.326	906.583	1123.700	2741.564	6958.240
180	1240.5060	1716.0416	2394.5706	3366.872	4765.356	6783.445	29078.223	130327.837
240	3617.5602	5744.4368	9224.1416	14949.519	24415.200	40128.421	306130.059	2434771.475
300	10348.9410	18961.7254	35177.4317	65910.730	124477.145	236583.783	3220612.151	45479902.572
360	29410.9747	62328.0564	133803.4324	290129.347	634017.719	1394020.802	33879877.843	849527908.174

Table III (*continued*)

n = No. Periods	Interest Rate per Period: $i^{(m)}/m$					
	6.000%	7.000%	8.000%	9.000%	10.000%	12.000%
1	1.000	1.000	1.000	1.00	1.00	1.00
2	2.060	2.070	2.080	2.09	2.10	2.12
3	3.184	3.215	3.246	3.28	3.31	3.37
4	4.375	4.440	4.506	4.57	4.64	4.78
5	5.637	5.751	5.867	5.98	6.11	6.35
6	6.975	7.153	7.336	7.52	7.72	8.12
7	8.394	8.654	8.923	9.20	9.49	10.09
8	9.897	10.260	10.637	11.03	11.44	12.30
9	11.491	11.978	12.488	13.02	13.58	14.78
10	13.181	13.816	14.487	15.19	15.94	17.55
11	14.972	15.784	16.645	17.56	18.53	20.65
12	16.870	17.888	18.977	20.14	21.38	24.13
13	18.882	20.141	21.495	22.95	24.52	28.03
14	21.015	22.550	24.215	26.02	27.97	32.39
15	23.276	25.129	27.152	29.36	31.77	37.28
16	25.673	27.888	30.324	33.00	35.95	42.75
17	28.213	30.840	33.750	36.97	40.54	48.88
18	30.906	33.999	37.450	41.30	45.60	55.75
19	33.760	37.379	41.446	46.02	51.16	63.44
20	36.786	40.995	45.762	51.16	57.27	72.05
21	39.993	44.865	50.423	56.76	64.00	81.70
22	43.392	49.006	55.457	62.87	71.40	92.50
23	46.996	53.436	60.893	69.53	79.54	104.60
24	50.816	58.177	66.765	76.79	88.50	118.16
25	54.865	63.249	73.106	84.70	98.35	133.33
26	59.156	68.676	79.954	93.32	109.18	150.33
27	63.706	74.484	87.351	102.72	121.10	169.37
28	68.528	80.698	95.339	112.97	134.21	190.70
29	73.640	87.347	103.966	124.14	148.63	214.58
30	79.058	94.461	113.283	136.31	164.49	241.33
31	84.802	102.073	123.346	149.58	181.94	271.29
32	90.890	110.218	134.214	164.04	201.14	304.85
33	97.343	118.933	145.951	179.80	222.25	342.43
34	104.184	128.259	158.627	196.98	245.48	384.52
35	111.435	138.237	172.317	215.71	271.02	431.66
36	119.121	148.913	187.102	236.12	299.13	484.46
37	127.268	160.337	203.070	258.38	330.04	543.60
38	135.904	172.561	220.316	282.63	364.04	609.83
39	145.058	185.640	238.941	309.07	401.45	684.01
40	154.762	199.635	259.057	337.88	442.59	767.09
41	165.048	214.610	280.781	369.29	487.85	860.14
42	175.951	230.632	304.244	403.53	537.64	964.36
43	187.508	247.776	329.583	440.85	592.40	1081.08
44	199.758	266.121	356.950	481.52	652.64	1211.81
45	212.744	285.749	386.506	525.86	718.90	1358.23
46	226.508	306.752	418.426	574.19	791.80	1522.22
47	241.099	329.224	452.900	626.86	871.97	1705.88
48	256.565	353.270	490.132	684.28	960.17	1911.59
60	533.128	813.520	1253.213	1944.79	3034.82	7471.64
72	1089.629	1850.092	3174.781	5490.19	9545.94	29133.47
84	2209.417	4184.651	8013.617	15462.20	29980.63	113527.42
96	4462.651	9442.523	20198.627	43510.13	94113.44	442324.25
108	8996.600	21284.260	50882.557	122399.56	295389.66	1723308.79
120	18119.796	47954.120	128149.912	344289.06	927080.69	6713993.79
180	598263.350	2779583.412	12977336.989	60607593.51	282282082.74	6026467710.61
240	19735859.576	161067740.347	1314048290.989	10668834933.79	85949714400.69	5409338944300.83
300	651040967.534	9333300844.926	133056672715.655	1878048799049.98	26170109961874.64	4855406048625677.00
360	21476338702.998	540831435348.694	13472927981770.390	330595356463107.30	7968317988173861.00	4358197580100368000.00

Answers to Odd-Numbered Exercises

CHAPTER 0

Exercises 0.1

1. -3 3. $\dfrac{-57}{7}$ 5. $\dfrac{11}{12t}$ 7. $\dfrac{-4}{3}$ 9. $\dfrac{-8}{5}$ 11. $\dfrac{-9}{8}$ 13. $\dfrac{86n}{3}$ 15. $\dfrac{1}{100}$ 17. $\dfrac{-5}{18}$ 19. $\dfrac{-41}{54}$

21. $\dfrac{2x - 15y}{24}$ 23. $\dfrac{7}{2}$

Exercises 0.2

25.
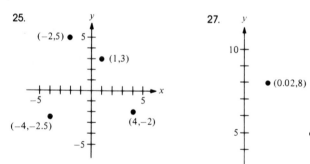

27.
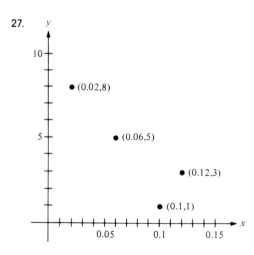

29. $A(-2, 1)$
$B(1, 5)$
$C(4, 6)$
$D(0, 2)$
$E(3, 3)$
$F(3, 0)$
$G(4, -1)$

31. $A(-.02, .4)$
$B(0, .6)$
$C(.05, 1.0)$
$D(.02, .4)$
$E(-.01, -.1)$
$F(.01, -.1)$
$G(.03, 0)$

33.
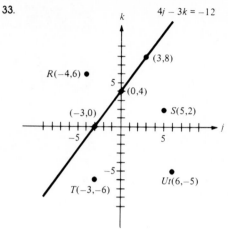

35.
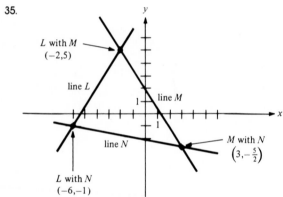

37.
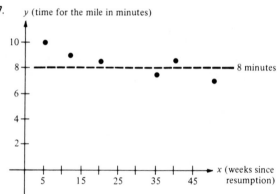

39.
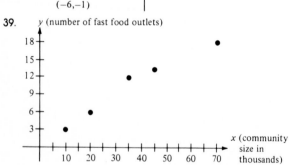

Exercises 0.3

41.

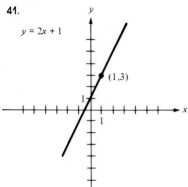

$y = 2x + 1$

(1,3)

43.

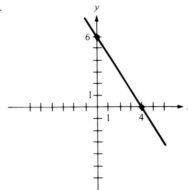

6

4

45.

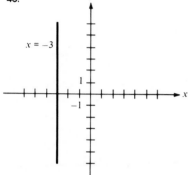

$x = -3$

47.

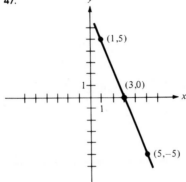

(1,5)

(3,0)

(5,−5)

49.

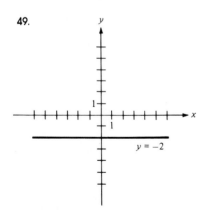

$y = -2$

51. $y = \dfrac{3}{5}x + 3$ **53.** $x = 13$ **55.** $y = 6$ **57.** $y = \dfrac{3}{2}x - 12$

59. $x = 5$ **61.** $y - 2 = -4(x - 5)$

63.

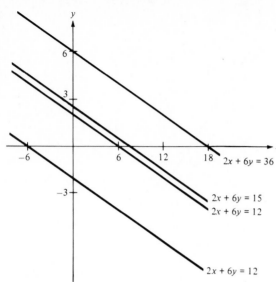

$2x + 6y = 36$

$2x + 6y = 15$

$2x + 6y = 12$

$2x + 6y = 12$

65. $y - 8 = \dfrac{5}{2}(x - 6)$ **67.** No

Exercises 0.4

69. $T = 2.50s + b$ **71.** $28 = 2.50s + b$ **73.** $T = 35f + 25i + 10s$ **75.** $T = 2s + .75e$

Exercises 0.5

77. $x = 35$ **79.** $x = 17$ **81.** $x = \dfrac{1}{3}$ **83.** $x = \dfrac{2}{5}$ **85.** $x = \dfrac{26}{7} \approx 3.71$ **87.** $x = \dfrac{345}{29} \approx 11.90$

89. $x = \dfrac{-51}{7} \approx -7.29$ **91.** $x = \dfrac{1100.50}{43} \approx 25.59$

CHAPTER 1

Exercises 1.1

1. $x = 3, y = -1$ **3.** $r = 2, s = -3, t = 4$ **5.** $x = 3, y = -1$ **7.** $r = 2, s = -3, t = 4$
9. $h = -1, j = 3, k = 1$ **11.** $r = 2, s = -1, t = 3, u = 3$

13.

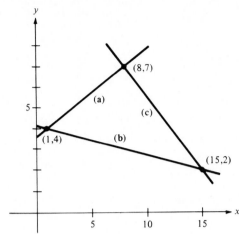

15. 28 Republicans, 12 Democrats

17. 15 pennies, 6 nickels, 8 dimes

19. 9 frammis, 24 widgets

21. 52 cars, 12 trucks, 5 buses

Exercises 1.2

23. The system has reduced to

$$x - 5y + \frac{1}{2}z = 0$$

$$y - \frac{8}{25}z = \frac{2}{25}$$

$$z = 6$$

25. The system has reduced to

$$x - \frac{1}{2}y = \frac{11}{80}$$

$$y = \frac{1}{8}$$

27. $x = 7$, $y = 10$, $z = -3$

29. $x = 6$, $y = 2$, $z = -3$ **31.** $r = \frac{202}{11}$, $s = 25$, $t = -\frac{147}{11}$, $u = -\frac{504}{11}$ **33.** $k = 10$, $p = 13$, $q = 3$

35. There are 35 horses, 42 mules, and 14 people on the trip.

Exercises 1.3

37. $v = 5$
$w = -2$
$x = .6$

39. $v = 2$
$w = 3$
$x = -1$

41. $v + .6x + 2z = 5$
$w - 3x + 4z = -1$
$y + 6z = 2$

43. $v = 9$
$w + 3y = 0$
$x + 5y = 5$
$0 = 7$
No solution

45. $a = -2$, $b = -3$, $c = \frac{1}{2}$

47. $x = \frac{46 - 14z}{13}$, $y = \frac{6 + z}{13}$, $z =$ any real number

49. $m = 4$, $n = 1$, $p = \frac{1}{2}$, $q = \frac{3}{2}$

51. The bottom row would say $0a + 0b + 0c = -1$, which is not possible. No solution.

53. We have $L = 5$ ounces, $M = 8$ ounces, $N = 3$ ounces.

Review Exercises

55.

System	Matrix
(a)	H
(b)	E
(c)	G
(d)	H
(e)	D, A, F
(f)	C
(g)	B

57. $x = 4, y = 0$ **59.** $a = 12, b = 8$ **61.** $m = \dfrac{21}{2}, n = 1$

63. $x = 9, y = -4, z = 2$ **65.** $x = \dfrac{19}{5}, y = \dfrac{4}{5}$ **67.** $x = -\dfrac{1}{11}, y = -\dfrac{14}{11}, z = \dfrac{9}{11}$

69. $r = -\dfrac{7}{10} - \dfrac{3}{10}c, s = \dfrac{3}{2} + c, t = \dfrac{4}{10} + \dfrac{1}{10}c, u = c$; c is any real number

71. $(p = 3, q = 0)$ **73.** Intersection point is $s = 3, t = -4$

75.

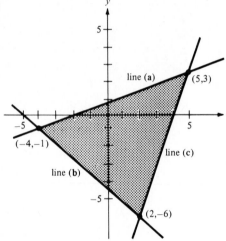

77. \$30   **79.** 50 cows at Creek Farm

81. $d_1 = 100$ km, $d_2 = 70$ km

CHAPTER 2

Exercises 2.1

1. 3×4 **3.** 1×2 **5.** 1×3 **7.** 3×1 **9.** $\begin{bmatrix} -5 \\ -4 \end{bmatrix}$ **11.** $\begin{bmatrix} 6 & -9 \\ 4 & 12 \\ 6 & x+7 \end{bmatrix}$ **13.** $\begin{bmatrix} 0 & 0 \\ 0 & 4 \\ 2 & 0 \\ -6 & -5 \end{bmatrix}$

15. $[w + m \quad 7 \quad m + 1]$ **17.** $\begin{bmatrix} 1 & -7 & -3 \\ -1 & -2 & 2 \\ 1 & 1 & 7 \end{bmatrix}$ **19.** "NP"   **21.** $\begin{bmatrix} 3 & -1 & 7 \\ 3 & 2 & 0 \\ 3 & 1 & 3 \end{bmatrix}$

23. $\begin{bmatrix} 0 & -7 & -3 \\ -1 & -3 & 2 \\ 1 & 1 & 6 \end{bmatrix} \neq \begin{bmatrix} 2 & -7 & -3 \\ -1 & -1 & 2 \\ 1 & 1 & 8 \end{bmatrix}$ so $(A - B) - C \neq A - (B - C)$

25. $x = -1$ **27.** $x = -7, y = 3$

29. $A - B = \begin{bmatrix} 50 & 10 & 50 \\ 40 & 5 & 26 \end{bmatrix}$

31.

"Matrix A"	weight	press
player #1	220	280
player #2	218	295
player #3	224	310
player #4	228	260

33. $B - A = \begin{bmatrix} 5 & 20 \\ 12 & 10 \\ 10 & 5 \\ 4 & 35 \end{bmatrix}$

35.

	person A	person B	
$D =$	26	18	CD players
	14	9	preamplifiers
	16	9	power amplifiers

37. $D - N = \begin{bmatrix} 12 & 6 \\ 10 & 4 \\ 10 & 4 \end{bmatrix}$

Exercises 2.2

39. $\begin{bmatrix} 14 \\ 6 \\ 7 \end{bmatrix}$

41. $\begin{bmatrix} 2 & 3 & 2 \\ 1 & 2 & 1 \\ 2 & 5 & 2 \end{bmatrix}$

43. $\begin{bmatrix} 10 \\ 7 \end{bmatrix}$

45. $\begin{bmatrix} 8 & 0 & -5 \\ -1 & 6 & 7 \end{bmatrix}$

47. $\begin{bmatrix} -2 & 9 \\ 1 & 6 \end{bmatrix}$

49. $\begin{bmatrix} 1 & 8 \\ 0 & 1 \\ 1 & 7 \end{bmatrix}$

51. "NP"   **53.** "NP"

55. (a) $\begin{bmatrix} 0 & 20 \\ 0 & 6 \\ 3 & 12 \end{bmatrix}$ (b) $\begin{bmatrix} 0 & 20 \\ 0 & 6 \\ 3 & 12 \end{bmatrix}$ (c) equal

57. (a) $\begin{bmatrix} 3 & 11 & 3 \\ 6 & 11 & 6 \end{bmatrix}$ (b) $\begin{bmatrix} 3 & 11 & 3 \\ 6 & 11 & 6 \end{bmatrix}$ (c) equal

Exercises 2.3

59. $\begin{bmatrix} 2 \\ 1 \\ -4 \end{bmatrix}$

61. $\begin{bmatrix} 3 & -2 & 3 \\ -1 & 1 & 0 \\ 2 & 5 & 1 \end{bmatrix}$

63. $\begin{bmatrix} 1 & 2 \\ 1 & 3 \\ 1 & 4 \\ 1 & 5 \end{bmatrix}$

65. $(A^T)^T = A$

67. (a) $\begin{bmatrix} 15 \\ 0 \end{bmatrix}$ (b) $\begin{bmatrix} 15 \\ 0 \end{bmatrix}$

69. $[2 \ \ 1 \ \ 4]$

71. (a) $\begin{bmatrix} 5 & 16 \\ 16 & 58 \end{bmatrix}$ (b) $\begin{vmatrix} 5 & 16 \\ 16 & 58 \end{vmatrix}$

73. $\begin{bmatrix} 2 & 1 & -2 \\ 0 & 2 & 1 \\ 3 & -1 & 5 \\ 2 & 1 & 4 \end{bmatrix}$

75. $\begin{bmatrix} 4 & -2 \\ -1 & 4 \\ 2 & 0 \end{bmatrix}$

77. $[2 \ \ 1 \ \ 4]$

79. (a) $[1 \ \ 2]$ (b) $[1 \ \ 2]$ (c) Yes. $E = \begin{bmatrix} 0 & 0 \\ \frac{1}{2} & 1 \end{bmatrix}$, for example.

81. I

Exercises 2.4

83. A has no inverse

85. $\frac{1}{6}\begin{bmatrix} 3 & 0 \\ -1 & 2 \end{bmatrix}$

87. $\frac{1}{11}\begin{bmatrix} 3 & 4 \\ -2 & 1 \end{bmatrix}$

89. $\frac{1}{6}\begin{bmatrix} 3 & 0 \\ -2 & 2 \end{bmatrix}$

91. A has no inverse

93. $\begin{bmatrix} 0 & -1 & 3 \\ \frac{1}{2} & 0 & -\frac{1}{2} \\ 0 & 1 & -2 \end{bmatrix}$

95. $\begin{bmatrix} 1 & 0 & 0 \\ 0 & \frac{1}{2} & 0 \\ 0 & 0 & \frac{1}{3} \end{bmatrix}$

97. $\begin{bmatrix} -5 & 3 \\ 2 & -1 \end{bmatrix}$

99. D has *no inverse*

101. $\frac{1}{2}\begin{bmatrix} 2 & -4 \\ 0 & 1 \end{bmatrix}$

103. $\frac{1}{4}\begin{bmatrix} -1 & 3 & -4 \\ 1 & -3 & 8 \\ 1 & 1 & -4 \end{bmatrix}$

105. $\begin{bmatrix} 0 & 0 & 1 \\ & & \frac{1}{2} \\ 1 & 0 & -\frac{1}{2} \\ -1 & 1 & 0 \end{bmatrix}$

107. $\frac{1}{10}\begin{bmatrix} 12 & -7 \\ -14 & 9 \end{bmatrix}$

109. $(AB)^{-1} = B^{-1}A^{-1}$

111. (a) $\begin{bmatrix} 7 & 11 \\ 8 & 14 \end{bmatrix}$ (b) $\frac{1}{10}\begin{bmatrix} 14 & -11 \\ -8 & 7 \end{bmatrix}$ (c) $\frac{1}{10}\begin{bmatrix} 14 & -11 \\ -8 & 7 \end{bmatrix}$

113. (a) $\frac{1}{4}\begin{bmatrix} -1 & 1 & 1 \\ 3 & -3 & 1 \\ -4 & 8 & -4 \end{bmatrix}$ (b) $\frac{1}{4}\begin{bmatrix} -1 & 1 & 1 \\ 3 & -3 & 1 \\ -4 & 8 & -4 \end{bmatrix}$ (c) $(D^T)^{-1} = (D^{-1})^T$

115. $x = 1, y = 2$

117. (a) $x = \frac{29}{19}, y = \frac{63}{19}$ (b) $x = 4, y = 2$

Review Exercises

119. $\begin{bmatrix} 3 & 3 & 4 \\ 5 & 2 & 2 \\ -4 & 4 & 7 \end{bmatrix}$

121. $\begin{bmatrix} 3 & 2 & 2 \\ 3 & 1 & 0 \\ -2 & 2 & 6 \end{bmatrix}$

123. (a) $\begin{bmatrix} -3 & 2 & 1 \\ 4 & 2 & -2 \\ 1 & 3 & 8 \end{bmatrix}$ (b) $\begin{bmatrix} -1 & 9 & 8 \\ -3 & 2 & 1 \\ 11 & 13 & 20 \end{bmatrix}$ (c) $\begin{bmatrix} -1 & 9 & 8 \\ -3 & 2 & 1 \\ 11 & 13 & 20 \end{bmatrix}$ (d) distributive law

125. $\begin{bmatrix} -3 & 3 & 1 \\ 6 & -5 & -2 \\ -2 & 2 & 1 \end{bmatrix}$

127. $\begin{bmatrix} 2 & 1 & 0 \\ 1 & 0 & 2 \\ 1 & 0 & 3 \end{bmatrix}$

129. $\begin{bmatrix} -4 & 2 & 3 \\ 1 & 1 & 3 \\ 0 & -2 & 5 \end{bmatrix}$

131. (a) $\begin{bmatrix} 3 & 3 & -2 \\ 2 & 1 & 2 \\ 2 & 0 & 6 \end{bmatrix}$ (b) $\begin{bmatrix} 3 & 3 & -2 \\ 2 & 1 & 2 \\ 2 & 0 & 6 \end{bmatrix}$ (c) $(A + B)^T = A^T + B^T$

133. $\begin{bmatrix} 0 & 3 & -2 \\ 1 & -6 & 4 \\ 0 & -1 & 1 \end{bmatrix}$ $\begin{bmatrix} 0 & 3 & -2 \\ 1 & -6 & 4 \\ 0 & -1 & 1 \end{bmatrix}$ $(A^T)^{-1} = (A^{-1})^T$

135.

	RAM Chips	Floppies	Ports
80286	324	24	48
80386	1512	96	192
80486	630	38	76

Interpretation: 324 RAM chips are used in the 18 80286 machines, 1512 RAM chips are used in the 60 80386 machines, and 630 RAM chips are used in the 22 80486 machines. Same interpretations apply for floppies and ports.

137.

RAM Chips	Floppies	Ports
[2466	158	316]

Interpretation: The product $T = [1 \ 1 \ 1] AM$ sums the columns of matrix AM. Thus, 2466 RAM chips are used in the 100 machines, while 158 floppy drives and 316 ports are used.

CHAPTER 3

Exercises 3.1

1. 37 grams   3. 76 grams   5. $10,550   7. $\begin{bmatrix} 10250 \\ 10350 \\ 10400 \\ 10800 \end{bmatrix}$ Salt Lake City   9. [$3240 $3350]

11. 5850 items   13. 17,175 items   15. $\begin{bmatrix} 460 \\ 500 \\ 500 \end{bmatrix}$ North 460, South 500, Central 500

17. Country Special $2025, Dieter's Delite $1400, Liver/Onions $640, El Grosso $4275   19. $8558.50

21. $1550   23. $\begin{bmatrix} \$490 \\ \$270 \\ \$375 \\ \$285 \end{bmatrix}$ Store A $490, Store C $375, Store B $270, Store D $285   25. $6540   27. $7350

Exercises 3.2

29. $\begin{array}{c} \\ V \\ W \\ X \\ Y \\ Z \end{array} \begin{array}{c} \begin{array}{ccccc} V & W & X & Y & Z \end{array} \\ \begin{bmatrix} 0 & 1 & 1 & 0 & 0 \\ 1 & 0 & 0 & 0 & 0 \\ 0 & 0 & 0 & 1 & 0 \\ 0 & 0 & 1 & 0 & 0 \\ 1 & 0 & 0 & 1 & 0 \end{bmatrix} \end{array} = M$

31.

33.

35. This is *not* a matrix of a dominance digraph, because M says that B dominates C and also that C dominates B.

37. This is not a dominance matrix, because M says that A dominates B and also that B dominates A.

39. This is a dominance matrix:
    A dominates B
    B dominates C
    C dominates A

41. (a) Number of two-step connections P_1P_3 is P_1P_3 entry in M^2. (Answer: 0)
    (b) Number of three-step connections P_1P_3 is P_1P_3 entry in M^3. (Answer: 0)
    (c) Number of connections P_1P_3 using three steps or fewer is sum of P_1P_3 entries in M, M^2, M^3. (Answers: $1 + 0 + 0 = 1$).

43. (a) M *does* represent a dominance matrix because no vertex which dominates another is also dominated by that other vertex, and in each pair of vertices one *does* dominate the other.
    (b) 1
    (c) 0
    (d) 0

45. M does *not* represent a dominance digraph because, for instance, B exports to C and C exports to B.

47. B can export, in two steps or less, to A (one way), to B (two ways), to C (one way) to D (two ways).

49. D *cannot* get goods to country A in two or fewer steps.

51.

$$
M = \begin{array}{c} \\ P_1 \\ P_2 \\ P_3 \\ P_4 \end{array}
\begin{array}{cccc} P_1 & P_2 & P_3 & P_4 \end{array}
\left[\begin{array}{cccc}
0 & 1 & 0 & 1 \\
0 & 0 & 1 & 0 \\
1 & 0 & 0 & 1 \\
1 & 0 & 1 & 0
\end{array}\right]
$$

53. There is one three-step connection from P_2 to P_3. This is P_2P_3, P_3P_4, P_4P_3

55. Two routes from P_1 to P_3 require no more than two intermediate stops. (This is P_1P_2, then P_2P_3 or P_1P_4, then P_4P_3)

57.

$$
M = \begin{array}{c} \\ P_1 \\ P_2 \\ P_3 \\ P_4 \\ P_5 \\ P_6 \end{array}
\begin{array}{cccccc} P_1 & P_2 & P_3 & P_4 & P_5 & P_6 \end{array}
\left[\begin{array}{cccccc}
0 & 1 & 0 & 0 & 0 & 0 \\
0 & 0 & 1 & 0 & 1 & 0 \\
0 & 0 & 0 & 1 & 0 & 0 \\
0 & 0 & 0 & 0 & 1 & 0 \\
0 & 1 & 0 & 0 & 0 & 1 \\
1 & 0 & 0 & 0 & 0 & 0
\end{array}\right]
$$

59. No. The P_1P_4 entry in $M + M^2$ is 0.   **61.** All six

63.
$$
\left[\begin{array}{cccccc}
1 & 2 & 2 & 1 & 3 & 1 \\
1 & 4 & 2 & 2 & 3 & 3 \\
1 & 1 & 1 & 1 & 2 & 1 \\
1 & 3 & 1 & 1 & 2 & 2 \\
2 & 3 & 3 & 1 & 4 & 2 \\
1 & 2 & 1 & 1 & 1 & 1
\end{array}\right]
$$

$(M + M^2 + M^3) + M^4$

65. We need four steps (3 intersections) to return to P_3.

67.

Food	Win	Loss
Q	3	1
Tos	2	2
B	2	2
E	2	2
T	1	3

69.

Food	Powers
Q	8
E	7
B	5
Tos	5
T	3

Exercises 3.3

71.

26	36	87	124	66	94	87	118	75	109	70	94	80
111	78	113	34	46	87	118	84	121	91	123	81	111
65	91	108	151	78	83	22	30	123	171	90	123	69
101	73	98	48	71	75	102	117	165	37	53	123	171

73. 89 120 36 49 131 183 38 54 66 97 63 93 49 66 123 171

75. $\begin{bmatrix} 18 \\ 21 \end{bmatrix} \begin{bmatrix} 27 \\ 7 \end{bmatrix} \begin{bmatrix} 18 \\ 2 \end{bmatrix} \begin{bmatrix} 27 \\ 11 \end{bmatrix} \begin{bmatrix} 4 \\ 17 \end{bmatrix} \begin{bmatrix} 25 \\ 18 \end{bmatrix} \begin{bmatrix} 5 \\ 27 \end{bmatrix} \begin{bmatrix} 11 \\ 4 \end{bmatrix} \begin{bmatrix} 5 \\ 13 \end{bmatrix}$

HE -W HO -L AU GH S- LA ST

$\begin{bmatrix} 27 \\ 23 \end{bmatrix} \begin{bmatrix} 10 \\ 5 \end{bmatrix} \begin{bmatrix} 5 \\ 21 \end{bmatrix} \begin{bmatrix} 8 \\ 27 \end{bmatrix} \begin{bmatrix} 13 \\ 18 \end{bmatrix} \begin{bmatrix} 21 \\ 27 \end{bmatrix} \begin{bmatrix} 3 \\ 2 \end{bmatrix} \begin{bmatrix} 10 \\ 6 \end{bmatrix} \begin{bmatrix} 13 \\ 27 \end{bmatrix}$

-M IS SE D- TH E- PO IN T-

77. $\begin{bmatrix} 4 \\ 27 \end{bmatrix} \begin{bmatrix} 5 \\ 13 \end{bmatrix} \begin{bmatrix} 10 \\ 13 \end{bmatrix} \begin{bmatrix} 12 \\ 18 \end{bmatrix} \begin{bmatrix} 27 \\ 10 \end{bmatrix} \begin{bmatrix} 6 \\ 27 \end{bmatrix} \begin{bmatrix} 13 \\ 10 \end{bmatrix} \begin{bmatrix} 23 \\ 21 \end{bmatrix} \begin{bmatrix} 27 \\ 25 \end{bmatrix}$

A - ST IT CH -I N- TI ME -G

$\begin{bmatrix} 4 \\ 13 \end{bmatrix} \begin{bmatrix} 18 \\ 21 \end{bmatrix} \begin{bmatrix} 22 \\ 5 \end{bmatrix} \begin{bmatrix} 27 \\ 6 \end{bmatrix} \begin{bmatrix} 2 \\ 27 \end{bmatrix} \begin{bmatrix} 23 \\ 2 \end{bmatrix} \begin{bmatrix} 5 \\ 5 \end{bmatrix}$

AT HE RS -N O- MO SS

79. $\begin{bmatrix} 21 \\ 4 \\ 22 \end{bmatrix}$ $\begin{bmatrix} 11 \\ 24 \\ 27 \end{bmatrix}$ $\begin{bmatrix} 13 \\ 2 \\ 27 \end{bmatrix}$ $\begin{bmatrix} 9 \\ 21 \\ 8 \end{bmatrix}$ $\begin{bmatrix} 27 \\ 21 \\ 4 \end{bmatrix}$ $\begin{bmatrix} 22 \\ 11 \\ 24 \end{bmatrix}$ $\begin{bmatrix} 27 \\ 13 \\ 2 \end{bmatrix}$ $\begin{bmatrix} 27 \\ 22 \\ 10 \end{bmatrix}$ $\begin{bmatrix} 5 \\ 21 \\ 27 \end{bmatrix}$

   EAR LY- TO- BED -EA RLY -TO -RI SE-

$\begin{bmatrix} 23 \\ 21 \\ 4 \end{bmatrix}$ $\begin{bmatrix} 6 \\ 5 \\ 27 \end{bmatrix}$ $\begin{bmatrix} 6 \\ 2 \\ 27 \end{bmatrix}$ $\begin{bmatrix} 4 \\ 12 \\ 13 \end{bmatrix}$ $\begin{bmatrix} 10 \\ 2 \\ 6 \end{bmatrix}$ $\begin{bmatrix} 27 \\ 26 \\ 2 \end{bmatrix}$ $\begin{bmatrix} 22 \\ 27 \\ 19 \end{bmatrix}$ $\begin{bmatrix} 4 \\ 12 \\ 15 \end{bmatrix}$

   MEA NS- NO- ACT ION -FO R-J ACK

81. B   e   w   a   r   e   !
    66 101 119 97 114 101 33

83. S   w   i   n   g   l   o   w   ,   s   w   e   e   t
    83 119 105 110 103 32 108 111 119 44 32 115 119 101 101 116 32

    c   h   a   r   i   o   t
    99 104 97 114 105 111 116 46

85. 73 115 110 44 116 32 109 97 116 104 32 102 117 110 63
    I   s   n   '   t   m   a   t   h   f   u   n   ?

Exercises 3.4

87. *Is* suitable   89. *Is not* suitable   91. Is unsuitable   93. Is unsuitable   95. $\begin{bmatrix} .2 & .1 & .3 \\ .2 & .4 & .3 \\ .6 & .5 & .4 \end{bmatrix}$

97. .1 dollars agriculture   99. .6 dollars agriculture   101. $x_1 = 50$, $x_2 = 45$ 103. $x_1 = 400.00$, $x_2 = 37.50$
    .4 dollars lumber   .2 dollars agriculture
    .5 dollars mining   .4 dollars agriculture

105. 0 dollars cattle per dollar of corn   107. Yes, production must be doubled.
    0 dollars corn per dollar of corn

109. 0 dollars corn per dollar of beans   111. Yes, $\frac{1}{2}$ external demand means $\frac{1}{2}$ total production.
    0 dollars beans per dollar of corn

113. $\begin{bmatrix} .04 & .12 \\ .08 & .04 \end{bmatrix}$ 115. $x_1 = 66$ horses and $x_2 = 27$ cows   117. $x_1 = 204$ horses, $x_2 = 648$ cattle

Review Exercises

119. $\frac{1}{20} \begin{bmatrix} 3 & 6 \\ 4 & 4 \end{bmatrix}$

121. Yes. Schedule a shirt production valued at 1,290.32 coconuts and shoe production valued at 322.58
    coconuts to fill an order for shirts valued at 1000 coconuts with all the shoes (valued at 322.58) used for
    internal consumption.

123. yards   inches   yards   125. $20,418   127. c_1 c_2 129. $\frac{1}{10} \begin{bmatrix} 4 & 3 \\ 4 & 1 \end{bmatrix}$
    fabric ribbing thread $17,221.50
    [2,150 16,800 58,400] $E = \begin{matrix} b_1 \\ b_2 \\ b_3 \end{matrix} \begin{bmatrix} 2 & 2 \\ 1 & 1 \\ 0 & 0 \end{bmatrix}$

    yards   inches   yards
    fabric ribbing thread
    [1,812.5 14,200 49,200]

131. To the nearest million, is 50 million in coal and 113 million in steel.

133.

135. 5200

	leisure	communi-cations	potatoes	flowers	
$PE =$	1350	825	1000	825	sports
	650	475	500	375	documentaries
	3200	1450	2250	2100	movies

2, 2 $PE = 475$

137.

	S	P	V	T	J	
Superintendent (S)	0	1	1	1	0	
Principal (P)	0	0	1	0	1	
Vice-principal (V)	0	0	0	1	0	$= M$
Math teacher (T)	0	1	0	0	0	
Janitor (J)	1	0	1	1	0	

139.

	S	P	V	T	J	
	0	2	2	2	1	S
	1	0	2	2	1	P
	0	1	0	1	0	V
	0	1	1	0	1	T
	1	2	2	3	0	J

$M + M^2$

141.

	S	P	V	T	J	
						S
						P
						V
	1	1	2	2	1	T
						J

"Teacher row" of
$M + M^2 + M^3$
has all positive
entries

143.

Brand	Power (sums of the row entries of $M + M^2$)
B	5
A	4
D	3
C	2

CHAPTER 4

Exercises 4.1

1.
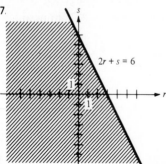

3.
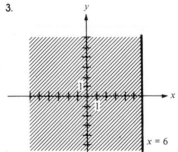

5.
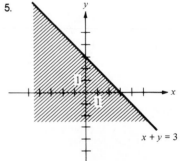

7.
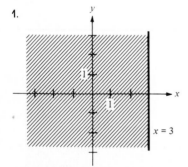

9.
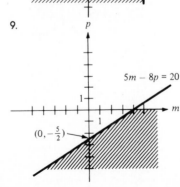

11.
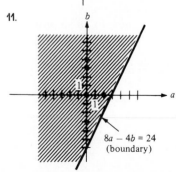

13.

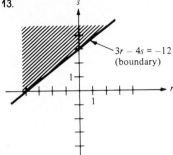

15.

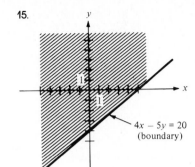

17.

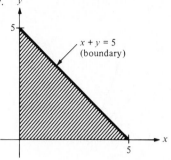

19.

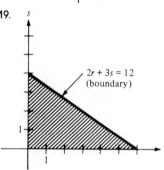

21.

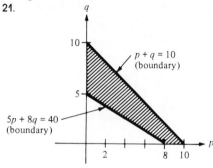

23.

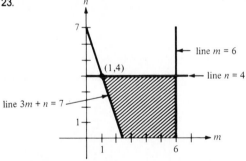

25. $(2, 4)$; $x + y \leq 5$ fails. $(-1, 1)$; $x \geq 0$ fails.
$(7, -3)$; $y \geq 0$ fails. $(3, 3)$; $x + y \leq 5$ fails.

27. $(1, 3)$; $3m + n \geq 7$ fails. $(5, 5)$; $n \leq 4$ fails.
$(6, -2.4)$; $n \geq 0$ fails.

29. We label the vertices A, B, C, and coordinates are
$A\ (0, 0)$
$B\ (0, 6)$
$C\ (3, 0)$

31. We label the vertices A, B, C, D, and coordinates are
$A\ (0, 2)$
$B\ (0, 5)$
$C\ (5, 0)$
$D\ (3, 0)$

33. The graph is the single point $(1, 0)$.

35. We label the vertices A, B, C, D, E, and coordinates
are
$A\ (0, 0)$
$B\ (0, 8)$
$C\ (4, 8)$
$D\ (7, 5)$
$E\ (2, 0)$

37.

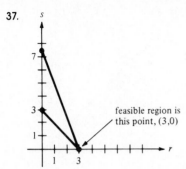

feasible region is
this point, (3,0)

39. Exercises 36, 37, and 38 show that the feasible regions may be a region such as a triangle as in Exercise 36, a single point such as in Exercise 37, or the empty set as in Exercise 38.

41.   **43.**

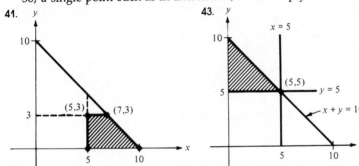

45. Vertices of the feasible region are (5, 0), (5, 3), (7, 3) and (10, 0).

47. Vertices of the feasible region are (0, 5), (0, 10), and (5, 5).

49.

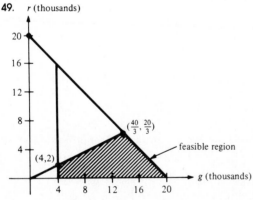

51. Vertices of the feasible region are (thousands) (4, 0), (4, 2), $\left(\frac{40}{3}, \frac{20}{3}\right)$, and (20, 0).

53.

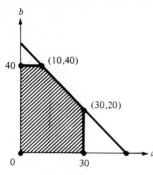

55. Vertices (dollars) are (0, 0), (0, 40), (10, 40), (30, 20), and (30, 0).

57.

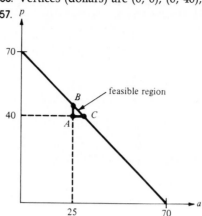

Exercises 4.2

59. Objective function $b = 6r - 3s + 2$ is maximum at (2, 0). Maximum is 14.

61. Objective function, $d = 6r + 5s + 10$, takes a maximum value of $26\frac{1}{3} = \frac{79}{3}$ at vertex $\left(\frac{4}{3}, \frac{5}{3}\right)$.

63. The maximum is 11 and occurs at $\left(\frac{4}{3}, \frac{5}{3}\right)$.

65.

Vertex	$p = 6a + 5b + 2$
(0, 0)	2
(0, 5)	27
(3, 7)	55
(6, 4)	58 (Maximum)
(4, 0)	26

67. Feasible vertices where t is maximum are (3, 7) and (6, 4) at which points $t = 45$.

69. The feasible region consists of the one point (2, 3). The value of $m = w + z + 17$ is 22.

71. The minimum is $\frac{146}{19}$ and occurs at $\left(\frac{126}{19}, \frac{25}{19}\right)$.

73.

Vertex	$r = 6 + 2m - 10p$
(0, 0)	6
(0, 2)	-14
$\left(\frac{5}{2}, \frac{13}{4}\right)$	$-\frac{43}{2}$ (Minimum)
(4, 1)	4
$\left(\frac{10}{3}, 10\right)$	$\frac{38}{3}$

75. $P = \$348,000$ at (60, 100); all the land is used.

77. $N = \$120,000$ at (40, 100); **not** all the land is used; 20 acres fallow.

79. Maximum of $\frac{22}{3}$ (thousands) at $c = \frac{50}{3}$ (thousands), $f = \frac{100}{3}$ (thousands). All money is invested.

81. Operational costs are minimized by running the Aurora plant 2 days and the Buffalo plant 6 days. This produces 720 extra plowshares. Minimum cost is $\$47,600$.

Exercises 4.3

83. Maximum $z = 20$ at $x_1 = 4$, $x_2 = 0$ 85. Minimum $z = -30$ at $x_1 = 0$, $x_2 = 10$

87. Maximum of $Z = 10$ at any point on the line $5x_2 + 8x_3 = 20$ between $(0, 4, 0)$ and $\left(0, 0, \frac{5}{2}\right)$, inclusive.

   For example, at $\left(0, \frac{4}{5}, 2\right)$ or at $\left(0, 2, \frac{5}{4}\right)$, we get $Z = 10$.

89. Minimum Z occurs at $(0, 0, 4)$. The minimum value is -16.

91. The maximum $Z = \frac{86}{3}$ at $\left(\frac{8}{3}, 0, 0, \frac{14}{3}\right)$

93. Maximum profit is 32 when we sell 40 cans of Dawn. All ingredients are used.

95. We have maximum profit $Z = \$1410$ when $a = 30$, $b = 0$, $c = 10$. No employee time is unutilized.

Exercises 4.4

97. **(a)** s is a minimum (105) at $(0, 3.5)$.
   (b) The minimum lattice-point value of s is 112, at $(4, 0)$.
   (c) No; the nearest lattice point to the vertex of part (a) produces $s = 118$. This fails by 6 to be a minimum lattice-point value.

99. **(a)** At a vertex, maximum $p = 2.4$ at $(5.2, 4.5)$.
   (b) At a lattice point, maximum $p = 1$ at $(5, 4)$.
   (c) Yes.

Review Exercises

101. The maximum is $\frac{375}{4}$ and occurs at $\left(0, \frac{15}{4}\right)$.

103. The maximum is $r = 2,050$ which occurs when $x_1 = 20$, $x_2 = 70$.

105. The minimum is $c = 45$ when $x_1 = 5$, $x_2 = 0$.

107. We have $x = -\frac{22}{5}$, $y = -\frac{18}{5}$, $z = -\frac{13}{5}$.

109. They make 400 tables each week of each type. All labor is used. $z = 25,200$ maximum.

111. Minimum cost will occur if factory A is scheduled for 100 work days and factory B for 300 work days. Minimum cost is $\$36,000,000$, and there will be an excess of 1000 intermediate-sized cars.

113. Build 60 type A and 40 type B homes. Unused materials: 80 units of glass. Maximum is $\$1,060,000$.

115. We import 200 chairs and 16 sideboards for a profit of $\$9,120$.

CHAPTER 5

Exercises 5.2

1. $4x_1 + x_2 \leq 9$ is in standard maximization form as given.
3. $-4x_1 + 6x_2 \leq 8$ is in standard maximization form as given.
5. The RHS constant, (-4), needs to have opposite sign. The problem cannot be made standard.
7. These inequalities both go the wrong way for a maximum, standard problem. The problem cannot be made standard.
9. $\left.\begin{array}{l} x_1 - 2x_2 + s_1 = 8 \\ 2x_1 + 4x_2 + s_2 = 5 \\ 3x_1 - 2x_2 + s_3 = 2 \end{array}\right\}$

11.

	x_1	x_2	s_1	s_2	s_3	z	RHS
s_1	4	2	1	0	0	0	8
s_2	1	-4	0	1	0	0	2
s_3	2	4	0	0	1	0	12
z	-4	-6	0	0	0	1	0

13.

	x_1	x_2	s_1	s_2	s_3	z	RHS
s_1	1	2	1	0	0	0	8
s_2	2	8	0	1	0	0	14
s_3	3	-2	0	0	1	0	10
z	-2	-5	0	0	0	1	0

15. We have basic variables x_1, x_2, z and nonbasic variables s_1, s_2. Values of the variables are $z = 14$, $x_1 = 7$ and $x_2 = 5$. We have $s_1 = s_2 = 0$.

17. We have $z = 48$ when $x_1 = 2$, $x_2 = 0$. Also $s_1 = 8$, $s_2 = 0$, $s_3 = 4$, and $s_4 = 4$.

19. (a) Basic variables are z, s_1, s_2, s_3 and nonbasic variables are x_1, x_2, x_3.
   (b) The readout from this tableau is $z = 0$ when $x_1 = x_2 = x_3 = 0$. Also, $s_1 = 24$, $s_2 = 14$, and $s_3 = 6$.
   (c) No solution (unbounded).

21. The pivot is the s_1 row, x_1 column entry. The next tableau is

	x_1	x_2	s_1	s_2	z	RHS
s_1	1	-2	1	0	0	8
s_2	0	2	0	1	0	3
z	0	-9	4	0	0	47

23. The pivot is the s_2 row, x_1 column entry. The next tableau is

	x_1	x_2	x_3	s_1	s_2	s_3	z	RHS
s_1	0	$\frac{7}{2}$	$-\frac{5}{2}$	1	$-\frac{1}{2}$	0	0	4
x_1	1	$-\frac{3}{4}$	$\frac{1}{4}$	0	$\frac{1}{4}$	0	0	1
s_3	0	2	-3	0	0	1	0	16
z	0	-5	-2	0	1	0	1	4

25. The pivot is the s_2 row, x_1 column entry. The next tableau is

	x_1	x_2	s_1	s_2	z	RHS
s_1	0	$\frac{1}{3}$	1	$-\frac{2}{3}$	0	4
x_1	1	$\frac{4}{3}$	0	$\frac{1}{3}$	0	10
z	0	$\frac{7}{3}$	0	$\frac{4}{3}$	0	40

We have maximum $z = 40$ when $x_1 = 10$ and $x_2 = 0$.

27. The pivot is the s_2 row, x_2 column entry.
The next tableau is

	x_1	x_2	s_1	s_2	z	RHS
s_1	$-\dfrac{1}{4}$	0	1	$-\dfrac{3}{4}$	0	$\dfrac{3}{2}$
x_2	$\dfrac{3}{4}$	1	0	$\dfrac{1}{4}$	0	$\dfrac{15}{2}$
z	$\dfrac{11}{2}$	0	0	$\dfrac{1}{2}$	1	15

We read $z = 15$ when $x_1 = 0$ and $x_2 = \dfrac{15}{2}$.

29.

	x_1	x_2	s_1	s_2	z	RHS
x_2	$-\dfrac{3}{2}$	1	$\dfrac{1}{2}$	0	0	6
s_2	-4	0	2	1	0	32
z	$-\dfrac{11}{2}$	0	$\dfrac{5}{2}$	0	1	30

This is still not optimal. However, all entries in the x_1 column are negative so the objective function is unbounded. z has no maximum.

31.

	x_1	x_2	s_1	s_2	s_3	z	RHS
x_1	1	0	$\dfrac{4}{3}$	$-\dfrac{1}{3}$	0	0	2
x_2	0	1	$-\dfrac{1}{3}$	$\dfrac{1}{3}$	0	0	7
s_3	0	0	$-\dfrac{2}{3}$	$-\dfrac{1}{3}$	1	0	4
z	0	0	$\dfrac{32}{3}$	$\dfrac{4}{3}$	0	1	136

We read $z = 136$ when $x_1 = 2$, $x_2 = 7$.

33.

	x_1	x_2	s_1	s_2	s_3	z	RHS
x_1	1	1	1	0	0	0	9
s_2	0	3	-1	1	0	0	21
s_3	0	1	-1	0	1	0	11
z	0	6	4	0	0	1	36

We read $z = 36$ when $x_1 = 9$, $x_2 = 0$.

CHAPTER 5 **649**

35.

	x_1	x_2	s_1	s_2	s_3	z	RHS
s_1	2	0	1	-4	0	0	0
x_2	1	1	0	1	0	0	2
s_3	7	0	0	5	1	0	22
z	6	0	0	2	0	1	4

$z = 4$ when $x_1 = 0$, $x_2 = 2$.

37

	x_1	x_2	s_1	s_2	z	RHS
x_1	1	0	$\frac{1}{3}$	$\frac{1}{3}$	0	8
x_2	0	1	$-\frac{2}{3}$	$\frac{1}{3}$	0	4
z	0	0	0	1	1	20

The solution is $x_1 = 8$, $x_2 = 4$, giving a maximum z of 20.

39.

	x_1	x_2	s_1	s_2	z	RHS
x_1	1	0	$\frac{1}{3}$	$\frac{1}{3}$	0	8
x_2	0	1	$-\frac{2}{3}$	$\frac{1}{3}$	0	4
z	0	0	$\frac{4}{3}$	$\frac{1}{3}$	1	12

We read $x_1 = 8$, $x_2 = 4$, and the maximum value of $z = 2x_1 - x_2$ is 12.

41.

	x_1	x_2	s_1	s_2	z	RHS
x_2	0	1	$\frac{1}{4}$	$-\frac{1}{4}$	0	1.5
x_1	1	0	0	1	0	6
z	0	0	$\frac{1}{4}$	$\frac{3}{4}$	1	7.5

We read $x_1 = 6$, $x_2 = 1.5$, and the maximum z is 7.5.

43.

	x_1	x_2	s_1	s_2	z	RHS
x_2	$\frac{1}{4}$	1	$\frac{1}{4}$	0	0	3
s_2	1	0	0	1	0	6
z	0	0	1	0	1	12

The solution is $x_1 = 0$, $x_2 = 3$, and the maximum value z is 12.

45.

	x_1	x_2	x_3	s_1	s_2	z	RHS
s_1	0	$\frac{5}{2}$	$-\frac{15}{4}$	1	$-\frac{1}{4}$	0	$\frac{55}{2}$
x_1	1	$\frac{1}{2}$	$\frac{1}{4}$	0	$\frac{1}{4}$	0	$\frac{25}{2}$
z	0	2	6	0	3	1	150

We read that $z = 150$ when $x_1 = \frac{25}{2}$, $x_2 = x_3 = 0$.

47.

	x_1	x_2	x_3	s_1	s_2	z	RHS
s_1	0	$\dfrac{5}{2}$	$-\dfrac{15}{4}$	1	$-\dfrac{1}{4}$	0	$\dfrac{55}{2}$
x_1	1	$\dfrac{1}{2}$	$\dfrac{1}{4}$	0	$\dfrac{1}{4}$	0	$\dfrac{25}{2}$
z	0	$\dfrac{1}{2}$	$\dfrac{1}{4}$	0	$\dfrac{1}{4}$	1	$\dfrac{25}{2}$

We read that $z = \dfrac{25}{2}$ when $x_1 = \dfrac{25}{2}$, $x_2 = x_3 = 0$.

49.

	x_1	x_2	x_3	s_1	s_2	z	RHS
s_1	17	11	0	1	4	0	240
x_3	4	2	1	0	1	0	50
z	4	2	0	0	1	1	50

We read that $z = 50$ when $x_3 = 50$ and $x_1 = x_2 = 0$.

51.

	x_1	x_2	x_3	s_1	s_2	z	RHS
x_1	1	0	0	$-\dfrac{1}{3}$	$\dfrac{2}{3}$	0	5
x_3	0	0	1	$-\dfrac{1}{3}$	$\dfrac{1}{6}$	0	1
z	0	1	0	$-\dfrac{1}{3}$	$\dfrac{2}{3}$	1	5

This is not optimal, but all elements in the new pivot column above the line are negative, telling us the solution is unbounded.

53. Maximum profit is \$905 obtained by making 450 boxes of Mix I and 50 boxes of Mix II.

55. The optimal solution is $x_1 = 450$ and $x_2 = 50$. Profit = \$905.

57.

	x_1	x_2	s_1	s_2	s_3	z	RHS
x_1	1	0	$-\dfrac{1}{4}$	$\dfrac{1}{2}$	0	0	250
s_3	0	0	-2	1	1	0	0
x_2	0	1	$\dfrac{1}{4}$	$-\dfrac{1}{4}$	0	0	250
z	0	0	.275	.15	0	1	1125

As predicted by the shadow price forecast, the optimum profit is $1125, but the solution is now to make 250 boxes of each mix.

59. The optimum solution consists of making 4466 of 3-Pack A and 1067 of 3-Pack B for a total profit of $3746.60.

61. The optimum solution is to make 4000 of the B 3-Packs, and none of the A or C 3-Packs. The resulting profit will be $4000.

63. The optimal solution is to make 3666 3-Packs of type A and 2667 3-Packs of type B (and none of type C).

65.

	x_1	x_2	x_3	s_1	s_2	s_3	z	RHS
s_1	0	$-\frac{1}{2}$	0	1	0	-2	0	40
x_3	0	0	1	0	1	-1	0	20
x_1	1	2	0	0	-2	4	0	40
z	0	10	0	0	0	40	1	1600

The final tableau reads $z = 1600$ when $x_1 = 40$, $x_2 = 0$, and $x_3 = 20$. The "0" in the z row for nonbasic variable s_2 indicates multiple solutions. Another solution is $x_1 = 60$, $x_2 = 0$, $x_3 = 10$.

67.

	x_1	x_2	x_3	s_1	s_2	s_3	z	RHS
s_1	0	$-\frac{1}{2}$	0	1	0	-2	0	0
x_3	0	0	1	0	1	-1	0	40
x_1	1	2	0	0	-2	4	0	40
z	0	10	0	0	0	40	1	2400

This final matrix reads $z = 2400$ when $x_1 = 40$, $x_2 = 0$, $x_3 = 40$.

Exercises 5.3

69.

	x_1	x_2	s_1	s_2	z^*	RHS
s_1	9	0	1	4	0	176
x_2	2	1	0	1	0	40
z^*	8	0	0	6	1	240

The maximum value of z^* is 240, when $x_1 = 0$ and $x_2 = 40$. Consequently, the minimum $z = -240$.

71.

	x_1	x_2	x_3	s_1	s_2	z^*	RHS
x_2	$\dfrac{7}{8}$	1	0	$\dfrac{1}{8}$	$\dfrac{1}{4}$	0	$\dfrac{17}{2}$
x_3	$\dfrac{5}{4}$	0	1	$-\dfrac{1}{4}$	$\dfrac{1}{2}$	0	7
z^*	8	0	0	0	2	1	48

The final tableau reads $z^* = 48$ when $x_1 = 0$, $x_2 = \dfrac{17}{2}$, $x_3 = 7$. Thus minimum $z = -$maximum $z^* = -48$ when $x_1 = 0$, $x_2 = \dfrac{17}{2}$, $x_3 = 7$.

The "0" in the z row under s_1 indicates multiple solutions. Another solution is $x_1 = 0$, $x_2 = 6$, $x_3 = 12$.

73. Maximize $z^* = 40y_1 + 20y_2$ with $y_1, y_2 \geq 0$ subject to $5y_1 + 3y_2 \leq 5$ and $7y_1 - 5y_2 \leq 3$.

75. Maximize $z^* = 10y_1 + 30y_2$ with $y_1, y_2 \geq 0$ subject to $6y_2 \leq 7$ and $y_1 + 4y_2 \leq 5$.

77. Maximize $z^* = 10y_1 + 12y_2$ with $y_1, y_2 \geq 0$ and subject to $y_1 + 2y_2 \leq 5$, $-5y_2 \leq 2$.

79. Minimum cost = \$937 with $x_1 = 59$ radio ads and $x_3 = 58$ newspaper ads and no TV.

81. Rounding x_1 and x_3 to the nearest integer without violating constraints, we have to take $x_1 = 59$, $x_2 = 0$, $x_3 = 58$. Then minimum cost = \$995.

83. We have $x_1 = x_2 = 84$ and $z = \$36{,}960$, but this is bettered by $x_1 = 84$, $x_2 = 83$ giving a minimum cost of \$36,720.

Review Exercises

85.

	x_1	x_2	s_1	s_2	z	RHS
x_1	1	0	$\dfrac{1}{5}$	$\dfrac{1}{5}$	0	$\dfrac{12}{5}$
x_2	0	1	$-\dfrac{1}{10}$	$\dfrac{2}{5}$	0	$\dfrac{14}{5}$
z	0	0	$\dfrac{3}{10}$	$\dfrac{4}{5}$	1	$\dfrac{38}{5}$

We read that $z = \dfrac{38}{5}$ when $x_1 = \dfrac{12}{5}$ and $x_2 = \dfrac{14}{5}$

87.

	x_1	x_2	s_1	s_2	z	RHS
x_1	1	0	$\dfrac{2}{3}$	$-\dfrac{1}{3}$	2	2
x_2	0	1	$-\dfrac{1}{3}$	$\dfrac{2}{3}$	0	8
z	0	0	$\dfrac{2}{3}$	$\dfrac{5}{3}$	1	38

The maximum z is 38 when $x_1 = 2$ and $x_2 = 8$.

89. Maximum $z^* = 8$ when $x_1 = 1$, $x_2 = 2$. Consequently, minimum $z = -8$ when $x_1 = 1$, $x_2 = 2$. The "0" in the z row of nonbasic variable s_2 indicates multiple solutions. Another optimal solution is $x_1 = \dfrac{5}{2}$, $x_2 = 1$.

91.

	y_1	y_2	s_1	s_2	s_3	z^*	RHS
s_1	0	0	1	$-\dfrac{1}{5}$	$-\dfrac{1}{5}$	0	60
y_2	0	1	0	$\dfrac{3}{500}$	$-\dfrac{1}{250}$	0	$\dfrac{6}{5}$
y_1	1	0	0	$-\dfrac{1}{500}$	$\dfrac{3}{1000}$	0	$\dfrac{11}{10}$
z	0	0	0	8	3	1	9100

For the primal (minimum) solution we read that the minimum $z = 9100$ when $x_1 = 0$, $x_2 = 8$ and $x_3 = 3$. Note: We do not use the BB factory.

93. The candy company should produce 3,200 Yum Yum bars and no Low Cal bars. Profit would be 12,800 (cents) = \$128 when $x_1 = 0$, $x_2 = 3,200$, $z = \$128$.

95. $z = \$4,700$ when $x_1 = \$12,500$, $x_2 = \$12,500$, $x_3 = \$25,000$.

97. $z = \$5,500$ income with all the money in money market securities; that is, $x_1 = x_3 = 0$, and $x_2 = 50,000$, with $z = 5,500$.

CHAPTER 6

Exercises 6.1

1.   Table Form

	B	B^c	
A	3	⑤	8
A^c	④	⑦	11
	7	12	19

(circled counts were given)

3.   Table Form

	S	S^c	
R	⑤	14	19
R^c	4	③	7
	⑨	17	㉖

5. (a)

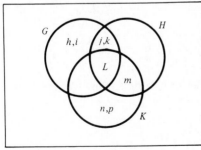

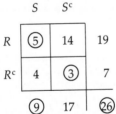

(b) $G \cap K = \{L\}$
(c) $n(H) = 4$
(d) $n(G \cup H) = 6$
(e) $n(G \cap H) = 3$
(f) $H^c \cap K = \{n, p\}$
(g) $G \cup (H \cap K) = \{h, i, j, k, L, m\}$

7.

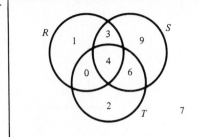

9.

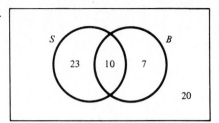

11.

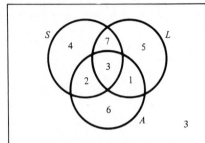

13.

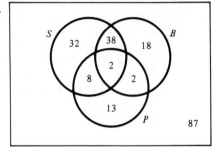

$n(S \cap B \cap P) = 2$
subscribe to all three

15. (a) In at least one subject, $n(H \cup P \cup S) = 100$.
  (b) In exactly one subject, $38 + 30 + 12 = 80$.
  (c) In at most two of the subjects, $n(H \cup P \cup S) - n(H \cap P \cap S) = 100 - 5 = 95$.
  (d) In none of these subjects, $n[(H \cup P \cup S)^c] = n(\varnothing) = 0$.

Exercises 6.2

17. 8 ways   **19.** 608,400   **21.** The tree has 32 paths, describing 32 possible burger variations
23. 48 ways   **25.** 19,656 ways   **27.** 3360 possible sequences of either 4 or 5 letters   **29.** 1024 ways
31. 125 ways   **33.** 50 ways   **35.** 60 ways   **37.** 24 ways

Exercises 6.4

39. {2a, 2d, 4a, 4g, 6a, 6f}   **41.** {1a, 1b, 1c, 3b, 3e, 3f, 5b, 5e}   **43.** {3b, 3e, 3f, 6a, 6f}   **45.** {3b, 3f, 6f}
47. $G = E \cap F$
49. A: "The digit is even"   **51.** C: "The digit is odd"
  B: "The letter is a F: "The letter is a consonant"
  vowel" D: "The letter is not a vowel"
                                  H: "3 divides the digit or the letter is a consonant"
53. D: "The letter is a vowel:
  E: 3 divides the digit evenly"
  H: "3 divides the digit or the letter is a consonant"
  B: "The letter is a vowel"
  C: "The digit is odd"
55. $S = \{$(U,U,U), (U,U,N), (U,N,U), (U,N,N), (N,U,U), (N,U,N), (N,N,U), (N,N,N)$\}$
57. $B = \{$(U,U,U), (U,U,N), (U,N,U), (U,N,N), (N,U,U), (N,U,N), (N,N,U)$\}$

59. $D = \{(U,N,N), (N,U,N), (N,N,U), (N,N,N)\}$ **61.** $G = \{(U,N,N), (N,N,N)\}$
63. $A = \{1H, 1T, 3H, 3T, 5H, 5T\}$ **65.** $C = \{5H, 5T, 6H, 6T\}$
67. $S = \{(A,B,C), (A,C,B), (B,A,C), (B,C,A), (C,A,B), (C,B,A)\}$
69. $A = \{(A,B,C), (A,C,B), (B,A,C), (C,A,B)\}$ **71.** $D = \{(A,B,C)\}$
73. $G = \{A,B,C), (A,C,B), (B,A,C), (B,C,A), (C,B,A)\}$ **75.** $A = \{(6,2), (5,3), (4,4), (3,5), (2,6)\}$
77. $C = \{(5,1), (5,2), (5,3), (5,4), (5,5), (5,6)\}$
79. $E = \{(1,4), (1,5), (1,6), (2,4), (2,5), (2,6), (3,4), (3,5), (3,6), (4,4), (4,5), (4,6), (5,4), (5,5), (5,6), (6,4), (6,5), (6,6)\}$
81. $A = \{(D,G,G)\}$ **83.** $C = \{(D,G,G), G\}$ **85.** $\{(K,B), (K,F), (K,S), (H,B), (H,F), (H,S)\}$
87. $\{(K,B), (K,S), (H,B), (H,S)\}$

Exercises 6.5

89. $P[A \cap B^c] = .17$ **91.** $P[z] = 0$ **93.** $P[t] = 1$ **95.** $.81$
97. (a) $P[g] = .05$ **(b)** $P[A] = .45$ **(c)** $.40$ **(d)** $.35$ **(e)** $P(A \cap B) = 0$
    (f) $P[A \cap C] = P\{f\} = .20$ **(g)** $P(B \cap C) = 0$ **(h)** $.85$
99. (a) $.15$ **(b)** $P[S] = 1$ **(c)** $.45$ **(d)** $.70$ **(e)** $P[A \cup B] = 1$
101. $.25$ **103.** $.86$ **105.** $.79$ **107.** $.96$ **109.** $.32$ **111.** $\frac{1}{2}$ **113.** $\frac{1}{2}$ **115.** $\frac{1}{8}$ **117.** $\frac{5}{8}$
119. $P[D] = 1$ **121.** $P[A \cap C] = 0$ **123.** $P[B] = \frac{5}{8}$ **125.** $P[B \cup C] = 1$
127. $T = \{(B,S,N), (B,N,S), (S,B,N), (S,N,B), (N,S,B), (N,B,S)\}$ **129.** $\frac{1}{3}$
131. $P[\text{admitted by at least one of } A \text{ or } B] = .9$ **133.** 85 to 15, which is 17 to 3 in favor   **135.** $\frac{175}{184}$
137. 6 to 94, which is 3 to 47

Exercises 6.6

139. $P(A) = \frac{28}{38} = \frac{14}{19}$ **141.** $\frac{1}{13}$ **143.** $\frac{1}{2}$ **145.** $\frac{1}{2}$ **147.** $\frac{1}{2}$ **149.** $\frac{7}{8}$ **151.** $\frac{7}{12}$ **153.** $P[C] = \frac{0}{36} = 0$
155. $P[A \cap C] = P[\varnothing] = 0$ **157.** $\frac{3}{4}$ **159.** $\frac{1}{2}$ **161.** $\frac{2}{13}$ **163.** $\frac{16}{52}$ **165.** $\frac{5}{6}$ **167.** $\frac{211}{216}$ **169.** $.75$
171. $P[\text{pair of threes}] = \frac{16}{2704} = \frac{1}{169}$

Exercises 6.7

173. $P[\text{visitor would return}] = \frac{887}{947}$ **175.** $P[\text{California car will not pass}] = \frac{65}{186}$
177. $P[\text{"D.O.A."}] = \frac{14}{88} = \frac{7}{44}$ **179.** 20%   **181.** $.14$ **183.** $.20$ **185.** $.18783$ **187.** 0.14 **189.** 0.69
191. 0.69 **193.** $\frac{27}{40}$ **195.** $\frac{19}{120}$

Review Exercises

197. $S = \{0, 1, 2, 3, 4, 5, 6\}$ **199.** $S = \{GGG, GGD, GDG, GDD, DGG, DGD, DDG\}$
201. $A = \{F\} \cup \{Sr\} = \{F, Sr\}$ **203.** $C = \{GGG, GDD, DGD, DDG\}$ **205.** 4   **207.** 24 such numerals

209. 64　　**211.** 64　　**213.** $340 - 64 = 276$　　**215.** 120

217. $P[\text{customer is in compliance}] = \dfrac{68}{85} = \dfrac{4}{5}$　　**219.** $P[P \cup T] = \dfrac{27}{60} = \dfrac{9}{20}$

221. $P[\text{numbers at least two apart}] = \dfrac{20}{36} = \dfrac{5}{9}$　　**223.** $P[A^c] = 1 - \dfrac{3}{5} = \dfrac{2}{5}$

225.

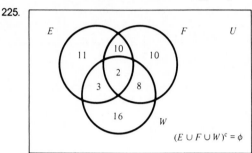

227. $\dfrac{37}{60}$　　**229.** $\dfrac{56}{95}$

231. $P[A \text{ first or } A \text{ last}] = \dfrac{4}{6} = \dfrac{2}{3}$　　**233.** total is 179　　**235.** 23 homes are frame and use electric heat

237. $P[\text{"frame or wood heat"}] = \dfrac{125}{200} = \dfrac{5}{8}$　　**239.** probability of failing $= \dfrac{2}{3 + 2} = \dfrac{2}{5}$

CHAPTER 7

Exercises 7.1

1. 56.　　**3.** 6720　　**5.** 8855　　**7.** 55,440　　**9.** 462　　**11.** 1050　　**13.** $\dfrac{14}{99}$　　**15.** 56

17. 120 assignment plans possible　　**19.** 210 ways　　**21.** 2,024　　**23.** 855 ways　　**25.** 10 distinct sets

27. .42　　**29.** 4017　　**31.** 4560 hands　　**33.** 1584 possible five-card hands　　**35.** 24 possible five-card hands

37. 3024 ways　　**39.** 1512 ways　　**41.** 252 possible committees　　**43.** 378 committees　　**45.** $\dfrac{28}{55}$　　**47.** $\dfrac{14}{55}$

49. 1287 hands　　**51.** 495 spade flushes, ace high　　**53.** 288 hands　　**55.** 54,912 possible hands

57. .0005　　**59.** .0002　　**61.** .0001　　**63.** 0.0212　　**65.** There are 3600 lineups possible.　　**67.** $\dfrac{2}{5}$

Exercises 7.2

69. 420　　**71.** 3,780　　**73.** 256 ways

75. $\dfrac{12!}{2!2!2!2!2!2!} \div 6! = 10,395$, assuming identical boxes. With distinguishable boxes, do not divide by 6!

77. $\dfrac{20!}{5!5!5!5!} \div 4! = 488,864,376$, assuming identical cars. With distinguishable cars, do not divide by 4!

79. 46 sets

Exercises 7.3

81. .65, .25, .65, .70   **83.** .15, .15, .35   **85.** $\frac{6}{13}, \frac{6}{13}$ **87.** $\frac{3}{13}, \frac{3}{5}$ **89.** $\frac{1}{2}, \frac{7}{13}$

91. A and C are *not* independent.   **93.** B and C are *not* independent.   **95.** $\frac{1}{4}$ **97.** $\frac{1}{10},$ **99.** $\frac{3}{20}$

101. $\frac{3}{4}$ **103.** We have independence of F and W.   **105.** The events are *not* mutually exclusive.

107. $P[B] = \frac{1}{2}$ **109.** $P[D] = \frac{1}{3}$ **111.** $P[A \cap C] = \frac{1}{3}$ **113.** $P[A \cap D] = \frac{1}{6}$ **115.** $P[C \cap D] = \frac{1}{3}$

117. $P[A \cup C] = P[S] = 1$ **119.** $P[B \cup C] = \frac{5}{6}$ **121.** $\frac{2}{3}$ **123.** $\frac{1}{2}$ **125.** $\frac{1}{2}$ **127.** $\frac{2}{3}$ **129.** $\frac{1}{4}$

131. B and D are mutually exclusive.   **133.** $\frac{1}{2}, \frac{5}{18}, \frac{1}{6}$ **135.** A and B are *not* mutually exclusive.   **137.** $\frac{1}{3}$

139. .415   **141.** $\frac{7}{47}$ **143.** $\frac{285}{585} = \frac{19}{39}$ **145.** Events are *dependent*

Exercises 7.4

147. Debbie agrees with probability = .21.   **149.** $\frac{25}{30} = \frac{5}{6}$ **151.** $\frac{850}{870} = .9770$

153. $P[F_2|F_1] \neq P[F_2]$ and the events are dependent   **155.** .9959   **157.** 38% will pass   **159.** $\frac{2}{27}$ **161.** $\frac{151}{216}$

163. Events are not mutually exclusive   **165.** L and B are *dependent*

Exercises 7.5

167. .6   **169.** $\frac{2}{5}$ **171.** $\frac{2}{3}$ **173.** .2857   **175.** .9333. Fire the gardener!   **177.** .043   **179.** .2326   **181.** .717

183. .4120   **185.** .58   **187.** $\frac{14}{29}$ **189.** $\frac{2}{5}$ **191.** $\frac{4}{9}$ **193.** $\frac{1}{3}$, and not $\frac{1}{2}$

Exercises 7.6

195. (a) .788   **(b)** $\sqrt[12]{.98} = .9983$ **197. (a)** .2401   **(b)** .9919   **199.** System is impossible
201. .9930 or 99.3%   **203.** System reliability .9741, cost $180
205. Reliability of component C must be at least .982325   **207. (a)** .8757   **209.** .5584
    (b) .990908

Review Exercises

211. 24,024   **213.** 1001   **215.** 210   **217.** $\frac{21}{55}$ **219.** .65, .55, .30   **221.** $P[B \cup C] = P\{a,b,d,e\} = .75$

223. $\frac{1}{3}, \frac{8}{13}$ **225.** A and C are dependent   **227.** They are *not* mutually exclusive

229. They are *not* mutually exclusive   **231.** .32   **233.** A and B are dependent   **235.** $\frac{1}{3}$

237. $P[\text{"at least one from Yale"}] = 1 - P[\text{"all from Harvard"}] = 1 - \frac{7}{33} = \frac{26}{33}$

239. $\frac{32}{75}$ **241.** $\frac{8}{25}$ **243.** .990909 **245.** $P[(3,\text{T})] = \frac{1}{12}$ **247.** $\frac{11}{162,435} = .000068$ **249.** $\frac{3}{4}$ **251.** 22

253. $\frac{7}{10}$ **255.** $\frac{6}{17}$ **257.** E and C are *not* mutually exclusive. **259.** $P[\text{"Good night's sleep"}] = \frac{31}{50}$

261. $\frac{16}{31}$ **263.** .5 **265.** .220 **267.** $\frac{9}{11}$ **269.** $\frac{9}{14}$ **271.** 6! (or 720) arrangements

273. $2^6 \cdot 6!$ (or 46,080) arrangements **275.** 126 are completely good **277.** Odds are 666 to 126

279. We count 6. **281.** $\frac{14}{55}$ **283.** $\frac{1}{55}$ **285.** 13 ways **287.** $\frac{3}{4}$ **289.** $\frac{3}{10}$

291. $C(27,6) \cdot C(21,6) \cdot C(15,5) \cdot C(10,5) \cdot C(5,5)$

$$= \frac{27!}{21!6!} \cdot \frac{21!}{15!6!} \cdot \frac{15!}{10!5!} \cdot \frac{10!}{5!5!} \cdot \frac{5!}{0!5!}$$

$$= \frac{27!}{6!6!5!5!5!} = 2.4311069 \times 10^{16}$$

CHAPTER 8

Exercises 8.1

1. Discrete **3.** Continuous **5.** Continuous **7.** Discrete **9.** Discrete **11.** $P[X \geq 4] = 0.30$

13. $P[X = 2] = \frac{1}{36}$ $P[X = 8] = \frac{5}{36}$ **15.** $P[Y = -5] = P[Y = 5] = \frac{1}{36}$

$P[X = 3] = \frac{1}{18}$ $P[X = 9] = \frac{1}{9}$ $P[Y = -4] = P[Y = 4] = \frac{1}{18}$

$P[X = 4] = \frac{1}{12}$ $P[X = 10] = \frac{1}{12}$ $P[Y = -3] = P[Y = 3] = \frac{1}{12}$

$P[X = 5] = \frac{1}{9}$ $P[X = 11] = \frac{1}{18}$ $P[Y = -2] = P[Y = 2] = \frac{1}{9}$

$P[X = 6] = \frac{5}{36}$ $P[X = 12] = \frac{1}{36}$ $P[Y = -1] = P[Y = 1] = \frac{5}{36}$

$P[X = 7] = \frac{1}{6}$ $P[Y = 0] = \frac{1}{6}$

17. $P[W = 0] = \frac{1}{9}$ **19.** $P[X = 0] = \frac{2}{7}$ **21.** $P[X = 0] = \frac{1}{5}$

$P[W = 1] = \frac{4}{9}$ $P[X = 1] = \frac{4}{7}$ $P[X = 1] = \frac{8}{15}$

$P[W = 2] = \frac{4}{9}$ $P[X = 2] = \frac{1}{7}$ $P[X = 2] = \frac{4}{15}$

23. $P[U = 0] = \frac{33}{91}$

$P[U = 1] = \frac{44}{91}$

$P[U = 2] = \frac{66}{455}$

$P[U = 3] = \frac{4}{455}$

25. $P[Y = 0] = \dfrac{1}{220}$

$P[Y = 1] = \dfrac{27}{220}$

$P[Y = 2] = \dfrac{27}{55}$

$P[Y = 3] = \dfrac{21}{55}$

29. $P[Y = 0] = \dfrac{19}{34}$

$P[Y = 1] = \dfrac{13}{34}$

$P[Y = 2] = \dfrac{2}{34}$

27. $P[Y = 0] = 0.2500$ $P[Y = 4] = 0.0450$

$P[Y = 1] = 0.3500$ $P[Y = 5] = 0.0100$

$P[Y = 2] = 0.2225$ $P[Y = 6] = 0.0025$

$P[Y = 3] = 0.1200$

31. $P[V = 0] = \dfrac{1}{3}$

$P[V = 1] = \dfrac{1}{2}$

$P[V = 2] = 0$

$P[V = 3] = \dfrac{1}{6}$

33. $P[Y = 0] = \dfrac{2}{27}$

$P[Y = 1] = \dfrac{37}{135}$

$P[Y = 2] = \dfrac{58}{135}$

$P[Y = 3] = \dfrac{2}{9}$

Exercises 8.2

35. 2.4   37. 5.2   39. −0.4   41. 2.4   43. $\mu_x = 7$, $E(X) = \mu_x = 7$, $E(X^2) = \dfrac{329}{6}$

45. $\mu_W = E(W) = \dfrac{4}{3}$, $E(W^2) = \dfrac{20}{9}$ 47. $-\dfrac{1}{6}$ 49. $E(X) = \dfrac{6}{7}$, $E(X^2) = \dfrac{8}{7}$ 51. $\dfrac{4}{5}$ 53. $\dfrac{3}{4}$

Exercises 8.3

55. $\sigma_x^2 = 0.24$, $\sigma_x = 0.4899$ 57. $\sigma_z^2 = 0.76$, $\sigma_z = 0.8718$ 59. $\sigma_y^2 = 3.84$, $\sigma_y = 1.9596$

61. $\sigma_w^2 = 6.24$, $\sigma_w = 2.4980$ 63. $\mu_y = 1.70$, $\sigma_y^2 = 1.51$, $\sigma_y = 1.2288$ 65. 3, 3

67. For the first distribution, $\mu = 3.0$ and $\sigma^2 = 0.8$. For the second distribution, $\mu = 3.0$ and $\sigma^2 = 0.10$.

69. $\sigma_x^2 = \dfrac{35}{6}$, $\sigma_x = 2.4152$ 71. (a) $\sigma_x = 0.5995$ (b) $\sigma_x = 0.5995$ 73. $\sigma_x = 32.37$

75. (a) 3.5   (b) 1.048   (c) 1.0237
    (d)

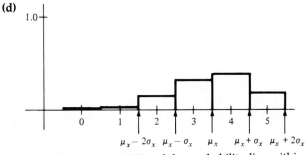

(e) All but 0.031, i.e., 0.969, of the probability lies within two standard deviations of the mean for this distribution.

Exercises 8.4

77. $p(0) = 0.262$ 79. $p(0) = 0.282$ 81. $p(0) = 0.168$ 83. $p(0) = 0.0000001$ 85. $p(0) = 0.160$
    $p(1) = 0.393$ $p(1) = 0.121$ $p(1) = 0.336$ $p(1) = 0.0000063$ $p(1) = 0.480$
87. 0.992   89. 0.522
91. $p(0) = 0.07776$ 93. $p(0) = 0.168$ $p(5) = 9.18 \times 10^{-3}$
    $p(1) = 0.2592$ $p(1) = 0.336$ $p(6) = 1.15 \times 10^{-3}$
    $p(2) = 0.3456$ $p(2) = 0.294$ $p(7) = 8.19 \times 10^{-5}$
    $p(3) = 0.2304$ $p(3) = 0.147$ $p(8) = 2.56 \times 10^{-6}$
    $p(4) = 0.0768$ $p(4) = 4.59 \times 10^{-2}$
    $p(5) = 0.01024$
95. $p(0) = 0.008$ $p(2) = 0.384$
    $p(1) = 0.096$ $p(3) = 0.512$
97. 0.834   99. 0.367   101. 0.043   103. 0.563   105. 0.998   107. 0.982   109. 0.939   111. 0.541
113. 0.598   115. 7.85×10^{-4} 117. $\mu = 30$, $\sigma = 3.464$ 119. $\mu = 6$, $\sigma = 1.897$
121. The required tree consists of 32 distinct paths. Of these, one consists entirely of successes, five contain
    exactly four successes, ten contain just three successes, ten contain exactly two successes, five contain
    just one success, and one consists of failures only. The respective probabilities are 3.2×10^{-4}, 6.4×10^{-3},
    5.12×10^{-2}, 0.2048, 0.4096, and 0.32768.
123. 0.451   125. $\mu = 1.5$, $\sigma = 1.162$ 127. 0.926   129. 0.997   131. 0.740   133. 0.749   135. 0.624
137. 1.265   139. (a) 0.345 (b) 0.346   141. 0.794   143. $\mu = 1.5$, $\sigma = 1.162$ 145. 0.678
147. .591   149. 0.472   151. 1.5
153. $p(0) = 0.00243$ $p(2) = 0.1323$ $p(4) = 0.36015$
    $p(1) = 0.02835$ $p(3) = 0.3087$ $p(5) = 0.16807$

Exercises 8.5

155. 0.4   157. 60   159. 0.4   161. 0   163. 1.0   165. 0.7   167. 0.9   169. 180

Exercises 8.6

171. 0.8413   173. 0.4772   175. 0.0228   177. 0.6826   179. 0.8413   181. 0.1587   183. 0.8185
185. 0.0228   187. $\frac{1}{2}$

Exercises 8.7

189. 0.3997   191. 0.3469   193. 0.0091   195. 0.1500   197. 0.7000   199. 0.9968, 49,840   201. 74.22%
203. 0.4260   205. about 452   207. 87.7   209. 0.9270   211. 25.12 kilokopeks   213. 0.8904   215. 416
217. 0.7682   219. 194   221. 0.0080   223. 12   225. 3.87 m   227. 0.0228   229. 0.5762   231. 0.001

Exercises 8.8

233. Normal approximation
235. We should not attempt normal approximation of this binomial distribution.
237. About 0.0548 (Exact answer: .057)   239. 0.6969 (Exact answer: .693)   241. 0.4943   243. 0.8790
245. 0.0071   247. $P[Y \geq 29.5]$ is negligible

Review Exercises

249.

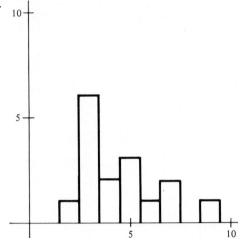

251. 4.5   **253.** (a) $\dfrac{2}{3}$ (b) $\dfrac{11}{12}$ (c) 1   (d) $\dfrac{25}{12}$ (e) $\sigma^2 = \dfrac{323}{144} \approx 2.243$, $\sigma = 1.498$ **255.** -2.6 **257.** -0.9

259. 70.5   **261.** 77.9   **263.** 54.5   **265.** 0.9544, or 95.44%   **267.** 0.6247   **269.** 89.72   **271.** 0.8212

273. 0.8212   **275.** 0.5793   **277.** 0.2025

279.

y	$p(y)$
0	$\dfrac{1}{5}$
1	$\dfrac{3}{5}$
2	$\dfrac{1}{5}$

281.
$$\mu = 1, \ \sigma^2 = \frac{2}{5}, \ \sigma = 0.6325 = \sqrt{\frac{2}{5}}$$

283. 0.914   **285.** 1   **287.** 0.980

289.

y	$p(y)$
0	$\dfrac{1}{81}$
1	$\dfrac{8}{81}$
2	$\dfrac{24}{81}$
3	$\dfrac{32}{81}$
4	$\dfrac{16}{81}$

291. $\mu_y = \dfrac{8}{3}$, $\sigma_y^2 = \dfrac{8}{9}$, $\sigma_y = 0.943$ **293.** 0.998   **295.** 0.650

CHAPTER 9

Exercises 9.1

1.

Class	Relative Frequency
5.0–5.2	0.075
5.3–5.5	0.325
5.6–5.8	0.275
5.9–6.1	0.175
6.2–6.4	0.150

3.

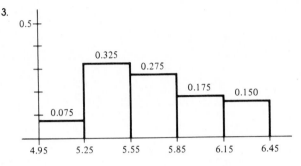

5.

(5.1–5.3) 5	3 3 2 2 1 3 3
(5.4–5.6) 5	4 6 4 6 5 5 6 5 5 5 5 6 6 5 5 6
(5.7–5.9) 5	8 9 8 8 9 8 9 8
(6.0–6.2) 6	1 0 2 2 0 1 2
(6.3–6.5) 6	3 4 4

7.

Class	Relative Frequency
33–43	$\dfrac{1}{42}$
44–54	0
55–65	$\dfrac{2}{7}$
66–76	$\dfrac{1}{2}$
77–87	$\dfrac{4}{21}$

9.

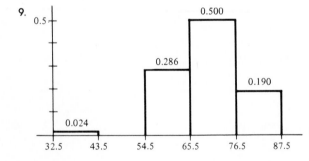

11.

Class	Relative Frequency
145–156	$\dfrac{2}{34} = \dfrac{1}{17} = 0.059$
157–168	$\dfrac{13}{34} = 0.382$
169–180	$\dfrac{14}{34} = \dfrac{7}{17} = 0.412$
181–192	$\dfrac{5}{34} = 0.147$

13.

15.

Stem	Leaf
14	9
15	9 4 8 9
16	7 6 6 0 8 9 3 5 0 2 8
17	5 8 6 7 0 7 0 6 4 0 8 7 7
18	9 4 4 2
19	0

17.

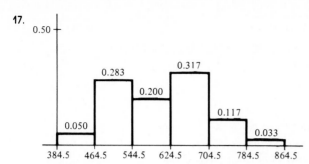

19. Here is a two-way stem-and-leaf display where we have used stems of 3, 4, 5, 6, and 7, but we have used only one digit for the leaves. (When there is more than one digit in the leaves, it is customary to drop all digits after the first.)

Yakima		Los Angeles
	3	9 8 9
	4	4 8 0 2 1 8 3 1 2 5 4 9 6 3 3 8 9
9 7	5	3 5 3 1
4 5 8 5 5 4 7 8 0 7 3 7 4	6	
2 4 2 8 2 4 5 6 1	7	
	8	

21.

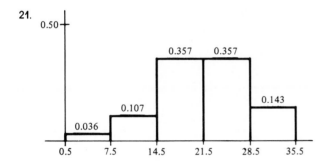

Exercises 9.2

23. $\overline{X} = 99.4$, median: 96.5   **25.** $\overline{X} = 5.705$, median: 5.6   **27.** $\overline{X} = 170.5$, median: 170
29. $\overline{X} = 6.8175$, median: 6.765   **31.** $\overline{X} = 21.07$, median: 22

Exercises 9.3

33. $S = 6.485$ **35.** $\overline{X} = 233$, median: 223.5   **37.** 42.5 lb   **39.** 2.16   **41.** 0.557   **43.** $s = .486$
45. $S = 7.12$. The range approximation for the standard deviation is 7.75.
47. The range approximation for the standard deviation S is 10.25.   **49.** 30.11

Exercises 9.4

51. 1.13   **53.** (135, 192.5, 214, 228, 258)   **55.** 135 is an outlier.   **57.** 3.18
59. 64 is an outlier.   **61.** (69, 71.5, 74.5, 84.25, 87). The data are skewed to the right.
63. There are no outliers.   **65.** (34, 63, 68.5, 73, 86). These data are skewed to the left.
67. 34 is an outlier.
69.

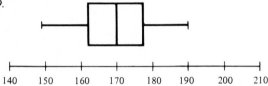

Exercises 9.5

71. 2   **73.** 1   **75.** $\frac{1}{2}$ **77.** $\frac{1}{2}$ **79.** $\frac{3}{2}$ **81.** 0.5000   **83.** .0013   **85.** .8400   **87.** .0013
89. 0.9917708

Exercises 9.6

91. $17.37 \leq \mu \leq 19.87$ is 90% interval; $17.10 \leq \mu \leq 20.10$
93. 90% confidence interval $24.2 \leq \mu \leq 24.8$. 95% confidence interval $24.13 \leq \mu \leq 24.87$.
95. 90% confidence interval $17.73 \leq \mu \leq 19.47$. 95% confidence interval $17.54 \leq \mu \leq 19.66$.
97. 90% confidence interval $24.29 \leq \mu \leq 24.71$. 95% confidence interval $24.24 \leq \mu \leq 24.76$.
99. 90% confidence interval $17.98 \leq \mu \leq 19.22$. 95% confidence interval $17.85 \leq \mu \leq 19.35$.
101. 90% confidence interval $24.35 \leq \mu \leq 24.65$. 95% confidence interval $24.32 \leq \mu \leq 24.68$.
103. 1.28   **105.** 1.56   **107.** 1.44   **109.** $285.4 \leq \mu \leq 290.6$ **111.** $260.5 \leq \mu \leq 299.5$
113. $311.5 \leq \mu \leq 368.5$ **115.** $316.6 \leq \mu \leq 363.4$ **117.** $46.14 \leq \mu \leq 47.86$
119. $18.86 \leq \mu \leq 23.28$. Here μ is the average wind velocity on Mt. Rainier.
121. μ represents the mean time to failure for *all* 75-watt light bulbs of this type.
123. $580.9 \leq \mu \leq 624.9$

Exercises 9.7

125. $0.439 \leq p \leq 0.695$ **127.** $0.5020 \leq p \leq 0.6980$
129. We may not use the normal approximation to set 95% confidence limits.   **131.** $0.2802 \leq p \leq 0.6798$
133. $0.5901 \leq p \leq 0.6899$ **135.** $0.5597 \leq p \leq 0.6403$ **137.** $0.1718 \leq p \leq 0.2682$

139. $0.8174 \leq p \leq 0.8969$

141. The binomial proportion p is the proportion of all cases in which batters who have a "zero ball, two strike" count get hits.

143. The parameter p represents the proportion of marriages, in which one of the partners is previously divorced, that last for at least five years.

Exercises 9.8

145. The experiment does not support Delmo's claim.

147. This experiment tends to support the hypothesis that A is the better golfer.

Review Exercises

149. $\mu = 2.948$. The median is 2.93.   **151.** (2.34, 2.76, 2.93, 3.1425, 3.64).

153. Here is a stem-and-leaf display: **155.** The range is 1.6. $S = 0.324$.

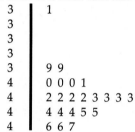

```
3 | 1
3 |
3 |
3 |
3 | 9 9
4 | 0 0 0 1
4 | 2 2 2 2 3 3 3 3
4 | 4 4 4 5 5
4 | 6 6 7
```

157.

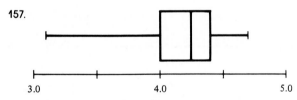

```
3.0        4.0        5.0
```

159. $\overline{X} = 16.6$. The median is 18.

161. The range is 20. The range approximation for the standard deviation is 6.7.

163.

```
0    5    10   15   20   25
```

165. $2.841 \leq \mu \leq 3.055$

167.

Class	Frequency
3.0–3.3	1
3.4–3.7	0
3.8–4.1	6
4.2–4.5	14
4.6–4.9	3

169. $4.088 \leq \mu \leq 4.353$. The parameter μ is to be thought of as the mean hay yield in tons over all one-acre plots.

171. .0228

173. We can be 95% confident that μ, the true average quantitative GRE score for all entering graduate students at Boondoggle A&M, satisfies $353.4 \leq \mu \leq 406.6$.

175. .0008. This experiment thus strongly supports the hypothesis that $\mu < 34{,}000$.

CHAPTER 10

Exercises 10.1

1. The missing probability is 0.2. The expected net payoff is −$0.50.   **3.** −1.50   **5.** $0.50 per play

7. −0.75

9. The probability of drawing two cards of the same suit is $\frac{4}{17} \approx 0.2353$. The probability of drawing two cards of the same rank is $\frac{1}{17} \approx 0.0588$. A "fair" cost to play would be $1.29.

11. The decision to play a game such as the one described by Exercise 10.10 probably reflects the relative insignificance of the cost per play in comparison with the potential winnings. The fact that the cost per play doesn't go to another person in the game, but to the post office for the most part, may also play a role in this decision.

13. The expected value of this insurance policy to its holder is $800. A premium that would be "fair" is $2000.

Exercises 10.2

15. Infant mortality is due primarily to disease and accidents. As the infant grows it becomes less susceptible to disease and more able to avoid accident—until it becomes more active at early adolescence and accidents become more frequent.

17. 0.99855   19. 0.99865

Exercises 10.3

21. Action B   23. Action A   25. Action A   27. The maximax choice of action is action C.
29. The expected value of action C is 4.1, while the expected value of action D is 4.8.
31. Expected values for actions E and F are 11.5 and 9, respectively.   33. Action E   35. Maximax strategy
37. $p = \frac{5}{14}$ 39. $\frac{2}{9}$ 41. 3 cranes   43. 4 cranes   45. This price structure favors the boat owner.
47. *Insuring* minimizes the maximum potential regret.   49. $p = 0.038$ 51. Stock 17 rutabagas daily.
53. Clyde should never order 20 rutabagas.   55. 15 rutabagas

Exercises 10.4

57. 18   59. Buy as much inventory as possible   61. $5.914
63. We must have a selling price of at least 21 cents before we will stock the fifteenth item.   65. −$0.08
67. $3.84   69. Five crates   71. At least $10.94   73. No more than $7.52 per crate

Exercises 10.5

75. Optimal row strategy is row 1; optimal column strategy is column 2; game value is −7.
77. Optimal row strategy is row 2; optimal column strategy is column 1; game value is 4.
79. Optimal row strategy is row 1; optimal column strategy is column 2; game value is 3.
81. Solution unknown.
83. Consider, for example, the matrix $\begin{bmatrix} a & b \\ c & d \end{bmatrix}$. If **a** and **b** are both saddle points, then **a** is minimum in row 1 and **b** is minimum in row 1. Thus $a \le b$ *and* $b \le a$, requiring $a = b$. If **a** and **c** are saddle points, then **a** and **c** are both maximum entries in column 1. Thus $a \ge c$ and $c \ge a$, requiring $a = c$. Even in a larger than 2×2 matrix, this argument is valid. We conclude that saddle point values on the same row or in the same column are identical.

85. Let M be a payoff matrix with two saddle points, s_1 and s_2. Suppose that s_1 is in row i_1 and column j_1, while s_2 is in row i_2 and column j_2. (We do not exclude the possibility that $i_1 = i_2$ or that $j_1 = j_2$, although we may suppose that $i_1 = i_2$ and $j_1 = j_2$ are not *both* true.) Let t be the entry that lies in row i_1 and column j_2 of M. Because s_1 and s_2 are saddle points, both are row minima and both are column maxima. Thus $s_1 \le t \le s_2$ (because s_1 and t lie in the same row while t and s_2 lie in the same column), or $s_1 \le s_2$. Let w be the entry that lies in row i_2 and column j_1. Then $s_2 \le w \le s_1$, or $s_2 \le s_1$. But if both of the inequalities $s_1 \le s_2$ and $s_2 \le s_1$ are true, then it follows that $s_1 = s_2$. Note that we also have $w = t = s_1 = s_2$.

87. Both authors should include the chapter and expect half the market.

Exercises 10.6

89. The row player's optimal strategy is $[0, 1]$, the column player's is $\begin{bmatrix} 1 \\ 0 \end{bmatrix}$, and the value of the game is 1.

91. The row player should play R1 with probability $p = \frac{4}{7}$ and R2 with probability $R2 = \frac{3}{7}$. The column player should choose C1 with probability $\frac{24}{35}$, C2 with probability $\frac{11}{35}$. The value of the game is $\frac{9}{7}$.

93. $\begin{bmatrix} \frac{5}{9}, \frac{4}{9} \end{bmatrix}, \begin{bmatrix} 0 \\ 0 \\ \frac{4}{9} \\ \frac{5}{9} \end{bmatrix}$, value $= \frac{25}{9}$

95. $P^* = [0.5 \quad 0.5]$, $Q^* = \begin{bmatrix} 0 & 0 & \frac{5}{12} & \frac{7}{12} \end{bmatrix}^T$, value of the game is $-\frac{1}{2}$

97. $P^* = \begin{bmatrix} \frac{1}{4} & \frac{3}{4} \end{bmatrix}$, game value is $\frac{7}{2}$, $Q^* = [0.5 \quad 0 \quad 0.5]^T$

99. 3.75 is the game value. Column player's strategy is $\begin{bmatrix} \frac{1}{4} & \frac{3}{4} & 0 & 0 \end{bmatrix}^T$. Row player's strategy is $\begin{bmatrix} \frac{5}{8} & \frac{3}{8} \end{bmatrix}$.

101. Row player's optimal strategy is $\begin{bmatrix} \frac{7}{8}, \frac{1}{8} \end{bmatrix}$, column player's optimal strategy is $\begin{bmatrix} \frac{3}{8}, \frac{5}{8} \end{bmatrix}^T$, and game value is $\frac{11}{8}$.

103. The pure strategy $[0, 1]$, expected payoff 2.6.

105. $P^* = [0.5 \quad 0.5]$, $Q^* = [0.3 \quad 0.7]^T$, "pleasure value" is 4.5.

107. $P^* = \begin{bmatrix} \frac{4}{7} & \frac{3}{7} \end{bmatrix}$, expected market share of $\frac{250}{7} = 35\frac{5}{7}$, $Q^* = \begin{bmatrix} \frac{2}{7} & \frac{5}{7} & 0 \end{bmatrix}^T$.

Exercises 10.7

109. Row player should always choose R1 and column player should always play C1. Game value is zero.

111. Row player should consistently play R4; column player should consistently play C2; game value is 2.

113. Maximize $z = x_1 + x_2 + x_3 + x_4$
subject to the constraints
$$10x_1 + x_2 + 9x_3 + 13x_4 \le 1;$$
$$12x_1 + 14x_2 + 6x_3 + 4x_4 \le 1;$$
$$9x_1 + 10x_2 + 11x_3 + 12x_4 \le 1;$$
$$x_1 \ge 0; x_2 \ge 0; x_3 \ge 0; x_4 \ge 0.$$

115. A 3 × 3 game with a saddle point in row 2, column 2, which is not a reducible game:
$$\begin{bmatrix} -3 & -1 & 3 \\ 1 & 0 & 1 \\ 2 & -1 & -2 \end{bmatrix}$$

Review Exercises

117. $0   **119.** Optimist would hold his stock for CALIPER's announcement.
121. Trade now for Boseo's DeSoto.   **123.** Stock 17 dozen roses. Expected profit is $62.20.   **125.** $67.12
127. Stock 17 dozen roses. His expected profit is then $80.36.   **129.** $-$0.65   **131.** 2.5 games

133. The expected number of bad cans is $\dfrac{55}{44} = 1.25$; the expected penalty is $1.25(\$50) = \$62.50$.

135. -0.438 **137.** $95,238.10   **139.** $202   **141.** Stock 8 bags, $210   **143.** $\dfrac{1}{9} \approx 0.1111$ **145.** $-\$1.984$

147. $P[\text{1-year-old male will live to age 6}] \approx .99512$; $P[\text{15-year-old male will live to age 20}] \approx .99188$. A one-year-old has a slightly better survival probability.

149. 70 pounds   **151.** $12.90   **155.** $P^* = \begin{bmatrix} 0 & \frac{2}{3} & 0 & \frac{1}{3} \end{bmatrix}$; game value $= 3$

157. $P^* = \begin{bmatrix} \frac{5}{12} & \frac{7}{12} \end{bmatrix}$; game value $= \dfrac{8}{3}$ **159.** Maximize $z = x_1 + x_2 + x_3$ subject to
$$
\begin{aligned}
2x_1 + 7x_2 + 6x_3 &\le 1 \\
10x_1 + x_2 + 7x_3 &\le 1 \\
12x_1 + 6x_2 + 4x_3 &\le 1 \\
x_1 + 8x_2 + 13x_3 &\le 1 \\
x_1, x_2, x_3 &\ge 0
\end{aligned}
$$

CHAPTER 11

Exercises 11.1

1. Is   **3.** Is not   **5.** Is not   **7.** Is   **9.** Is not   **11.** Is not   **13.** Is   **15.** $P = \begin{bmatrix} 0.4 & 0.4 & 0.2 \\ 0.7 & 0.0 & 0.3 \\ 0.3 & 0.6 & 0.1 \end{bmatrix}$

17. 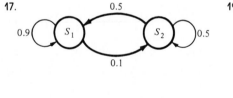   **19.**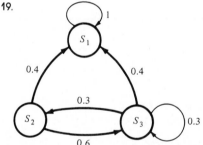

21. $P^2 = \begin{bmatrix} 0.74 & 0.26 \\ 0.65 & 0.35 \end{bmatrix}$ and $P^3 = \begin{bmatrix} 0.722 & 0.278 \\ 0.695 & 0.305 \end{bmatrix}$. The first row of P^2 gives the probabilities that the system, starting in state 1, will be in states 1 and 2 after two transitions. The entries in the first row of P^3 give the probabilities that the system, starting in state 1, will be in states 1 and 2 after three transitions.

23. $P^2 = \begin{bmatrix} 1.00 & 0.00 & 0.00 \\ 0.58 & 0.30 & 0.12 \\ 0.56 & 0.10 & 0.34 \end{bmatrix}$ and $P^3 = \begin{bmatrix} 1.000 & 0.000 & 0.000 \\ 0.736 & 0.060 & 0.204 \\ 0.702 & 0.170 & 0.128 \end{bmatrix}$. From the first rows P^2 and P^3, we see that if the system begins in state 1, it will certainly be in state 1 after either two or three transitions.

25.
$$P = \begin{array}{c} \text{H} \\ \text{M} \\ \text{N} \end{array} \begin{array}{ccc} \text{H} & \text{M} & \text{N} \\ \begin{bmatrix} 0.60 & 0.30 & 0.10 \\ 0.20 & 0.70 & 0.10 \\ 0.05 & 0.30 & 0.65 \end{bmatrix} \end{array}$$

27. 0.425   **29.** 0.532   **31.** 0.468   **33.** $P = \begin{array}{c} \text{A} \\ \text{B} \end{array} \begin{array}{cc} \text{A} & \text{B} \\ \begin{bmatrix} 0.30 & 0.70 \\ 0.90 & 0.10 \end{bmatrix} \end{array}$ **35.** 0.316

37. $P = \begin{array}{c} \\ C \\ B \end{array} \begin{array}{cc} C & B \\ \begin{bmatrix} 0.5 & 0.5 \\ 0.8 & 0.2 \end{bmatrix} \end{array}$ 39. 0.56   41. 0.74   43. 0.586   45. 0.70   47. 0.65   49. 0.4925

51. $P^3 = \begin{array}{c} \\ S \\ \text{C-S} \end{array} \begin{array}{cc} S & \text{C-S} \\ \begin{bmatrix} 0.421675 & 0.578375 \\ 0.3305 & 0.6695 \end{bmatrix} \end{array}$. The entries in the first row give, respectively, the probabilities that

Pam will sew and that she will cross-stitch the third project after the current one if she is sewing the current one. The entries in the second row give the same probabilities if she is cross-stitching the current project.

53. 0.752

Exercises 11.2

55. $\pi_1 = [0.65 \quad 0.35]$, $\pi_2 = [0.525 \quad 0.475]$, $\pi_3 = [0.4625 \quad 0.5375]$
57. $\pi_1 = [0.45 \quad 0.55]$, $\pi_2 = [0.425 \quad 0.575]$, $\pi_3 = [0.4125 \quad 0.5875]$
59. $\pi_1 = [0.25 \quad 0.75]$, $\pi_2 = [0.325 \quad 0.675]$, $\pi_3 = [0.3625 \quad 0.6375]$
61. $\pi_1 = [0.23 \quad 0.77]$, $\pi_2 = [0.277 \quad 0.723]$, $\pi_3 = [0.2723 \quad 0.7277]$
63. $\pi_1 = [0.27 \quad 0.73]$, $\pi_2 = [0.273 \quad 0.727]$, $\pi_3 = [0.2727 \quad 0.7273]$
65. $\pi_1 = [0.22 \quad 0.54 \quad 0.24]$, $\pi_2 = [0.386 \quad 0.366 \quad 0.248]$, $\pi_3 = [0.3346 \quad 0.4158 \quad 0.2496]$
67. $\pi_1 = [0.46 \quad 0.30 \quad 0.24]$, $\pi_2 = [0.314 \quad 0.438 \quad 0.248]$, $\pi_3 = [0.3562 \quad 0.3942 \quad 0.2496]$
69. $\pi_1 = [0.35 \quad 0.45 \quad 0.20]$, $\pi_2 = [0.355 \quad 0.405 \quad 0.240]$, $\pi_3 = [0.3455 \quad 0.4065 \quad 0.2480]$
71. $\pi_1 = [0.28 \quad 0.36 \quad 0.36]$, $\pi_2 = [0.344 \quad 0.384 \quad 0.272]$, $\pi_3 = [0.3424 \quad 0.4032 \quad 0.2544]$
73. $\pi_1 = [0.34 \quad 0.30 \quad 0.36]$, $\pi_2 = [0.326 \quad 0.402 \quad 0.272]$, $\pi_3 = [0.3478 \quad 0.3978 \quad 0.2544]$ 75. P is regular
77. P is not regular   79. P is regular   81. P is regular
83. $\begin{bmatrix} 0.6875 & 0.3125 \\ 0.6250 & 0.3750 \end{bmatrix}$. The entry in the ith row and jth column of this matrix gives the probability that the system will be in state j after four transitions, given that it started in state i.

85. $\begin{bmatrix} 1 & 0 \\ 0 & 1 \end{bmatrix}$. The system never changes state.

87. $\begin{bmatrix} 0.3175 & 0.1250 & 0.5575 \\ 0.1800 & 0.1050 & 0.7150 \\ 0.1975 & 0.1075 & 0.6950 \end{bmatrix}$. The entry in the ith row and jth column of this matrix gives the probability that the system will be in state j after four transitions, given that it started in state i.

89. $\begin{bmatrix} 0.7376 & 0.2296 & 0.0328 \\ 0.3280 & 0.5880 & 0.0840 \\ 0.3280 & 0.5880 & 0.0840 \end{bmatrix}$. The entry in the ith row and jth column of this matrix gives the probability that the system will be in state j after four transitions, given that it started in state i.

91. $\pi = \begin{bmatrix} \frac{2}{3} & \frac{1}{3} \end{bmatrix}$ 93. $\pi = \pi P$ for every vector π 95. $\pi = \begin{bmatrix} \frac{2}{9} & \frac{1}{9} & \frac{2}{3} \end{bmatrix}$ 97. $\pi = \begin{bmatrix} \frac{5}{9} & \frac{7}{18} & \frac{1}{18} \end{bmatrix}$

99. The rows of P^4 seem to be tending toward $\pi = \begin{bmatrix} \frac{2}{3}, \frac{1}{3} \end{bmatrix}$. P is regular.

101. P is not regular.

103. The rows of P^4 are tending rather slowly toward $\pi = \begin{bmatrix} \frac{2}{9} & \frac{1}{9} & \frac{2}{3} \end{bmatrix}$. P is regular.

105. The nature of the collection of fixed-point vectors for a non-regular matrix is undetermined. There may be a unique fixed-point probability vector, and there may be infinitely many such.

107. P is regular   109. Expected waiting time 3 buys   111. $\begin{array}{c} \\ C \\ I \\ \text{Int} \end{array} \begin{array}{ccc} C & I & \text{Int} \\ \begin{bmatrix} .5 & .4 & .1 \\ .6 & .4 & 0 \\ .8 & .2 & 0 \end{bmatrix} \end{array}$

113. $r = \dfrac{1}{18}, q = \dfrac{7}{18}, p = \dfrac{10}{18}$ **115.**

$$P = \begin{array}{c} \\ A \\ N \end{array} \begin{array}{cc} A & N \\ \left[\begin{array}{cc} \dfrac{2}{5} & \dfrac{3}{5} \\ \dfrac{7}{10} & \dfrac{3}{10} \end{array} \right] \end{array}$$

117. $\pi = \left[\dfrac{7}{13}, \dfrac{6}{13} \right]$ **119.** $\dfrac{13}{7}$ trips

121. $\pi_1 = \left[\dfrac{103}{200} \quad \dfrac{11}{40} \quad \dfrac{21}{100} \right] = [.515 \quad .275 \quad .210]$

123. In the long run, $\dfrac{46}{89}$ proportion of the people will shop at Albertson's, $\dfrac{31}{89}$ at Alpha Beta, and $\dfrac{12}{89}$ elsewhere.

125. P is regular **127.** $\pi = \left[\dfrac{1}{3} \quad \dfrac{1}{3} \quad \dfrac{1}{3} \right]$ **129.** Three years **131.** P is regular

133. In the long run, he spends $\dfrac{7}{13}$ of the time in Eastern Colorado **135.**

$$\begin{array}{c} \\ A \\ B \\ C \end{array} \begin{array}{ccc} A & B & C \\ \left[\begin{array}{ccc} .4 & .4 & .2 \\ .4 & .2 & .4 \\ .2 & .1 & .7 \end{array} \right] \end{array}$$

137. $P^2 = \left[\begin{array}{ccc} .36 & .26 & .38 \\ .32 & .24 & .44 \\ .26 & .17 & .57 \end{array} \right]$. The conditional probability for being in state j in 2 moves given now in state i is the i, jth element of P^2.

139. 3.3 exams **141.** 0.21 **143.** $\pi = \left[\dfrac{4}{21}, \dfrac{11}{21}, \dfrac{6}{21} \right]$

Exercises 11.3

145. Regular **147.** Regular **149.** Neither regular nor absorbing **151.** Regular **153.** Absorbing

155.
$$\begin{array}{c} \\ 2 \\ 1 \end{array} \begin{array}{cc} 2 & 1 \\ \left[\begin{array}{c|c} 1 & 0 \\ \hline 0.7 & 0.3 \end{array} \right] \end{array}$$

157.
$$\begin{array}{c} \\ 3 \\ 1 \\ 2 \end{array} \begin{array}{ccc} 3 & 1 & 2 \\ \left[\begin{array}{c|cc} 1 & 0 & 0 \\ \hline 0.3 & 0.4 & 0.3 \\ 0.4 & 0.6 & 0.0 \end{array} \right] \end{array}$$

159.
$$\begin{array}{c} \\ 3 \\ 1 \\ 2 \end{array} \begin{array}{ccc} 3 & 1 & 2 \\ \left[\begin{array}{c|cc} 1.0 & 0.0 & 0.0 \\ \hline 0.0 & 0.4 & 0.6 \\ 0.0 & 1.0 & 0.0 \end{array} \right] \end{array}$$

161. State 1 is absorbing; states 2 and 3 are transient. The probability of being absorbed in 4 steps from state 2 is 0.9375, while the probability of being absorbed within 4 steps from state 3 is 0.8268.

163. State 1 is absorbing; state 2 is transient. The probability of being absorbed within four steps from state 2 is 0.3439.

165. States 1 and 2 are absorbing; states 3 and 4 are transient. The probability of being absorbed by state 1 from state 3 (resp., state 4) within four steps is 0.2000 (resp., 0.3776). The probability of being absorbed by state 2 from state 3 (resp., state 4) within four steps is 0.8000 (resp., 0.6216).

167. $\left[\begin{array}{cc} \dfrac{10}{9} & 0 \\ \dfrac{5}{12} & \dfrac{5}{4} \end{array} \right]$ **169.** $\dfrac{5}{3}$ **171.** $\left[\begin{array}{ccc} \dfrac{3}{2} & \dfrac{1}{6} & \dfrac{2}{3} \\ \dfrac{1}{6} & \dfrac{61}{54} & \dfrac{2}{27} \\ \dfrac{5}{6} & \dfrac{5}{54} & \dfrac{40}{27} \end{array} \right]$ **173.** $\dfrac{5}{4}$ **175.** $\left[\begin{array}{c} 1 \\ 1 \end{array} \right]$ **177.** 1 **179.** $\left[\begin{array}{cc} \dfrac{1}{5} & \dfrac{4}{5} \\ \dfrac{17}{45} & \dfrac{28}{45} \end{array} \right]$

181. $\left[\begin{array}{cc} \dfrac{1}{10} & 0 \\ \dfrac{3}{8} & \dfrac{1}{5} \end{array} \right]$ **183.** $\dfrac{2}{5}$ **185.** $\left[\begin{array}{ccc} \dfrac{1}{3} & \dfrac{9}{61} & \dfrac{9}{20} \\ \dfrac{1}{9} & \dfrac{7}{61} & \dfrac{1}{20} \\ \dfrac{5}{9} & \dfrac{5}{61} & \dfrac{13}{40} \end{array} \right]$ **187.** $\dfrac{1}{5}$ **189.**

$$\begin{array}{c} \\ \$0 \\ \$3 \\ \$1 \\ \$2 \end{array} \begin{array}{cccc} \$0 & \$3 & \$1 & \$2 \\ \left[\begin{array}{cc|cc} 1 & 0 & 0 & 0 \\ 0 & 1 & 0 & 0 \\ \hline 0.7 & 0 & 0 & 0.3 \\ 0 & 0.3 & 0.7 & 0 \end{array} \right] \end{array}$$

191. $\dfrac{100}{79}$

193. $\dfrac{30}{79}$

195.

$$\begin{array}{c c c c c} & F & C & P & A \\ F & \dfrac{2}{5} & \dfrac{1}{5} & \dfrac{3}{10} & \dfrac{1}{10} \\ C & \dfrac{2}{5} & \dfrac{3}{10} & \dfrac{1}{4} & \dfrac{1}{20} \\ P & \dfrac{3}{5} & 0 & \dfrac{2}{5} & 0 \\ A & 0 & 0 & 0 & 1 \end{array}$$

197. .126

199.

$$\begin{array}{c c c c} & F & C & P \\ F & \dfrac{35}{4} & \dfrac{5}{2} & \dfrac{65}{12} \\ C & \dfrac{65}{8} & \dfrac{15}{4} & \dfrac{45}{8} \\ P & \dfrac{35}{4} & \dfrac{5}{2} & \dfrac{85}{12} \end{array}$$

201. $\dfrac{5}{2}$

203. $\dfrac{55}{3}$ years

205. $\dfrac{31}{35}$

207.

$$\begin{array}{c c c c c} & N & D & P & T \\ N & \dfrac{7}{10} & \dfrac{1}{5} & \dfrac{1}{10} & 0 \\ D & \dfrac{3}{10} & \dfrac{1}{2} & \dfrac{1}{10} & \dfrac{1}{10} \\ P & 0 & 0 & 1 & 0 \\ T & 0 & 0 & 0 & 1 \end{array}$$

209. $\dfrac{6}{25}$

211. $\dfrac{7}{10}$

213. $\dfrac{20}{3}$ days

215. $\dfrac{3}{5}$

217. $\dfrac{7}{9}$

Review Exercises

219. $\pi_1 = [0.385 \quad 0.615]$, $\pi_2 = [0.2845 \quad 0.7155]$, $\pi_3 = [0.31465 \quad 0.68535]$
221. $\pi_1 = [0.37 \quad 0.63]$, $\pi_2 = [0.289 \quad 0.711]$, $\pi_3 = [0.3133 \quad 0.6867]$
223. $\pi_1 = [0.31 \quad 0.69]$, $\pi_2 = [0.307 \quad 0.693]$, $\pi_3 = [0.3079 \quad 0.6921]$ **225.** Regular   **227.** Regular
229. Not a transition matrix, neither regular nor absorbing
231. Absorbing, state 2 is the only absorbing state

233.

$$P = \begin{array}{c c c} & H & L \\ H & 0.60 & 0.40 \\ L & 0.60 & 0.40 \end{array}$$

235. $\pi = [0.60 \quad 0.40]$

237.

$$P = \begin{array}{c c c c} & H & J & M \\ H & 0.4 & 0.3 & 0.3 \\ J & 0.4 & 0.5 & 0.1 \\ M & 0.2 & 0.2 & 0.6 \end{array}$$

239. $\pi = \left[\dfrac{1}{3}, \dfrac{1}{3}, \dfrac{1}{3}\right]$

241.

$$P = \begin{array}{c c c c} & WN & WR & WS \\ WN & 0.40 & 0.30 & 0.30 \\ WR & 0.25 & 0.00 & 0.75 \\ WS & 0.10 & 0.10 & 0.80 \end{array}$$

243. Given that it is windy and snowy today, the probability that it will be windy and nice three days hence is 0.160, the probability that it will be windy and rainy then is 0.118, and the probability that it will then be rainy and snowy is 0.722.

245. $\dfrac{148}{25}$ days   **247.** $\pi_1 = [0.1675 \quad 0.1150 \quad 0.5480 \quad 0.1695]$, $\pi_2 = [0.253425 \quad 0.149025 \quad 0.452050 \quad 0.145500]$

249. $\pi = \left[\dfrac{1285}{2819} \quad \dfrac{537}{2819} \quad \dfrac{729}{2819} \quad \dfrac{268}{2819}\right]$
$\approx [.4558 \quad .1905 \quad .2586 \quad .0951]$

251.

$$P = \begin{array}{c c c c c} & \{\ \} & \{A\} & \{B\} & \{A, B\} \\ & 1 & 0 & 0 & 0 \\ & 0 & 1 & 0 & 0 \\ & 0 & 0 & 1 & 0 \\ & 0.02 & 0.18 & 0.08 & 0.72 \end{array} \begin{array}{l} \{\ \} \\ \{A\} \\ \{B\} \\ \{A, B\} \end{array}$$

253. $\dfrac{25}{7}$ **255.** $\dfrac{9}{14}$ **257.** $\dfrac{1}{14}$ **259.** 0.69   **261.** $\pi = \left[\dfrac{2}{3} \quad \dfrac{1}{6} \quad \dfrac{1}{6}\right]$ **263.** Six exams

265. $\pi_1 = [0.6875 \quad 0.3125]$ 267. $\pi = \begin{bmatrix} \frac{1}{5} & \frac{4}{5} \end{bmatrix}$ 269.

$$P = \begin{array}{c} \\ \text{S} \\ \text{L} \\ \text{BO} \\ \text{OB} \end{array} \begin{array}{cccc} \text{S} & \text{L} & \text{BO} & \text{OB} \\ \begin{bmatrix} 0.50 & 0.40 & 0.00 & 0.10 \\ 0.30 & 0.60 & 0.06 & 0.04 \\ 0.00 & 0.00 & 1.00 & 0.00 \\ 0.00 & 0.00 & 0.00 & 1.00 \end{bmatrix} \end{array}$$

271. $\pi_2 = [0.330 \quad 0.480 \quad 0.096 \quad 0.094]$ 273. 10 months   275. $\frac{25}{4}$ large-profit months   277. $\frac{4}{5}$ 279. $\frac{5}{8}$

281.

$$P = \begin{array}{c} \\ \\ \end{array} \begin{array}{cc} \text{L} & \text{R} \\ \begin{bmatrix} 0.8 & 0.2 \\ 0.7 & 0.3 \end{bmatrix} \begin{array}{c} \text{L} \\ \text{R} \end{array} \end{array}$$

283. 0.225   285.

$$P = \begin{array}{ccc} \text{A} & \text{B} & \text{C} \\ \begin{bmatrix} 0.70 & 0.20 & 0.10 \\ 0.05 & 0.90 & 0.05 \\ 0.60 & 0 & 0.40 \end{bmatrix} \begin{array}{c} \text{A} \\ \text{B} \\ \text{C} \end{array} \end{array}$$

287. $\pi_1 = [0.50 \quad 0.20 \quad 0.30]$, $\pi_2 = [0.54 \quad 0.28 \quad 0.18]$ 289. $\frac{10}{3}$ years

CHAPTER 12

Exercises 12.1

1. $53.33   3. $81.67   5. $225.00   7. $129.60   9. $375.00   11. $95.38   13. $162.25   15. $115.06
17. $322.19   19. $1962.52   21. $162.80   23. $485.56   25. $336.88   27. $a^n = 1.262477$, $A = \$3156.19$
29. $a^n = 1.266770$, $A = \$3166.93$ 31. $a^n = 2.4325353$, $A = \$29190.42$ 33. $a^n = 1.27121525$, $A = \$18{,}559.74$
35. $a^n = 1.095445$, $A = \$4381.78$ 37. 68.14%   39. 416%   41. $392.68   43. $2900
45. In case (a) 8% compounded daily will have a two-year compound accumulation factor of $\left(1 + \frac{.08}{360}\right)^{720} \approx$

1.17349. This is preferable to 8.25% compounded annually, which gives a 2-year compound accumulation factor of $(1.0825)^2 = 1.171806$.   47. (a) $83.33 (b) $2083.33   49. 8.4 mo
51. (a) $64,593,420.17 (b) $35,458.87 (c) $46,929,425.36   53. $4824   55. $1524

Exercises 12.2

57. 8.16%   59. 12.36%   61. 10.25%   63. 6.17%   65. 8%
67. 6.6% compounded semi-annually is the better investment.
69. The better investment is 9% compounded quarterly.
71. (a) 6.56%
    (b) 6.15%
    (c) 5.54%
    (d) 6.71%
    The best investment is (d), followed in decreasing order by (a), (b), and (c).
73. Effective rate for 5% compounded daily is $\left(1 + \frac{0.05}{360}\right)^{360} = 5.13\%$. Because the effective rate for 5.3%
    compounded quarterly exceeds 5.3%, it is the better investment.
75. (a) The borrower received $9200.
    (b) $r = 13.04\%$

Exercises 12.3

77. $4208.40   79. $7350.30   81. $3712.35   83. $618.79   85. $146,017.90   87. $58,823.31

89. $105,428.87   **91.** 23.79%   **93.** 17.45%   **95.** 25%   **97.** 20.56%   **99.** $3415.07   **101.** $3083.19
103. 7.02%   **105.** $4037.64   **107.** 37.97%

Exercises 12.4

109. The second option is the more valuable.   **111. (a)** You should make the investment.
                                                     (b) You should make the investment.
113. It is not a good investment.   **115.** Accept the offer!

Exercises 12.5

117. $8807.98   **119.** $15,937.42   **121.** $22,129.13   **123.** $346,255.22   **125. (a)** $1360.22   **127.** $655.19
                                                                                                      (b) $2491.15
                                                                                                      (c) $6378.62

129. (a) $9834.03   **131.** $40,607.44; $2,337,991.59   **133.** $156,116.15
       (b) $254.22
135. (a) Three years is $4115.27   **137. (a)** At 8%, this yields $36,589.21
       (b) Four years is $5752.07   **(b)** At 9%, this yields $38,702.86
       (c) Five years is $7542.41   **(c)** At 10%, this yields $40,969.00
                                              (d) At 11%, this yields $43,399.63

Exercises 12.6

139. $89.97   **141.** $96.50   **143.** $792.23   **145.** $853.14   **147.** $310.15
149. (a) $10,455.08   **(b)** $34,505.80
151. (a) $31598.90   **153. (a)** $14,600.73   **155. (a)** $513.18
       (b) $607,287.73   **(b)** $31,423.73   **(b)** $24.55 per quarter, or a total of $491.00
157. $11.94 per quarter   **159. (a)** $579.01
                                      (b) $53,881.19

161. (a) $686.08
       (b) $560.57 has been paid against principal, $7672.39 is the interest paid
       (c) $135,824 in interest
       (d) $66,468.49
       (e) $60,362.64
       (f) $612.24
163. Loan with points is the better alternative

Review Exercises

165. $451.50   **167.** $144.87   **169.** $983.33   **171.** $8532.60   **173.** $49,178.78   **175.** $4456.67
177. $5186.33   **179.** $631,486.40   **181.** 9.73%   **183.** 10.43%   **185.** 16.08%   **187.** $12,491.94
189. $351,083.09   **191.** $93,977.10   **193.** $8337.70   **195.** 19.22%   **197.** 37.22%   **199.** 5.82%
201. $13,954.01   **203.** $189,258.42   **205.** $65,047.97   **207.** $34,520.52   **209.** $545.48   **211.** $908.12
213. $273.95   **215.** $3019.21   **217.** $24,937.86   **219. (a)** 9.44%   **(b)** 7.42%   **221.** $5157.21
223. Investment (a) is the better.   **225.** 47 quarters   **227.** 11.166%   **229. (a)** 5.127%   **(c)** 5.268%
                                                                                            (b) 5.198%   **(d)** 5.3%

231. $3638.21   **233.** $11,042.99

Index

A

Absorbing state, 541–542
Accumulated value, 570, 575
Algorithm, 153
Amortization, 606–614
Annuity, 599–614
  definition, 599
  future value, 601–603
    table, 627
  present value, 608–614
  sinking fund, 603–604
APR (annual percentage rate),
  583–585
Arrangements, *see* Permutations
Array, 403
ASCII code, 102

B

Banker's Rule, 571
Basic variable, 24, 157
Bayes' theorem, 292–298
  algebraic statement, 297
  tree diagram approach, 293–295
  Venn diagram description, 296
Binomial
  experiment, 349
  probability distribution, 348–351
    approximating hypergeo-
      metric, 357
    approximating normal, 381
    mean of, 354
    standard deviation, 354
    table, 621
Box plot, 417–419

C

Canonical form of absorbing
  chain, 544–545
Central Limit Theorem, 427–432,
  434
Chebyshev's theorem, 341
Combinations, 263–265
  of k objects from among n, 264
Comparison date, 592–593, 597
Composite numbers, xix
Compound accumulation factor,
  576
  table, 623
Conditional probability, 276–281
  definition, 278
  diagram interpretation, 279
Constraint, 119
Continuous compounding, 578
Coordinate plane applications,
  xxiii–xxv
Coordinate systems, xiv, xxiv
Counting
  alternatives, 273–274
  combinations, 264
  permutations, 261–262
  using tree diagrams, 274–275
Counts of arrangements and sets,
  258–275
Cryptography, 99–104

D

Data (qualitative and quantitative),
  395–396
Doubling your money, 579–580
Dual problem, 186–194; *see also*
  Linear programming

E

Effective rate of interest, 583–585
Empirical rule, 410–411
Equations of value, 594–597, 600,
  608

Equilibrium probability vector,
  530–531
Events
  independent, 279
  mutually exclusive, 291

F

Feasible region, 125
Feasible solution, 125, 135, 158
  obvious basic, 158
Five-Number Summary, 417–419
Fractions and their arithmetic,
  xv–xx
Frequency distribution, 396–398
Fundamental Counting Principle,
  219–221
Future value, 574–575
  of annuity, 601–603
  with compound interest, 575
  with continuous compounding,
    578
  with simple interest, 570

G

Gambler's Ruin, 544–558
  simulation, 554–558
Game theory
  choosing a strategy, 464–472
    Bayesian solution, 467–469
    maximax ("optimist's") crite-
      rion, 466
    maximin ("pessimist's") crite-
      rion, 466
    minimax regret, 467
    regret table, 467
  fair game, 458–459
  fair insurance premium, 463–
    464

Game theory (*cont.*)
gross value of game, 458
insurance as "game", 460–464
inventory management, 469–472, 474–480
demand frequencies/probabilities, 470
item expected value, 476–478
LASP, 471
lowest acceptable selling probability, 471
marginal analysis, 474–480
marginal profit, 480
salvage value, 471
stock level expected value, 471
matrix games, 482
algebraic solution of 2×2, 495–498
dominant rows/columns, 502–503
expected payoff, 490
Fundamental Theorem, 492
game value, 485
graphic solution of $2 \times m$, 498–500
mixed strategy 2×2, 487–500
nonstrictly determined, 486
optimal mixed strategy, 490–497
pure strategy, 483
reduced game matrix, 503
saddle point, 483–485
simplex method for large games, 504–508
strategy vectors, 489–490
net value of game, 458
outcomes and values, 455–456
payoff matrix, 482
payoff tables, 456, 458, 465
strictly determined, 481–486
two-party, zero-sum, 459
value of game, 457
Graph theory
applications, 86–96
airline routing, 98
communication network, 90–91
power of sports teams, 91–95
preference relations, 95–96, 99
trade relations, 86–89, 97
digraphs, 86–98
directed graphs, 86
dominance digraphs, 91–96

edges, 86
nodes or vertices, 86
two-step connections, 87–88

H
Histogram, 344, 351–353
relative frequency, 398
Human mortality, 461–463
Hypothesis testing, 422, 444–449
null and alternative hypotheses, 444
philosophy of, 422, 444–449
P-values, 445–449
Type I and II errors, 444–445, 447

I
Independent events
definition, 279
testing for, 280
Input-output models, 104–114
Insurance, 460–464
fair premium, 463–464
Integer programming, 146–147
Integers, xiv
Interest, 570
compound, 573
effective rate, 583–585
nominal rate, 585–586
simple, 570
Banker's Rule, 571
exact, 571
ordinary, 571
Interest conversion period, 573
Internal demand, 106
Interquartile range (IQR), 415–417, 419–420
Inventory management, 469–472, 474–480; *see also* Game theory

L
Leontief models, 104–114
closed model, 106–110
open model, 110–113
technical matrix, 106
LINDO, 179, 195–205
Linear equations
changing forms of, xxxi–xxxii, xlvii–xlix
graphing technique, xxviii–xxx
graphs
horizontal or vertical, xxix

intercepts, xxx
oblique, xxviii
slope of, xxxii–xxxiv
parallel lines, xli
point-slope form, xxxvi–xxxvii
graphing, xxxiv–xxxvii
slope-intercept form, xxxviii
standard form, xxviii, xlv
two-point form, xxxix–xl
Linear inequalities, 120–125
changing form, 123
definition, 120
graphing, 121–125
strict, 122
weak, 122
Linear programming
basic and nonbasic variables, 157
basic solution, 157
classic problem, 132
computer solution, 195–205
constraint, 119
description of, 130–133
dual problem, 188–194
feasible region, 125
bounded, 126
unbounded, 126–127
feasible solution, 135, 155–158
obvious basic, 158
feasible vertex, 127–128
functional constraints, 154
graphical solution, 127–128
graphic methods, 130–137
implicit constraints, 120
initial simplex tableau, 167–168
integer programming, 146–147
multiple optimal solutions, 175–176
nonnegativity constraints, 120, 154
objective function, 119
constant value lines, 130–131
maximizing/minimizing, 130–134
obvious basic feasible solution, 158
optimization, 119
sensitivity analysis, 177–180, 195–204
shadow prices, 177–180, 195–204
slack variables, 156–157
solution by simplex method, 154–170

standard maximization problems, 154
standard minimization problems, 186–187
in three variables, 139–141
in two variables, 134–135
unbounded solutions, 176–177
using LINDO, 195–205

M

Markov chains
  absorbing, 540–558
    canonical form, 544–545
    capture probabilities, 552
    ever reach probabilities, 552
    fundamental matrix, 548
  brand switching in, 521–525
  finite, 515–566
  first returns in regular chain, 535
  Gambler's Ruin problem, 545–558
  recursive process in, 528–530
  regular, 531–535
  states in, 542
Markov property, 518
Matrix
  absorbing, 541–558
  addition and subtraction, 43
  associative properties, 44, 55
  coefficient, 63
  commutative properties, 44, 53
  corresponding elements, 42
  decoding, 101
  definition, 41
  dimensions, 41
  elements, 41
  encoding, 100
  equality, 42
  fundamental in absorbing chain, 548
  identity, 59–60
  incidence, 81–82, 87, 90, 95
  input-output, 106
  inverse
    definition, 65
    procedure for finding, 66–69
  multiplication, 47–58
    applications, 77–85
    by a scalar, 47–48
    distributive law for, 56
    row vector times column vector, 49

of two matrices, 51
  regular, 531–536
  square, 42
  stochastic, 519–520
  symmetric, 62
  technical, 106
  transition, 518
  transpose, 60–61
  zero, 45
Measures of central tendency (mean, median, mode), 403–404
MINITAB
  matrix operations, 72–73
  simulation of Central Limit Theorem, 431–432
  simulation of Gambler's Ruin, 554–558
Mutually exclusive events, 291

N

Natural numbers, xiii
Nominal rate of interest, 589
Nonbasic variable, 157
Normal distribution, 366–368
  applying, 372–374
  approximation to binomial, 381
  properties, 367
  standard (z) scores, 370, 374
  table, back cover
Number line, xiv

O

Odds, 237
Orderings, *see* Permutations
Origin, xiv
Outlier, 406, 419–420

P

Parameter, 421–422
Partition, 212
Permutations
  definition, 261
  of k objects from among n, 261–262
  of n objects, 261
  of "some alike" objects, 271–272
Pivot (column, element, row), 162
Population, 393–395, 397, 421–423, 428–429
Power of a vertex, 135–137

Preference rankings, 95–96, 99
Present value, 575, 588, 592–598
  of annuity, 607–609
Prime numbers, xix
Principal, 570
Probability
  additive law, 235–236
  of any two events, 284
  complement rule, 237
  discussed, 223–224
  empirical, 247
  equally likely models, 240–242
  events, 228
    certain, 233
    impossible, 233
    probability, 33
  model, 236
  multiplicative rule, 280–290
  objective, 247
  random experiments, 224
  relative frequency, 245–246
  rules for assigning, 236
  sample space, 225
  subjective, 248
  transition, 518
  transition matrix, 520
  in tree diagrams, 285–287
  of two independent events, 288
  vector, 519
    equilibrium, 530–531
    initial, 526
    m-step, 528
Probability density function, 361
Probability distribution, *see* Random variable
  Chebyshev's theorem, 341
  expected value, 331
  mean, 330
  parameter, 329
  standard deviation, 340–341
  variance
    computing formula, 339
    definition, 337

Q

Quartiles and percentiles, 414–420

R

Random variable, 320; *see also* Probability distribution
  continuous, 325, 361

Random variable (*cont.*)
  probability density function, 361
  definition, 319
  discrete, 324
  histogram, 321
  probability distribution for, 320
Rational numbers, xiv
Real number line, xxiii
Real numbers, xxi
  distributive property, x
Reliability, 300–309; *see also* Systems reliability
Row and column vectors, 41

S

Sample
  mean, 403–406
    sampling distribution, 424–432
  median, 403–406
  mode, 404
  range, 409, 411–412
  standard deviation, 408–410
  variance, 408–410
Sampling distribution, 422–432
  Central Limit Theorem, 427–432, 434
Sensitivity analysis, 177–181, 197–204
Sets
  complement, 213
  definition, xiii, 211
  elements in, 211
  empty, 214
  exhaustive, 212
  intersection, 213
  mutually exclusive, 212
  subsets, 212
  union
    count, 217
    definition, 213
  universe, 213
Simple discount interest, 587
Simple random sample, 394
Simplex method, 154–194
  computer solution, 195–205
  dual problem, 186–194

geometric interpretation, 159, 166–167
  initial tableau, 160, 168
  minimization problems, 186–194
  multiple optimal solutions, 174–176
  optimal tableau, 163, 169
  procedure, 169
  sensitivity analysis, 197–204
  shadow prices, 177–181
  slack variable, 156
  unbounded solutions, 176
Sinking fund, 603–604
Standard error of the mean, 427, 435–438, 440
Standard maximization problem, 154
Standard minimization problem, 187
  dual problem, 188–191
Statistic, 402
Statistics
  descriptive, 393, 395–403
    graphical displays, 395–400, 417–419
    numerical measures, 402–406, 408–410, 414–416
  inferential, 393, 421–449
    confidence intervals, 434–438, 440–442
    hypothesis testing, 422, 444–449
Stem-and-leaf display, 398–400
Symmetry and skewness, 404–406, 411, 417–419
Systems of linear equations
  consistent, 26
  dependent, 26–27
    general solution, 35
    multiple solutions, 26
    parameters, 27–29, 31–33
    particular solution, 35
  equivalent systems, 6–8
  general plan for solving, 34–35
  inconsistent, 26
  independent, 26–27
  matrix solution methods, 17–24
    augmented matrix, 18
    basic variables, 24

coefficient matrix, 18
    elementary row operations, 18–19
    Gaussian elimination, 18–22
    Gauss-Jordan elimination, 23
    leading row entry, 23
    row echelon form, 19
  solving by elimination, 6–13
  solving by graphing, 4
  solving by substitution, 2–4, 13–14
  three variables: graphic illustration, 30, 34
Systems reliability, 300–309
  definition, 303–304
  mixed series/parallel, 306–307
  parallel
    definition, 303–304
    reliability, 305
  redundancy in, 304
  reliability defined, 300
  reliability of, 300–309
  series
    definition, 301
    reliability, 302

T

Taste testing, 95, 99
Time diagrams, 592–597, 600, 607
Transition diagram, 519
Transition probability, 518
Tree diagrams, 219
Trivial Subsets, 259
Tukey's Five-Number Summary, 417–419

V

Variable
  basic and nonbasic, 157
  random, 320
  slack, 156
Venn diagrams, 210–215

W

Whole numbers, xiv
Word problems: solution plan, xliv–xlvi, 15–16